HEAT ENGINES

HEAT ENGINES

(A FIRST TEXT-BOOK)

BY

A. C. WALSHAW

PH.D., M.SC., D.I.C., A.C.G.I., M.I.MECH.E.

HEAD OF THE DEPARTMENT OF MECHANICAL AND PRODUCTION ENGINEERING,
COLLEGE OF TECHNOLOGY, BIRMINGHAM

With diagrams and illustrations

LONGMANS, GREEN AND CO
LONDON ◆ NEW YORK ◆ TORONTO

LONGMANS, GREEN AND CO LTD
6 & 7 CLIFFORD STREET LONDON W 1
BOSTON HOUSE STRAND STREET CAPE TOWN
531 LITTLE COLLINS STREET MELBOURNE

LONGMANS, GREEN AND CO INC
55 FIFTH AVENUE NEW YORK 3

LONGMANS, GREEN AND CO
20 CRANFIELD ROAD TORONTO 16

ORIENT LONGMANS LTD
CALCUTTA BOMBAY MADRAS
DELHI VIJAYAWADA DACCA

FIRST PUBLISHED 1938
SECOND EDITION 1944
NEW IMPRESSIONS . . . 1946 and 1947
THIRD EDITION 1949
NEW IMPRESSIONS . . . 1951 and 1953
FOURTH EDITION 1956

PRINTED IN GREAT BRITAIN
SPOTTISWOODE, BALLANTYNE AND CO LTD
LONDON AND COLCHESTER

PREFACE TO FOURTH EDITION

This fourth edition is a result of deletion, re-arrangement and addition of material. A number of paragraphs, diagrams, examples and exercises have been replaced by new ones. A further effort has been made towards simplicity of expression and the clearing of difficulties, especially in connection with units. A note on units and dimensions has been included preliminary to the text in order to induce students to be *dimension-conscious* from the start and also to emphasize the difference between the two types of formulae, namely, "physical" and "numerical," which occur in engineering science and in the applied sciences generally.

To eliminate difficulties which arise in students' minds regarding force, weight and mass, a small letter is used in the abbreviation for the unit of mass (*e.g.* lb. for pound mass) and a capital letter to signify force (*e.g.* Lb. for pound force), the two being interconnected by Newton's second law of motion (force=mass × acceleration) in the definition of the standard pound-force, namely,

$$1 \text{ Lb.} = 1 \text{ lb.} \times g_0$$

the last quantity usually being taken as

$$32\cdot2 \text{ ft./sec.}^2 = g_0 = 981 \text{ cm./sec.}^2$$

=the acceleration due to the pull of gravity in London.

$$\text{Thus} \quad \left[\frac{\text{lb.} \times 32\cdot2 \text{ ft.}}{\text{Lb.} \times \text{sec.}^2}\right] = 1 \text{(unity)} = \left[\frac{\text{Lb.}}{\text{lb. } g_0}\right]$$

called the Newtonian unity bracket. Other unity brackets resulting from definitions or measurements of equivalent quantities

$$\text{such as} \quad \left[\frac{2\cdot54 \text{ cm.}}{\text{inch}}\right], \quad \left[\frac{\text{min.}}{60 \text{ sec.}}\right], \quad \left[\frac{33{,}000 \text{ ft.-Lb.}}{\text{h.p. min.}}\right]$$

etc. (see page xxiv), and the Joule unity bracket $\left[\frac{778 \text{ ft.-Lb.}}{\text{B.Th.U.}}\right]$ are used in worked examples in the text to illustrate the ease and sureness of the method of reducing and converting units by a procedure which becomes almost mechanical and fool-proof. This is a development of the Stroud convention (dealt with in the

Note on page xix) which has been used in the Royal Naval College, Greenwich and in training establishments of the Royal Navy since the first world war.

My thanks are due to the firms for permission to use diagrams, and to the Senate of London University and Council of the Institution of Mechanical Engineers for allowing the inclusion of questions selected from the B.Sc. (Engineering) and Associate Membership Examinations.

The additions to the text make the book more complete as a first text-book, the main purpose of which remains that of rendering service complementary to present-day methods of teaching and introducing this subject to students.

A. C. W.

Birmingham, 1956

PREFACE

THIS book is intended to serve as an introductory text-book for students preparing for first examinations in the subject of heat engines and applied thermodynamics.

The scope of the book is such as to cover first examinations of the Final B.Sc. and Associate Membership examinations in this subject and, although the book as a whole may perhaps go somewhat beyond the Ordinary National Certificate stage, the treatment is such as to serve these students, who will have no difficulty in selecting particular sections according to their requirements.

A statement on the aims and plan of the book follows this preface, and it is hoped that, having regard to its size and scope, the book achieves these ends.

As it is too difficult, and well-nigh impossible, to acknowledge adequately the many sources of knowledge and information to which I have had recourse over a period of years, I make a general acknowledgement with an expression of grateful thanks to all those lecturers, authors of books and papers, and firms who have helped me to come by the greater part of the knowledge dealt with and presented in this book. My thanks are also due to several of my friends who have been kind enough to read the typescript or the proofs of the book. I am specially grateful to Dr. W. Abbott, H.M.I., and Dr. J. G. Docherty, D.Sc.; to my colleagues Mr. F. Y. Poynton, M.Sc., and Dr. E. S. Gyngell, Ph.D., and to my brother, Mr. R. S. Walshaw, M.A., B.Sc.

London, 1938.

AIMS AND PLAN OF THE BOOK

(*a*) To describe and establish fundamental principles underlying the subject of heat engines.

(*b*) To describe and illustrate by means of diagrams and sketches simple practical applications of those principles.

(*c*) To show by means of calculations and exercises the applications of fundamental principles in engineering problems.

(*d*) To describe the principles underlying the testing of engines, together with methods of analysing the observations made and drawing up reports on trials of heat engine plant.

With these four aims in view it has been the plan, as nearly as is possible, to present the various sections of the subject in such a way that each succeeding section is built on the ideas and material which have preceded it, and to present the subject-matter and sequence of ideas so as to result in a gradual and continuous development of the subject from chapter to chapter.

The sequence chosen is such that the book divides itself into three parts :

I. Introductory Work on Heat and Heat Engines.

II. Steam and Steam Engine Plant.

III. Compressors and Internal Combustion Engines.

In working out this plan only an elementary knowledge of physics, chemistry, and mathematics has been assumed.

The exercises (i) included at the ends of the chapters are mostly elementary in character and within the reach of students dealing with the subject-matter for the first time. It is felt, however, that to include a few exercises (ii) of a slightly more difficult type will stretch the student's mind in the direction of the ideas which are awaiting him in a more advanced course.

A few fully worked out reports on typical trials have been included, mainly to illustrate the method which can be applied to all types of engineering plant. The numerals on the report sheets of these trials can be used as data for additional exercises.

The symbols used in the book are those recommended in the pamphlet " Engineering Symbols and Abbreviations " issued by the British Standards Institution, and Callendar's steam tables (fourth edition) have been used throughout.

CONTENTS

PART II

STEAM AND STEAM ENGINE PLANT

PART III

COMPRESSORS AND INTERNAL COMBUSTION ENGINES

SUPPLEMENT

KEY TO MAIN USE OF SYMBOLS AND ABBREVIATIONS

Symbol.	Signification.
A	Area; rate of mass flow of air; energy in air stream.
a	Area; acceleration; local speed of sound; suffix or subscript after reversible or ideal adiabatic processes.
B	Energy delivered as brake power (b.h.p.).
b	Specific volume of water at freezing point; energy to drive feed and extraction pumps; numerical value of brake horse-power.
C	Specific heat; cycles per unit time; power to drive a compressor.
C_v, C_p	Specific heats of gases at constant volume and constant pressure.
${}_MC_v$, ${}_MC_p$	Molecular specific heats of gases at constant volume and constant pressure.
c	A constant; numerical value of cycles per unit time.
D, d	Diameter.
E	Internal energy; energy rejected in exhaust.
f	Rate of flow of fuel; frictional coefficient; number of molecules per mol.
F	Force; energy in fuel supply; diagram factor.
G	Negative of Gibbs' function; energy lost in flue gases.
g	Acceleration due to gravity.
H	Enthalpy or total heat of gas and vapour.
h	Enthalpy or total heat of gas and liquid.
i	Numerical value of indicated horse-power.
J	Joule's equivalent, i.e. the Joule unity bracket; energy in jacket-water streams.
k	Coefficient of conductivity.
L	Latent heat; length.
l	Length.
lb.	Pound mass.
Lb.	Pound force.
£	Pound sterling.
M	Mass per mol; " molecular weight."
$\mathcal{M}$	Mach number.
m	Mass; rate of mass flow.
m.e.p.	Mean effective pressure.
N	Number of mols; speed of revolution.
n	Index of expansion; fraction of stroke at which cut-off takes place; number of revolutions per minute.
P, p	Pressure.
$\mathcal{P}$	Power.
h.p.	Horse-power.

Symbol.	Signification.
Q	Quantity of heat.
q	Dryness fraction; rate of flow of heat.
R	Characteristic gas-constant; overall ratio of expansion; radius.
$\mathcal{R}$	Universal gas-constant.
r	Ratio of expansion or compression; radius; heat lost by radiation.
S	Energy supplied in steam; force exerted by spring balance.
s	Specific heat of solids; spring strength; suffix or subscript indicating dry saturated steam; specific gravity.
T	Absolute temperature; torque.
t	Time; ordinary temperature; numerical value of torque.
U, ΔH	Change in total heat, enthalpy or " heat drop."
u	Suffix after real uncooled processes, i.e. practical heat-insulated or adiabatic processes.
V	Volume; velocity.
V_c	Clearance volume.
V_k	Stroke volume.
V_s	Specific volume of dry saturated steam.
v	Velocity.
W	Work or mechanical energy; weight; energy in cooling water streams.
w	Specific weight, i.e. weight density ($w = \rho g$); specific volume of water; suffix or subscript indicating water at saturation temperature.
x	Distance; linear displacement.
z	Height above a datum; ratio of absolute temperatures at the extremes of reversible (i.e. ideal) adiabatic processes.
α, β	Angles.
γ	Ratio C_p/C_v of gases.
η	Efficiency.
ρ	Density, i.e. mass density ($\rho = m/V$).
ϕ	Entropy.
ω	Angular velocity.
θ	Angle.

NOTE ON UNITS AND DIMENSIONS, PHYSICAL AND NUMERICAL FORMULAE, AND THE STROUD CONVENTION

THE object of this note is:

(a) to make students "dimension-conscious" at the beginning of their engineering studies,
(b) to point out and emphasize the difference between *physical* and *numerical* formulae, which students of engineering encounter and have to use, and
(c) to present a simple method of overcoming all difficulties with units and dimensions when developing and using formulae.

In analysis, symbols—P, V, T, Q, E, H, m, v, t, φ, ω, etc.—may be used to represent either *numbers only* (i.e. numerics, e.g. 5, 32·2, etc.) or *physical quantities* (a physical quantity being composed of a number multiplied by a unit or standard measure, e.g. a mass of 5 lb., an acceleration of 32·2 ft./sec.²) according to the convention adopted at the beginning of an analysis, thus resulting in *numerical* or *physical* formulae, respectively.

The Stroud convention (after the late Professor Stroud of Leeds University) **is that symbols are used to represent physical quantities, *i.e.* numbers × units.**

Physics is concerned with inanimate nature and its laws. Therefore, a *physical quantity* is always, and can only be, specfied by a *unit or standard measure* (the unit being of the same nature as the quantity being measured), a *number* showing how many times that unit is contained in a given quantity, and a *sign* indicating direction as in the case of a force or flow of heat. Thus, **a physical quantity is specified by ± a number multiplied by a unit or standard measure.** For example, using the Stroud convention, we should refer to:—

(i) A mass *m* of 5 lb., not a mass of *m* lb., since in the latter case *m* represents a *number only*, namely, 5, whereas in the former case the symbol *m* represents the *complete physical quantity* (number × unit), namely, 5 lb.

(ii) An acceleration, *g*, of 32·2 ft./sec.², not *g* ft./sec.², since in the latter case the symbol *g* merely represents the *number* 32·2, whereas in the former case *g* represents the *physical quantity* in any system of units e.g., $g = 32 \cdot 2$ ft./sec.² $= 981$ cm./sec.², etc.

(iii) A rotational angular velocity of $\omega = 15$ revolutions/sec., and an angular acceleration of, say $\alpha = -3$ radian/sec.² (i.e. an angular retardation of 3 radian/sec².).

(iv) A pressure of fifteen pounds per square inch as P=15 lb. wt./in.^{2}, 15 lb_f/in.^{2} or 15 Lb./in.^{2}—**the abbreviation Lb. is used throughout this book for the standard pound force in order to distinguish clearly between pound mass (lb.), pound force (Lb.) and pound sterling (£),** each of which is *different in kind* from either of the others, i.e. *they are different physical quantities.* **This recognition is fundamental.**

It follows that in **physical formulae,** all of which express inter-relationships (or state a balance) between certain physical quantities as, for example, in Newton's second law of motion **F=ma,** the numbers and the units or measures are, in accordance with the Stroud convention, included in the symbols representing the quantities concerned. Thus, *the Stroud convention is merely that symbols are used to represent complete quantities* as, for instance, Q=−8 B.Th.U. which means that 8 B.Th.U. have left a substance. The negative sign can, however, be rendered unnecessary by using suffixes or subscripts, e.g. Q_i may represent inflow, and Q_o outflow of heat across a boundary surrounding an engine or any energy transformer (see trials on plant).

In a **numerical formula,** such as $b=\frac{2\pi tn}{33,000}$ (see p. 65) which gives the *number* (b) of brake horse-power transmitted by a rotating shaft, *symbols represent numbers only*, the numbers (t and n) required for substitution being obtained by measuring quantities in the units specified at the beginning of the analysis by use of which the formula was originally deduced. Thus, in the numerical formula $b=\frac{2\pi tn}{33,000}$ the symbol t represents the *number* of Lb.-ft. of torque on the shaft, and n represents the *number* of revolutions per minute of the transmission shaft, otherwise the formula will not give the *number* (b) of horse-power transmitted; i.e. the torque or couple C=t Lb.-ft., and the angular speed of the shaft is $\omega=n$ rev./min. and the power transmitted is $\mathcal{P}=b$ h.p., where t, n and b are numbers (or numerics) only and C, ω and $\mathcal{P}$ are physical quantities (numbers × units).

Similarly, *all numerical formulae are based on particular units as also are empirical formulae,* which are usually deduced from graphs plotted as a result of observations made using definite measures or units during laboratory tests and experiments. *Physical formulae are not restricted to any particular units or systems of units but are equally valid in all systems,* e.g. the physical formula for power ($\mathcal{P}$) transmitted by a shaft rotating at an angular speed ω and exerting a torque or couple C is $\mathcal{P}=C\omega$ as shown on page 65.

Since both types of formulae (physical and numerical) are used in engineering, it is essential that students should

(i) Appreciate the difference between them,
(ii) Be in no doubt as to how to derive and use the two types of formulae (see pages 63, 99, 252),

(iii) Be able to convert one type into the other when necessary (see pages 154, 192, 251).

A few physical formulae in the text have been transformed into their equivalent or corresponding numerical formulae (see p. 252) in order to illustrate the difference between them, and also to emphasize the importance of units. Although students often omit units (presumably with the idea of saving time) when the arithmetical stages of the more straightforward problems have been reached, it is essential that students should be "dimension-conscious" and that a check be kept on units.

"Dimensions" is the word used in science when distinguishing between the different kinds or qualities of physical quantities in nature, e.g. *mass*, *length* and *time* are different in kind or quality from one another and are regarded as *the three fundamental dimensions* in the mechanical sciences. When the quality or intensity of heat is involved in problems, *temperature* is usually added as a fourth fundamental dimension.

Heat, work, and energy are quantities which have the same "dimension" and, therefore, all may be measured by means of one standard unit of energy—say the ft. Lb., B.Th.U. or kilowatt-hour.

Units are "yardsticks" or standard measures by means of which the magnitudes of physical quantities may be measured, e.g. ft., sec., lb., £, Lb., ° F. (or, more strictly, F degree), are all standard measures (or units) of quantities having different dimensions. The ratio of any two of all the possible units of the *same* kind or "dimension" (i.e. of the same kind of physical quantity) are related purely by numerical factors,

$$\text{e.g. } \frac{\text{foot}}{\text{inch}}=12;\ \frac{\text{hour}}{\text{sec.}}=3{,}600;\ \frac{\text{B.Th.U.}}{\text{ft.-Lb.}}=778;$$

$$\text{or } \left[\frac{\text{ft.}}{12\text{ in.}}\right]=1 \text{ (i.e. unity)}=\left[\frac{3{,}600\text{ sec.}}{\text{hour}}\right]=\left[\frac{778\text{ ft.-Lb.}}{\text{B.Th.U.}}\right]$$

are "unities" or "unity brackets"; others are given later.

FORCE.—The standard gravitational (or engineers') unit of force is the weight in London of the standard pound mass of platinum kept in the Standards Office of the Board of Trade. Thus, a pound mass of any substance weighs one pound (i.e. is attracted to the earth by one standard pound force) in London. If, also, the particular substance costs one pound, we see that the word "pound" is used for three things which are *different in kind* (i.e. have different "dimensions") and which, therefore, need distinguishing as pound mass, pound force, and pound sterling—the abbreviations being lb., Lb., and £, respectively, which effectively indicate that the three pounds are different in kind.

The foot (ft.) is the fundamental unit of length in the foot-pound-second (f p.s.) system and, by definition, **it is equal to one-third of the standard yard which is kept in the National Physical Laboratory.**

The fundamental **unit of time is the second which, by definition, is the $\frac{1}{86400}$ part of the mean solar day,** *i.e.* of the average interval of time between successive transits of the sun across a meridian of the earth.

These three fundamental units (ft., lb., and sec.) are involved in **Newton's second law of motion (F= ma).** This law, when applied to balance or weigh the pull of the earth on a mass *m*, is usually written $W = mg$. Hence, taking the value of the acceleration caused by the gravitational pull in London as $g_0 = 32 \cdot 2$ ft./sec.², the force caused by the pull of gravity on a mass *m* in London is $W_0 = mg_0$. Therefore, **the standard pound force is 1 Lb. = 1 lb. × 32·2 ft./sec.². This never changes no matter how the value of g changes on or above the earth.**

Hence, $\left[\frac{\text{Lb. sec.}^2}{\text{lb.} \times 32 \cdot 2 \text{ ft.}}\right] = 1$ **(unity), and is called the "Newtonian Unity Bracket" which interconnects the pound force (Lb.) and the pound mass (lb.).**

The weight, gravitational pull or force exerted by the earth on a mass *m* at any point where the acceleration due to gravity is *g* is $W = mg = \frac{W_0}{g_0} g = \frac{g}{g_0}$ times its weight (W_0) in London, but in most engineering problems *on the earth* the variation in the value of g can usually be neglected.

"Poundal" is alternatively used as a unit of force in physics and **"slug"** as a unit of mass in aeronautics. From the table on the following page, based on Newton's second law and definitions, it will be clear that

$$\frac{\textbf{Lb.}}{\textbf{Pdl.}} = 32 \cdot 2 = \frac{\textbf{slug}}{\textbf{lb.}}$$

Examples in the text show how the use of Newtonian and other unity brackets enable the process of reduction and checking of units (i.e. of ensuring that consistent units or standard measures are used) and dimensions (i.e. of ensuring that all the terms being added or subtracted in an equation are the same in kind) to be *carried out on paper rather than mentally* and, therefore, almost with certainty as to accuracy when the arithmetical stage of any problem or calculation has been reached.

Correct equations relating physical quantities are always dimensionally homogeneous, for *the terms of an equation must have the same dimensions before an addition or subtraction can be done, e.g.* 2 ft. + 8 sec. cannot be done. Also, it is obvious that the numbers or numerics of the terms composing a dimensionally-correct equation

Force	Mass	Acceleration	Newtonian Unity Bracket
$F = m \times a$			$\left[\frac{F}{ma}\right] = 1 = \left[\frac{ma}{F}\right]$
1 Lb.	1 lb.	32·2 ft./sec.^{2}	$\left[\frac{\text{lb.} \times 32\cdot2 \text{ ft.}}{\text{Lb. sec.}^2}\right] = 1$
1 Pdl.	1 lb.	1 ft./sec.^{2}	$\left[\frac{\text{Pdl. sec.}^2}{\text{lb. ft.}}\right] = 1$
1 Lb.	1 slug	1 ft./sec.^{2}	$\left[\frac{\text{Lb. sec.}^2}{\text{slug. ft.}}\right] = 1$
1 Dyne	1 gram.	1 cm./sec.^{2}	$\left[\frac{\text{gram. cm.}}{\text{Dyne sec.}^2}\right] = 1$
1 Newton	1 kilogram	1 metre/sec.^{2}	$\left[\frac{\text{Newton sec.}^2}{\text{kilogram metre}}\right] = 1$

cannot be added or subtracted unless they are those of the same standard unit, e.g. 4 B.Th.U. + 3,112 ft.-Lb., although dimensionally correct (the quantities being of the same kind, namely, energy), cannot be added until *measured with the same standard measure or unit*, the B.Th.U., in which case

$$4 \text{ B.Th.U.} + 3{,}112 \text{ ft.-Lb.} \left[\frac{\text{B.Th.U.}}{778 \text{ ft.-Lb.}}\right] = 8 \text{ B.Th.U.}$$

The symbol J is often used "to represent Joule's equivalent," namely 1 B.Th.U. of heat per 778 ft.-Lb. of work. When used in this sense, it is the ratio of the same quantity of energy and is, **therefore, unity as represented by** $\left[\frac{778 \text{ ft.-Lb.}}{1 \text{ B.Th.U.}}\right]$ **which is called the "Joule unity bracket."** Thus, J, when used for this ratio, is not a quantity in the physical sense of being a numeral × a unit, but is merely a unity bracket for the conversion of units as used above. *It is, therefore, unnecessary to include J in algebraic analysis*—in fact it does not arise where symbols are used to represent physical quantities in accordance with the Stroud convention; for the ratio of the equivalence between different forms of energy, e.g. work and heat, as well as for all other quantities, of the same dimension, is only required when a problem has reached the last stage where arithmetic and consistency of units in physical formulae will compel the use of "unity brackets" for the reduction of different units to one and the same standard measure or unit (see Examples on pages **72, 88, 252**).

It is clear, also, that **a radian, being the ratio of two equal lengths of arc and radius, is unity.** Thus, 1 revolution of a crank is 2π, although to write **1 rev.** $=$ 2π **radn.** is a help to most students, it being understood however, that "radian" is the name given to the angle whose circular measure is unity.

Other well-known unity brackets resulting either from definitions or measurements of equivalent quantities are:—

$$\left[\frac{\text{h-p. min.}}{\text{33,000 ft.-Lb.}}\right], \left[\frac{360^\circ}{\text{rev.}}\right], \left[\frac{\text{mile}}{\text{5,280 ft.}}\right], \left[\frac{\text{rev.}}{2\pi}\right], \left[\frac{9^\circ\text{ F.}}{5^\circ\text{ C.}}\right]$$

$$\left[\frac{\text{h-p.}}{\text{746 Watt}}\right], \left[\frac{\text{5 C.H.U.}}{\text{9 B.Th.U.}}\right], \left[\frac{453\cdot 6\text{ gm.}}{\text{lb.}}\right], \left[\frac{\text{2240 lb.}}{\text{ton}}\right]$$

$$\left[\frac{1\cdot 98\times 10^6\text{ ft.-Lb.}}{\text{h.p. hour}}\right], \left[\frac{\text{C.H.U.}}{453\cdot 6\text{ cal.}}\right]\times\left[\frac{\text{9 B.Th.U.}}{\text{5 C.H.U.}}\right]=\left[\frac{\text{B.Th.U.}}{\text{252 cal.}}\right]$$

$$\left[\frac{6\cdot 23\text{ gal.}}{\text{ft.}^3}\right]$$

—a gallon being defined as the volume of 10 lb. of pure water at 62° F. in the standard atmosphere of 30 inches of mercury.

Since multiplying any quantity by unity [1] does not alter the quantity but enables the unit by means of which a physical quantity is measured to be changed, any appropriate unity bracket may be inserted in equations whenever conversion of units is required in the last (the arithmetical) stage of a problem or calculation.

After use it will be realised that the advantages of using symbols according to the Stroud convention, and of using unity brackets, are:—

(i) Units need not be specified at the beginning of any algebraic analysis since they are only needed in the arithmetical stage in which each symbol in a physical formula is replaced by a number × a unit.

(ii) Analysis in symbols is independent of any particular system of units. Thus, any system of units or standard measures can be used in the final (arithmetical) stage of a problem—a mixture of units being reduced to one consistent system by the use of appropriate unity brackets.

(iii) By the use of unity brackets the process of conversion of units is rendered almost mechanical and is done in writing rather than mentally, hence each line of working can be seen and easily checked at any time.

Also, a numerical or empirical formula based on one system of units can be changed by a sure and almost mechanical process into a formula based on any other system of units (see p. 154).

(iv) All "*g* difficulties" are eliminated.

(v) If any quantity, having a dimension, is omitted during analysis, or from a formula, the resulting unit or measure of the final quantity will be seen to have worked out incorrectly and will, therefore, force another check to be made on the analysis and working. This item alone justifies the adoption of the *Stroud convention of using symbols to represent physical quantities in the first analysis*. Numerical formulae can easily be deduced from the resulting physical formulae, if desired (see pages **63**, **65**, **252**).

Worked examples in the text show the ease and sureness with which the method can be applied. A little practice in using the method in exercises will convince students of this; and although it may sometimes appear unnecessary to write units down every time the values of symbols are put into physical formulae, it is essential to do so if one is to be certain of avoiding mistakes with units, dimensions, and "*g*",—mistakes which are all too often made by students of heat engines and other mechanical sciences.

PART I

INTRODUCTORY WORK ON HEAT AND HEAT ENGINES

CHAPTER 1

HEAT, ENERGY, AND POWER

(i) HEAT

1. On the Nature of Heat.—Heat is a form of energy. It is without weight, as is proved when heat is applied to water, which changes into the same weight of steam. Heat cannot, therefore, be a material substance.

Heat produced by mechanical effort was observed by Rumford who noted the large amount of heat evolved during the boring of cannon. Two blocks of ice can be melted by rubbing them together as was shown by Davy in 1799.

The heat in a substance is associated with the motion of its molecules. The hotter the substance the more vigorous are the vibration and motion of its molecules. If heat is applied continuously to a solid it relaxes the cohesion of the molecules, and a point is reached at which the vibration of the molecules is such that the solid changes into liquid in which the molecules can move about more freely. On further addition of heat to the liquid the motion of the molecules is increased still more, and a point is reached at which the liquid begins to change into vapour and then becomes gas. The heat applied dissociates the molecules of liquid from one another so that they fly apart and remain separate in the gaseous state. Heat in a substance may, therefore, be regarded as molecular energy. Radiant heat, however, which travels with the velocity of light, does not require a material medium for its transmission.

The pressure exerted by a gas in a vessel is due to the impact of the molecules on the sides of the vessel. The hotter the gas the greater the pressure, because the more violent is the motion of the molecules which, by molecular impact, cause a bigger force on the sides of the vessel.

With these notions in mind on the nature of heat, the molecular condition of the water and steam in the interior of a boiler can be imagined, as can that of the gases in the cylinder of an internal combustion engine.

2. Transfer of Heat.—It is a law of nature that if there is a difference of temperature, heat will flow from a hotter to a colder substance. This flow or transfer of heat may take place by conduction, convection, and radiation.

(i) **Conduction.**—Transmission of heat by conduction requires a material medium—solid, liquid, or gaseous, but is chiefly thought of in connection with solids. Hot and cold bodies in contact interchange heat by the process of conduction. If one end of a bar of iron is placed in a fire, heat will travel along to the other end by conduction.

Materials vary widely in their conducting powers or conductivities. Engineers use bad conductors to prevent loss of heat. Asbestos lagging is often used on steam pipes, steam-engine cylinders, heaters and boilers. Liquids and gases are bad conductors; they are readily heated by convection but not by conduction.

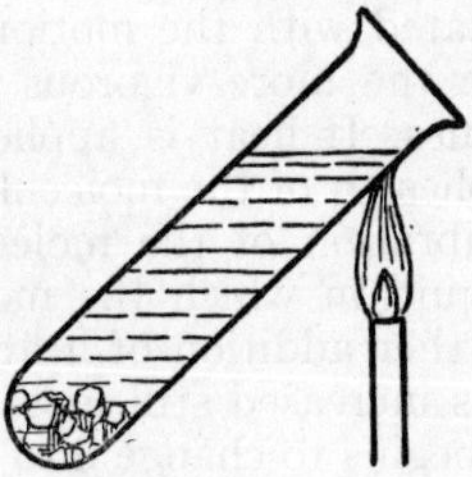

FIG. 1.1—*Conduction of heat.*

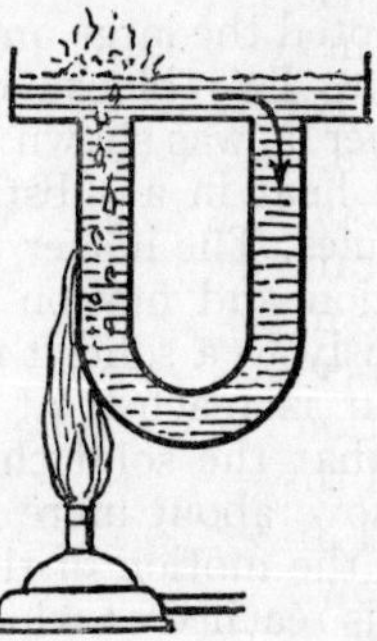

FIG. 1.2—*Convection of heat.*

The following list shows the conducting powers of a few materials in British Thermal Units per hour from face to face through a cube of material of 1 ft. side with a temperature difference of 1° F.

Copper	220	Water	0·35	Wool	0·02
Brass	63	Ice	1·0	Cotton	0·035
Iron	35	Firebricks	0·3 to 1·0	Cork	0·025

To show that water is a bad conductor of heat, take a test-tube nearly full of cold water and hold the upper end near the flame, as shown in fig. 1.1. The water boils at its free surface but the temperature of the water at the bottom of the tube remains almost unchanged. A piece of ice can be held at the bottom of the tube and remain unmelted for a long time.

(ii) **Convection.**—Convected or carried heat is transmitted from one place to another by circulating currents.

Transmission of heat by convection can only occur in liquids and gases. Since movement of fluid is involved in the mixing of warmer particles with cooler particles of the fluid causing the temperature distribution to change with time, convection may be regarded as a special case of conduction because the transference of heat from molecule to molecule takes place by conduction.

Natural or free convection currents are due solely to differences of density caused by differences in temperature at various points in the fluid, whereas forced convection is brought about by means of a fan or pump which maintains the relative motion between the fluid and the heating surface.

In the apparatus of fig. 1.2, if heat is applied to one leg of the U-tube, circulation is immediately set up because the heated and less dense water in the hot leg rises whilst the colder and denser liquid in the other leg flows downwards.

(iii) Radiation.—For transmission of heat by radiation a material medium is not necessary. All substances, whether solid, liquid, or gaseous, emit energy by radiation dependent on their temperatures. Hot bodies give off heat by means of rays which radiate in all directions in straight lines with a speed of 186,000 miles per second. The sun showers heat on the earth in this way. Radiation falling on a body may be reflected, absorbed, or transmitted through the body.

Heat from burning coal in a boiler furnace is transferred to the crown and sides of the furnace by radiation, and it passes through the furnace plates and tubes by conduction, whilst the water in the boiler is heated by convection.

3. Temperature.—Temperature is a measure of the hotness of a substance or of the intensity of heat, *i.e.* of the molecular activity of a substance, and is a property determining whether or not a substance is in thermal equilibrium with other bodies. *Thus temperature is a measure of quality or grade of heat, and should not be confused with quantity of heat.*

The substance, mercury, which expands with heat and contracts with cold, is used in ordinary thermometers to indicate temperature, but very high temperatures are usually measured by some form of pyrometer. A temperature scale assigns a number to every thermal state and provides a means of measuring the temperature of any particular body. The equal increments of the relative or apparent expansion of mercury enclosed in a glass tube correspond to equal rises of temperature.

Two well-known scales, Centigrade (first used by Celsius in 1742) and Fahrenheit (first used in 1665) are such that between the freezing-point and boiling-point of water at atmospheric pressure there are 100 divisions and 180 divisions respectively, as shown in fig. 1.3. One Centigrade degree is therefore $\frac{9}{5}$ times as big as one Fahrenheit degree

or $\left[\frac{9\text{ F. deg.}}{5\text{ C. deg.}}\right]$, **usually written** $\left[\frac{9^\circ\text{ F.}}{5^\circ\text{ C.}}\right]$, **is unity.**

Example.—50° C.$=\frac{9}{5}\times 50$ Fahrenheit degrees above freezing-point.

or$=90+32$ above the zero on the Fahrenheit thermometer.

$\therefore$ 50° C. would read 122° F. on the Fahrenheit scale.

50° F.$=(50°-32°)$ F. above freezing-point,

or$=\frac{5}{9}\times 18=10$ Centigrade degrees above freezing-point.

$\therefore$ 50° F. would read 10° C. on the Centigrade scale.

It will be obvious that on ordinary thermometers the readings depend on the physical properties of the materials (such as mercury and glass) used in their construction. *The perfect thermometer would, however, show equal rises of temperature on its scale for equal additions of heat to the thermometric substance used in it,* and in 1848 Kelvin perceived the need of a scale of temperature which would be independent of the properties of any particular substance. Carnot's reversible engine (see p. 346), which is independent of the nature of the working substance and in which equal quantities of work are done owing to equal falls in temperature, forms the basis of Kelvin's absolute thermodynamical scale of temperature (see p. 352). It will, however, be sufficient for the purposes of this book to think of and use absolute temperature as indicated in the next paragraph.

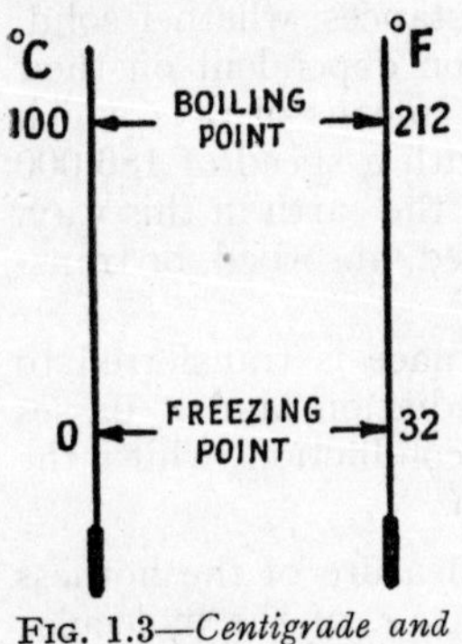

FIG. 1.3—*Centigrade and Fahrenheit thermometers.*

4. Absolute Temperature.—The absolute zero of temperature is the zero below which temperature cannot fall—it being the limit of temperature below which a body cannot be cooled by any process whatever. This limit has never yet been reached, and its exact position is uncertain within a small fraction of a degree.

The zeros on the ordinary Centigrade and Fahrenheit scales were chosen arbitrarily—being the temperature of melting ice in the one case and the temperature of a mixture of ice, water, and salt in the other—the latter producing the lowest temperature which could be achieved in the days when the Fahrenheit scale was introduced. The temperature of melting ice on the

Fahrenheit scale was taken as 32° which, therefore, corresponds to 0° on the Centigrade scale. We shall see later (p. 275) that the absolute zero of temperature is taken to be −273° C. or −460° F., and temperatures measured from this zero are called *absolute temperatures*. The boiling-point of water at atmospheric pressure is, therefore, 273° C.+100° C.=373° C. above absolute zero, and is usually written 373° abs. C., or 672° abs. F.

An important thing with regard to the absolute scale of temperature is that if one of the "permanent" gases, such as air, hydrogen, or nitrogen, is used as the expanding substance for measuring temperatures, it is found that the scale of such a gas-thermometer is practically identical with Kelvin's absolute thermodynamical scale provided that the pressure of the gas is very low, for then the gas behaves very nearly as would a perfect gas. The gas-thermometer is therefore used when a very accurate estimation of temperature is required.

We may note that °F. when used as a unit to measure *differences* of temperature should strictly be written " F. degree "; e.g. 65° F. denotes *a position* on the ordinary Fahrenheit scale corresponding to a position denoted by 525° abs. F. on the absolute Fahrenheit scale, but *the unit of measurement, namely, the Fahrenheit degree, is the same on both scales.* Thus, although a difference of temperature of, say, 25 degrees on both the ordinary and absolute scales should strictly be written as a difference of 25 F. deg., it is customary to write 25° F. for this temperature difference. The abbreviation ° abs. F. has been retained in the text to help students to realise that, in certain cases, the absolute scale of temperature is involved; but it should be understood that *° F. is the abbreviation used for the same unit of measurement as ° abs. F.*, and that these two, when signifying the unit *F. deg.*, can, therefore, be cancelled with one another where temperature differences are concerned, for the Fahrenheit degree is the same measure on both scales—it being merely the datum that is different.

5. Measurement of Quantity of Heat.—To measure quantity of heat, a definite mass (1 lb.) of a particular substance (water) is selected, and the quantity of heat required to raise its temperature by a definite amount (1°) is taken to be unit quantity of heat.

The British Thermal Unit is defined on the Fahrenheit temperature scale, and the Centigrade Heat Unit on the Centigrade scale of temperature. Thus:

1 B.Th.U. is the quantity of heat required to raise the temperature of 1 lb. of water by 1° F. and 1 C.H.U. is the quantity of heat required to raise the temperature of 1 lb. of water by 1° C.

It is found, however, that these quantities vary slightly according to which part of the scale the 1° rise in temperature is made, being slightly different, for instance, when the rise is from 4° to 5° than if the rise is, say, from 91° to 92°. Because of this, the units of heat may be defined more strictly in the following way:

1 *mean B.Th.U. is the* $\frac{1}{180}$*th part of the quantity of heat required to raise the temperature of* 1 *lb. of water from* 32° *F. to* 212° *F.; and* 1 *mean C.H.U. is the* $\frac{1}{100}$*th part of the quantity of heat required to raise the temperature of* 1 *lb. of water from* 0° *C. to* 100° *C.—both at the standard barometric pressure of* 30 *in. of mercury.*

1 C.H.U. is therefore $\frac{9}{5}$ times as big as 1 B.Th.U. or

$$\left[\frac{5\ \text{C.H.U.}}{9\ \text{B.Th.U.}}\right] \textbf{ is unity.}$$

Example.—How many B.Th.U. or C.H.U. are required to raise the temperature of 10 lb. of water from 60° F. to 150° F.?

Rise in temperature = 90° F., i.e. 90 Fahrenheit degrees.

∴ Heat required to raise 10 lb. of water 90° F. = 900 B.Th.U.,

$$\text{which is equal to } 900\ \cancel{\text{B.Th.U.}}\left[\frac{5\ \text{C.H.U.}}{9\ \cancel{\text{B.Th.U.}}}\right] = 500\ \text{C.H.U.}$$

6. Specific Heat and Water Equivalent.—The specific heat of a substance may be defined as the quantity of heat required to raise the temperature of 1 lb. of the substance by 1°.

Alternatively, specific heat may be defined as the ratio

$$\frac{\text{heat to raise temperature of mass } m \text{ of substance by amount } \delta\text{T}}{\text{heat to raise temperature of same mass of water by same amount}}$$

which, being the ratio of two quantities of heat, is a pure number, say $|s|$—the verticals being used to emphasize that s is a number only, i.e. is non-dimensional. Because the heat required to raise the temperature of 1 lb. of water by 1° F. is called a British Thermal Unit, it follows that the heat required to raise the temperature of 1 lb. of substance by 1° F. is $|s|$B.Th.U. Hence, the heat required to raise the temperature of $|m|$ lb. of the substance by $|\delta t|$ °F. is

$$|m| \times |s|\text{B.Th.U.} \times |\delta t| = \frac{\text{M}}{\text{lb.}} \times |s|\text{B.Th.U.} \times \frac{\delta\text{T}}{°\text{F.}} = \text{M} \times |s|\frac{\text{B.Th.U.}}{\text{lb. °F.}} \times \delta\text{T}$$

where the mass of substance is $\text{M} = |m|\text{lb.}$, i.e. $|m| = \frac{\text{M}}{\text{lb.}}$, and the rise in temperature is $\delta\text{T} = |\delta t|°\text{F.}$, i.e. $|\delta t| = \frac{\delta\text{T}}{°\text{F.}}$, and in which it is realised that M and δT are *physical quantities*—each being composed of *a number* × *a unit,* whereas $|m|$ and $|\delta t|$ are numerics, i.e. represent numbers only.

Thus we may write that the heat δQ required to raise the temperature of a mass M of substance by a temperature difference δT is given by the formula

$$\delta Q = M \times C \times \delta T,$$

where $C = |s| \frac{\text{B.Th.U.}}{\text{lb. °F.}}$ in British units or $|s| \frac{\text{calorie}}{\text{grm. °C.}}$ in C.G.S. units, *i.e. C is a number × a measure or unit and* $|s|$ *is a number only.*

In words, the formula states that **the heat added to a substance is equal to the mass × specific heat × rise in temperature.**

The specific heat of mercury is

$$C = 0{\cdot}033 \frac{\text{B.Th.U.}}{\text{lb. °F.}} = 0{\cdot}033 \frac{\text{C.H.U.}}{\text{lb. °C.}} = 0{\cdot}033 \frac{\text{calorie}}{\text{grm. °C.}},$$

the numerical part $|s| = 0{\cdot}033$ being the same in the three systems of units.

Example.—Find the rise in temperature produced on the Centigrade and Fahrenheit scales due to the application of 180 B.Th.U. or 100 C.H.U. to 5 lb. of water. If the initial temperature of the water is 50° F. what is its final temperature?

Heat added = mass × specific heat × rise in temperature.

$$\delta Q = M \times C \times \delta T.$$

$$\text{i.e., } 180 \text{ B.Th.U.} = 5 \text{ lb.} \times 1 \frac{\text{B.Th.U.}}{\text{lb. °F.}} \times \delta T.$$

$$\text{Hence, } \delta T = \frac{180° \text{ F.}}{5} = 36° \text{ F.} = 36° \text{ F.} \left[\frac{5° \text{ C.}}{9° \text{ F.}}\right] = 20° \text{ C.}$$

The initial temperature of the water is 50° F. or $\frac{5}{9}(50-32)$° C. = 10° C. Therefore, after application of heat, the final temperature would be 86° F. or 30° C.

The numerical values of the specific heats of a few substances are given in the table on the following page. They usually have different values for the three states: solid, liquid, and gaseous (the latter at constant pressure and at constant volume).

Example.—The numeric of the specific heat of iron is 0·113. 1 lb. of iron is raised to a temperature of 100° C. by immersion in boiling water and then taken out and quickly suspended in 2 lb. of water, which initially is at a temperature of 10° C. Find the resulting

Substance	Solid	Liquid	Gaseous at	
			Constant Pressure	Constant Volume
Mercury.	0·0314	0·0333	—	—
Water.	0·47 to 0·5	1·00	0·478 (at 100° C.)	0·390
Paraffin.	—	0·60	—	—
Lead.	0·0314	0·0402	—	—
Air.	—	—	0·240	0·171
Oxygen.	—		0·240	0·171
Nitrogen.	—	—	0·235	0·170
Hydrogen.	—	—	3·405	2·402

temperature t of the mixture if the temperature variation of the containing vessel is neglected.

Heat lost by iron = heat gained by water.

Mass of iron × Specific heat of iron × Drop in temperature of iron = Mass of water × Specific heat of water × Rise in temperature of water.

$$\therefore 1\ \text{lb}_i \times 0\cdot 113\ \frac{\text{C.H.U.}}{\text{lb}_i\ {}^\circ\text{C.}} \times (100^\circ\ \text{C.} - t) = 2\ \text{lb}_w \times 1\ \frac{\text{C.H.U.}}{\text{lb}_w\ {}^\circ\text{C.}}\ (t - 10^\circ\ \text{C.})$$

$$\therefore 11\cdot 3\ \text{C.H.U.} + 20\ \text{C.H.U.} = (2 + 0\cdot 113)\ \frac{\text{C.H.U.}}{{}^\circ\text{C.}} \times t.$$

$$\therefore 31\cdot 3 = 2\cdot 113\ \frac{t}{{}^\circ\text{C.}}$$

$$\therefore \frac{t}{{}^\circ\text{C.}} = \frac{31\cdot 3}{2\cdot 113} = 14\cdot 81 \text{ or } t = 14\cdot 81^\circ\ \text{C.}$$

$\therefore$ Resulting temperature of mixture is $t = 14\cdot 81^\circ$ C.

Water Equivalent.—That mass of water requiring the same amount of heat to raise its temperature by one degree as will raise the temperature of a body by one degree is called the water equivalent of the body.

Example.—A copper calorimeter of mass 20 grm. and of specific heat 0·095 has, therefore, a water equivalent given by

$$20\ \text{grm}_c \times 0\cdot 095\ \frac{\text{calorie}}{\text{grm}_c\ {}^\circ\text{C.}} \times 1^\circ\ \text{C.} = m_w \times 1\ \frac{\text{calorie}}{\text{grm}_w\ {}^\circ\text{C.}} \times 1^\circ\ \text{C.}$$

or $\quad 1\cdot 9 = \frac{m_w}{\text{grm}_w}$, i.e. equivalent mass of water is 1·9 grm.

To Find the Specific Heat of a Solid by the Method of Mixtures.—If a solid of mass M, fig. 1.4, is heated in a liquid until its temperature is t and then suddenly plunged into a calorimeter containing water the temperature of which is t_i initially and t_f finally, the specific heat C of the solid can be found in the following way, if losses are neglected:

$$\left[\begin{array}{l}\text{Heat given out by metal (M)}\\ \text{due to a fall in temperature}\\ \text{from } t \text{ to } t_f\end{array}\right] = \left[\begin{array}{l}\text{Heat gained by water (W) and}\\ \text{calorimeter (A) due to a rise}\\ \text{in temperature from } t_i \text{ to } t_f.\end{array}\right]$$

$$\therefore\ M.C(t-t_f)=W.C_w(t_f-t_i)+A.C_c(t_f-t_i)$$

$$\therefore\ C=\frac{(W.C_w+A.C_c)(t_f-t_i)}{M(t-t_f)}=\text{the specific heat of the solid.}$$

If M is a mass of lead weighing 1·1 Lb. and the temperature of the liquid is 98° C., the calorimeter being made of iron of specific heat

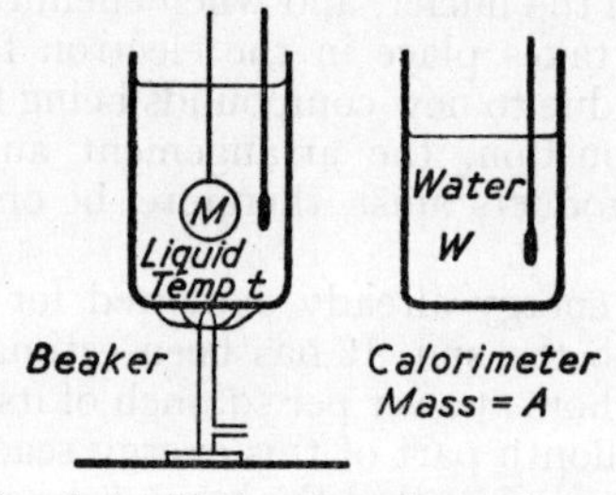

Fig. 1.4.—*Estimation of specific heat.*

0·116 C.H.U./lb.°C. and of mass 0·66 lb., and a change in temperature from 20° C. to 23° C. is produced in 0·77 lb. of water, the specific heat of lead is

$$C=\frac{\left(0\cdot 77\ \text{lb}_w.\times 1\ \dfrac{\text{C.H.U.}}{\text{lb}_w.\ {}^\circ\text{C.}}+0\cdot 66\ \text{lb}_i.\times 0\cdot 116\ \dfrac{\text{C.H.U.}}{\text{lb}_i.\ {}^\circ\text{C.}}\right)(23-20)^\circ\ \text{C.}}{1\cdot 1\ \text{lb}_d.\ (98-23)^\circ\ \text{C.}}$$

$$=0\cdot 031\ \text{C.H.U. per lb. }^\circ\text{C. or }0\cdot 031\ \text{B.Th.U. per lb. }^\circ\text{F.}$$

(ii) ENERGY

7. Forms and Sources of Energy.—*Energy may be thought of as capacity for doing work.* Steam in a boiler contains energy (pressure energy together with heat energy), and work can be obtained from it by means of, say, a steam engine or turbine.

A small proportion of the heat energy in the furnace of a locomotive is ultimately changed into the energy of motion of the train. If the brakes are applied to the moving train the energy of motion is changed back again into heat by friction between the brake blocks and the wheels.

Heat energy is mostly obtained from the chemical energy contained in the substances of the earth. The three elements: carbon, hydrogen, and sulphur are present in most of the fuels used by engineers, whether the fuel be solid (*e.g.* coal), liquid (*e.g.* petrol or oil), or gaseous (*e.g.* coal gas or producer gas).

When 1 lb. of carbon is burned completely to carbon dioxide, 14,550 B.Th.U. are liberated.

When 1 lb. of hydrogen is burned completely to steam, 62,000 B.Th.U. are liberated.

When 1 lb. of sulphur is burned completely to sulphur dioxide, 4,000 B.Th.U. are liberated.

The chemical properties of atoms depend upon the electron formations around the nuclei; and when chemical compounds are formed a change takes place in the electron formations. When energy is released due to new compounds being formed as a result of ordinary combustion, the arrangement and motion of the electrons in the products must, therefore, be one of lower energy content.

The sources of energy already exploited for producing power owe their origin to the sun. It has been estimated that the sun radiates about 50 horse-power per sq. inch of its surface, but only about a 2,000 millionth part of this energy reaches the earth. At some future date it may be that the heat of the sun will be directly converted into work. Another possibility is that of allowing the sun's energy to produce vegetation in large quantities, say in tropical regions, of such a character that alcohol and other fuels may be produced therefrom.

Also, it is now possible to make available for use by the engineer the stock of energy stored away in atoms by the process of nuclear fission.

It is known that radium (which is very costly) gives out in 45 minutes as much energy as could raise its own weight of water from freezing-point to boiling-point, and several thousand years would pass before a piece of radium ceased to give out energy in this way.

Eddington has estimated the temperature on the surface and at the centre of the sun (and stars) to be of the order of 10,000° F. and 36,000,000° F., respectively, and suggests that nuclear energy is released at this temperature by the process known as nuclear fission—this being the reason for the continual stream of energy which radiates from the sun.

The process of nuclear fission shows that large quantities of energy are released by certain types of matter with a consequent reduction of mass in accordance with Einstein's relationship $\delta e = c^2 \delta m$, where c is the speed of light (186,000 miles per second), δe is the amount of energy released due to a reduction of mass δm. Thus in the process of nuclear fission the separate laws of conservation of energy and conservation of mass need to be replaced by one law of conservation of mass plus energy. In ordinary combustion, however, the separate laws concerning conservation of mass and conservation of energy apply. The steady production of energy by the process of nuclear fission requires a slow chain-reaction analogous to the self-propagating process of ordinary combustion in which any heat released is sufficient to ignite neighbouring fuel which in turn releases more heat, and so on. Slow chain reactions in the process of nuclear fission have been produced, but at temperatures high enough for use in plant such as boilers.

At present, however, engineers derive energy mainly from the ordinary process of combustion and transform energy and generate power by means of boilers, steam engines, internal-combustion engines, water possessing potential energy and harnessed to work in the water turbines of electric power stations, chemical processes in batteries, and a few other means such as the wind and the tides.

8. Calorific Value of Fuel.—The expression " calorific value of a fuel" is just another term for the heating value of unit mass of fuel when burnt completely. Two calorific values are met with in practice:

The Higher Calorific Value (H.C.V.) or gross calorific value of a fuel is the quantity of heat which is liberated per unit mass of fuel burnt when the products of combustion are cooled down to the atmospheric temperature (say 60° F.) of the fuel and oxygen before combustion. The steamformed due to the combustion of hydrogen is thus condensed and, therefore, gives up its latent heat and also some of its sensible heat (p. 101).

The Lower Calorific Value (L.C.V.) or net calorific value of a fuel is the higher calorific value less the latent heat of the steam formed by the combustion of hydrogen in the fuel and the evaporation of moisture in the air supplying the oxygen.

i.e. L.C.V. = H.C.V. − L × [Pounds of moisture in air used + 9 × lb. of hydrogen per lb. of fuel.]

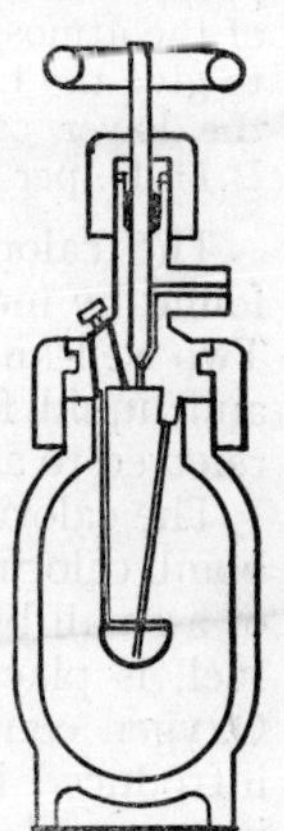

FIG. 1.5—*Bomb calorimeter.*

Thus, to estimate the L.C.V. involves the assumption that the whole of the hydrogen in the fuel has been burnt to water; that the exact amount of hydrogen in the fuel is known; and that the moisture in the air supplying the oxygen is known. It assumes, therefore, that a chemical analysis has been made. Since, however, the value of the latent heat of steam (L) depends upon pressure, and the exact pressure of the steam, together with the partial pressures of other gases in the products of combustion, can only be found if the volumetric analysis of the products is known, the finding of the correct value of L from steam tables is not so straightforward as might at first appear. It is usual, however, when L.C.V. is to be estimated, to take L=1,055 B.Th.U. per lb., *i.e.*, the latent heat at 68° F., this being the saturation temperature corresponding to a steam pressure of 0·34 Lb. per sq. in. abs.

In spite of this agreed fixing of L for purposes of calculating L.C.V., it is more satisfactory to use the H.C.V. or gross calorific value since the latter is the direct experimental figure which represents the heating value of a fuel reckoned from atmospheric temperature (usually specified as 60° F.) as the datum. It is an indication of inefficiency of fuel-burning plant if this heat (H.C.V.) is not fully used. In fact, there is no convincing argument for using the so-called L.C.V. in any problem.

Example.—A fuel-oil containing 13 per cent. of hydrogen by weight was found by experiment to have a higher calorific value of 19,260 B.Th.U. per lb. It is known that 0·13 lb. of hydrogen burns to produce $9 \times 0 \cdot 13 = 1 \cdot 17$ lb. of steam. Hence, neglecting the moisture of the atmosphere, the latent heat to be subtracted from the H.C.V. to give the L.C.V. is $1 \cdot 17 \times 1{,}055 = 1{,}235$ B.Th.U. per lb. of fuel, and the lower calorific value of the fuel-oil is $19{,}260 - 1{,}235 = 18{,}025$ B.Th.U. per lb.

The calorific values of solid, liquid, and gaseous fuels are found by means of calorimeters designed to suit the type of fuel. Two well-known calorimeters for finding the calorific values of gas and liquid fuels are Boys' and Junkers', respectively. These are referred to again on pp. 450, 463).

The calorific value of a solid fuel can be found by means of the bomb calorimeter shown in fig. 1.5. A quantity of fuel in the form of a small briquet, which has been pressed from finely powdered fuel, is placed in the crucible at the centre of the steel bomb. Oxygen contained in a cylinder at about 300 Lb. per sq. in. is introduced into the bomb which is then closed and immersed in a vessel of water. The fuel is ignited by means of a small electrically-heated coil which is placed near the briquet. The water in the vessel is stirred continuously, and its temperature is noted before ignition and at intervals of time, both during and after the process of burning, in order to estimate, from the cooling curve, the loss in temperature during the combustion period. The estimated loss in temperature during the combustion period is added to the observed rise to give the true rise in temperature which would be produced by the heat liberated if no heat was lost by radiation and convection. The heat produced by the fuel is then calculated, being the product of the water equivalent of the bomb plus water in the vessel, and the corrected rise in temperature.

Example.—The observations made during a test of coal were: Weight of briquet, 1·36 Grm. Weight of ash, 0·093 Grm. Weight of water in vessel, 1,400 Grm. The water equivalent of the calorimeter had been previously determined as 227 grm. Initial temperature of water, 10·6° C. Highest temperature of water, 17·4° C. Temperature observations made at noted intervals of time:

Time in Mins.	0	0·5	1	1·5	2	2·5	3	3·6	4
Temp. in °C.	10·6	10·8	11·2	12·4	13·4	14·4	15·4	16·0	15·6

Time in Mins.	5	5·5	6	7	8	9	11	14	16
Temp. in °C.	17·4	17·4	17·4	17·4	17·3	17·2	17·15	17	16·9

The time of burning was from 0 to 5 minutes, with an apparent rise in temperature of water 17·4° C.−10·6° C.=6·8° C.

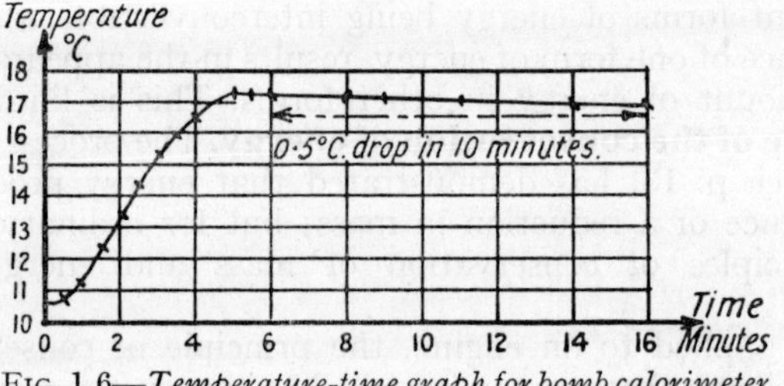

Fig. 1.6—*Temperature-time graph for bomb calorimeter.*

From the cooling curve of fig. 1.6, the rate of fall of temperature due to radiation at the end of the combustion period $=\frac{0 \cdot 5}{10}=0 \cdot 05°$ C. per minute. From this rate, and an application of Newton's law of cooling, a corrected temperature-time graph can be drawn; but in practice it is found that to assume the average rate of temperature fall during the combustion period is half the rate at the end of the period, is a good approximation. Thus, the temperature lost due to radiation during the 5-min. experiment $=0\cdot025\dfrac{°\text{C.}}{\text{min.}}\times 5\text{ min.}=0\cdot125°\text{ C.}$

$\therefore$ True rise in temperature produced by the burning of fuel $=6\cdot8°\text{ C.}+0\cdot125°\text{ C.}=6\cdot925°\text{ C.}$

$\therefore$ Heat produced by a mass of 1·36 grm. of coal

$$=(1400+227)\text{grm}_w.\times 1\,\frac{\text{calorie}}{\text{grm}_w.\,°\text{ C.}}\times 6\cdot925°\text{ C.}$$

$$\therefore \text{Calorific value of the sample of coal}=\frac{1,627\times 6\cdot925\text{ calories}}{1\cdot36\text{ grm. of fuel}}$$

$$=8,280\text{ calories per grm. of coal.}$$

$$=8,280\frac{\text{cal.}}{\text{grm.}}\left[\frac{453\cdot6\text{ grm.}}{\text{lb.}}\right]\left[\frac{\text{C.H.U.}}{453\cdot6\text{ cal.}}\right]\left[\frac{9\text{ B.Th.U.}}{5\text{ C.H.U.}}\right]$$

$$=14,900\text{ B.Th.U. per lb. of coal.}$$

This is the higher or gross calorific value because the temperature of the gases at the end of the experiment being nearly atmospheric, namely, 17·4° C. or 63·3° F. means that any steam formed will have condensed and, therefore, have given up its heat.

9. Conservation of Energy and the First Law of Thermodynamics.—It is usually assumed that *in ordinary processes matter is neither created nor destroyed*, though it may be made to take different forms, visible or invisible. Similarly, *energy can take many different forms but cannot be created or destroyed.* **The sum total of energy in a closed system always remains the same**—different forms of energy being interconvertible, *i.e.* the disappearance of one form of energy results in the appearance of the same amount of energy in other forms. This is known as **the principle of the conservation of energy.** The process of nuclear fission (see p. 13) has demonstrated that energy produced is a consequence of a reduction in mass; but for ordinary processes the principles of conservation of mass and energy can be applied.

When applied to an engine, the principle of conservation of energy tells us that energy supplied to the engine = energy converted into work + energy rejected from the engine.

Example.—An internal-combustion engine is supplied with $\frac{1}{10}$ lb. of fuel per minute having a heating value of 18,000 B.Th.U. per lb. If 30 per cent. of the energy supplied is converted into useful mechanical energy or work, find the quantity of heat rejected per minute.

Heat supplied to engine $=0 \cdot 1 \times 18{,}000 = 1{,}800$ B.Th.U. per minute.
Work done by engine $=0 \cdot 3 \times 1{,}800 = 540$ B.Th.U. per minute.
$\therefore$ Heat rejected from engine $=1{,}260$ B.Th.U. per minute,
which would be the sum of the heat rejected to exhaust, to engine cooling water, and to the surrounding air.

The First Law of Thermodynamics.—*The first law of thermodynamics is merely the principle of the conservation of energy coupled with the fact that heat is a form of energy.* It may be stated in the form of a verbal equation as:

$$\left[\textbf{Heat added to a substance}\right] = \left[\textbf{Increase in internal energy of the substance}\right] + \left[\textbf{External work done by the substance}\right]$$

Symbolically, it may be written: $\boldsymbol{\delta Q = \delta E + \delta W}$.

This "first law equation" is easily understood by reference to fig. 1.7, in which a fluid or gas S, is enclosed in a cylinder by means of a load, W, on a movable piston. The heat added to the substance by means of the burner, B, goes either into the substance itself and so increases its temperature, or to do work in forcing up the loaded piston. That is, the heat (δQ) supplied by B goes to increase the internal molecular energy (δE) and to do external work (δW) by lifting the load. Hence, $\delta Q = \delta E + \delta W$.

W
S
B

Fig. 1.7—*First law of thermodynamics.*

Alternatively, the first law of thermodynamics may be stated thus: **When heat is produced by the expenditure of work or mechanical energy** (for example, heat produced due to friction from the work spent in rubbing two materials together) **a definite amount of heat is produced for every unit of work spent.** And conversely, **when mechanical energy is produced from heat energy a definite quantity of heat goes out of existence for every unit of work done.** This confirms the notion that heat is a form of energy.

The first law states that heat and work are interconvertible, and *it is true for all processes,* i.e. for imaginary ideal processes as well as for real processes, since the law is merely a statement of the law of conservation of energy.

10. Joule's Equivalent.—An elaboration of the apparatus shown diagrammatically in fig. 1.8 was used by Joule in 1843 to determine the equivalence between heat and work. Paddles P fixed to spindle S rotate in a volume of water V because the weight W (778 Lb.) descends as the rope unwinds from barrel B.

When W has descended 1 ft., then 778 ft.-Lb. of work have been done. This energy appears as heat in the water owing to friction caused by the paddles in the water. A thermometer would show (with more perfect apparatus) that 778 ft.-Lb. of work produces a rise in temperature of 1° F. in a mass of 1 lb. of water—that is, **778 ft.-Lb. are equivalent to 1 B.Th.U.** Thus, Joule estimated the heat equivalent of work, not the mechanical equivalent of heat. If this quantity of heat is divided by itself in equivalent work units we get the **Joule unity brackets**

$$\left[\frac{\textbf{1 B.Th.U.}}{\textbf{778 ft.-Lb.}}\right], \left[\frac{\textbf{1400 ft.-Lb.}}{\textbf{1 C.H.U.}}\right] \textbf{ and } \left[\frac{\textbf{4·19}\times\textbf{10}^7\textbf{ ergs}}{\textbf{calorie}}\right]$$

(see also p. xxiii).

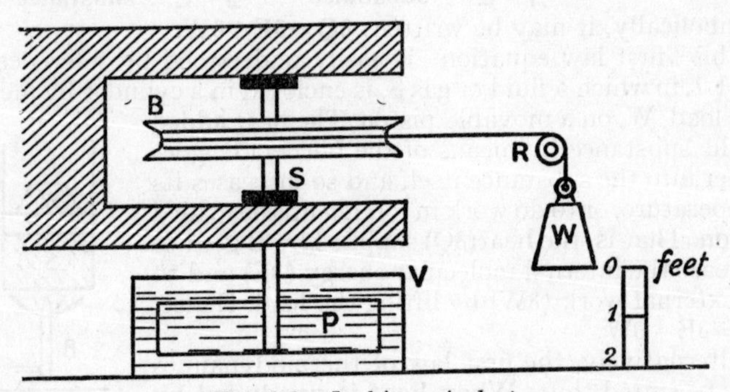

FIG. 1.8—*Joule's equivalent.*

One must not be misled by the phrase "mechanical equivalent of heat" *into thinking that a given quantity of heat can be converted wholly into mechanical energy, for it should be noted here that while it is true that any quantity of mechanical energy can be changed into its equivalent amount of heat, the converse of this is not true.*

We shall see later (*p.* 350) *that in accordance with the second law of thermodynamics there is a definite limit to the amount of mechanical energy which can be obtained from a given quantity of heat energy.*

In fact, the maximum amount of mechanical energy or work theoretically available from an amount of heat Q will be proved (p. 351) to be $Q\left(\frac{T_1-T_2}{T_1}\right)=Q-Q\frac{T_2}{T_1}$, where T_1 and T_2 are the absolute temperatures of the heat received and rejected respectively by a perfect engine—say, one working on the Carnot cycle (p. 346). Thus, conversion of heat into work, even if a perfect engine could be used, falls short of complete conversion by an amount $Q\frac{T_2}{T_1}$ which is consequently called "unavailable energy."

Example 1.—The frictional force produced by a brake on the circumference of a 7-ft. diameter flywheel which is rotating at $\omega = 90$ revolutions per minute is F=600 Lb. Find the quantity of heat produced per second due to the friction of the brake.

Mechanical energy or work dissipated by the brake per unit time

=Frictional force × speed of brake rim.

$$= F \times r\omega = 600 \text{ Lb.} \times 3\cdot5 \text{ ft.} \times \frac{90 \text{ rev.}}{60 \text{ sec.}}\left[\frac{2\pi}{\text{rev.}}\right]\left[\frac{\text{B.Th.U.}}{778 \text{ ft.-Lb.}}\right]$$

$$= 25\cdot4 \text{ B.Th.U. per sec.}$$

Example 2.—(*a*) A gas is contained in a vertical cylinder by means of a movable piston on which there is a constant load of 778 Lb. Heat is applied such that the piston rises 2 ft., and it is estimated, by taking initial and final gas temperatures, that the increase in internal energy is 0·5 B.Th.U. Find the quantity of heat supplied to the gas, neglecting radiation losses.

Work done by gas in lifting 778 Lb. through a height of 2 ft. =1,556 ft.-Lb. which is equivalent to 2 B.Th.U.

Increase in internal energy of gas=0·5 B.Th.U.

∴ By the first law of thermodynamics, the heat supplied to the gas=2·5 B.Th.U.

(*b*) If the cylinder is now placed in a bath containing 20 lb. of water until the piston has fallen by a vertical distance of 1 ft., find the decrease in the internal energy of the gas if the temperature of the water in the bath rises by 4° F. Neglect the water equivalent of piston and cylinder, and neglect radiation losses.

Heat abstracted from gas = Heat gained by water in bath,

$$= 20 \text{ lb.} \times 1 \frac{\text{B.Th.U.}}{\text{lb. } ^\circ\text{F.}} \times 4^\circ \text{F.} = 80 \text{ B.Th.U.}$$

Work done *by* gas due to piston falling 1 ft. = 778 Lb. × (−1) ft. = −778 ft.-Lb. which is equivalent to −1 B.Th.U.

∴ By first law of thermodynamics: Increase in internal energy of gas = Heat added to gas − Work done *by* the gas.

$$= -80 \text{ B.Th.U.} - (-1 \text{ B.Th.U.})$$
$$= -79 \text{ B.Th.U.}$$

That is, there is a decrease in internal energy of 79 B.Th.U.

(iii) POWER

11. Power, and the Horse-power-hour Unit.—Power is defined as the time rate of doing work. It is a measure of working capacity—that is, of how much work an engine can do in unit time.

It should be noted that in the definition of work (force × displacement) no reference is made to the time taken to do the work. Herein lies the difference between work and power. The ft.-Lb. unit is a measure of work, whereas the ft-Lb. per second unit is a measure of power. Thus, energy expended or produced per unit of time is a measure of power.

Horse-power.—The unit, 1 horse-power, is defined as 33,000 ft.-Lb. per minute, being James Watt's estimate of the rate at which a horse could work. It is equivalent to 550 ft.-Lb. per second or to 746 Watt, or 0·746 kilowatt.

Also 1 horse-power is equivalent to

$$33{,}000\,\frac{\cancel{\text{ft.-Lb.}}}{\text{min.}}\left[\frac{\text{B.Th.U.}}{778\ \cancel{\text{ft.-Lb.}}}\right]=\mathbf{42\cdot 41\ B.Th.U.\ per\ minute.}$$

Example.—A horse walks round in a circle at 3 miles per hour exerting a constant horizontal force of 250 Lb. on an arm which turns the wheels of a primitive corn mill. Find the rate at which the horse is working in the horse-power units of the engineer.

$$3\text{ miles per hour}=3\,\frac{\cancel{\text{mile}}}{\cancel{\text{hour}}}\times\left[\frac{5{,}280\text{ ft.}}{\cancel{\text{mile}}}\right]\times\left[\frac{\cancel{\text{hour}}}{3{,}600\text{ sec.}}\right]=4\cdot 4\,\frac{\text{ft.}}{\text{sec.}}$$

∴ The horse is working at the rate of 250 × 4·4 ft.-Lb. per sec., or

$$250\ \cancel{\text{Lb.}}\times 4\cdot 4\,\frac{\cancel{\text{ft.}}}{\cancel{\text{sec.}}}\times\left[\frac{\text{h.p.}}{550\,\frac{\cancel{\text{ft.-Lb.}}}{\cancel{\text{sec.}}}}\right]=2\text{ h.p.}$$

That is, one horse is developing 2 horse-power units as engineers reckon them.

Horse-power-hour.—The expression "one horse-power-hour" is a contracted way of saying one horse-power developed for one hour. 1 horse-power-hour is thus 33,000 ft.-Lb. per minute developed for 60 min. $=33{,}000\,\frac{\text{ft.-Lb.}}{\text{min.}}\times 60\text{ min.}=1{,}980{,}000$ ft.-Lb.

The horse-power unit is therefore a definite quantity of energy, being equivalent to 1,980,000 ft.-Lb. of work, or to 2,545 B.Th.U. or to 0·746 kilowatt-hour unit of electrical energy.

By means of this unit the fuel consumption of engines, for the doing of this definite amount of work, can be compared. One always sees in reports on engine trials the consumption of fuel per b.h.p.-hour expressed prominently as a most important item.

The unit is dealt with further on p. 73.

EXERCISES ON CHAPTER I

1. Describe what happens when heat is applied continuously to a solid, a liquid, a gas.

2. What is temperature? How can it be measured and how does it differ from quantity of heat?

3. Convert 5°, 41°, 158°, 266° Fahrenheit to Centigrade, and 1°, −30°, 90°, 120° Centigrade to Fahrenheit.

4. The mercury in a Fahrenheit thermometer rises by 45°; how many degrees would this correspond to on a Centigrade thermometer?

5. What is the difference between temperatures measured on the absolute scale and those measured on ordinary scales?

6. Express the answers of Question 3 in absolute units.

7. In what respect does a British Thermal Unit differ from a Centigrade Heat Unit?

8. Find the equivalent of 100 B.Th.U. in C.H.U.

9. How many units of heat are required to raise 1 lb. of water from 55° F. to 212° F.? Convert the result into units of work.

10. A weight of 1 Ton is lifted by means of an engine through a vertical distance of 400 ft. What amount of heat is converted into work by this act?

11. How much water at 60° F. must be mixed with 1 lb. of water at 212° F. so that the resulting temperature shall be 120° F.?

12. 1 lb. of lead shot at a temperature 100° C. and of specific heat 0·031 is poured into 12 oz. of water contained in an iron vessel of mass 10 oz. the specific heat of which is 0·116. Find the final temperature of the mixture if the initial temperature of the water and calorimeter is 20° C.

13. The following figures, given by Callendar, show the numerical values of the specific heat of water at different temperatures.

Temperature °C.	−5	0	5	10	15	20
Specific heat.	1·0158	1·0094	1·0054	1·0027	1·0011	1·0000
Temperature, °C.	25	30	35	40	45	50
Specific heat.	0·9992	0·9987	0·9983	0·9982	0·9983	0·9987
Temperature °C.	55	60	65	70	75	80
Specific heat.	0·9992	1·0000	1·0008	1·0016	1·0024	1·0033
Temperature, °C.	85	90	95	100	120	140
Specific heat.	1·0043	1·0053	1·0063	1·0074	1·0121	1·0176
Temperature, °C.	160	180	200			
Specific heat.	1·0238	1·0308	1·0384			

Plot a curve on a temperature base showing the variation of specific heat with temperature

14. How does power differ from heat, work, or any other form of energy?

15. If 14,400 B.Th.U. are evolved when 1 lb. of a certain brand of coal is burned, calculate the energy stored in 1 ton of this coal and express it in C.H.U., B.Th.U., ft.-Lb. units, horse-power-hours, and in kilowatt-hour units.

16. The boiler in a central-heating system is situated in the basement of a house, and the rooms in three stories have to be heated by means of hot water circulating through radiators. Draw a diagrammatic sketch showing a system by which hot water can be made to circulate.

17. Fuel-oil of density 58 lb. per cu. ft. and calorific value 18,000 B.Th.U. per lb. is used to fire a set of steam boilers A certain brand of coal having a calorific value of 14,400 B.Th.U. per lb. and density, when stacked in bunkers of 52 lb. per cu. ft. is sometimes used to fire the boilers. Express in horse-power-hour units the energy which can be stored in a ship of 40,000 cu. ft. bunker or tank capacity if (*a*) coal only is used, (*b*) oil only is used.

18. (*a*) If the energy available for tractive purposes in a locomotive is 4 per cent. of the heat energy produced by burning coal in the boiler furnace, calculate the quantity of coal consumed by the locomotive per horse-power-hour of effective work if each lb. of coal liberates 14,400 B.Th.U.

(*b*) What weight of coal will be consumed per hour by the locomotive when pulling a train, weighing 390 Tons, at an average speed of 50 m.p.h. against frictional resistances of 15 Lb. per Ton on a level track?

19. An oil engine rejects to the exhaust, to engine cooling water, and to surrounding air a sum total of 75 per cent. of the energy supplied. If the useful mechanical work is equivalent to 50 horse-power, find the consumption in lb. of fuel per minute if the fuel-oil used has calorific value of 18,000 B.Th.U. per lb.

20. What is meant by the *mechanical equivalent of heat*? Outline any one method by which its value may be determined experimentally.

A train weighing 500 Tons descends an incline of gradient 1 in 56 at a uniform speed of 35 m.p.h., the engine being shut off. Neglecting heat losses, calculate the rate of rise of temperature of the wheels and brakes, assuming their weights to be 30 Tons and 15 Tons respectively, and the numerical values of the specific heats of their materials 0·12 and 0·34 respectively. (I.Mech.E., Sec. A.)

21. (i) Describe, with the aid of a sketch of apparatus, how to estimate the higher and lower calorific values of a fuel.

(ii) One-tenth of a grm. of the liquid fuel $C_{12}H_{26}$ was placed in a bomb calorimeter, the water equivalent of which was 460 grm. The bomb was surrounded by 1,900 grm. of water which rose in temperature by 0·83° F. above that of the atmosphere after the fuel was fired. Taking 1,055 B.Th.U. as the latent heat of 1 lb. of steam formed by the combustion of the hydrogen in the fuel, estimate the higher and lower calorific values of the fuel in B.Th.U. per lb. and state the assumptions made. The atomic weights of hydrogen, carbon, nitrogen and oxygen may be taken as 1, 12, 14 and 16, respectively.

CHAPTER 2

THE FUNCTION AND ESSENTIALS OF A HEAT ENGINE: TYPES OF HEAT ENGINES AND ENGINE GEAR

1. The Function of a Heat Engine.—The function of a heat engine is to transform heat energy into mechanical energy and render the latter available for doing useful work. *A heat engine is, therefore, merely an energy transformer*, although it may take many different and complicated forms.

In 1824 Carnot concluded that heat can produce mechanical energy or work by flowing from one level of temperature to another through an engine in a way analogous to that of water falling from one level to another and doing work in passing over a water-wheel proportional to the quantity descending and to the height through which the water falls.

On p. 18 it was pointed out that *because of a law of Nature known as the second law of thermodynamics* (*also see p.* 350) *there is a definite limit to the amount of mechanical energy that can be obtained from heat energy*. Engineers desire to get the maximum of mechanical energy from any quantity of heat energy supplied to an engine; that is, they aim at getting the maximum efficiency of transformation of heat into work. Modifications in the designs of engines and developments of new ideas are constantly being carried out with this end in view. The selection of a particular type of power plant is usually based on a compromise between various demands concerning power output, efficiency, space, weight, capital cost and running costs.

2. The Essentials of a Heat Engine.—There are three primary or basic essentials underlying the working of all heat engines. They are:

(i) *A source of heat* which supplies heat to the working agent of the engine—a fraction of the heat supplied being changed into work.

(ii) *A working agent*, which alternately takes in and rejects heat, expanding and contracting when doing so, and overcoming the resistance opposing these changes.

(iii) *A sink* or receiver into which heat can be rejected.

All types of heat engines have these three essentials; the rest of the mechanism and parts fitted to engines is gear and apparatus necessary for the successful operating and functioning of the three essentials.

Theoretically, the working agent may be solid, liquid, or gaseous; but practically, water vapour and gases, in steam and internal-combustion engines, respectively, have, up to the present, been predominant. We will, however, first consider an engine in which a solid metal bar constitutes the working agent.

3. A Solid-bar Heat Engine.—Fig. 2.1 shows diagrammatically a "solid-bar" engine in which the three essentials of a heat engine are obviously seen as:

(i) *the source of heat*, in the form of a fuel burner;

(ii) *the working agent*, in the form of a metal bar which expands when heat is applied by the burner, and contracts when the cold water spray is turned on;

(iii) *the sink*, into which heat can be rejected, is seen as the cold-water spray, which, when turned on, abstracts heat and carries it away from the metal bar.

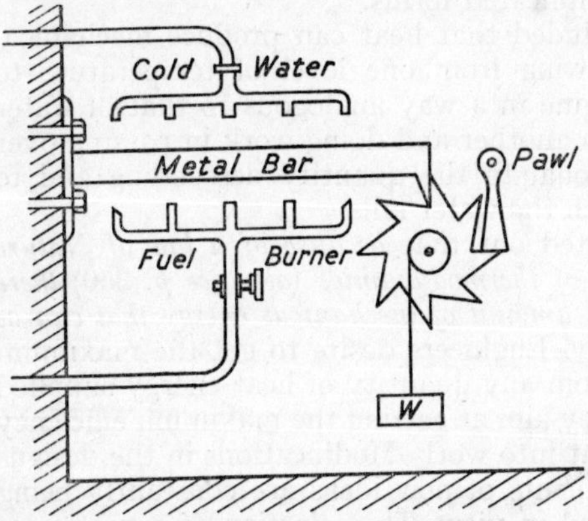

FIG. 2.1—*Solid bar heat engine.*

By alternately applying heat and cold the metal bar can be made to expand and contract, and by means of the rachet wheel and pawl it can be made to do work in raising the weight W.

This type of engine would, however, be too slow in its working and too inefficient to be of much practical use.

It will be noticed that the same metal bar is used time after time as the working agent, but we shall see that in actual steam and internal-combustion engines where water vapour and gases, respectively, form the working agents (both of which expand when heated and contract when cooled), a fresh supply of the working agent is taken in by the engine each cycle, and, after doing work, is rejected either into a condenser or into the atmosphere.

In the next section we shall consider various types of engines in actual practical use, pointing out the three essentials of a heat engine in each case.

TYPES OF HEAT ENGINES, AND ENGINE GEAR

Most working engines can be placed in one or the other of two categories, namely, (i) steam engines (including turbines), (ii) internal-combustion engines (petrol, paraffin, gas, and oil engines). Typical engines in each category will now be considered.

(i) STEAM ENGINES

4. Simple Steam Engines.—Fig. 2.2 shows a section through a vertical steam engine in which steam can be admitted alternately to one side of the piston and then the other, thus making the engine *double-acting*. The figure shows the piston at top-dead-centre (or inner-dead-centre) and the slide valve about to admit high-pressure steam to the top side of the piston. The underside of the piston has, in this position, a through passage to exhaust which may lead into the atmosphere if the engine is non-condensing, or into a condenser at a pressure less than that of the atmosphere if the engine is of the condensing type.

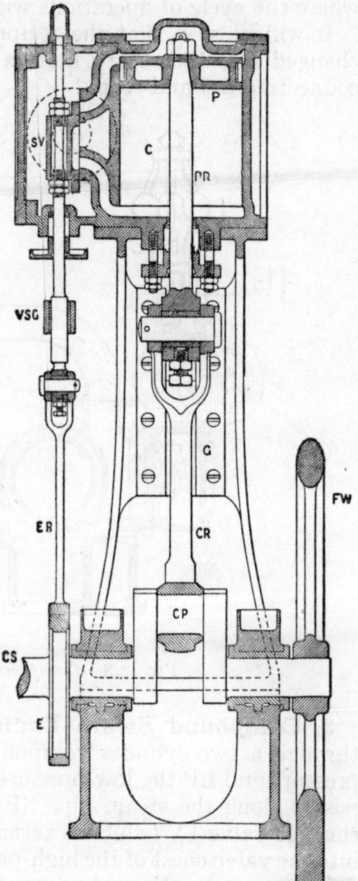

As steam is admitted to the top side, the piston moves downwards owing to the resultant force caused by the difference between high-pressure steam, which is in communication with the boiler, on the top side, and low-pressure steam, which is in communication with the exhaust pipe, on the underside of the piston. When the piston has reached bottom-dead-centre (or outer-dead-centre) the eccentric will have

FIG. 2.2—*Steam engine.*

moved the slide valve such that high-pressure steam is about to enter the underside of the piston while the top side is in communication with the low-pressure steam flowing along the exhaust pipe. There will then be a resultant upward force, and the piston will move up to top-dead-centre (or inner-dead-centre) again, where the cycle of operations will commence to be repeated.

It will be seen that the reciprocating motion of the piston is changed into the rotary motion of the flywheel by means of a connecting rod and crank.

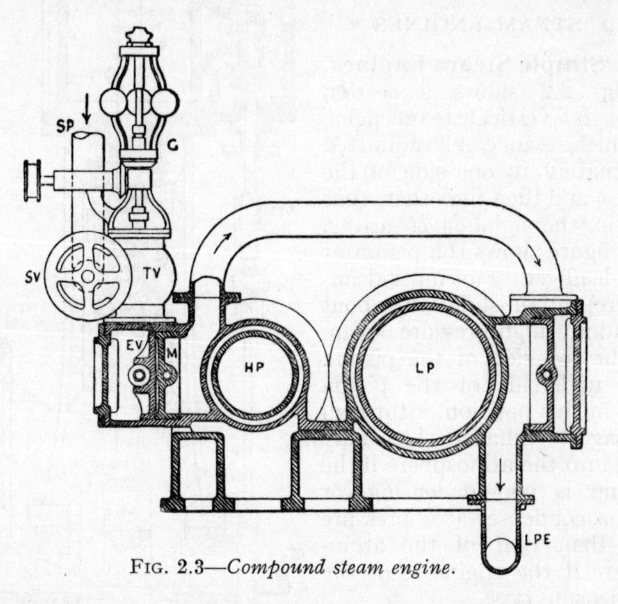

FIG. 2.3—*Compound steam engine.*

5. Compound Steam Engines.—Fig. 2.3 shows a section through a two-cylinder compound engine, HP being the high-pressure and LP the low-pressure cylinder. Steam from the boiler passes along the steam pipe SP through the stop valve SV and throttle valve TV (which is actuated by the centrifugal governor) into the valve chest of the high-pressure cylinder, in which a Meyer expansion valve M works actuated by two eccentrics which are fitted on the crankshaft. After doing work in the high-pressure cylinder the steam is exhausted into the pipe shown connecting the two cylinders. The pipe acts as a *receiver* until the steam is admitted to the low-pressure cylinder by a simple D slide valve. The steam does work in the LP cylinder before being rejected into the exhaust pipe LPE which conveys the steam to the condenser.

Multi-cylinder steam engines are the outcome of increased boiler pressures which are still being increased; and surface condensers have made low back-pressures possible. Compound engines still have many uses, especially on steam locomotives, and triple and quadruple-expansion engines are fitted in cargo vessels.

6. De Laval Steam Turbine.—Fig. 2.4 shows a section through a De Laval steam-turbine in which steam from the boiler

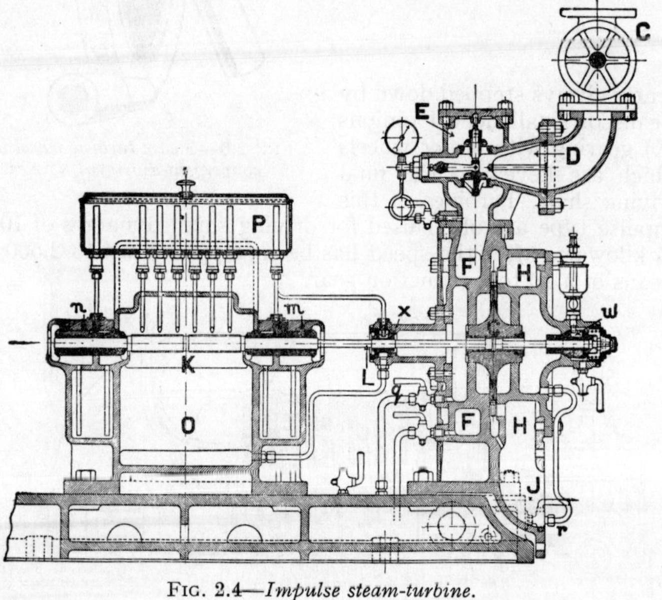

FIG. 2.4—*Impulse steam-turbine.*

flows through the stop-valve C and strainer D into the steam chest F. The amount of steam flowing is regulated by means of the governor valve E. From F the steam passes through nozzles (fig. 2.5) on to the blades of the turbine wheel G as illustrated by fig. 2.6. On leaving the wheel the steam flows into the exhaust chamber H, from which it flows via pipe J to the condenser. The turbine shaft rests in the plain bearings n, m, x, and spherical bearing w. Most of the lubrication is done from the oil tank P. The speed of such a turbine is of the order of 25,000 r.p.m., which is much too fast for driving ordinary machinery, and the speed is

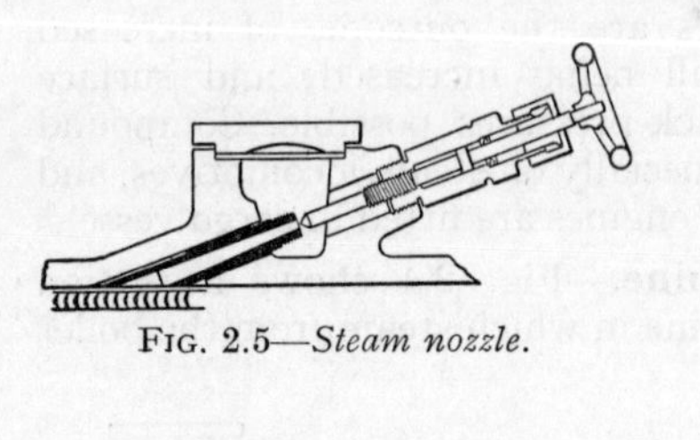

FIG. 2.5—*Steam nozzle.*

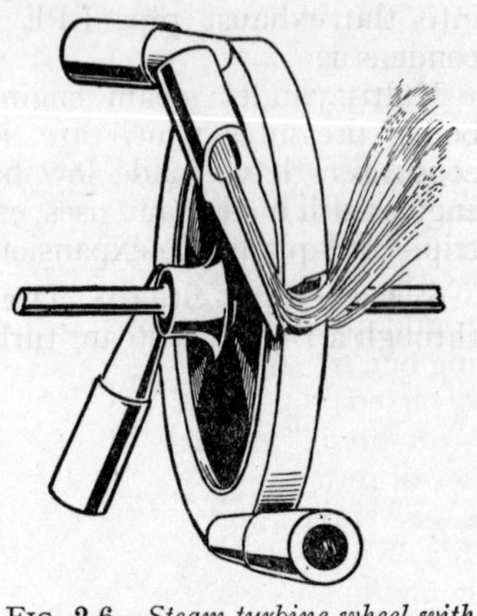

FIG. 2.6—*Steam turbine wheel with convergent-divergent nozzles.*

nearly always stepped down by means of small helical pinions (K) gearing with larger wheels which are keyed to the final driving shaft. Turbines of this impulse type are often used for driving small dynamos of 10 to 15 kilowatts after the speed has been stepped down to 2,500 by means of a 10 to 1 reduction gear.

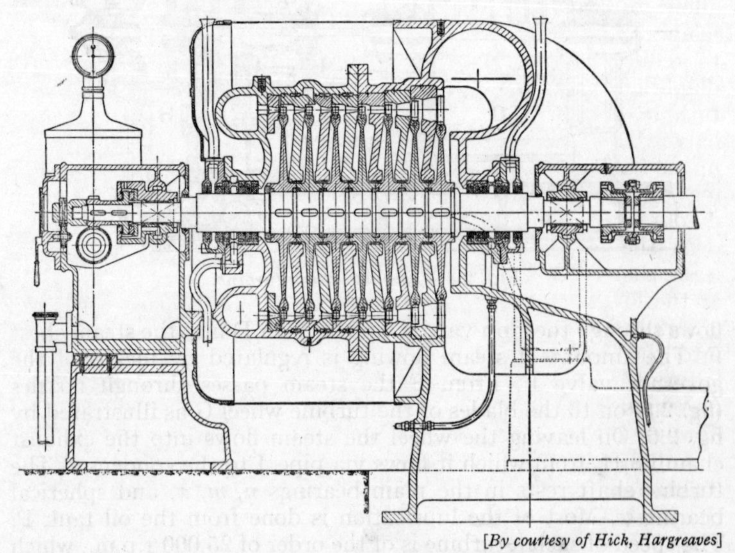

[By courtesy of Hick, Hargreaves]

FIG. 2.7—*Multi-stage impulse turbine.*

7. Multi-stage Turbine.—Fig. 2.7 is a section through a seven-stage turbine of 1,750 kilowatts output which runs at 5,000 r.p.m., each moving wheel having one set of blades.

Fig. 2.8 shows nozzles and blading for two of the stages. The steam flows through the fixed blades or nozzles and the velocity increases due to a fall of pressure between the inlet and outlet sides of the nozzles. The nozzles direct the high-velocity steam on to the moving blades, where work is done in forcing the wheel round at the expense of the kinetic energy of the steam. On leaving one set of moving blades the steam is received by the next set of fixed blades or nozzles and redirected, with an increased velocity, on to the next set of moving blades, and so on through the seven stages.

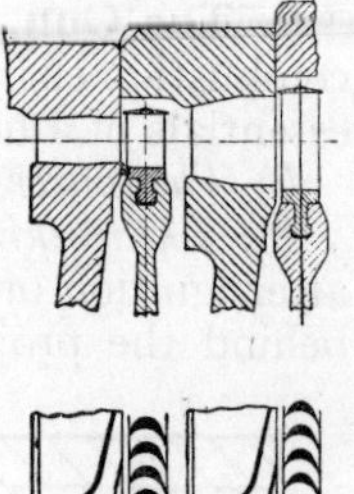

Fig. 2.8—*Convergent nozzles and rotor blades.*

The high-pressure end of the turbine casing is made of cast-steel or close-grained cast-iron, according to conditions of steam pressure and temperature, whilst the low-pressure or exhaust end of the turbine is of cast-iron. The casing is fixed axially at the low-pressure end, whilst at the high-pressure end the bearing block slides on a key in the bedplate to allow for expansion. The turbine wheels are made of high-tensile steel and highly finished to reduce steam friction on the discs. The diaphragms forming the walls between the turbine stages are made of steel and in halves, the top halves being secured to the upper half of the casing so that when opening up the turbine for inspection the half diaphragms are lifted with the casing.

At the high-pressure end the small amount of steam which leaks past the gland rings is drawn off into the condenser, whilst at the low-pressure end a small amount of high-pressure steam is supplied to "pack" the gland, thus preventing air being drawn into the condenser and reducing the vacuum. Glands of the labyrinth type are fitted to larger turbines using high steam-pressures. Velocity diagrams for turbine blading may be seen in Chapter 12.

8. The "Three Essentials" of Steam Engines and Turbines.—In the above, and in all steam engines and turbines, the three basic essentials are:

(i) *The source of heat,* which is the furnace of the boiler supplying heat to the water and so changing it into steam.

(ii) *The working agent,* which is "water stuff" (H_2O) changing state as it passes round the plant and may be superheated steam, wet steam, or water according to which particular organ of the plant it happens to be in.

(iii) *The sink,* which is the atmosphere in the case of a non-condensing engine (all the exhaust steam being rejected into the atmosphere), and in the case of a condensing engine "the sink" is the cooling water of the condenser, into which the heat from the exhaust steam is rejected.

(ii) INTERNAL COMBUSTION ENGINES

9. The Gun.—The gun is perhaps the simplest of all internal-combustion engines. Referring to fig. 2.9 we can see how the three essentials of a heat engine appear in the firing of a gun, namely:

(i) *The source of heat* is the chemical energy in the explosives E.

(ii) *The working agent* is the gases or the products of combustion after ignition of the explosives. An enormous pressure is created behind the projectile P which acts as a piston. The projectile

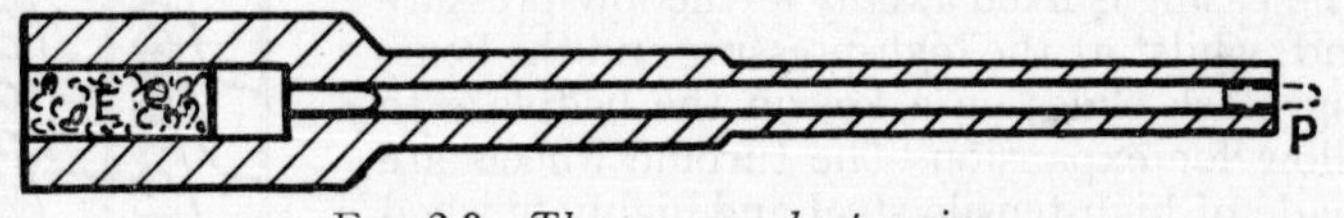

Fig. 2.9—*The gun as a heat engine.*

is shot out the barrel of with high velocity due to the pressure of the gases expanding along the barrel of the gun.

(iii) *The sink* is the atmosphere, into which the resulting smoke and hot gases are rejected.

10. Petrol, Paraffin, Gas, and Oil Engines.—These engines work either on the four-stroke cycle or on the two-stroke cycle—that is, in the one case they complete one cycle every four strokes of the piston or every two revolutions of the crank, and in the other they make one complete cycle every two strokes or each revolution of the crank. Engines working on either cycle may be designed for electric-ignition or compression-ignition according to the speed, size, and type of fuel used.

11. The Four-stroke Cycle.—Fig. 2.10 illustrates in a simple diagrammatic way the four strokes of the piston or two revolutions of the crank which make up the cycle of operations of a four-stroke gas engine.

Diagram I shows the gas and air valves open for the suction or charging stroke.

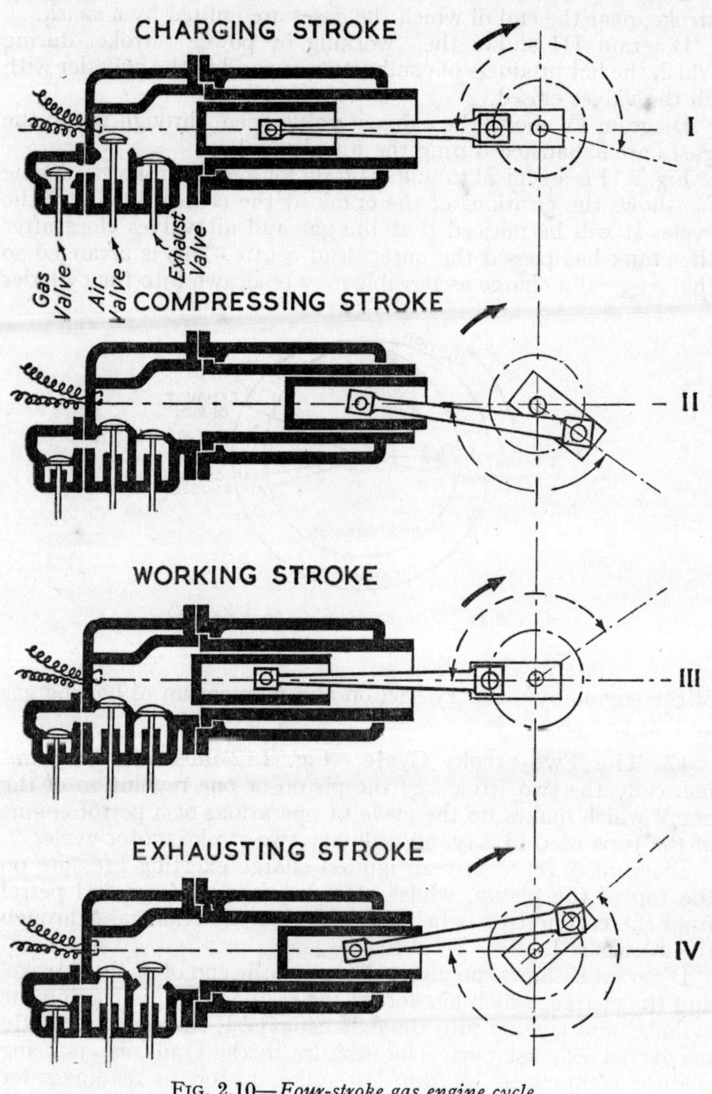

FIG. 2.10—*Four-stroke gas engine cycle.*

Diagram II shows all the valves closed during the compression stroke, near the end of which the gases are ignited by a spark.

Diagram III shows the "working or power" stroke, during which the hot products of combustion expand in the cylinder with all the valves closed.

Diagram IV shows the exhaust valve open, through which the gases are exhausted during the fourth stroke.

Fig. 2.11 is a typical timing diagram for a four-stroke gas engine *i.e.* shows the positions of the crank at the critical points of the cycle. It will be noticed that the gas and air valves close after the crank has passed the outer dead centre. This is arranged so that as great a charge as possible may be drawn into the cylinder

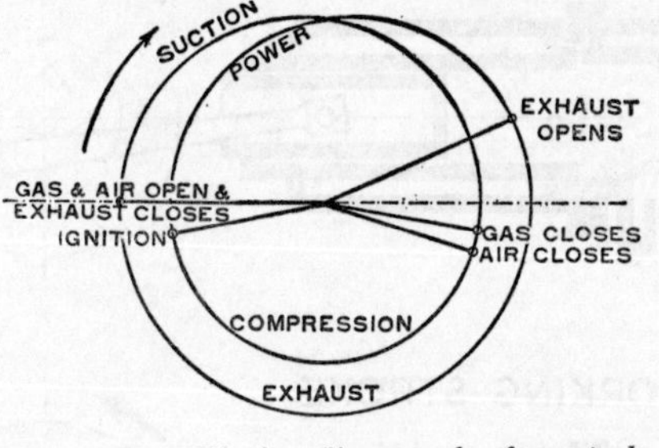

FIG. 2.11—*Timing diagram for four-stroke engine.*

of the engine by ordinary suction and momentum of flowing gas and air (see also p. 44).

12. The Two-stroke Cycle.—Fig. 2.12 illustrates diagrammatically the two strokes of the piston or one revolution of the crank which makes up the cycle of operations of a petrol engine of the type used in, say, an ordinary two-stroke motor-cycle.

Diagram A represents an ignited charge exerting pressure on the top of the piston, whilst a fresh mixture of air and petrol from the carburettor is being drawn into the crankcase through the inlet port I.

Diagram B shows the piston almost at the end of its first stroke, and the charge, which has forced the piston down, is leaving the cylinder and passing into the exhaust pipe E through the partly uncovered exhaust port. The mixture in the crankcase is being slightly compressed by the descending piston in readiness for passing through the transfer port G as soon as it is uncovered by the piston.

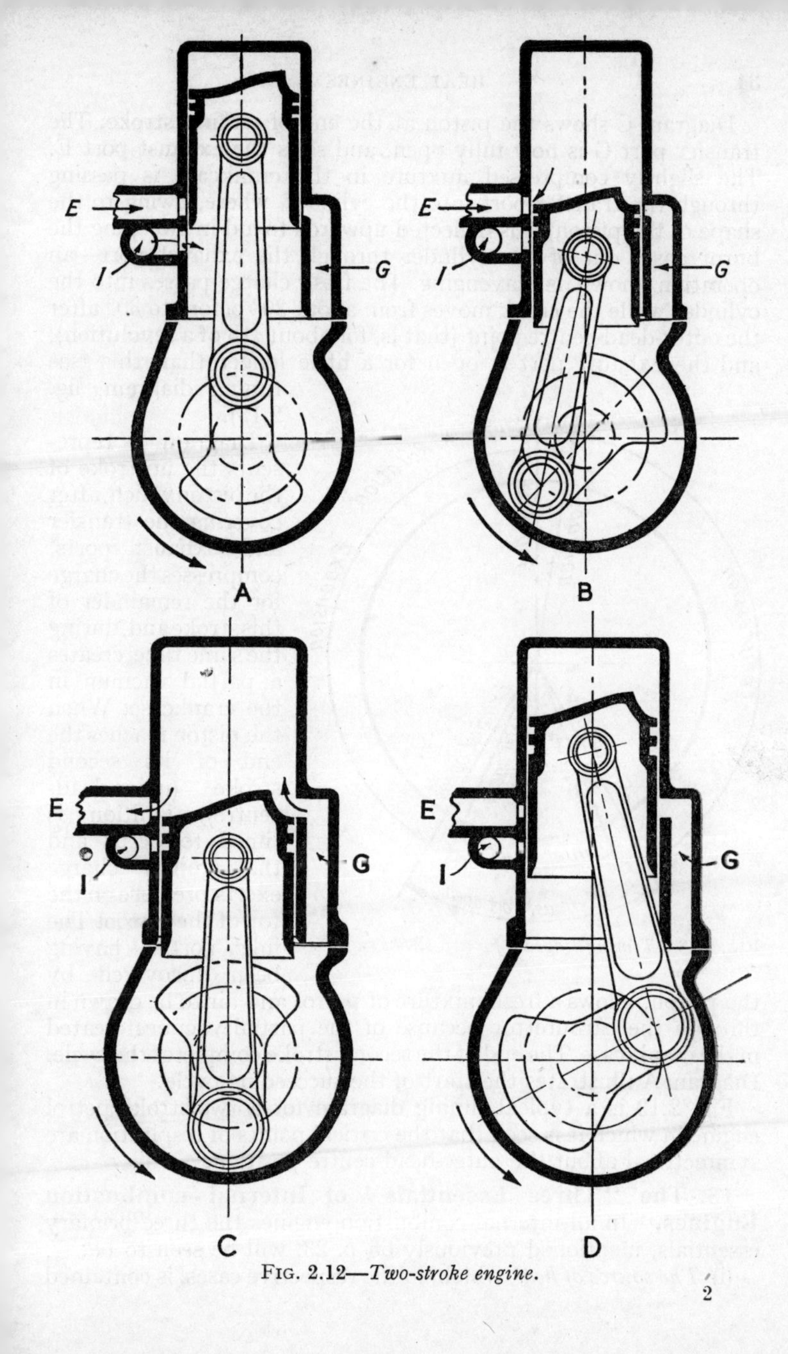

FIG. 2.12—*Two-stroke engine.*

Diagram C shows the piston at the end of its first stroke. The transfer port G is now fully open, and so is the exhaust port E. The slightly compressed mixture in the crankcase is passing through the transfer port into the cylinder, where, owing to the shape of the piston, it is deflected upwards to aid in sweeping the burnt gases out of the cylinder through the exhaust port—an operation known as scavenging. The fresh charge passes into the cylinder while the crank moves from about 30° before to 30° after the outer-dead-centre point (that is, for about $\frac{1}{6}$th of a revolution), and the exhaust port is open for a little longer than this (see timing diagram, fig. 2.13).

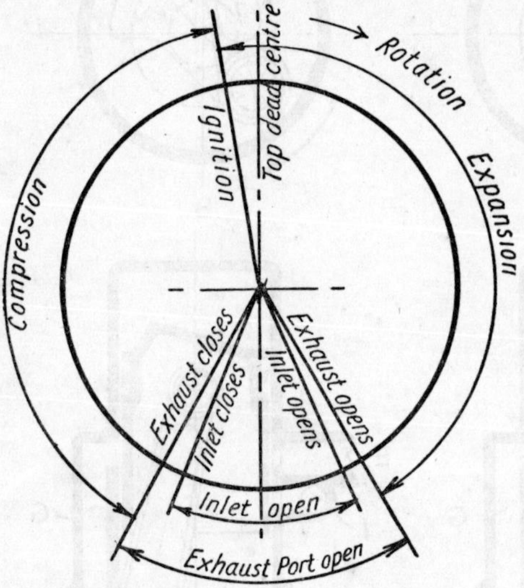

Diagram D represents the upstroke of the piston which, after covering the transfer and exhaust ports, compresses the charge for the remainder of this stroke and, during the same time, creates a partial vacuum in the crankcase. When the piston reaches the end of its second stroke (inner-dead-centre), ignition is timed to occur and the ignited charge exerts pressure on the top of the piston. The inlet port I, having been uncovered by the piston, allows a fresh mixture of petrol and air to be drawn in through the carburettor because of the partial vacuum created in the crank-case. The end of the second stroke completes the cycle. Diagram A illustrates the start of the succeeding cycle.

FIG. 2.13—*Timing diagram for two-stroke engine.*

Fig. 2.13 is a typical timing diagram for a two-stroke petrol engine in which it is seen that the critical points of respiration are symmetrical about the outer-dead-centre position.

13. The "Three Essentials" of Internal-combustion Engines.—In all internal-combustion engines the three primary essentials, mentioned previously on p. 23, will be seen to be:

(i) *The source of heat*, which, in the respective cases, is contained in the chemical energy of the petrol, paraffin, gas, or oil, according to the type of engine.

(ii) *The working agent*—made up of air plus a small amount of fuel resulting in products of combustion after ignition of the fuel-air mixture has occurred.

(iii) *The sink,* which is the atmosphere into which the hot exhaust gases are rejected.

14. Distinction between Internal-combustion Engines.—Air forms the greater part of the working agent in internal-combustion engines and supplies the oxygen necessary for the combustion of carbon and hydrogen contained in the fuels:—petrol, paraffin, gas, and oil. Heat is released when the fuel-air mixture is ignited, thus creating a high temperature and pressure in the working agent. The products of combustion, if burning is complete, are CO_2, H_2O, O_2, and N_2.

The distinction between different types of internal-combustion engines is made according to the kind of fuel used to produce the heat. Petrol, paraffin, gas, and oil engines are all engines in which the bulk of the working agent is *air*—the ratio of air to fuel by weight being about 15 to 1 in the case of liquid fuels.

The mechanisms for changing heat into work, and the designs of internal combustion engines, differ according to the kind of fuel used, the speed and the amount of power required.

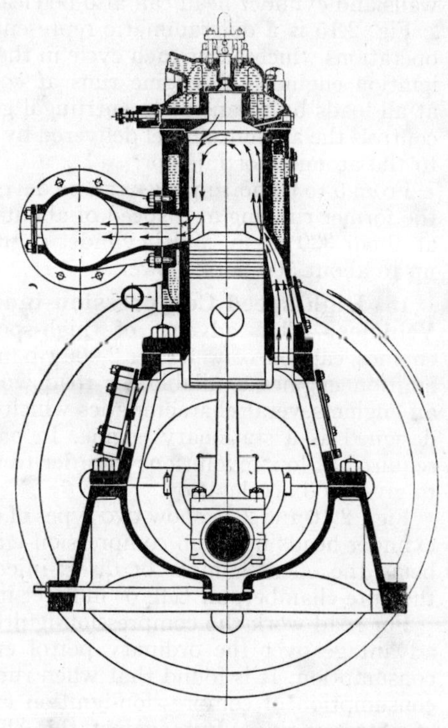

Fig. 2.14—*Compression-ignition two-stroke engine.*

15. Two-stroke Compression-ignition Heavy-oil Engine.—Fig. 2.14 shows a section through a compression-ignition engine which works on the two-stroke cycle. It will be seen that air is drawn into the crankcase from the atmosphere before flowing (as indicated by the arrows) to recharge the cylinder and assist in expelling the exhaust gases of the previous cycle. The air is compressed to a pressure of about 450 Lb. per sq. in. before the fuel-oil is injected at a pressure of about 1,200 Lb. per sq. in. through the injector which is placed centrally in the top of the combustion chamber. A maximum pressure of about 750 Lb. per sq. in. is reached due to combustion in the cylinder. The engine is started up by means of compressed air, which is admitted to the cylinder through a valve to be seen on the left of the cylinder head. On the right of the cylinder head will be seen a channel by means of which the pressures in the cylinder can be recorded on an indicator which can be screwed in after the plug has been removed. The water-cooling spaces of the cylinder walls and cylinder head can also be clearly seen.

Fig. 2.15 is a diagrammatic representation of the sequence of operations which occur each cycle in the two-stroke compression-ignition engine. The engine runs at constant speed maintained at all loads by means of a centrifugal governor (fig. 2.25), which controls the amount of fuel delivered by the fuel pump (fig. 17.12) to the atomiser or injector.

From 5 to 90 horse-power can be developed in a single cylinder, the former running at a speed of about 750 r.p.m. and the latter at about 330 r.p.m. Multi-cylinder engines of this type are made up to about 500 horse-power.

16. High-speed Compression-ignition Engines for Road Vehicles.—The advent of high-speed compression-ignition engines, capable of well over 2,000 r.p.m., has made compression-ignition engines available for road work, which demands from an engine several characteristics which it need not possess when designed as a stationary engine. In particular a high torque is required at low revolutions in order to reduce gear-changing and to give good acceleration.

Figs. 2.16 and 2.17 show two types of combustion chambers and cylinder heads fitted on compression-ignition engines, the former being the open-chamber or direct-injection type and the latter the ante-chamber, air cell, or indirect-injection type.

For road work the compression-ignition oil engine has one big advantage over the ordinary petrol engine, namely lower fuel consumption. It is found that when running on average load the consumption of compression-ignition engines is about half that of petrol engines. But against this should be set the inherent disadvantages of the former heavier engines owing to higher

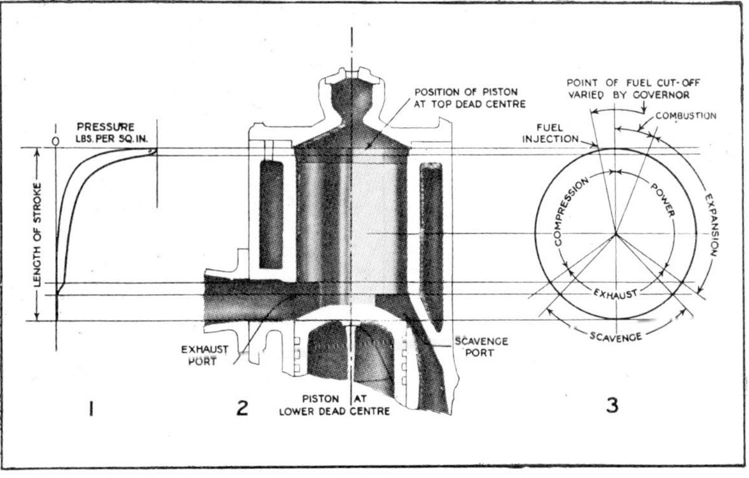

FIG. 2.15—*Two-stroke compression-ignition engine.*

[*By courtesy of Leyland Motors*]

FIG. 2.16—*Direct-injection.*

FIG. 2.17—*Indirect-injection.*

WATER COOLED CYLINDER HEAD
OIL COOLED PISTON
SPHERICAL SMALL END BEARING
OIL SUPPLY FOR PISTON COOLING
PISTON COOLING OUTLET PIPE
LUBRICATING OIL FILTER
CYLINDER & BLOWER CALIBRATER LUBRICATOR
CONNECTING ROD
WHITE METALLED MAIN BEARINGS
LUBRICATING OIL STRAINER
OIL PUMPS
ATOMISER
EXHAUST THERMOMETER
TWIN EXHAUST VALVES
EXHAUST MANIFOLD
MONOBLOC CONSTRUCTION
CYLINDER LINER
SCAVENGE PORTS
AIR PASSAGE
MULTISEAL PISTON RINGS
WATER INLET MANIFOLD
AIR INLET SILENCER & FILTER
SCAVENGING BLOWER
BLOWER & CAMSHAFT DRIVING GEARS
INSPECTION DOOR
BALANCED CRANKSHAFT
MAIN OIL PRESSURE RAIL
QUICK RELEASE FOR COVER
OIL TIGHT CYLINDER HEAD COVER
EXHAUST VALVE ROCKERS
EXHAUST VALVE PUSH RODS
INSPECTION DOORS
FUEL PUMP
CAMSHAFT
INSPECTION DOOR

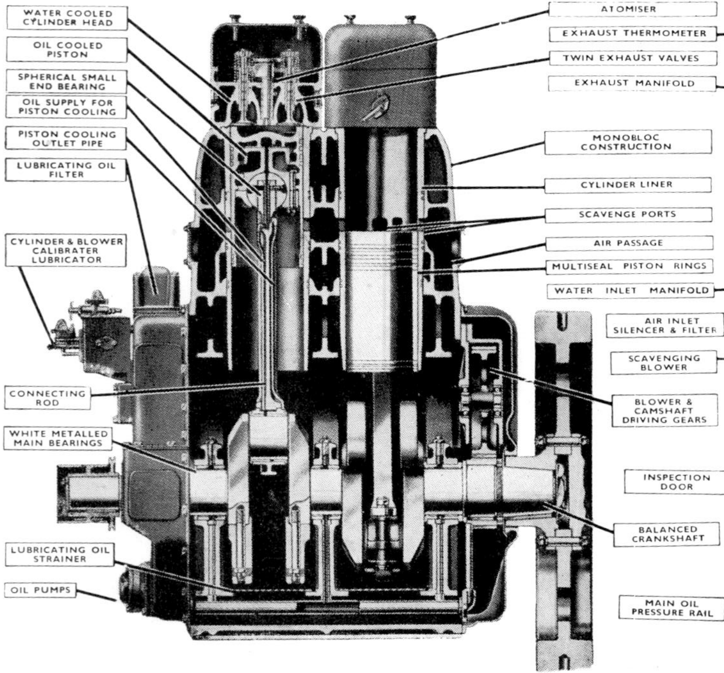

FIG. 2.18. *Uniflow compression-ignition engine.* FIG. 2.19.

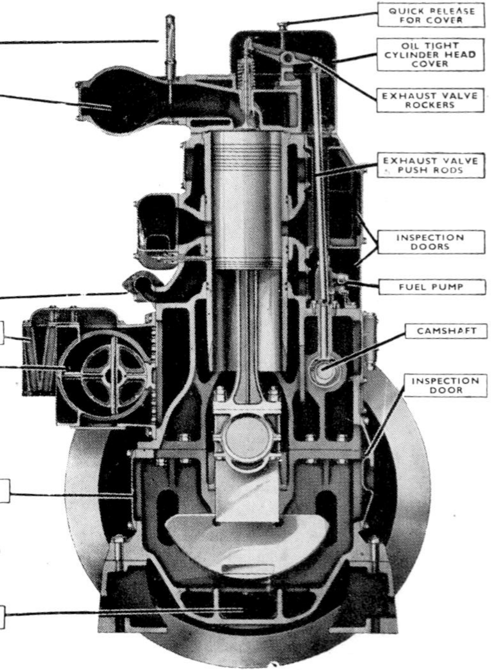

compression ratios than in petrol engines, and higher pressures which result in greater wear on cylinders and bearings; rougher running and greater noise, and a thicker exhaust than from petrol engines.

A modern omnibus petrol engine will develop **130** horse-power with a weight of about **10** Lb. per horse-power, and a high-speed compression-ignition engine **150** horse-power with a weight of about **13** Lb. per horse-power. The latter, however, shows a greater mileage per gallon of fuel than the petrol engine, and this is a very important point in its favour. Also the high torque which is needed at low revolutions in road vehicles is higher in compression-ignition engines than in spark-ignition engines.

17. The Uniflow Compression-ignition Engine.—This engine works on the two-stroke cycle, but instead of crankcase-compression the fresh air, which assists in ejecting the exhaust gases while recharging the cylinder, is forced into the cylinder under pressure from a blower. The blower is driven by gears from the crankshaft and delivers air at about 1·5 Lb. per sq. in. above atmospheric into the cylinder through swirl ports.

Uniflow or through-scavenge is employed, the scavenge ports being controlled by the pistons, and the products of combustion passing from the cylinders through exhaust valves housed in the cylinder heads. Figs. 2.18 and 2.19 show sections through the engine in which the principle of uniflow scavenging can be clearly seen. The essential idea behind this is to get quicker and more complete removal of the exhaust gases from the cylinder and also to get a greater amount of air into the cylinder for the succeeding cycle. Owing to better scavenging and an increased mass of air in the cylinder a higher speed is possible, and a greater power can be developed per cylinder.

Such engines will develop about 62·5 horse-power per cylinder at a speed of 500 r.p.m. The engine shown is made with two to six cylinders, 8·5 in. bore and **13** in. stroke, rated at **125** to **375** b.h.p. at 500 r.p.m.

18. Gas - turbine and Turbo - jet Engines.—A propeller-driving gas turbine as fitted in medium-speed aircraft is shown in fig. 2.20. It consists of an axial-flow compressor driven by a two-stage turbine mounted on the same shaft, a number of combustion chambers disposed equidistant round the engine, a separate turbine-wheel driving the propeller, and an exhaust or jet pipe at the rear. Thus, the engine is an internal-combustion gas-turbine engine driving an airscrew propeller and producing "thrust" by means of a jet of hot gases ejected, with high velocity, rearwards.

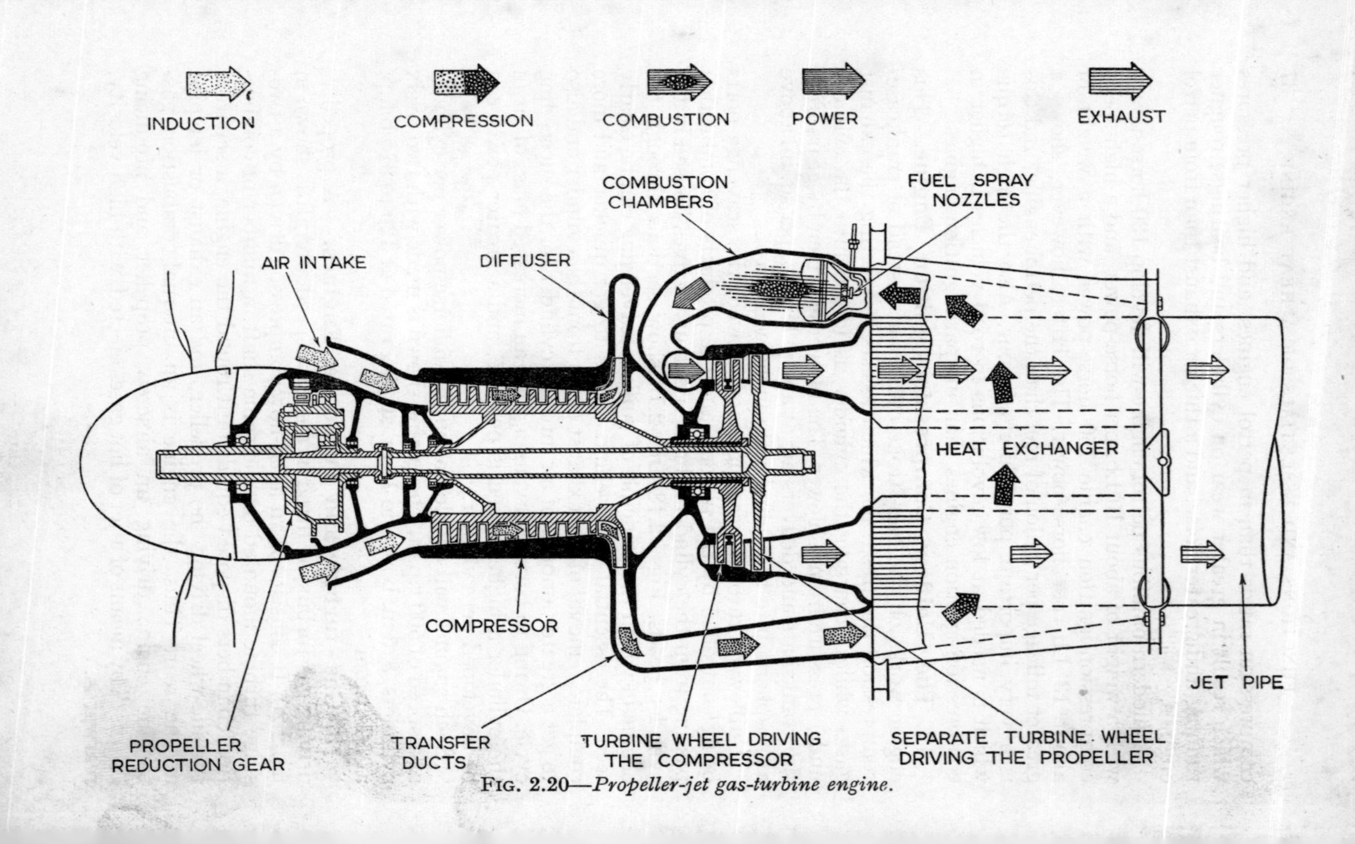

FIG. 2.20—*Propeller-jet gas-turbine engine.*

During flight, air from the atmosphere rams itself into the entry duct and then enters the compressor from which it is delivered at a higher pressure into the combustion chambers via transfer ducts and the heat exchanger. Kerosene or paraffin is delivered by fuel pumps through the nozzles of the burners into the combustion chambers where continuous combustion takes place. The fuel supply is governed by a throttle valve under the control of the pilot, but an automatic device may control the fuel supply according to altitude.

The gases resulting as products of combustion pass, with high velocity, through a ring of guide vanes or nozzle-blades which direct the gases on to the first turbine blade wheel which has

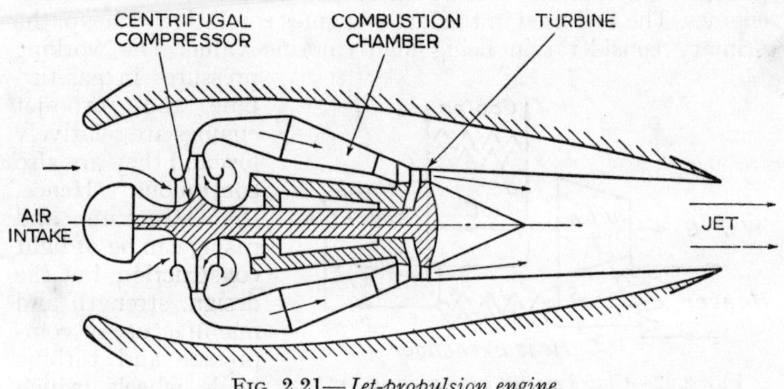

FIG. 2.21—*Jet-propulsion engine.*

two rings of moving blades on one disc mounted on the same shaft as the compressor rotor. The gases are then directed by another ring of fixed guide-vanes on to the moving blades of a second turbine wheel which drives the propeller through reduction gearing. Thus, some of the energy of the hot gases is utilised in driving the compressor and propeller, and the remainder flows along the jet pipe towards the rear and produces a forward thrust or propulsive force on the aircraft dependent on the amount and speed of the gas flowing along the jet pipe.

A jet-propulsion or turbo-jet aero engine having a double-entry centrifugal compressor mounted on the forward end of the turbine shaft is illustrated diagrammatically in fig. 2.21. The shaft revolves at a speed of about 14,000 r.p.m.

The engine is started by a motor and igniters which are fitted in, say, two of the combustion chambers. Shutting off the fuel supply, of course, stops the engine. The fuel-oil and lubricating-oil pumps, electric generator, starting motor, and other accessories are usually fitted at the front of the engine.

It will be seen that these jet engines comprise (i) an air-intake duct, (ii) a rotary compressor, (iii) combustion chambers, (iv) a turbine, and (v) a jet or tail pipe.

There is practically no vibration or out-of-balance force in these engines, and no heavily loaded bearings. The problem of lubrication is very simple relative to that in reciprocating-piston aero engines, and cooling is also very much simplified. There are no valves, and injection of fuel and burning are continuous processes. Thus, timed ignition, which is vital in internal-combustion piston-engines, is dispensed with in internal-combustion turbine-engines. The fuel used in the latter engines is relatively cheap, the primary consideration being high calorific value. The working pressures in gas-turbine and turbo-jet engines are relatively low and they are also continuous. Hence, the structure and casing can be of light construction, but the design, strength and manufacture of compressor and turbine blade wheels, which revolve at the rate of 10,000 to 16,000 r.p.m., must be attended to with great care and precision. The weight per horse-power of turbo-jet engines is about one-third of that of reciprocating-piston internal-combustion engines of equivalent output. Hence, for military use where high power and speed are the primary considerations, reciprocating-piston engines have been superseded by turbo-jet engines. Gas turbine plant is not limited in application to aircraft but can be used in ships, locomotives, and in electric generating stations.

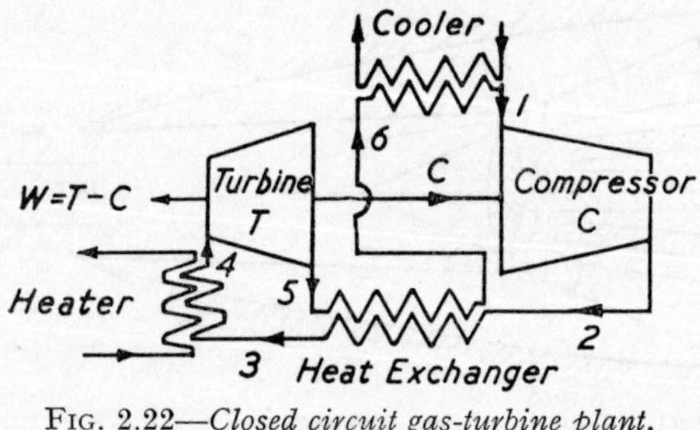

FIG. 2.22—*Closed circuit gas-turbine plant.*

In such plant the working agent may be replaced each cycle as in the open circuit type of plant shown diagrammatically in fig. 16.14, or alternatively the working agent may be confined within a closed circuit for repeated use in successive cycles of operation as in fig. 2.22 which also has a heat exchanger.

Open-circuit gas-turbine plant such as those illustrated in figs. 2.20, 2.21 and 16.14 are internal-combustion engines of the rotary type in which oxygen for combustion of fuel is supplied by the air ... ering from the atmosphere, whereas, in closed-circuit plant t... working agent receives heat from an external source as in fig. ... 2. In both types the working agent, which is mainly air co... ning 2 or 3 per cent. CO_2 and H_2O after combustion in the f... er case and pure air in the latter, flows continuously throu... the component units which form an aerodynamic plant in w... the problems of smoothness of gas-flow are of prime imp... nce.

A... ntages of the closed circuit are that the working agent rem... s free from pollution of products of combustion and hence the ... erior of the plant remains clean; also, the working air can be ... d at a higher pressure than that in an open-circuit plant. Di... vantages of the closed-circuit plant are that large and costly he... ng and cooling surfaces are needed, and a small quantity of ... under high pressure has to be pumped into the system to m... e up for the leakage.

... . Uses and Development of Internal - combustion ...gines.—Each of the above types of engines has its own field ... usefulness. There is, however, some overlapping, and in a ... cases it may be difficult to say which is the best type to use.

In favour of internal-combustion engines is the fact that they ...e not restricted to the use of a closed circuit for the working ...gent as is the case in steam engine and steam-turbine plant, for ...iston internal-combustion engines take the greater part of their ...orking agent from the surrounding air and reject the products of combustion into the atmosphere.

Regarding compression-ignition engines, it may be said that for slow and moderate speeds (*i.e.* say piston speeds less than 1,500 ft. per min.) the 2-stroke holds sway with the 4-stroke, but that the 4-stroke is superior at high speeds.

In heavy road-vehicles compression-ignition engines develop up to 150 horse-power at about 2,000 r.p.m. on a fuel consumption less than 0·4 lb. per b.h.p.-hour, *i.e.* with a thermal efficiency of about 33 per cent. on fuel oil of calorific value 19,200 B.Th.U. per lb. This is nearly 10 per cent. greater than is achieved in corresponding petrol engines. Where, however, reduction in weight per horse-power is of prime importance, as in aeronautical engines, there is no rival to the internal combustion engine either in the form of a reciprocating-piston engine or rotary gas-turbine with jet propulsion when high speeds of flight are required.

One of the most important problems facing engine designers is the reduction of the total weight of engines in relation to power, *i.e.* the weight-power ratio. In marine oil-engine installations, for instance, where it is desirable to have a low weight to power ratio, the single-acting four-stroke engine with its separate scavenge stroke each cycle has to give way (even if supercharged) to the single-acting two-stroke engine, since the ratio of weight to power is against the four-stroke. In ships of short engine-room, the opposed piston two-stroke or the double-acting two-stroke may be installed. Also, it may be noted that a requirement of marine propulsion is opposite to that of road vehicles in that high torque is required at the top end of the speed range.

From a thermodynamic point of view the oil engine is the most efficient prime mover, and the compression-ignition engine seems to have advantages over other types sufficient to warrant development towards using it in aircraft of moderate speeds. A comparatively low rate of fuel consumption and consequent high thermal efficiency are in its favour, and the risk of fire is less when oil is carried instead of petrol as a fuel. Intensive research and development may, however, result in the efficiency of the gas turbine and jet engines being increased to such a degree that piston engines will be superseded altogether in aircraft.

20. Lubrication and Cooling of Internal - combustion Engines.—Mineral oils are used for lubricating engines. There are two methods in which the lubrication of engines is achieved, known as the wet and dry sump methods. In the former method the base of the crankcase or sump is the reservoir for the oil in which a pressure-pump is usually submerged for the purpose of forcing the oil along pipes to the moving parts of the engine. In the dry sump method as used, say, in the reciprocating-piston engines of aircraft, scavenge pumps drain the sump and deliver the oil into a cooler from which it flows into a separate reservoir tank. Pressure-pumps start the cool oil in the reservoir flowing again through the lubricating system of the engine, first to the main bearings and big ends and then, with a reduced pressure, to the camshaft and rockers of the valve-operating gear and auxiliaries of the engine. The oil finally drains back into the sump from which it is withdrawn by the scavenge pumps and delivered again into the reservoir via the oil cooler.

Pistons and gudgeon pins of small engines are often lubricated by splash of oil when the big ends strike the oil in the crankcase sump. A baffle plate can be placed to prevent an excess of oil being thrown up into the cylinder.

It is necessary to keep the temperatures of the moving parts of engines low enough for efficient lubrication. Air-cooling and liquid-cooling are the two methods employed. In the former method thin fins are usually cast round the engine cylinders and on the cylinder heads to increase the surface area from which a stream of air can abstract heat. In the case of liquid-cooling, ducts cast in the cylinder blocks of engines are filled with water, or "anti-freeze" mixture if temperatures are likely to be lower than 32° F., and connected to a radiator or syphon tank from the bottom of which cooler liquid flows into the base of the cylinder block while the hotter liquid flows from the upper part of the engine into the top part of the radiator tank.

21. Valve-timing of Internal-combustion Engines.—For the successful running of internal-combustion engines the precise timing of the opening and closing of inlet and exhaust valves, and the exact point at which ignition or injection of fuel takes place in engines, are of fundamental importance.

In engines working on the two-stroke cycle the exhaust ports are required to open first so as to allow the major portion of the exhaust gases to escape and the pressure in the cylinder to drop to about that of the atmosphere before the inlet ports are opened.

In the case of spark-ignition engines, an explosive mixture enters the cylinders at a pressure slightly above that of the gases in the cylinders of two-stroke engines, thus forcing out more of the products of combustion of the previous cycle and, at the same time, recharging the cylinder for the next cycle.

It is generally desirable to arrange for the closure of exhaust ports while the inlet ports are still open so that the fresh charge can be packed into the cylinder under slight pressure—a process known as pressure-charging or supercharging. The simple crank-case scavenge two-stroke engine shown in fig. 2.12 or 2.14, which uses the piston as the operator of inlet and exhaust ports while at the same time operating the crankcase as a pump, will not achieve this since the critical events of port opening and closing are symmetrical about the outer-dead-centre as shown in figs. 2.13 and 2.15. If, however, the exhaust and inlet ports are separated by the length of the cylinder, as in fig. 2.19, the desirable conditions can be achieved, since the piston operates the inlet ports and an independent camshaft and push-rod operates the rocker arm of the exhaust valve situated in the cylinder head.

In the case of four-stroke engines, similar fundamental principles of valve operation apply. The exhaust valve must be timed to commence opening early so that it is fully open by the time the exhaust stroke or positive expulsion of the products of combustion commences as the piston passes outer-dead-centre. Also, the inlet valve should be timed to open so that it is well open by the time the induction stroke commences at inner-dead-centre, and the closure of the inlet valve needs to be delayed for as long as is practicable after the piston has passed the outer-dead-centre position in order to allow time for the induction, or forcing, of as much of the new charge as possible into the cylinder before it is scaled for compression.

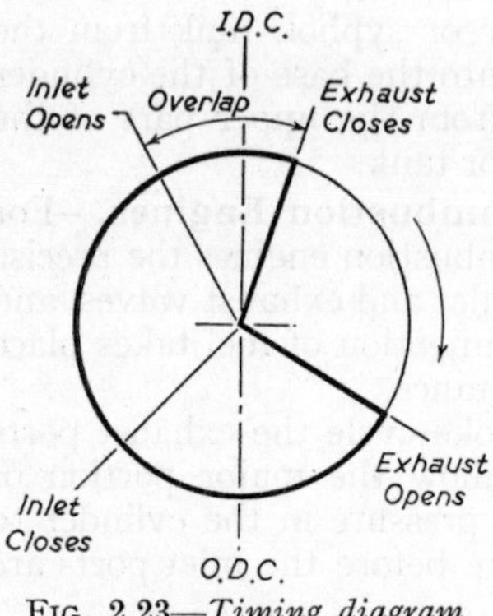

FIG. 2.23—*Timing diagram showing overlap.*

Ignition or fuel-injection in both two-stroke and four-stroke engines should be as early as the speed of the engine will permit. In high-speed engines it is possible to have a considerable "overlap" during which period the inlet and the exhaust ports are both open, as represented in fig. 2.23. This is possible because the quick flow of gases along the exhaust pipe is not arrested the moment the inlet valve opens. The exhaust valve can be kept open until the point when reversal of flow of the gases in the exhaust pipe would arrest further scavenging of combustion products from the cylinder.

(iii) GOVERNORS, FLYWHEELS, AND IGNITION

22. Governors.—Governors are fitted to engines for the purpose of securing, as nearly as possible, a uniform rate of rotation of the crankshaft, and for preventing variation of speed when fluctuations of load or boiler pressure occur. None of the governors applied to engines is able to accomplish this *perfectly*, because, being themselves driven by the engines they have to govern, they cannot begin to act until a change of speed has first occurred.

Governing is usually achieved by means of some form of centrifugal governor, the motion of the sleeve of which is taken through levers to control either the amount of fuel or steam entering a particular engine.

The effects of throttle governing and cut-off governing of steam engines can be seen on indicator diagrams of figs. 11.17 and 11.18.

23. The Spring-loaded Governor.—Fig. 2.24 shows a spring-loaded governor.

The balls move outwards as the speed rises, and lift the sleeve S by means of the bell-crank levers B. The load on the spring can be adjusted by means of the lock-nuts N. One of the advantages of using a spring is that the central spindle of the governor is not restricted to the vertical position. The sleeve S would be connected through link work to the inlet valve of a steam engine or to the fuel valve or throttle of an internal combustion engine.

Fig. 2.25 shows a spring-loaded governor as fitted to compression-ignition engines of the type illustrated in fig. 2.14. The governor is mounted vertically and driven from the crankshaft by means of gearing. The revolving parts are totally enclosed in an

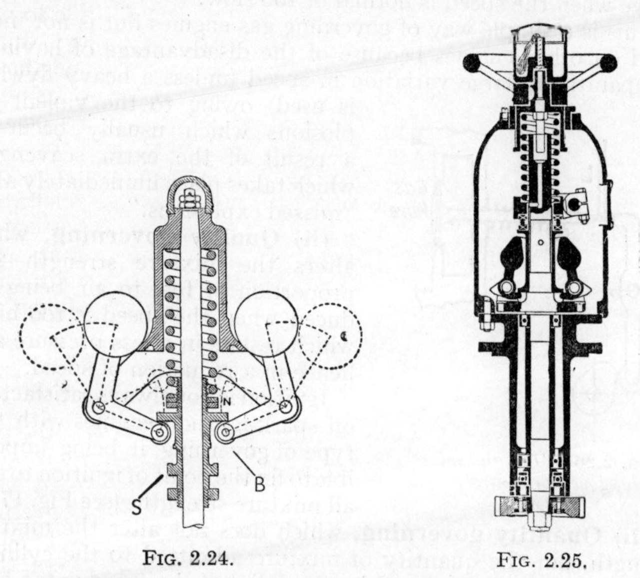

FIG. 2.24. FIG. 2.25.

Spring-loaded centrifugal governors.

oil-tight casing and the load on the springs can be regulated by means of the external hand-wheel at the top.

The governor controls the amount of fuel injected into the cylinder by actuating a spill-valve on the fuel pump (fig. 17.12) which allows a certain proportion of the fuel delivered by the fuel-pump plunger to be by-passed back to the fuel-supply side. It can be imagined from fig. 2.25 that as the speed increases centrifugal action on the masses results in a motion of the governor sleeve. This motion is transmitted through link rods to the shaft K which controls the spill-valve plunger, N, of the fuel pump, fig. 17.12. The speed variation can be limited to about 3 per cent. with this type of governor.

24. Methods of Governing Internal - combustion Engines.—We have seen in the cases just considered that the motion of the sliding sleeve of the governor causes a lever to be moved which has control on the inlet or supply-side of the engine. The lever which is given the control can be used for:

(i) "Hit and Miss" governing of gas engines, in which lever L, fig. 2.26, is lifted and made to miss opening the gas valve when the speed is too high, and to be directly in line ready for opening the valve when the speed is normal or too slow.

This is a simple way of governing gas engines but is not much used on other engines because of the disadvantage of having a comparatively large variation in speed (unless a heavy flywheel is used) owing to the violent explosions which usually occur as a result of the extra scavenging which takes place immediately after "missed explosions."

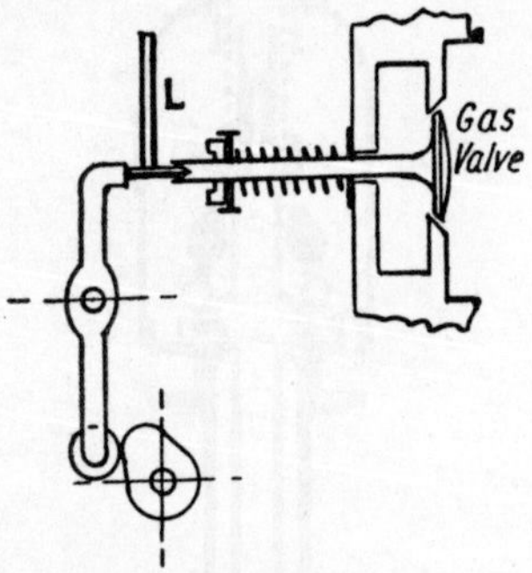

FIG. 2.26—*"Hit and miss" governor control.*

(ii) Quality governing, which alters the mixture strength—the proportion of fuel to air being reduced when the speed is too high, which results in a less pressure and hence in a reduction of speed.

Ignition is not always satisfactory on spark-ignition engines with this type of governing, it being impossible to fix the point of ignition to suit all mixture strengths (see Fig. 17.1).

(iii) Quantity governing, which does not alter the mixture strength, but the quantity of mixture admitted to the cylinder is regulated—being reduced by throttling if the speed is too high and increased if the speed is too low. If the speed is too high less charge is admitted to the cylinder for compression and, therefore, there is less pressure created by combustion. Less work is done during that particular cycle and, consequently, there is a reduction of speed.

Since, with this method of governing, there is an impulse each cycle due to the explosion of a correct mixture, it has the advantage of giving a more even turning moment and closer limits of speed variation. For these reasons quantitative governing is preferred on spark-ignition engines.

(iv) Governing of Compression-ignition Engines.—This is achieved by some form of control on the amount of fuel injected into the cylinder per cycle. In most compression-ignition engines a centrifugal governor actuates link rods which operate some device on the fuel pump for by-passing a portion of the fuel which would otherwise be injected into the engine cylinder.

Thus, compression-ignition engines employ quality governing, the amount of fuel injected into each cylinder per cycle being controlled according to the speed of the engine. Since, however, in such an engine the temperature of the air after compression is the same in each cycle, the question of poor combustion of a "weak mixture" does not arise, for combustion is always assured (see fig. 17.6) by the temperature of the air after compression no matter how small the amount of fuel injected.

Figs. 17.7 and 17.12 illustrate fuel pumps fitted to modern compression-ignition engines and also show the arrangements for by-passing fuel necessary to governing the engine (see p. 390).

25. Governing of a Laval Turbine.—Fig. 2.27 illustrates the method of governing the Laval impulse turbine of fig. 2.4. Centrifugal force on governor masses fixes the position of the vertical

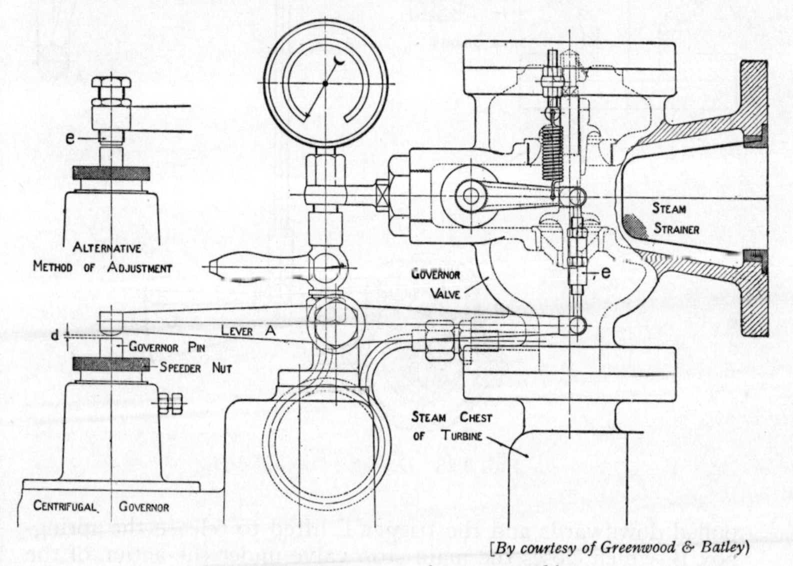

[*By courtesy of Greenwood & Batley*)

FIG. 2.27—*Governing of a steam turbine.*

governor pin, and from fig. 2.27 it will be seen how the position of this pin controls the double-beat steam valve by means of lever A. The distance *d* can be adjusted by means of the nut and screw at e, which are firmly locked when d has been set to the correct amount.

An emergency governor of the type shown in fig. 2.28 is fitted to safeguard against overspeeding. The unbalanced ring H takes up a position, if the speed is about 15 per cent. above normal, such that the lever J will be struck. Thus the rod K will be

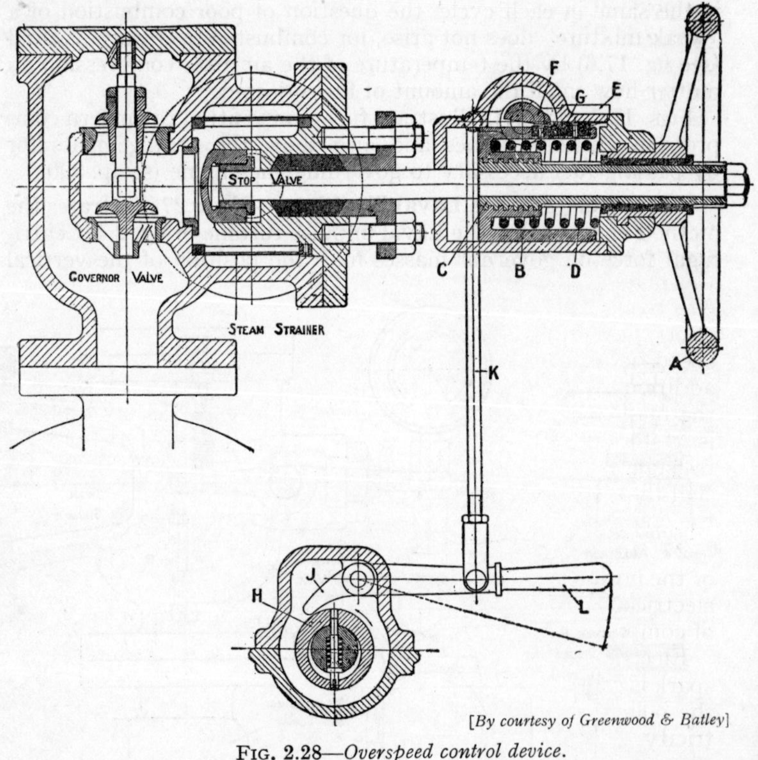

[By courtesy of Greenwood & Batley]

FIG. 2.28—*Overspeed control device.*

pulled downwards and the trigger F lifted to release the spring-box B, which closes the main stop valve under the action of the spring D. The main steam supply will thus be cut off and the turbine will come to rest. When the turbine is normally being shut down it is advisable to use this trip mechanism by pulling down the level L in order to ensure that the mechanism is in working order.

Large turbines are usually governed by means of pressure of oil which regulates the position of the steam supply valve. An example of this is described on p. 265.

26. Flywheels.—Flywheels are fitted to engines with the object of evening-out the fluctuations of speed which would occur during each cycle of operations if they were not fitted.

The turning effort on the crank pin of an engine varies considerably during each revolution. There is, therefore, a tendency to fluctuation of speed. This is counteracted by means of flywheels fitted to the crankshafts of reciprocating engines. The driving wheels on locomotive engines serve the purpose of flywheels.

When the turning effort on the crank pin during a portion of a revolution is greater than the resistance due to the load, the speed of the engine increases; and conversely, when the resistance is greater than the turning effort, the speed of the engine is reduced. Owing to its great mass and the distance of the bulk of the mass from its centre of rotation, the flywheel resists very effectively tendencies to changes of speed. Any excess of turning effort, instead of causing immediate and excessive change of speed, is absorbed by the flywheel and gives a relatively small additional kinetic energy to the large store already contained in the mass and motion of the flywheel. The energy thus absorbed is restored when the turning effort falls below the opposing resistances—the kinetic energy of the flywheel then being slightly reduced. In this way an almost uniform rate of rotation of the crank can be maintained.

27. Ignition in Internal - combustion Engines.—Ignition or the initiation of combustion in engine cylinders can be achieved electrically as in spark-ignition engines, or by utilising the heat of compression as in compression-ignition engines.

Electric-ignition is usually employed in all but oil engines. A spark is caused to cross the points of a plug, the air or gas between the points of which offers great resistance to the passage of electricity. A high voltage of, say, 8,000 volts is necessary and is generated either by a magneto or by a coil system. The primary coil is supplied with low-voltage current from a battery, and the high-voltage current of the secondary coil is led to the sparking plug via a distributor through insulated cables. The higher the pressure of the fuel-air mixture in the gap between the points of the plug, the higher the voltage necessary for forcing a discharge of electricity from the central electrode to the body of the plug.

The spark is timed to occur at a precise point relative to the position of the piston, for it is necessary that the period of time between the initiation of the spark and the point at which maximum pressure in the cylinder is reached should be such that the maximum pressure occurs when the crankshaft is beyond inner-dead-centre by about 12 to 16 degrees in order that a high power may be obtained from the engine. If the spark occurs too early a relative large amount of unnecessary work has to be done in compressing the ignited gases, whereas, if the spark occurs too late the maximum pressure is not only late in the stroke but reduced in magnitude since the piston will have travelled down the cylinder and the ignited gases will have to fill a larger volume when the maximum temperature is reached than if the spark had occurred earlier. When weak fuel-air mixtures are used the spark must be timed to occur earlier than when rich mixtures are used since weak mixtures burn at a slower rate than rich mixtures (see fig. 17.1).

Large engine-cylinders sometimes need two plugs in order to initiate flame propagation at two separate points and reduce the length of flame-travel from any given centre of ignition and, also, to reduce the time taken to reach maximum pressure in the cylinder. Aero engines usually have two magnetos supplying independent plugs in each cylinder—one of the two plugs being fitted on the inlet side and one on the exhaust side of the cylinder.

Overheated plugs may cause pre-ignition and it is, therefore, necessary that some heat shall be able to flow from the plugs in order to avoid the fusing of deposits on the points and so causing a short. The plugs should, however, remain sufficiently hot to burn off any oil which may become deposited, as when the engine is left "ticking over" on the slow-running jet for lengthy periods.

In spark-ignition engines there is a more or less homogeneous fuel-air mixture in the cylinder during compression, while in compression-ignition engines fuel is not injected into the air until nearly the end of the compression stroke. Also, in spark-ignition engines propagation of combustion proceeds from the point where the sparking plug is fitted, whereas in compression-ignition engines each particle of fuel injected into the air is a potential centre from which combustion may begin. If, however, the strength of the fuel-air mixture is correct the rate of flame propagation after the spark has occurred is very rapid in spark-ignition engines, and combustion is complete before exhaust begins unless the mixture is very weak.

CHAPTER 3

MEASUREMENT OF WORK AND POWER, CONSUMPTION AND EFFICIENCY

1. Measurement of Work.—Work is defined as force × displacement measured in the direction of the force. If, as in fig. 3.1, a constant force F moves the load D through a distance

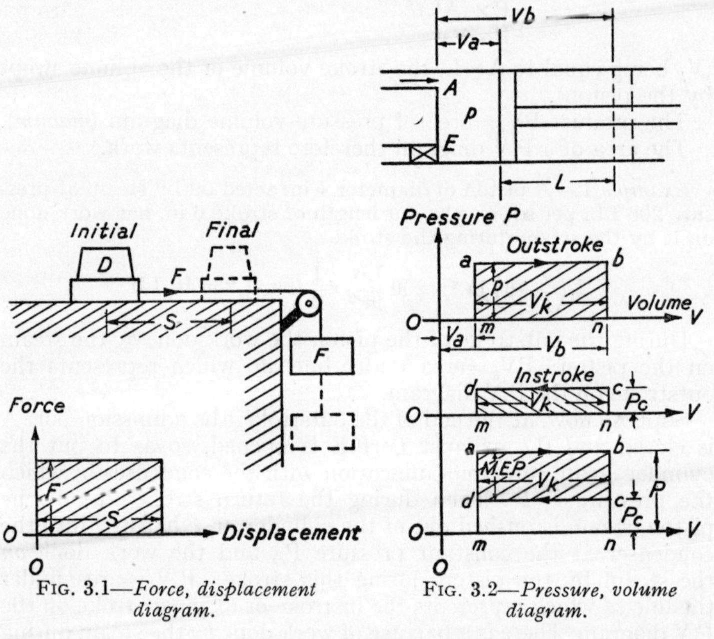

FIG. 3.1—*Force, displacement diagram.*

FIG. 3.2—*Pressure, volume diagram.*

S the work done is F × S, and this product will be seen to represent the area of the force-displacement diagram. We see, therefore, that *work, or mechanical energy, can be represented as an area on a force-displacement diagram.*

Example.—A locomotive pulling a train with a force of $\frac{1}{3}$ Ton over a distance of 1 mile does 1,760 ft.-Ton units of work or $3 \cdot 94 \times 10^6$ ft.-Lb.

Considering next the piston and cylinder of fig. 3.2 in which steam at the constant absolute pressure P is admitted for the full length of the stroke L, the force on the piston will be constant throughout the stroke and, in Lb. units, equal to the pressure of steam in Lb. per sq. ft. × area of piston in sq. ft., or to the pressure of steam in Lb. per sq. in. × area of piston in sq. in.

That is, the force on the piston $= P \times A$

and, assuming that movement of the piston is resisted by an external opposing force equal to that on the face of the piston, the work done per stroke

$$= (PA) \times (L)$$
$$= P \times (AL)$$
$$= P \times V_k$$

(V_k being equal to $A \times L$, the stroke volume or the volume swept by the piston).

The product PV_k = area of pressure-volume diagram (*mabnm*).

The area of a P,V diagram therefore represents work.

Example 1.—A piston of diameter 4 in. acted on by steam at pressure 200 Lb. per sq. in. abs. for length of stroke 6 in. has work done on it by the steam during the stroke

$$= \left(\frac{\pi}{4} . 16\right) \text{in.}^2 \times 200 \frac{\text{Lb.}}{\text{in.}^2} \times \frac{1}{2} \text{ ft.} = 1{,}256 \text{ ft.-Lb.}$$

During the outstroke of the piston the work done *by* the steam on the piston $= PV_k$ = area under line *ab*, which represents the outstroke on the P,V diagram.

Suppose now, at the end of the outstroke, the admission port A is closed and the exhaust port E is opened, so as to put the cylinder steam into communication with the condenser in which the pressure is P_c. Then during the return stroke (*cd*) of the piston, steam is pushed out of the cylinder or exhausted into the condenser at the constant pressure P_c, and the work done *on* the steam by the piston during this stroke $= P_cV_k$ = area under the line *cd* which represents the instroke or exhaust stroke on the P,V diagram. There is a balance of work done *by* the steam during the two strokes forming the cycle (or per revolution of the crank)

= work done *by* the steam during outstroke — work done *on* steam during instroke.

$= PV_k - P_cV_k$.

$= (P - P_c)V_k$.

= area *abcda*.

or = mean effective pressure (m.e.p.) × stroke volume (V_k).

Example 2.—A single-acting steam engine of piston diameter 6 in. and stroke 9 in. admits steam for the full stroke at 100 Lb. per sq. in.

gauge pressure and exhausts into the atmosphere at 15 Lb. per sq. in. absolute pressure. Find the work done per cycle and the horse-power developed if the crank of the engine makes 120 revolutions per minute.

$$\text{Work done per cycle} = \text{PLA} = \left((115-15)\frac{\text{Lb.}}{\text{in.}^2}\right)\times\left(\frac{9}{12}\text{ft.}\right)\times\left(\frac{\pi}{4}\times 36\ \text{in.}^2\right)$$

$$=2{,}120 \text{ ft.-Lb.}$$

Hence, if C represents the number of cycles traced out per unit of time, the rate of work done

$$=\text{PLAC}=2{,}120\text{ ft.-Lb.}\times\frac{120}{\text{min.}}$$

$$=2{,}120\times 120\frac{\text{ft.-Lb.}}{\text{min.}}\left[\frac{\text{h.p. min.}}{33{,}000\text{ ft.-Lb.}}\right]$$

$$=7\cdot 7 \text{ horse-power,}$$

i.e. work is being done at the rate of 7·7 horse-power.

Absolute Pressure.—It will have been noticed that in the above example the fact that absolute pressure = gauge pressure + atmospheric pressure has been used. This is dealt with again on page 99.

If instead of being admitted for the full length of the stroke steam is cut off by the valve early in the stroke, then, as the piston moves forward for the remainder of the stroke, the pressure of the steam in the cylinder will gradually fall. This is *expansive* working of steam.

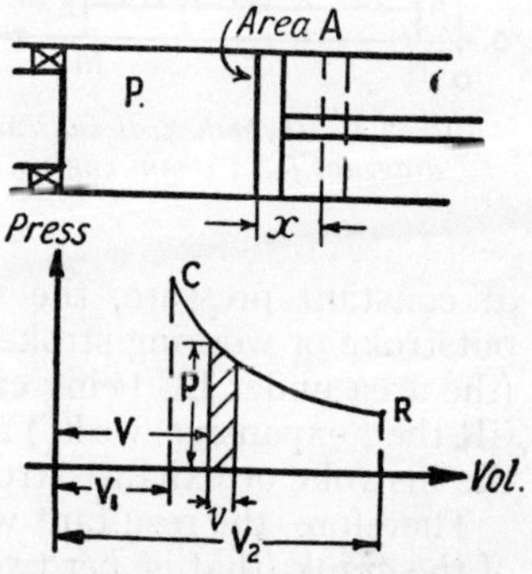

Supposing the trace on the P,V diagram of fig. 3.3 from the point of cut-off to the point of release, when the exhaust port opens, is CR, then at the instant when the piston is in the position shown (the volume in front of the piston being V and the pressure in the cylinder being P), the force on the piston of area A at that instant is PA. If the piston then moves through the small distance x (the corresponding increase in volume being $Ax=v$), the work done during the small displacement against an equal opposing force is

$$=(PA)\times(x)$$
$$=P\times(Ax)$$
$$=Pv=\text{area of shaded strip on the P,V diagram.}$$

FIG. 3.3.—*Expansion of steam.*

Therefore, the total work done by the steam during balanced or fully-resisted expansion (see p. 289 for statements on "reversible" expansion) from cut-off to release=sum of all such strips from C to R=area under the expansion curve CR. The area will be in ft.-Lb. units if P is measured in Lb. per sq. ft. and V in cu. ft.

The area under the curve CR can be found by counting squares, by the mid-ordinate method, or by means of some instrument for measuring areas, as, for instance, a planimeter (fig. 3.17).

2. Hypothetical Indicator Diagrams.—In a single-acting steam engine which admits steam from the beginning of the stroke at B to the point of cut-off C (fig. 3.4), and then expands the enclosed steam from cut-off to release along the expansion curve CR, and during the return stroke EA exhausts the steam

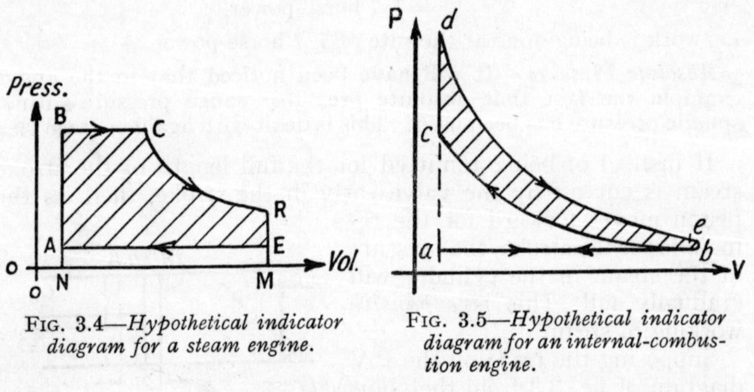

Fig. 3.4—*Hypothetical indicator diagram for a steam engine.*

Fig. 3.5—*Hypothetical indicator diagram for an internal-combustion engine.*

at constant pressure, the work done *by* the steam during the outstroke or working stroke BCR is given by the area NBCRMN (the area under BC being called the "flow work" and that under CR the "expansive work") and the work done *on* the steam during the instroke or exhaust stroke EA is given by the area MEANM.

Therefore, the resultant work done *by* the steam per revolution of the crank (that is, per two strokes, or per cycle)

=area (NBCRMN—MEANM).
=area of the diagram BCREAB, which is called a "hypothetical indicator diagram" since it is theoretical and drawn as a result of making several assumptions.

Fig. 3.5 shows the P,V diagram for a four-stroke internal combustion engine in which the theoretical work done per cycle (that is, per 2 revolutions of the crank or per 4 strokes of the piston) is given by the enclosed area *bcdeb* of the P,V or indicator diagram.

In this hypothetical diagram

ab represents	the suction stroke	1st revolution	one cycle.
bc ,,	the compression stroke		
cd ,,	ignition at inner-dead-centre		
de ,,	the expansion stroke	2nd revolution	
ea ,,	the exhaust stroke		

The above two diagrams are theoretical only. Such diagrams are what we get by hypothesis, and as such are usually referred to as "hypothetical indicator diagrams."

3. The Principles of Recording Indicator Diagrams.—We have seen that an area on a P,V diagram represents work

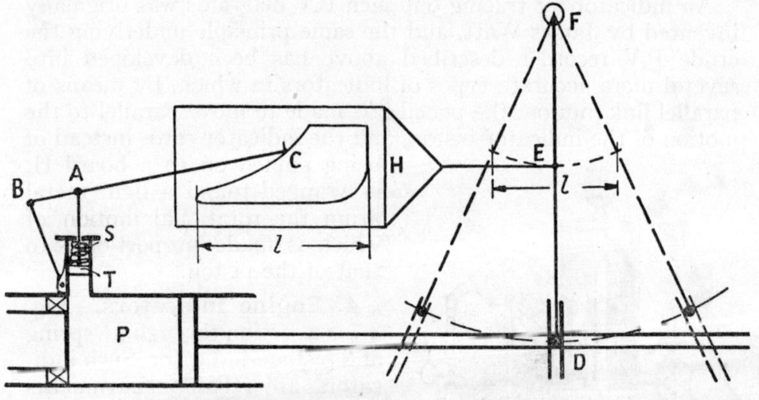

FIG. 3.6—*Principle of an engine indicator.*

done. If, therefore, a means can be devised whereby the pressure and volume in the cylinder of an engine are traced on a diagram having rectangular axes, the actual work done by the engine per cycle can be estimated from the resulting indicator diagram.

In order to record a P,V diagram with rectangular axes the tracing point must have a vertical motion proportional to the pressure in the cylinder and, at the same time, a horizontal motion proportional to the motion of the piston giving a record of volume.

Referring to fig. 3.6 it will be seen that the motion of the point A depends upon the compression of the spring S, and is therefore proportional to the pressure in the cylinder acting on the small piston T. The pencil C, therefore, moves proportional to pressure P, and in an almost vertical direction—the motion of A being amplified in the ratio $\frac{BC}{BA}$.

The point D is fixed on the piston rod, and therefore moves proportionately to the volume swept out by the piston. Hence, also, the point E moves the card (pinned to the board H) in a horizontal direction proportional to the swept volume of the piston—the motion of D being reduced in the ratio $\frac{FE}{FD}$.

In this way a diagram can be traced on the card having rectangular axes P and V, and the area enclosed by the P,V diagram represents (within certain limits) the work done by the working fluid during that particular cycle.

An indicator for tracing out such P,V diagrams was originally invented by James Watt, and the same principle underlying the crude P,V recorder described above has been developed into several more accurate types of indicators in which, by means of parallel link motion, the pencil C is made to move parallel to the motion of the indicator piston, and the indicator card, instead of being pinned on to a board H, is wrapped round a light metal drum the rotational motion of which is made proportional to that of the piston.

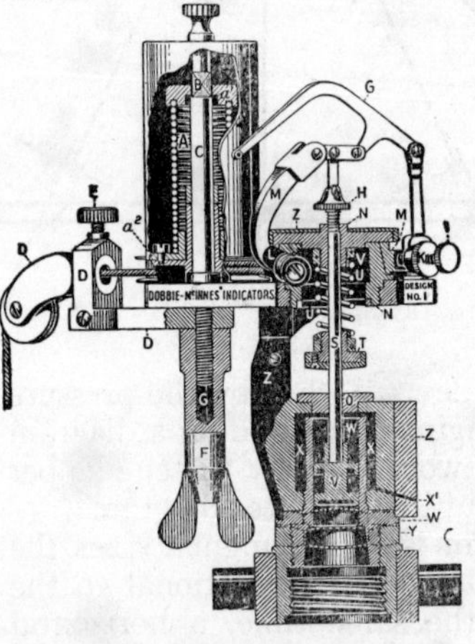

FIG. 3.7—"*Spring and piston*" *indicator.*

4. Engine Indicators.—Fig. 3.7 is a section through a "spring and piston" indicator. Such indicators are reliable instruments for slow and moderate speed engines, but for high speeds they are not so reliable because of the inertia effects of the moving parts and the friction of the pencil and mechanism. These defects have led to the development of electrical indicators.

The "Farnboro" indicator, illustrated in figs. 3.8 and 3.9, has been developed for use on high-speed engines. Small holes are punched by electric sparks through a paper which revolves on a drum connected to the engine crankshaft. Pressure variations in

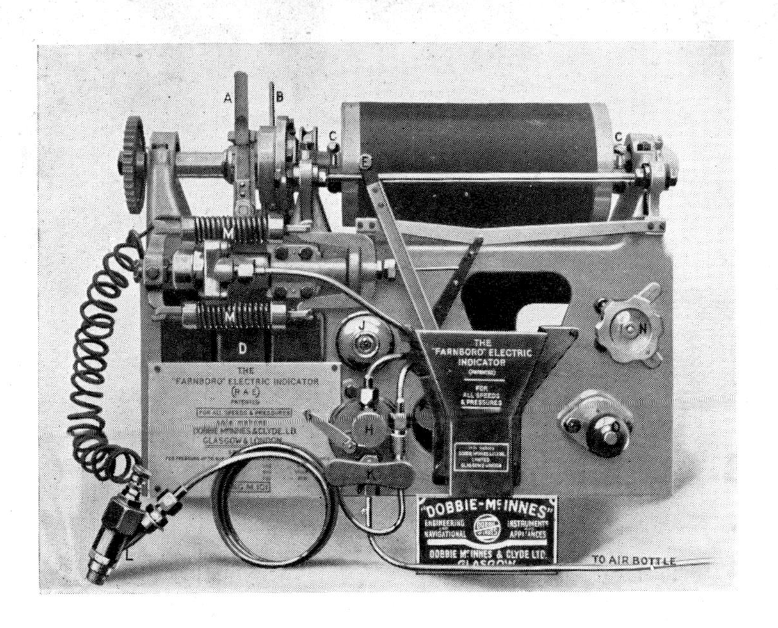

FIG. 3.8—*"Farnboro" indicator.*

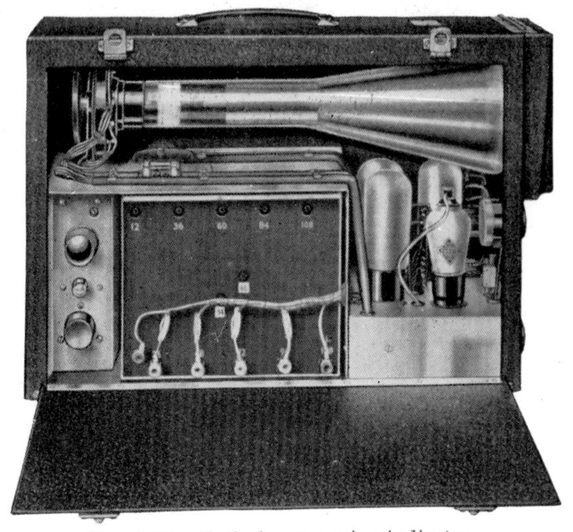

Fig. 3.11—*Cathode ray engine indicator.*

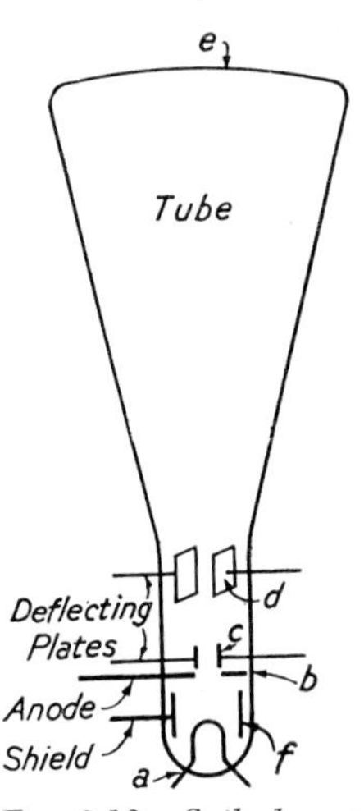

Fig. 3.12—*Cathode ray tube.*

the cylinder of the fastest running engines can be recorded by this instrument.

It can be used on engines where the cylinders are inaccessible to ordinary indicators, *e.g.* aeroplanes in flight, racing cars on the track. Features of this indicator are that inertia is practically

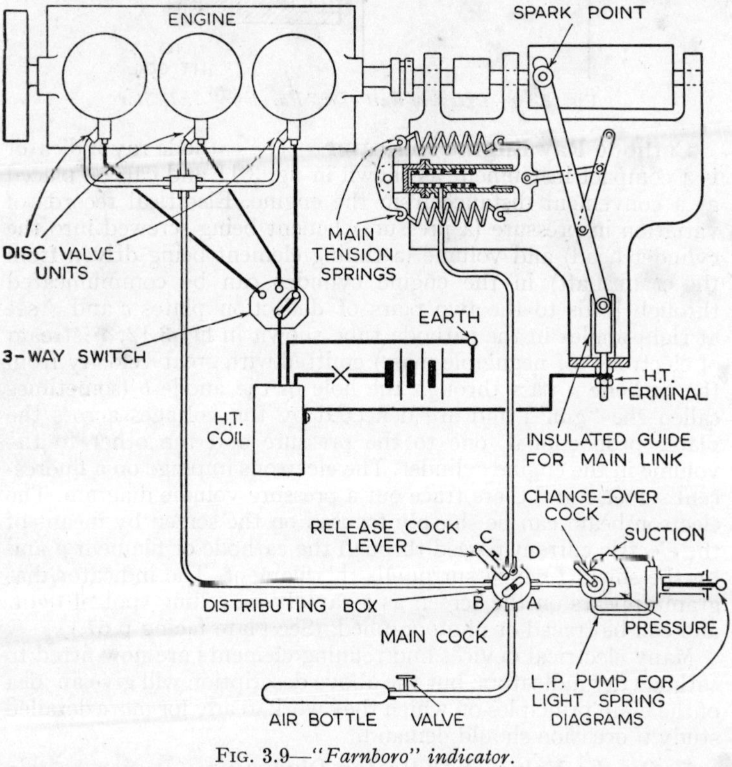

FIG. 3.9—*"Farnboro" indicator.*

eliminated, since the disc, fig. 3.10, against which the pressure in the engine cylinder is balanced on the other side by pressure from an air bottle, weighs only 1·5 Grm., and the record is transmitted by means of a spark the instant that contact of the disc valve breaks. Also, the indicator diagram is built up over the period of a large number of cycles. Such diagrams are to be preferred because of any lack of uniformity there may be in consecutive cycles.

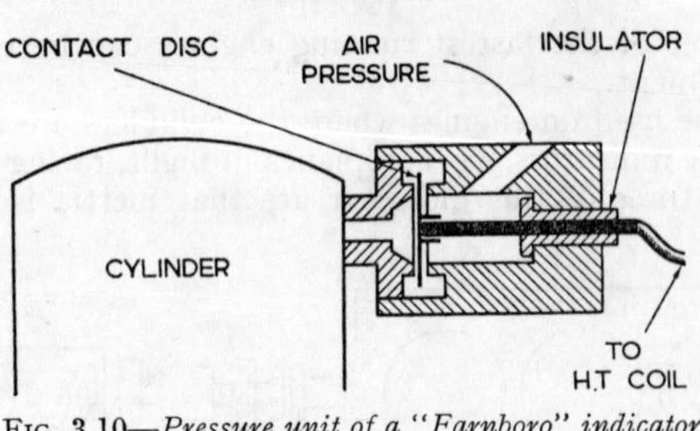

FIG. 3.10—*Pressure unit of a "Farnboro" indicator.*

Cathode Ray Engine Indicator.—The cathode ray indicator is a compact instrument as shown in fig. 3.11 and can be placed at a convenient distance from the engine. Electrical records of variation in pressure (a pressure element being screwed into the cylinder head) and volume (a timing element being driven from the crankshaft) in the engine cylinder can be communicated through leads to the two pairs of deflection plates *c* and *d* set at right-angles in the cathode tube shown in fig. 3.12. A stream of electrons (of negligible mass) emitted with great velocity from the cathode *a* pass through the hole in the anode *b* (sometimes called the "gun") and are deflected by the voltages across the plates proportional, one to the pressure and the other to the volume in the engine cylinder. The electrons impinge on a fluorescent screen *e* and there trace out a pressure-volume diagram. The electron beam can be sharply focused on the screen by means of the electric current passed through the cathode or filament *a* and by the shield *f* which surrounds the filament. The indicator diagram appears on the screen as a rapidly-travelling spot of light, and can be traced or photographed. (See plate facing p 57.)

Many electrical devices and refining elements are now fitted to cathode ray indicators, but the above description will give an idea of the main principles on which they work, ready for more detailed study if occasion should demand.

5. On the Value of Indicator Diagrams.—It may be said that indicator diagrams taken from slow-running engines (*e.g.* steam engines and gas engines) are fairly reliable when taken with the "spring and piston" type of indicator provided there is no sudden rise of pressure causing oscillations in the indicator spring. *Despite the inevitable internal swirling of a fluid expanding or being compressed in a cylinder, the area of a reliable indicator diagram does represent the actual work done on the face of the piston. But because of the energy in the swirling and eddying motion or turbulence of the* *fluid in the cylinder, the area of an actual indicator diagram is less than that which would appear if expansion and compression could be perfect, i.e. free from eddies and turbulence (see p. 289 for statements on "reversibility")*.

In the case of high-speed internal combustion engines in which high pressures and rapid rates of rise of pressure occur, it is contended that indicator diagrams from spring and piston indicators are unreliable—the error being more than 5 per cent. Even the cathode ray indicator, which is recognised as being most useful in high-speed work, is not above suspicion, owing to difficulties of phasing and the employment of a very large amplification.

6. Actual Indicator Diagrams. Fig. 3.13 shows a common form of indicator diagram taken from a single-acting, non-condensing steam engine.

Admission commences at A, and AB shows the rise of pressure in the cylinder as the steam enters; BC shows how the pressure of the admission steam varies up to the cut-off point C; CD shows the expansion of the steam from cut-off to the release point D, which will be seen to occur just before the end of the stroke; DE shows the drop in pressure when the exhaust port opens at D; EF shows the back pressure, or the pressure acting against the piston, until the exhaust port closes at F, the point of compression; FA shows compression of the steam (called "cushion steam") trapped in the cylinder and clearance space at the point of compression.

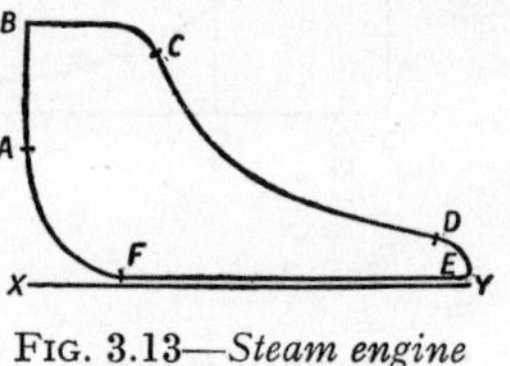

Fig. 3.13—*Steam engine indicator diagram.*

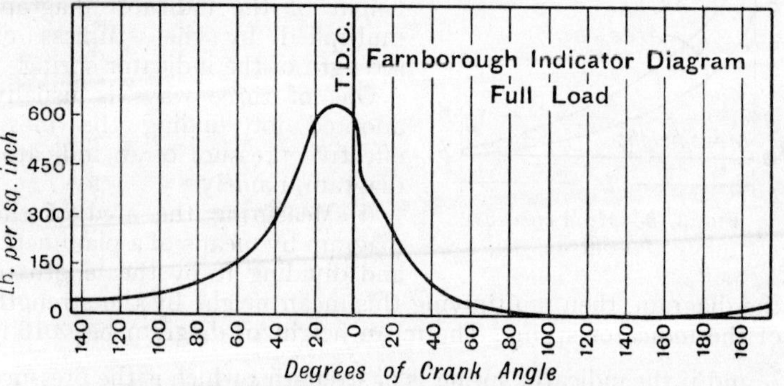

Fig. 3.14—*Indicator diagram on crank angle base.*

Fig. 3.14 shows the diagram taken from a compression-ignition engine with the "Farnboro" indicator, and fig. 3.15 shows the same data converted to a pressure-volume diagram.

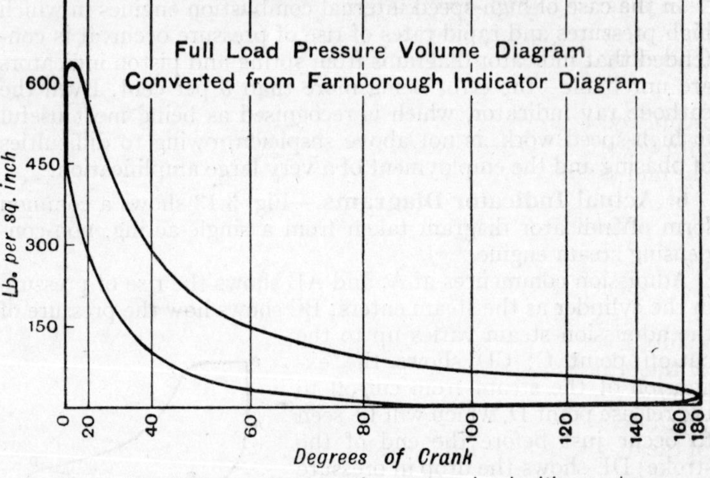

Fig. 3.15—*Indicator diagram of a compression-ignition engine.*

7. Mean Effective Pressure.—Mean effective pressure is that pressure which if acting on the piston for the whole length of the stroke would do the same amount of work as is actually done by the working agent during a complete cycle. It is equal to the mean height of the indicator diagram multiplied by the stiffness or strength of the indicator spring.

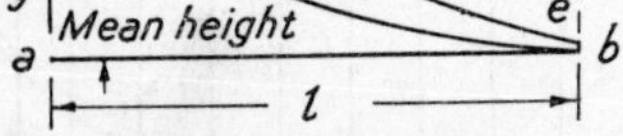

Fig. 3.16—*Mean effective pressure.*

One of three ways is usually adopted for finding the mean effective pressure of an indicator diagram, namely:

(i) Measuring the area of the diagram by means of a planimeter and dividing it by the length of the diagram, then multiplying this mean height by the strength of the indicator spring. The mean height of diagram fig. 3.16 is $\frac{a}{l}$, and if the indicator spring is of strength s which is the pressure rise needed in the cylinder to move the pencil by unit distance vertically on the indicator card, then the m.e.p. $=\frac{a}{l}\times s$. That is, the area *bcdeb* = area *abfga*.

In diagram fig. 3.16 $a=0\cdot24$ in.^{2} and $l=1\cdot44$ in.

$\therefore$ mean height of diagram $=0\cdot167$ in.

Therefore, if the spring strength $s=500$ Lb./in.^{2} per inch of height,

the m.e.p. $=83\cdot5$ Lb. per sq. in.

(ii) By the mid-ordinate method, which is to divide the diagram into ten strips of equal widths and then find the average height of the mid-ordinates.

$$\text{Mean height} = \frac{\text{sum of the ten mid-ordinates}}{10} \text{ or } \frac{\Sigma h_m}{10},$$

$$\text{hence, m.e.p.} = \left(\frac{\Sigma h_m}{10}\right) \times s.$$

(iii) By setting the points of the planimeter to the exact length of the indicator diagram and noting the planimeter reading after tracing round the diagram. This reading, divided by a constant (because of the design of the planimeter), gives the mean height of the diagram. Thus, the

$$\text{m.e.p.} = \left(\frac{\text{planimeter reading}}{\text{a constant}}\right) \times \text{spring strength}.$$

Fig. 3.17 is an illustration of a planimeter.

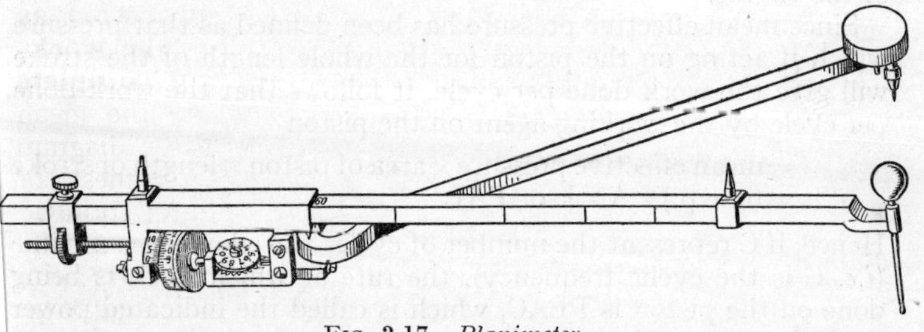

FIG. 3.17—*Planimeter.*

8. The Calibration of Indicator Springs and Pressure Gauges.—Fig. 3.18 illustrates a dead-weight gauge tester by means of which pressure gauges and indicator springs can be calibrated.

A pressure gauge G, from which accurate readings are required, can be calibrated by fitting it with union U to the pipe E, which communicates with a small cylinder C in which fits an accurately ground plunger P supporting the dead weights W. The cylinder C and pipe E are filled with oil, and the weights W are made to float by screwing down piston N. The pressure of the oil can be accurately found, being equal to the total weight W divided by the area of the plunger, and the corresponding pressure indicated by the pointer can be observed on the scale of the gauge. By applying a series of weights W to the plunger the whole range of the gauge scale can be traversed, and a calibration curve drawn showing gauge readings against actual pressures.

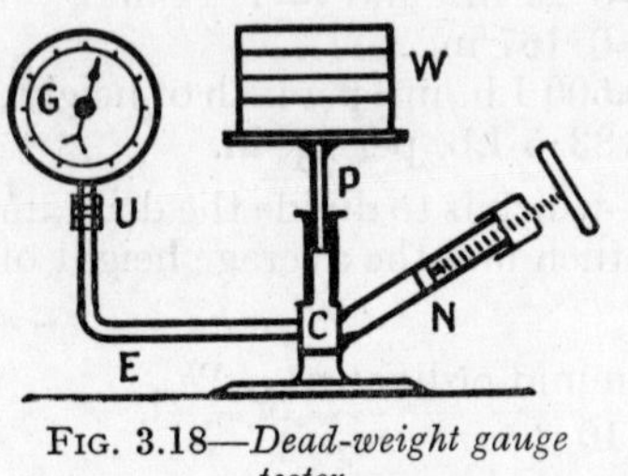

FIG. 3.18—*Dead-weight gauge tester.*

An engine indicator can be fitted by means of an adapter on to the pipe E, and, by applying weights to the plunger, the pressure required to move the pencil of the indicator a distance of 1 in. on the indicator card can be found. In this way strengths of indicator springs can be checked.

9. Indicated Horse-power.—Indicated horse-power is the power developed in the cylinder of an engine and is usually estimated from an indicator diagram. It represents the rate at which work is being done on the face of the piston by the working agent of the engine.

Since mean effective pressure has been defined as that pressure which if acting on the piston for the whole length of the stroke will give the work done per cycle, it follows that the work done per cycle by the working agent on the piston

$$= \text{mean effective pressure} \times \text{area of piston} \times \text{length of stroke}$$
$$= (\text{m.e.p.}) \times A \times L \text{ or PAL}$$

Hence, if C represent the number of cycles traced out in unit time (*i.e.* C is the cyclic frequency), the rate at which work is being done on the piston is PLAC, which is called the indicated power $\mathcal{P}_i$. If, however, it is decided to measure the physical quantities in the usual particular units, namely, stroke L in ft. such that $L=l$ ft.; $A=a$ in.^{2}; m.e.p.$=P=p$ Lb./in^2.; $C=c$/min. and indicated power $\mathcal{P}_i=i$ horse-power$=i$.h.p., where l, a, p, c and i are *numbers only* as distinct from L, A, P, C and $\mathcal{P}_i$ which are *quantities*, *i.e.* numbers × units, then **the physical formula** $\mathcal{P}_i=$**PLAC** (which is independent of any particular system of units and therefore correct in all systems) **has the corresponding**

numerical formula $\boldsymbol{i=\frac{plac}{33,000}}$, which is restricted to the units already stated.

The numerical formula $i=\frac{plac}{33,000}$ can be deduced from the physical formula $\mathcal{P}_i$=PLAC by first writing the latter in the form

$$\left(\frac{\mathcal{P}_i}{\text{h.p.}}\right)=\left(\frac{\text{P}}{\text{Lb./in.}^2}\right)\left(\frac{\text{L}}{\text{ft.}}\right)\left(\frac{\text{A}}{\text{in.}^2}\right)\left(\frac{\text{C}}{\text{1/min.}}\right)\left\{\frac{\text{Lb.}}{\text{in.}^2}\times\frac{\text{ft.}\times\text{in.}^2}{\text{h.p.}}\times\frac{1}{\text{min.}}\right\}$$

and then, since L=l ft., writing $\frac{\text{L}}{\text{ft.}}=l$, $\frac{\text{A}}{\text{in.}^2}=a$, etc. and operating on the last bracket with a unity bracket involving horse-power,

i.e.,
$$i=plac\left\{\frac{\text{Lb.}}{\text{in.}^2}\times\frac{\text{ft. in.}^2}{\text{h.p.}}\times\frac{1}{\text{min.}}\right\}\left[\frac{\text{h.p. min.}}{33,000\text{ ft. Lb.}}\right]$$

$$i=\frac{plac}{33,000}.$$

Thus, the indicated power is $\mathcal{P}_i=i$ h.p.$=\left(\frac{plac}{33,000}\right)$ horse-power.

This formula, as all numerical formulae, is tied to specific units: if units other than those previously specified are used, then a constant other than 33,000 would need to be deduced for use in the formula.

I.H.P. of Two-stroke Engines.—If the engine works on the two-stroke cycle—that is, tracing out one complete cycle every two strokes or every revolution of the crank—then the cycles, c, traced per minute=the revolutions per minute of the crank, n, and the indicated horse power is given by the numerical formula

$$i=\frac{plan}{33,000}$$

Example 1.—A single-cylinder two-stroke petrol engine has a piston diameter 3 in. and a stroke of 6 in. Find the horse-power developed in the cylinder of the engine if the m.e.p. is 33 Lb. per sq. in. when the crank makes 1,000 revolutions per min.

$$i\text{.h.p.}=\frac{plan}{33,000}\text{ horse-power}=33(\tfrac{1}{2})\left(\frac{\pi}{4}9\right)\frac{1{,}000}{33{,}000}\text{ h.p.}=3\cdot53\text{ h.p.}$$

I.H.P. of Four-stroke Engines.—If the engine works on the four-stroke cycle—that is, traces one complete cycle every four-strokes or every two revolutions of the crank—then the cycles per minute = half the number of revolutions per minute of the crank, i.e. $c=\frac{n}{2}$, and the i.h.p.$=\left(\frac{pla}{33,000}\times\frac{n}{2}\right)$ h.p.

Example 2.—Find the indicated horse-power of a four-cylinder four-stroke engine of piston diameter 4 in. and stroke 7 in. if the m.e.p. in each cylinder is 44 Lb. per sq. in. when the crank is making 1,200 r.p.m.

$$\text{i.h.p. of each cylinder} = \left(\frac{44}{33{,}000}\right)\left(\frac{7}{12}\right)\left(\frac{\pi}{4}16\right)\frac{1{,}200}{2}\ \text{h.p.} = 5\cdot 87\ \text{h.p.}$$

$$\therefore\ \text{i.h.p. of engine} = 4 \times 5\cdot 87 = 23\cdot 5\ \text{h.p.}$$

I.H.P. of Double-acting Steam Engines.—In a double-acting steam engine the steam is admitted to both sides of the piston each in turn, thus tracing out two cycles per revolution of the crank—that is $c=2n$, and if an average m.e.p. is taken for both sides of the piston, the indicated horse-power of the engine can be calculated from the numerical formula

$$i.\text{h.p.} = \left(\frac{2\ plan}{33{,}000}\right)\ \text{h.p.}$$

Example 3.—A double-acting steam engine has a mean piston area of 50 sq. in. and a stroke of 1 ft. Calculate the i.h.p. developed by the engine if the average m.e.p. for both sides of the piston is 50 Lb. per sq. in. and the crank makes 220 r.p.m.

$$i.\text{h.p.} = \frac{2 \times 60 \times 1 \times 50 \times 220}{33{,}000}\ \text{h.p.} = 40\ \text{h.p.}$$

The general physical formula (*i.e.* in which symbols represent physical quantities composed of numbers × units) for indicated power, namely, $\mathcal{P}_i = \text{PLAC}$, and the corresponding numerical formula, namely, $i = \dfrac{plac}{33{,}000}$ (in which symbols represent numbers only—definite measures or units having been used to get them, *e.g.* p represents the number of Lb./in.^{2} of mean effective pressure, *i.e.* $\text{P} = p$ Lb. per in.^{2}; l the number of feet in the stroke, *i.e.* $\text{L} = l$ ft.; a the number of square inches on the face of the piston and c the number of cycles traced per minute) show that a given indicated horse-power can be obtained in a variety of ways provided that the product PLAC remains the same. For instance, if P is increased, then A, L, or C may be reduced; or if the speed of the engine is increased, then C, the cyclic frequency, is increased, and P, L, or A may be reduced, but still resulting in the same power being developed.

Development of the steam engine has resulted in an increase in the steam pressure and piston speed—that is, P and C have been increased, thus allowing of a reduction in A and L, and therefore the same power has been developed in a smaller engine.

The same development has taken place in internal-combustion engines, but to a far greater extent. High speeds in internal-combustion engines admit of high powers being developed in comparatively small engines.

10. Brake Horse-power.—Brake or shaft horse-power is a measure of the useful power available from an engine. If a constant force F (fig. 3.19) be applied to the rim of a flywheel of radius R, say, by means of a rope unwinding with a velocity V thus making the wheel, fixed to a shaft on which there is an equal and opposite torque T=FR, revolve with a constant angular speed of $\omega=\frac{V}{R}$, then the power expended=force × velocity

$$\text{or power } \mathcal{P}=F\times V=FR\times\frac{V}{R}=T\omega$$

i.e. *shaft power=torque × angular velocity.*

FIG. 3.10 —*Brake or shaft horse-power.*

This general physical formula $\mathcal{P}=T\omega$ has a corresponding numerical formula for brake horse-power expended, namely, $b=\frac{2\pi tn}{33{,}000}$, in which n represents the number of revolutions per minute of the shaft and wheel, and t represents the torque in Lb.-ft. If units other than these are used then the latter formula will not give correct horse-power expended.

During engine tests, a torque is usually applied by means of some kind of brake opposing the rotation of the crankshaft or flywheel.

Thus, if T=t Lb.-ft. is the opposing torque exerted by the brake on the engine crankshaft which is revolving at $\omega=n$ r.p.m., the number of horse-power transmitted through the crankshaft to the brake must be

$$b=\frac{2\pi tn}{33{,}000} \text{ i.e. brake horse-power}=\left(\frac{2\pi tn}{33{,}000}\right) \text{h.p.}$$

This numerical formula can be deduced from the general physical formula for power absorbed by a brake, namely, $\mathcal{P}_b=T\omega$ by forcing specific or desired units into the physical formula, i.e., first writing the latter in the form

$$\left(\frac{\mathcal{P}_b}{\text{h.p.}}\right)=\left(\frac{T}{\text{Lb. ft.}}\right)\left(\frac{\omega}{\text{rev./min.}}\right)\left\{\frac{\text{Lb. ft.}}{\text{h.p}}\times\frac{\text{rev.}}{\text{min.}}\right\}$$

Then writing $T = t$ Lb. ft.; $\omega = n$ rev./min. and $\mathcal{P}_b = b$.h.p. (i.e., t, n and b are numbers or numerics only and T, ω and $\mathcal{P}$ are physical quantities composed of numbers × units) and proceeding to reduce the last bracket by means of appropriate unity brackets, we get

$$b = tn\left\{\frac{\text{Lb. ft.}}{\text{h.p.}} \times \frac{\text{rev.}}{\text{min.}}\right\}\left[\frac{\text{h.p. min.}}{33{,}000 \text{ ft. Lb.}}\right]\left[\frac{2\pi}{\text{rev.}}\right]$$

$$= \frac{2\pi tn}{33{,}000}, \text{ i.e. } \mathcal{P}_b = b\text{.h.p.} = \left(\frac{2\pi tn}{33{,}000}\right) \text{horse-power.}$$

The opposing friction-brake produces heat, which has to be carried away by means of cooling water flowing round the brake wheel rim.

B.h.p. is usually measured in one of three ways—either by means of a rope brake, a water brake, or an electric brake, according to the speed and power of the engine.

(i) The Rope Brake.—Fig. 3.20 shows one type of rope brake in which the weights of the lengths of the rope relative to the dead weight, W, and to the spring-balance load, S, are sufficiently large to warrant inclusion. It will be seen that the resultant torque opposing the rotation of the wheel is:—

$$= F_1\left(R + \frac{D}{2}\right) - F_2\left(R + \frac{D}{2}\right)$$

$$= (F_1 - F_2)\left(R + \frac{D}{2}\right).$$

$$= \left[(W + \text{weight of } l_1) - (S - \text{weight of } l_2)\right]\left(R + \frac{D}{2}\right)$$

$$\therefore \text{Torque} = \left[(W - S) + (\text{weight of rope } l_1 + l_2)\right]\left(R + \frac{D}{2}\right).$$

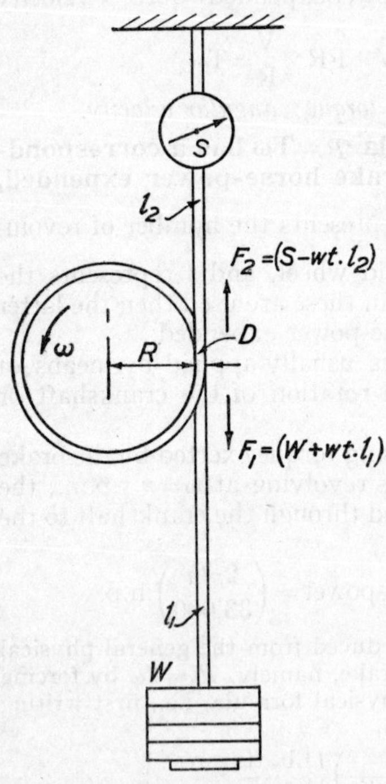

Fig. 3.20—*Rope brake.*

In most cases, however, the weight of the hanging rope is negligible compared with W. Also, in some cases, the diameter

D of the rope is negligible compared with the radius R of the flywheel, thus giving a resultant torque T=(W−S)R, and

$$b=\frac{2\pi(w-s)\,rn}{33{,}000}$$

where w and s represent the number of Lb. force of dead load and spring balance, r is the number of feet in the radius of the brake drum, and n is the number of revolutions per minute of the brake drum, i.e.

$$W=w\text{Lb.};\ S=s\text{ Lb.};\ \omega \text{ or } N=n \text{ rev./min. and } R=r \text{ ft.}$$

Example.—The brake rim of a gas engine is 4 ft. 6 in. diameter and is bolted on to one of the flywheels. A rope 1 in. diameter is passed round the rim to form a brake. The dead load on the end of the rope is 90 Lb. and the mean spring-balance reading 1·8 Lb. If the flywheel makes 225 r.p.m., find the b.h.p. of the engine and the quantity of heat produced per minute due to friction between the rope and the brake rim.

$$\text{Torque } T=(W-S)\left(R+\frac{D}{2}\right)=(90-1\cdot 8)\left(\frac{54}{24}+\frac{1}{24}\right)\text{ Lb.-ft.}=t\text{ Lb.-ft.},$$

where T is a quantity (number × unit) and t is a number only.

$$\therefore b.\text{h.p.}=\left(\frac{2\pi tn}{33{,}000}\right)\text{h.p.}=2\pi(88\cdot 2)\left(\frac{55}{24}\right)\frac{225\text{ h.p.}}{33{,}000}=8\cdot 68\text{ h.p.}$$

The heat equivalent of this brake horse-power is

$$8\cdot 68\ \text{h.p.}\left[\frac{33{,}000\text{ ft. Lb.}}{\text{h.p. min.}}\right]\left[\frac{1\text{ B.Th.U.}}{778\text{ ft. Lb.}}\right]$$

$$=8\cdot 68\times\frac{33{,}000}{778}\,\frac{\text{B.Th.U.}}{\text{min.}}=368\text{ B.Th.U./min.}$$

which is produced at the brake rim due to work being changed back into heat by friction between the rope and the metal rim of the brake wheel.

(ii) The Water Brake.—Fig. 3.21 illustrates a type of water brake in which a rotor of cup-shaped recesses rotates so as to shear across swirling water which is supplied continuously to adjacent cup-shaped recesses in a stationary casing. The shearing and change of momentum of the water provide the torque against which the engine under test is set to work, and the heat produced is carried away by the stream of water flowing through the brake. The rate of flow of water can be regulated by means of an external handwheel operating internal sluice plates, and thus the torque exerted by the brake can be controlled. Weights hung on the casing at a known leverage, and such as to keep it balanced against the torque exerted by the engine, constitute the opposing torque from which the b.h.p. of the engine can be calculated.

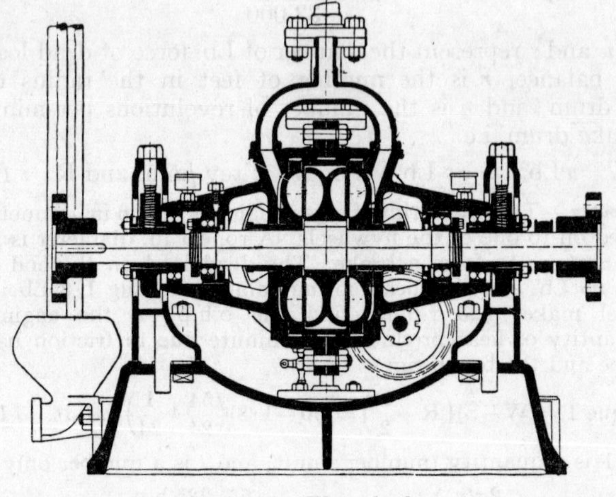

FIG. 3.21—*Water brake.*

(iii) The Electric Brake.—An electric brake is illustrated in fig. 3.22, in which the engine shaft is coupled to the armature A of

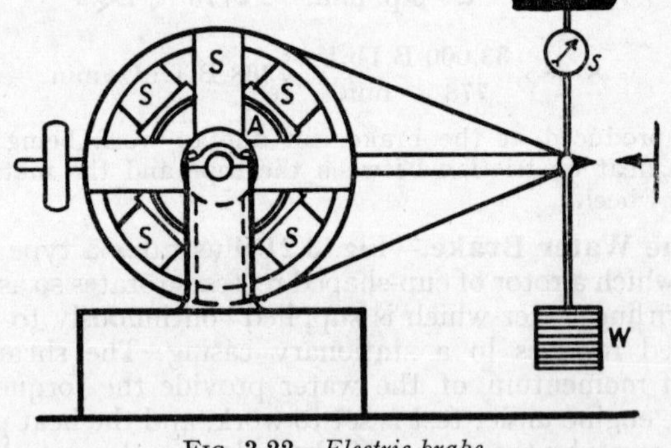

FIG. 3.22—*Electric brake.*

a dynamo which rotates in a swinging field S. When the field current is switched on the armature tends to pull round the field housing in the same direction as the rotation of the engine under test, but the field housing is kept stationary by means of an opposing torque, exerted by weights W hung on the arm. The dead load and average spring balance reading acting at a known leverage are sufficient data for an estimation of opposing torque, which, together with speed, enable a calculation for b.h.p. to be made.

11. Friction Horse-power.—An engine develops i.h.p. in the cylinder, but owing to the friction and resistances in the mechanism of the engine (piston friction, friction at bearings, etc.), the power available for work at the brake wheel is less than that developed in the cylinder by the amount necessary to overcome the frictional resistances of the moving parts. That is, b.h.p. = i.h.p. − f.h.p.; and friction horse-power is:—f.h.p. = i.h.p. − b.h.p. Thus, if the i.h.p. and b.h.p. of an engine are measured accurately, an accurate figure for f.h.p. can be obtained by subtraction. *In cases where the i.h.p. cannot be obtained accurately the f.h.p. can be estimated by shutting off the fuel and then continuing to rotate the engine crankshaft at the same speed by means of an electric motor.* The electric power or torque required for motoring the engine in this way can easily be obtained, and a figure obtained for the f.h.p. of the engine at that particular speed. If an electric brake is used for measuring b.h.p., the dynamo, after generating power during the engine test, can be used as an electric motor for motoring the engine in order to find the f.h.p. The sum of the measured b.h.p. and f.h.p. is taken as the i.h.p. (see Exercise 12, page 94).

Of the mean effective pressure estimated from indicator cards it is often useful to know how much of this indicated m.e.p. is usefully employed in producing shaft power or brake horse-power. Thus, we define (b.m.e.p.) brake mean effective pressure as that part of the m.e.p. which goes to develop the b.h.p.

Example.—A gas engine of piston diameter 7 in. and stroke 16 in. was tested when running at a speed of 225 r.p.m. The m.e.p. was estimated to be 109·6 Lb. per sq. in. when the explosions per minute were $69 = e$. A rope brake was used on a rim 4 ft. 6 in. diameter, and a dead load of 90 lb. together with a spring balance load of 1·8 Lb. on a rope 1 in. diameter constituted the opposing torque. Calculate the i.h.p. and b.h.p. of the engine, and deduce the power absorbed by engine friction. Also, calculate the b.m.e.p.

Using numerical formulae we get

$$i = \frac{plae}{33{,}000} = \left(\frac{109\cdot 6}{33{,}000}\right)\left(\frac{16}{12}\right)\left(\frac{\pi}{4}49\right)69 = 11\cdot 7,$$

i.e., indicated power $= \mathcal{P}_i = i$.h.p. $= 11\cdot 7$ h.p.,

$$\text{and}\quad b=\frac{2\pi(w+s)\left(r+\frac{d}{2}\right)n}{33{,}000}=\frac{2\pi(90-1\cdot8)\left(\frac{54+1}{24}\right)225}{33{,}000}=8\cdot7,$$

i.e., brake power $\mathcal{P}_b=b$.h.p.$=8\cdot7$ h.p.

$\therefore$ f.h.p.$=i$.h.p.$-b$.h.p.$=(11\cdot7-8\cdot7)$h-p$=3$ h.p.

Brake mean effective pressure can be deduced from the physical formula $\mathcal{P}_b=p_b\text{LAC}$ which can be changed into a numerical formula by writing $\mathcal{P}_b=b$ horse-power$=b$.h.p.;

$$\text{L}=l\text{ ft.};\ \text{A}=a\text{ in.}^2;\ \text{C}=e/\text{min.}$$

Thus, $\mathcal{P}_b$, L, A, C and p_b are physical quantities each being composed of a numbers × a unit, and b, l, a, e are numerics, i.e. numbers only.

Hence, from the physical formula, we get—

$$p_b=\frac{\mathcal{P}_b}{\text{LAC}}=\frac{b.\text{h.p.}}{l\text{ ft.}\times a\text{ in.}^2\times\dfrac{e}{\text{min.}}}\left[\frac{33{,}000\text{ ft. Lb.}}{\text{h.p. min.}}\right]$$

$$=\left(\frac{b\times33{,}000}{lae}\right)\frac{\text{Lb.}}{\text{in.}^2}$$

$$\text{Or b.m.e.p.}=p_b=\left(\frac{b\times33{,}000}{lae}\right)\frac{\text{Lb.}}{\text{in.}^2}$$

$$=\frac{8\cdot7\times33{,}000}{\frac{16}{12}\left(\frac{\pi}{4}\times49\right)69}=81\text{ Lb. per sq. in.}$$

12. Power Developed by a Turbo-jet Engine in Flight.—If the turbo-jet engine of fig. 2.21 flies with a speed of 500 m.p.h. in a stationary atmosphere, the air enters the engine duct with a velocity of

$$500\,\frac{\text{mile}}{\text{hour}}\left[\frac{5280\text{ ft.}}{\text{mile}}\right]\left[\frac{\text{hour}}{3600\text{ sec.}}\right]=\mathbf{733\text{ ft./sec.}}$$

relative to the duct. If after passing through the compressor, combustion chambers, turbine and tail pipe the gas leaves with a velocity of 1233 ft./sec. relative to the duct (*i.e.* with a velocity of 1233−733=500 ft./sec. relative to the earth) the change in velocity of the gas during its passage from entry to exit is 500 ft./sec.

Hence, if the rate of mass flow of air through the engine is 64·4 lb./sec. and the slight increase due to fuel is neglected, the rate of change of momentum is 64·4 lb./sec. × 500 ft./sec.

Hence, by Newton's second law of motion, namely

Force=rate of change of momentum

or **F=$\dot{\text{M}}\times\Delta$V, where $\dot{\text{M}}$ is the rate of mass flow of gas and ΔV is its increase in velocity.**

we deduce that the thrust created is

$$F=64\cdot 4\frac{\text{lb.}}{\text{sec.}}\times 500\frac{\text{ft.}}{\text{sec.}}\left[\frac{\text{Lb. sec.}^2}{\text{lb.}\times 32\cdot 2\text{ ft.}}\right]=1000\text{ Lb.}$$

and the power developed in flight is

Power = Thrust × velocity of aeroplane

or **$\mathcal{P}$ = F × V**

$$=1000\text{ Lb.}\times 733\frac{\text{ft.}}{\text{sec.}}\left[\frac{\text{h.p. sec.}}{550\text{ ft.-Lb.}}\right]$$

$$=1332\text{ h.p.}$$

13. Engine Efficiencies.—The efficiency of any piece of mechanism may be defined, in a simple way, as $\frac{\textbf{output}}{\textbf{input}}$.

Mechanical Efficiency.—The mechanical efficiency of an engine

$$=\frac{\text{mechanical output}}{\text{mechanical input}}=\eta_m$$

$$=\frac{\text{mechanical energy available at the brake or flywheel}}{\text{mechanical energy put into the moving mechanism at the piston}}$$

$$=\frac{\text{b.h.p.}}{\text{i.h.p.}}=\frac{\text{i.h.p.}-\text{f.h.p.}}{\text{i.h.p.}}=1-\frac{\text{f.h.p.}}{\text{i.h.p.}}=\eta_m$$

This last expression shows, as we should expect, that the smaller the friction the greater is the mechanical efficiency.

Example.—Calculate the mechanical efficiency of the gas engine during the test recorded in the example on p. 69.

Turning back to the previous example we find that

$$i=11\cdot 7,\ b=8\cdot 7,\ \therefore f=3.$$

Hence,

$$\text{mechanical efficiency}=\frac{b\text{.h.p.}}{i\text{.h.p.}}=\frac{8\cdot 7\text{ h.p.}}{11\cdot 7\text{ h.p.}}=0\cdot 743\text{ or }74\cdot 3\text{ per cent.}$$

Thermal Efficiency.—The thermal efficiency of an engine

$$=\frac{\text{thermal equivalent of mechanical energy output}}{\text{thermal equivalent of chemical energy input}}$$

$$=\frac{\text{heat equivalent of the power developed}}{\text{heat content of fuel supplied to the engine developing the power}}$$

But there are two horse-powers, namely, i.h.p. and b.h.p., from which we can find heat equivalents. Thus two thermal efficiencies can be found:

(i) Thermal efficiency on the i.h.p. basis, or indicated thermal efficiency

$$\eta_i = \frac{\text{heat equivalent of the indicated power}}{\text{heat content of fuel supplied to the engine}}$$

$$= \frac{\text{i.h.p.}\left[\dfrac{33{,}000 \text{ ft.-lb.}}{\text{h.p. min.}}\right]\left[\dfrac{\text{B.Th.U.}}{778 \text{ ft.-lb.}}\right] = i \times \dfrac{33{,}000}{778} \text{ B.Th.U./min.}}{\text{mass of fuel (lb./min.)} \times \text{calorific value of fuel (B.Th.U./lb.)}}$$

where i is the *number* of horse-power.

(ii) Thermal efficiency on the b.h.p. basis, or brake thermal efficiency

$$\eta_b = \frac{\text{heat equivalent of the brake power}}{\text{heat supplied to the engine}}$$

$$= \frac{b \times \dfrac{33{,}000}{778} \text{ B.Th.U./min.}}{\text{mass of fuel (lb./min.)} \times \text{cal. val. (B.Th.U./lb.)}}$$

where b is the *number* of horse-power available at the brake.

In the case of a gun, the thermal efficiency is the ratio of the kinetic energy imparted to the projectile to the potential energy in the explosive charge.

Example.—If the gas used per minute by the engine of the example on p. 69 was 4·19 cu. ft. and had a calorific value of 497 B.Th.U. per cu. ft., calculate the brake thermal efficiency of the engine and its efficiency on the i.h.p. basis during that particular test.

Brake thermal efficiency

$$= \frac{\text{heat equivalent of b.h.p.}}{\text{heat supplied to engine}}$$

$$= \frac{8 \cdot 7 \text{ h.p.}\left[\dfrac{33{,}000 \text{ ft. lb.}}{\text{h.p. min.}}\right]\left[\dfrac{\text{B.Th.U.}}{778 \text{ ft. lb.}}\right]}{4 \cdot 19 \dfrac{\text{ft.}^3}{\text{min.}} \times 497 \dfrac{\text{B.Th.U.}}{\text{ft.}^3}}$$

i.e., $$\eta_b = \frac{8 \cdot 7 \times 33{,}000 \text{ B.Th.U./min.}}{4 \cdot 19 \times 497 \times 778 \text{ B.Th.U./min.}} = 0 \cdot 177 \text{ or } 17 \cdot 7 \text{ per cent.}$$

Similarly, the thermal efficiency on i.h.p. basis

$$= \frac{11 \cdot 7 \times \dfrac{33{,}000}{778}}{4 \cdot 19 \times 497} = 0 \cdot 238 \text{ or } 23 \cdot 8 \text{ per cent.}$$

Here we may note that the *greatest* brake thermal efficiency of a modern steam turbine is of the order of 34 per cent. and of an internal-combustion engine about 40 per cent., the latter being a compression-ignition engine.

14. Fuel Consumption.—The fuel consumption of engines is usually measured and expressed in two ways: (i) in lb. of fuel per hour, from which the cost of running an engine for a period of time can be calculated; and (ii) in lb. per b.h.p.-hour, which gives us the lb. of fuel required by an engine to do the definite amount of work equal to 1 h.p.-hour or 1,980,000 ft.-Lb.

The horse-power unit, being a definite amount of work, serves chiefly as a means by which to compare the fuel consumptions of an engine at different power outputs; for the engine can, as it were, be set to do the definite amount of work 1 h.p.-hour no matter what particular power it is developing at the time, and the amount of fuel necessary for the doing of it can be found and compared with that required for doing the same amount of work at any other power.

Consumptions of fuel expressed in lb. per b.h.p.-hour are, in effect, consumptions in lb. per 1,980,000 *ft.-Lb. of work, and a curve plotted over the range of power output (no load to overload) for an engine will reveal the particular brake power at which the engine can be run with least consumption of fuel, per b.h.p.-hour and, therefore, with maximum thermal efficiency.*

The expression for brake thermal efficiency shows that the power at which there is minimum consumption per b.h.p.-hour is also the power at which the brake thermal efficiency is a maximum; for, brake thermal efficiency is

$$\eta_b = \frac{\text{heat equivalent of brake power}}{\text{rate of consumption of fuel} \times \text{calorific value of fuel}}$$

or, in specific units,

$$\eta_b = \frac{(b.\text{h.p.})\left[\dfrac{33{,}000\ \text{ft.-Lb.}}{\text{h.p. min.}}\right]\left[\dfrac{60\ \text{min.}}{\text{hour}}\right]\left[\dfrac{\text{B.Th.U.}}{778\ \text{ft.-Lb.}}\right]}{f\text{-lb. of fuel/hour} \times q\ \text{B.Th.U./lb. of fuel}}$$

where b, f and q are numbers only

$$= \frac{b\left(\dfrac{33{,}000 \times 60}{778}\right)\dfrac{\text{B.Th.U.}}{\text{hour}}}{(f \times q)\ \dfrac{\text{B.Th.U.}}{\text{hour}}}$$

i.e.

$$\eta_b = \frac{\text{a constant number, namely } \left(\dfrac{33{,}000 \times 60}{778 \times q}\right)}{(f/b) \text{ which is the number of lb. of fuel consumed per b.h.p.-hour}}$$

Therefore, when the denominator (f/b) is a minimum, the fraction giving brake thermal efficiency (η_b) will be a maximum as on fig. 3.23.

Example.—The following figures are results obtained from observations made during a trial of a four-cylinder petrol engine:

Brake horse power .	5·8	7·2	8·75	10·9	12·65	14·1	15·3	16·6
Fuel consumption, lb. per b.h.p.-hour .	0·935	0·87	0·81	0·735	0·71	0·70	0·705	0·73

Plot a curve showing fuel consumption against power developed, and estimate from it the power at which to run the engine to give greatest economy of fuel and cost.

If the calorific value of the petrol used was 19,260 B.Th.U. per lb., calculate the thermal efficiency in each case and plot a curve showing how it varies with power.

Thermal efficiency on the b.h.p. basis

$$=\frac{\frac{33{,}000}{778}\times 60}{\text{fuel lb. per b.h.p.-hour}\times\text{cal. val. of fuel in B.Th.U. per lb.}}$$

$$=\frac{\frac{33{,}000}{778}\times\frac{60}{19{,}260}}{\text{fuel lb. per b.h.p.-hour}}=\frac{0\cdot 132}{\text{lb. per b.h.p.-hour}}$$

which, for the above trial, gives:

Brake thermal efficiency%	14·1	15·2	16·3	18	18·6	18·9	18·75	18·1

When plotted, these figures give the curves shown in fig. 3.23, from which it will be seen that the most economical power is at M in the region of 14 b.h.p., because at this particular power the amount of fuel necessary for doing 1,980,000 ft.-Lb. of work (*i.e.* 1 h.p.-hour) is a minimum. At any other power the graph shows that to do this same amount of work would require more fuel and therefore be more expensive. It will be noticed that at the point M, where the fuel consumption per b.h.p.-hour is a minimum, the brake thermal efficiency is a maximum.

A modern large steam engine has a minimum consumption of about 10 lb. of steam per b.h.p.-hour; a large turbine about 8; a heavy oil engine has a consumption of the order 0·37–0·4 of fuel-oil; and a high-speed compression-ignition engine about 0·35 lb. per b.h.p.-hour.

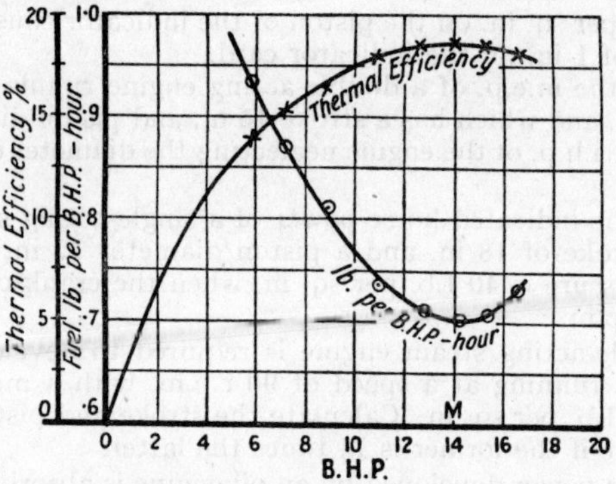

Fig. 3.23—*Engine curves.*

EXERCISES ON CHAPTER 3

(i)

1. If a constant force of 10,000 Lb. acts on the piston of an engine having a stroke of 2 ft., calculate the work done during the stroke, and the diameter of the piston if the force is due to steam exerting a resultant pressure of 100 Lb. per sq. in.

2. (*a*) The piston of a single-acting steam engine has a diameter 30 in. and stroke 48 in. Steam is admitted to the engine at a pressure of 90 Lb. per sq. in. gauge until the point of cut-off at half stroke. Assuming the expansion of steam from cut-off to the end of the stroke obeys the law PV=constant, draw a P,V diagram to scale and from it estimate the work done during the outstroke of the piston.

(*b*) If the exhaust pressure is atmospheric and equal to 15 Lb. per sq. in. absolute for the whole of the instroke, estimate the m.e.p. of the diagram if clearance volume is neglected. Hence calculate the work done per cycle and the horse-power developed if the crank makes 100 r.p.m.

3. A petrol engine has a diameter of piston 3·5 in. and a stroke 4 in. What is the mean height of the indicator diagram of area 4·12 sq. in. and length 3·85 in.? If the strength of the indicator spring is such that the indicator pencil moves a height 1 in. due to 70 Lb. per sq. in. on the piston of the indicator, find the m.e.p. of the diagram and the work done per cycle.

If the engine works on the four-stroke cycle, making 800 cycles per minute, what is the horse-power developed? State also the speed of the engine in revolutions per minute.

4. An indicator diagram is divided into 10 equal strips and the sum of the mid-ordinates of the 10 strips is 7·77 in. Find the m.e.p. of the diagram if the strength of the indicator spring is such that 40 Lb. per sq. in. on the piston of the indicator causes a vertical movement of 1 in. on the indicator card.

If this is the m.e.p. of a double-acting engine running at a speed of 120 r.p.m. and which has a stroke 15 in. and piston diameter 1 ft., calculate the i.h.p. of the engine neglecting the diameter of the piston rod.

5. Find the indicated horse-power of a single-acting steam engine having a stroke of 18 in. and a piston diameter 12 in. if the mean effective pressure is 40 Lb. per sq. in. when the crank of the engine makes 90 r.p.m.

6. A single-acting steam engine is required to develop 37 horse-power when running at a speed of 90 r.p.m. with a mean effective pressure 40 Lb. per sq. in. Calculate the stroke and piston diameter of the engine if the former is $1\frac{1}{2}$ times the latter.

7. (*a*) The power developed by an oil engine is absorbed by means of a rope brake on a flywheel 4 ft. $11\frac{1}{2}$ in. diameter. The dead load on the rope is 84 Lb. and the average reading of the spring balance is 15 Lb. If the engine speed is 230 revolutions per minute and the rope is $\frac{1}{2}$ in. diameter, calculate the b.h.p. of the engine.

(*b*) If the mechanical efficiency is 82 per cent., what is the i.h.p. of the engine and the horse-power expended in overcoming the frictional resistances?

8. The oil fuel used in an oil engine has a calorific value of 18,000 B.Th.U. per lb. When tested the engine is found to develop 80 b.h.p. with an oil consumption of 35 lb. per hour. Calculate the thermal efficiency on the i.h.p. basis if the mechanical efficiency of the engine is 80 per cent.

9. A marine engine is found to develop one horse-power-hour for every 2 lb. of coal consumed in the furnace of the boiler. What is the thermal efficiency of the plant if the coal used has calorific value of 14,500 B.Th.U. per lb.?

10. A gas engine consumes 230 cu. ft. of coal gas per hour when developing 10 i.h.p. and 7·6 b.h.p. If the calorific value of the gas is equivalent to 330,000 ft.-Lb. per cu. ft., calculate the thermal efficiencies of the engine on the i.h.p. basis and on the b.h.p. basis, Find also the mechanical efficiency of the engine and the consumption in cu. ft. per b.h.p.-hour and per i.h.p.-hour.

11. The following figures are results obtained from observations made during a variable load trial of a uniflow steam engine:

Brake horse power . .	21	42	63·5	82	106	130
Steam consumption per b.h.p. per hour . . .	17·7	16·3	15·7	15·5	15·7	16·8

Plot a curve showing steam consumption per b.h.p.-hour against b.h.p. developed, and estimate from it the most economical power at which to run the engine.

12. A gas engine working on the four-stroke cycle was designed to develop 25 b.h.p. at 260 r.p.m. and tested over a range of power outputs when using gas having a calorific value of 540 B.Th.U. per cu. ft. The following results were obtained from the trials:

Brake horse power . .	30	20	14·5	13·3	12·25	6·12
Gas consumption per b.h.p.-hour . . cu. ft.	16·7	15·8	17·25	18·1	19·0	27·8

Calculate the thermal efficiency of the engine at each of the above powers, and plot curves showing how the consumption and brake thermal efficiency of the engine varies over the range of b.h.p. developed.

Estimate from the graphs the best power at which to run the engine and the cost of running the engine per hour at this particular power if the price of the gas is 42*d*. per 1,000 cu. ft.

(ii)

13. The dimensions of a double-acting steam engine are: piston diameter 8·47 in.; stroke 12·1 in.; piston rod diameter 1·45 in.; brake-wheel diameter + diameter of rope 3·9 ft.

A trial of 48 minutes' duration was made. The total number of revolutions of the crank during that time was 4,973. The m.e.p. for the outstroke, i.e. for the head end of the cylinder, was found to be 16 Lb. per sq. in., and the m.e.p. for the instroke, i.e. for the crank end of the cylinder, was 13·6 Lb. per sq. in. The dead load on the rope brake was 113·5 Lb., and the average reading of the spring balance, 24·1 Lb.

Calculate:

(*a*) The i.h.p., b.h.p., and f.h.p. of the engine.

(*b*) Express the above powers as heat equivalents in B.Th.U. per min.

14. Find the amount of feed water used during a journey of $2\frac{1}{2}$ hrs. by a locomotive developing 1,200 i.h.p. and using 38 lb. of feed per i.h.p. hour. If the steam raised per lb. of coal burned is 9 lb., what is the total weight of coal fired during the journey?

What is the power available for tractive purposes if the mechanical efficiency of the engine is 85 per cent.?

15. A four-stroke gas engine having a stroke of 30 in. and piston diameter 21 in. is designed to develop 160 b.h.p. when running at the constant speed of 170 r.p.m. A series of tests on the engine when

using town gas of calorific value 540 B.Th.U. per cu. ft. gave the following results:

Brake horse power . . .	160	120	80	40	20
Brake thermal efficiency . .	0·296	0·273	0·236	0·168	0·113

Calculate the gas consumption in cu. ft. per b.h.p.-hour and the cost of running the engine per hour for each power if the price of gas is 42*d*. per 1,000 cu. ft., and plot curves on a b.h.p. base to show how the thermal efficiency, the gas consumption, and the cost of running vary with power output.

Estimate from the graphs the best power at which to run the engine and calculate the m.e.p. at this particular power, assuming that identical working cycles occur every two revolutions and a mechanical efficiency of 80 per cent.

16. An oil engine firing every other revolution is loaded by means of a rope brake mounted on a mean diameter of 4·5 ft., the dead weight being 60 Lb. and the spring balance reading 4 Lb. The speed is 250 r.p.m., the bore and stroke 6 and 9 in. respectively, and the m.e.p. 87 Lb. per sq. in.

Determine:

(*a*) the mechanical efficiency;

(*b*) the thermal efficiency on the i.h.p. basis, if the engine uses 2·69 lb. of oil per hour of calorific value 18,000 B.Th.U. per lb. [Part I, B.Sc. Lond.]

17. A jet-propulsion engine mounted on a test bed draws in 63 lb. of air per sec. and consumes 1 lb. of fuel per sec. of calorific value 18,000 B.Th.U. per lb. The air enters the intake duct with a speed of 400 ft. per sec., and the products of combustion leave the tail pipe with a velocity of 1,800 ft. per sec. relative to the pipe. Calculate the static thrust of the engine. If this thrust is maintained when the engine is in an aircraft flying at 400 ft. per sec., calculate the horse-power expended in flight and the overall efficiency.

CHAPTER 4

THE TESTING OF ENGINES: AND REPORT ON A GAS ENGINE TRIAL

1. THE TESTING OF ENGINES

WHATEVER claims are made as a result of theory regarding the performance of heat engine plant, *the final appeal must be made to experimental facts and measured results*. (See the Appendix for theory and practice forming a cycle of operations known as Scientific Method.) It was pointed out on p. 23 that the function of a heat engine is to transform heat energy into mechanical energy. Some engines do this more efficiently than others—that is, they change a greater amount of the heat energy supplied into mechanical energy than do other types of engines. Also, in general, there is one particular power at which to run an engine such that its thermal efficiency is greatest. One reason for testing engines is to find this particular power, for engineers desire an engine to yield a maximum of mechanical energy from a minimum of heat energy which they have to supply in the form of fuel. In other words, they desire the thermal efficiency, that is, the ratio

$$\frac{\text{output of mechanical energy from the engine}}{\text{input of heat energy to the engine}},$$

to be as high as possible.

When running an engine at any power or at a particular speed we want to know how much of the energy supplied in the fuel is actually being transformed into mechanical energy available at the engine flywheel or crankshaft for driving belts, gears, dynamos, road wheels of cars, and other uses to which the different types of engines can be put. We also want to know how the energy, which is supplied in the fuel, splits up, and how much flows along the various energy streams through the engine (for instance, heat flowing to exhaust and heat flowing to engine cooling water) with a view to finding out if any of the heat which is flowing to waste can be diverted into the useful stream of mechanical energy and so yield a greater amount of work available at the flywheel or at the driving shaft of the engine.

The chief objects in view when engines are tested over the full range of output may be stated briefly as follows:

(i) to measure the mechanical energy or power output of the engine;

(ii) to measure the consumption of fuel;

(iii) to estimate the performance or efficiency of the engine;

(iv) to draw up a heat account or heat balance sheet for the engine showing the quantities of energy flowing along the different energy streams of the engine.

Also, it may be that it is desired to check the specification given by the makers of a certain engine. In this connection the following note of the British Engineering Standards Association is of interest, "The rated output of the engine shall be the load in b.h.p. which it is capable of carrying continuously for a period of 12 hours at its rated speed when working under the following conditions: barometric pressure 30 inches of mercury; atmospheric temperature 62° F."

The method of analysing heat engine plant and of drawing up reports on engine trials is made logical and rational if carried out in the following way:

(*a*) Make a diagrammatic sketch or Line Diagram of the plant;

(*b*) Deduce the Energy Equation and Energy Stream Diagram from the Line Diagram;

(*c*) The form of the Report Sheet can be deduced from the Energy Stream Diagram (the report sheet being merely a tabulation in appropriate sections of the observations necessary for calculating the items which appear on the Energy Stream Diagram, together with a section on engine efficiencies and another on deductions);

(*d*) Engine Curves and other graphical representations can be made of the numerical results tabulated in the Report Sheet;

(*e*) Conclusions and criticisms can be made from the Graphs, Curves, and Report Sheet.

In this way all heat engine plant can be analysed—each step being deduced from the one which precedes it. This will be seen more clearly when considering the engine trials and reports which follow, and which, it should be noted, are drawn up under the six sub-sections:

I. Object of Trial.

II. The Plant—

(*a*) Diagrammatic Sketch or Line Diagram.

(*b*) Energy Equation and Energy Stream Diagram for the Plant.

(*c*) Description of Plant and Method of Testing.

III. Report Sheet giving mean values of the observations made during tests, and results derived therefrom.

IV. Specimen Set of Calculations of the results of one of the tests entered on the Report Sheet.

V. Graphical Representations of Results, and Engine Curves.

VI. Conclusions and Criticisms.

The apparatus involved in the testing of engines and the methods employed for measuring the several quantities required are very varied. Points with regard to a few of them will be best brought out by reference to the brief reports of the trials which come later in the text.

2. REPORT ON A GAS ENGINE TRIAL

OBJECT OF TRIAL

To obtain a power-consumption curve and mechanical and thermal efficiency curves for the engine when tested over a range of power from no load to full load. Also, to draw up a heat account for the engine over this range of power.

THE PLANT

(*a*) *Diagrammatic Sketch or Line Diagram.*—This sketch or Line Diagram shows in a diagrammatic way those features of the plant which are necessary for deducing the energy equation and energy stream diagram on which the remainder of the report is built up.

It will be noticed that the plant under test has been enclosed by a boundary line (fig. 4.1) shown broken. The engine within the boundary can be regarded as an energy transformer receiving

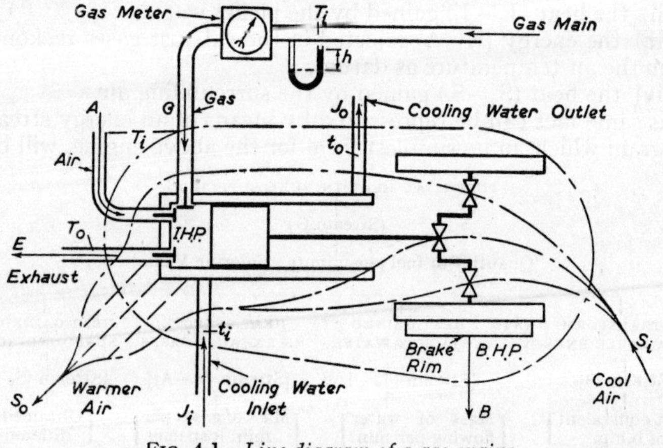

FIG. 4.1—*Line diagram of a gas engine.*

energy contained in the chemical elements of the fuel, and transforming it into heat energy, a part of which is changed into mechanical energy or work. Assuming, now, that the engine has been running for a sufficient length of time for it to be working steadily, then no energy will be accumulating within the boundary and we can, therefore, make the statement that the sum total of the energy per minute flowing into the boundary must be equal to the sum total of the energy per minute flowing out of the boundary along the various energy streams.

(*b*) *Energy Equation and Energy Stream Diagram for the Plant.*—The energy streams flowing into and out of the boundary are indicated by means of arrows, and the fact that the sum of the rate at which energy is flowing along the streams indicated by arrows pointing into the boundary must equal the sum total of the rate of flow of energy along the streams indicated by arrows pointing out of the boundary, can be shown by means of the following energy equation:

$$G+A+J_i+S_i=B+E+J_o+S_o$$

where the letters represent the energy per unit of time flowing along the respective streams into and out of the boundary. Rearranged the energy equation can be written:

$$G=B+(J_o-J_i)+(E-A)+(S_o-S_i)$$

which, in words, states that the potential energy supplied in the gas stream (G) is divided up, in going through the engine, into:

(i) the heat transformed into mechanical energy which leaves the boundary along the brake horse-power stream (B),

(ii) the heat (J_o-J_i) gained by the jacket water,

(iii) the energy (E—A) rejected in the exhaust gases reckoned from the air temperature as datum,

(iv) the heat (S_o-S_i) gained by the surrounding air.

This same fact can be represented by means of an energy stream diagram which, in its simplest form for the above engine, will be:

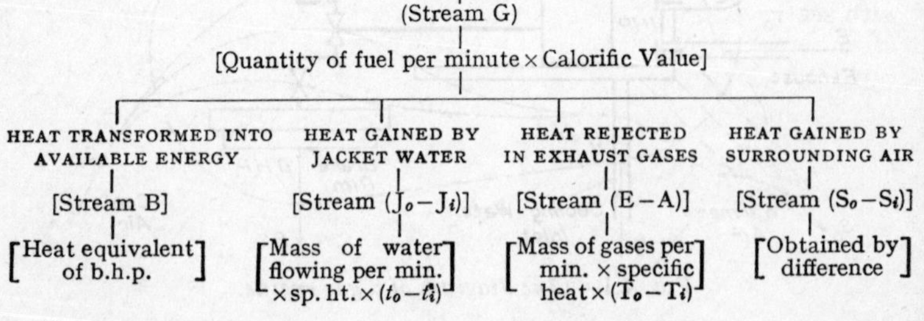

(*c*) *Description of Plant and Method of Testing.*—The engine tested was a four-stroke gas engine rated at 10 b.h.p. when making 225 r.p.m. The governor was of the "hit and miss" type. The gas-supply-valve was set at a constant opening throughout the series of tests. Ignition was controlled by a magneto actuated by the half-speed camshaft. The gas supply was passed through a meter which was read every 2 minutes. A water-manometer tube and a thermometer recorded the pressure of the gas above that of the atmosphere and the temperature of the gas at inlet (T_i). The air supply to the air valve of the engine was not measured in this simple trial, and no observations were made on the exhaust gases.

The i.h.p. of the engine was estimated from diagrams taken with a standard type of spring and piston indicator, and the number of explosions was counted per minute. The b.h.p. was obtained from observations made on the spring balance and dead load of a rope brake passed round the brake rim fitted to one of the two flywheels; revolutions per minute were estimated by means of a speedometer.

The mass of engine cooling water flowing per minute was obtained by collecting in tanks and weighing, and its rise in temperature was obtained from observations made on thermometers placed in the inlet and outlet pipes.

The duration of each test was 20 minutes. Observations were made on the various instruments and apparatus every 2 minutes and entered immediately on a log sheet. The mean values of the observations made during each 20-minute test were obtained for a trial of six tests made over the power range from full load to no load, and the six sets of mean values were entered on the following Report Sheet.

[It will be noticed that the form of the Report Sheet is deduced from the items appearing on the Energy Stream Diagram, being merely a tabulation in sections of the observations necessary for calculating the heat quantities appearing on that diagram, together with sections giving a heat account, efficiencies, and deductions.]

REPORT SHEET FOR TRIAL OF NATIONAL GAS ENGINE

ENGINE DATA: Piston Diameter, 7 in. Stroke, 16 in. Clearance volume, 0·067 cu. ft. Compression ratio, 6·32.
Diameter of brake rim, 4 ft. 6 in. Diameter of brake rope, 1 in.

DATE OF TRIAL.

Number of Test.		1	2	3	4	5	6
Duration of Test.	min.	20	20	20	20	20	20
POWER.							
Revolutions per minute, n		225·8	225	227·3	227·7	232	239
Number of explosions per minute, e		82·6	69	56·8	48	35	19·3
Mean effective pressure, p,	Lb. per sq. in.	106·9	109·6	114·8	109·7	123·6	123
i.h.p. $=\frac{plae}{33{,}000}$	h.p.	13·7	11·7	10·1	8·2	6·7	3·7
Brake, dead load, w,	Lb.	110	90	70·6	50	30	0
Spring balance, s,	Lb.	2·2	1·8	1·5	1·3	0·9	0
b.h.p. $=\frac{2\pi(w-s)}{33{,}000}\left(\frac{r+d}{2}\right)n$	h.p.	10·6	8·7	6·9	4·8	2·9	0
Heat equivalent of b.h.p.	B.Th.U. per min.	450	370	293	218	123	0
ENGINE COOLING WATER.							
Rate of flow of cooling water,	lb./min.	18·2	18·5	14·8	11·2	10·8	8·7
Inlet temperature, t_i,	°C.	21·61	22·51	21·0	21·78	21·9	20·75
Outlet temperature, t_o,	°C.	40·05	37·5	34·4	40·96	37·67	31·23
Rise in temperature (t_o-t_i),	°C.	18·44	14·99	13·4	19·18	15·77	10·48
Heat carried away by engine cooling water, $=[\text{mass per min.}\times(t_o-t_i)]\times\frac{9}{5}$	B.Th.U./min.	605	500	357	388	306	164
HEAT SUPPLIED TO ENGINE,							
Gas used as recorded by meter, V,	cu. ft./min.	5·24	4·48	3·8	3·15	2·43	1·53
Manometer reading, h,	in water	4·3	4·75	4·65	5·0	4·9	4·9
Pressure of gas above atmospheric $\left[=0{\cdot}49\times\frac{h}{13{\cdot}6}\right]$	Lb. per sq. in.	0·16	0·17	0·17	0·18	0·18	0·18
Atmospheric pressure,	Lb. per sq. in.	14·75	14·75	14·75	14·75	14·75	14·75
Absolute pressure of gas used, p,	Lb./sq. in.	14·91	14·92	14·92	14·93	14·93	14·93
Temperature of gas used, t,	°C.	21·5	23·3	23·3	20·6	22·9	22·1
Absolute temperature of gas used, $(T=273+t)$	°abs.C	294·5	296·3	296·3	293·6	296·2	295·1
Volume of gas used at s.t.p. $\left[=\frac{pV}{14{\cdot}7}\frac{273}{T}\right]$	cu. ft./min.	4·93	4·19	3·55	2·98	2·27	1·44
Calorific value of gas.		497 B.Th.-U. per cu. ft. at s.t.p.					
Heat supplied to the engine	B.Th.U./min.	2,450	2,080	1,760	1,480	1,130	716

Number of Test.		1		2		3		4		5		6	
Duration of Test.	min.	20		20		20		20		20		20	
HEAT ACCOUNT) in B.Th.U. per minute and percentages).													
Heat supplied to the engine.		2,450	100%	2,080	100%	1,760	100%	1,480	100%	1,130	100%	716	100%
Heat equivalent to b.h.p.		450	18·3%	370	17·7%	293	16·6%	218	13·7%	123	10·9%	0	0%
Heat to engine cooling water.		605	24·6%	500	24·0%	357	20·2%	388	26·2%	306	27·1%	164	22·9%
Heat to exhaust gases, and Heat loss to surrounding air.	By difference.	1,395	57·1%	1,210	58·3%	1,110	63·2%	874	60·1%	701	62·0%	552	77·1%
		2,450	100%	2,080	100%	1,760	100%	1,480	100%	1,130	100%	716	100%
EFFICIENCIES.													
Mechanical efficiency $\left(\frac{\text{b.h.p.}}{\text{i.h.p.}}\right)$	per cent.	77·4		74·3		68·3		58·5		43·3		0	
Thermal efficiency (b.h.p. basis)	per cent.	18·3		17·7		16·6		13·7		10·9		0	
Thermal efficiency (i.h.p. basis)	per cent.	24·7		23·8		24·2		23·4		25·2		21·9	
" Air Standard " thermal efficiency.		$=1-\left(\frac{1}{r_c}\right)^{\gamma-1}=1-\left(\frac{1}{6\cdot32}\right)^{0\cdot4}=52\cdot1\%$											
Relative efficiency (b.h.p. basis) $=\frac{\text{Brake thermal efficiency}}{\text{" Air Standard " efficiency}}$	per cent.	35·2		34·0		31·9		26·3		20·9		0	
DEDUCTIONS.													
Horse-power absorbed in friction (f.h.p. =i.h.p. − b.h.p.)		3·1		3·0		3·2		3·4		3·8		3·7	
Consumption of gas as used,	cu. ft. per hr.	311·4		268·8		228·0		189·0		145·8		91·8	
Gas as used in cu. ft. per b.h.p.-hour.		29·6		30·9		33·1		39·4		50·2		—	
Cost of running per hour at $8\frac{1}{2}d.$ per therm (=100,000 B.Th.U.)	pence	12·5		10·6		9·0		7·5		5·7		3·6	

SPECIMEN SET OF CALCULATIONS FOR TEST

(See Report Sheet on pages 84–85.)

Power.

Indicated Horse-power.

Explosions or Cycles $= C = 82\cdot6$ per min. $= c$/min.

M.e.p. $= P = 106\cdot9$ Lb. per sq. in. $= p$ Lb./in.^{2}

Piston diameter $= 7$ in. $\therefore$ Area $= A = \frac{\pi}{4} 49$ in.$^2 = a$ in.^{2}

Stroke $= L = 16$ in. $= \frac{16}{12}$ ft. $= l$ ft.

Where the capital letters C P A L represent complete quantities (numbers × units) and the small letters, *c*, *p*. *a*, *l*, represent numbers only.

Thus, using the physical formula in which symbols represent physical quantities composed of numbers × units, the indicated power is

$$\mathcal{P}_i = PLAC = 106\cdot9 \frac{\text{Lb.}}{\text{in.}^2} \times 16 \text{ in.} \times \frac{\pi}{4} 49 \text{ in.}^2 \times \frac{82\cdot6}{\text{min.}}$$

$$= 106\cdot9 \times 4\pi \times 49 \times 82\cdot6 \frac{\text{Lb. in.}}{\text{min.}} \left[\frac{\text{h.p. min.}}{33{,}000 \text{ ft. Lb.}}\right] \left[\frac{\text{ft.}}{12 \text{ in.}}\right]$$

$$= 13\cdot7 \text{ h.p.}$$

Alternatively, using the numerical formula in which symbols represent numbers only—the units or measures having been specified beforehand in order to get the numbers and also to deduce the formula, the *number* of indicated horse-power developed is

$$i = \frac{plac}{33{,}000} = \frac{106\cdot9 \times \frac{16}{12} \times \frac{\pi}{4} 49 \times 82\cdot6}{33{,}000} = 13\cdot7.$$

Therefore, *i*.h.p. $= 13\cdot7$ h-p. $= \mathcal{P}_i =$ indicated power.

Brake Horse-power.

Brake drum speed $= \omega = 225\cdot8$ rev./min. $= n$ rev./min.

Brake dead-load $= W = 110$ Lb. $= w$ Lb.

Spring-balance load $= S = 2\cdot2$ Lb. $= s$ Lb.

Radius of brake rim $= R = 2\frac{1}{4}$ ft. $= r$ ft.

Diameter of rope $= D = 1$ in. $= \frac{1}{12}$ ft. $= d$ ft.

Thus, using the physical formula, the brake power is

$$\mathcal{P}_b = T\omega = (W - S)\left(R + \frac{D}{2}\right)\omega$$

$$= (110\ \text{Lb.} - 2 \cdot 2\ \text{Lb.})(27\ \text{in.} + 0 \cdot 5\ \text{in.})\ 225 \cdot 8\ \frac{\text{rev.}}{\text{min.}}$$

$$= 107 \cdot 8 \times 27 \cdot 5 \times 225 \cdot 8\ \text{Lb. in.}\ \frac{\text{rev.}}{\text{min.}}\left[\frac{\text{h.p. min.}}{33{,}000\ \text{ft.-Lb.}}\right]\left[\frac{\text{ft.}}{12\ \text{in.}}\right]\left[\frac{2\pi}{\text{rev.}}\right]$$

$$= \frac{2\pi \times 107 \cdot 8 \times \frac{27 \cdot 5}{12} \times 225 \cdot 8}{33{,}000}\ \text{h.p.}$$

$$= 10 \cdot 6\ \text{h.p.}$$

Alternatively, using the numerical formula, the *number* of brake horse-power developed is

$$b = \frac{2\pi tn}{33{,}000} = \frac{2\pi(w - s)\left(r + \frac{d}{2}\right)n}{33{,}000}$$

$$= \frac{2\pi(110 - 2 \cdot 2)\left(2 \cdot 25 + \frac{1}{24}\right)22 \cdot 58}{33{,}000} = 10 \cdot 6.$$

Therefore, b.h.p. $= 10 \cdot 6$ h.p. $= \mathcal{P}_b =$ power absorbed or dissipated by the brake.

Engine Cooling Water.

Mass of cooling water flowing M $= 18 \cdot 2$ lb./min.
Inlet temperature $= 21 \cdot 61°$ C.
Outlet temperature $= 40 \cdot 05°$ C.
Rate at which heat is carried away by engine cooling water = rate of mass flow × specific heat × rise in temperature, or

$$\delta Q = M \times C \times \delta T.$$

$$= 18 \cdot 2\ \frac{\text{lb.}}{\text{min.}} \times 1\ \frac{\text{B.Th.U.}}{\text{lb. °F.}} \times (40 \cdot 05 - 21 \cdot 61)°\ \text{C.}\left[\frac{9°\ \text{F.}}{5°\ \text{C.}}\right]$$

$$= 605\ \text{B.Th.U./min.}$$

Heat Supplied to Engine.

Volume of gas used as recorded by meter $= V = 5 \cdot 24$ cu. ft. per min.
Absolute pressure of gas used = pressure above atmospheric + atmospheric pressure

$$= 4 \cdot 3\ \text{in.}\ H_2O\left[\frac{1\ \text{in. Hg.}}{13 \cdot 6\ \text{in.}\ H_2O}\right]\left[\frac{0 \cdot 49\ \text{Lb./in.}^2}{1\ \text{in. Hg}}\right] + 14 \cdot 75\ \text{Lb./in.}^2$$

i.e. $P = 0 \cdot 16\ \text{Lb./in.}^2 + 14 \cdot 7\ \text{Lb./in.}^2 = 14 \cdot 91\ \text{Lb./in.}^2$ abs.

Absolute temperature of gas used $= T = 273 + 21 \cdot 5 = 294 \cdot 5°$ abs. C.

∴ Volume of gas used reduced to s.t.p.

$$= V_n = \frac{PV}{T}\frac{T_n}{P_n} = \frac{14 \cdot 91 \text{ Lb./in.}^2 \times 5 \cdot 24 \text{ ft.}^3\text{/min.} \times 273° \text{ abs. C.}}{294 \cdot 5° \text{ abs. C.} \times 14 \cdot 7 \text{ Lb./in.}^2}$$

$= 4 \cdot 93$ cu. ft. per minute at s.t.p.

Calorific value of gas $= 497$ B.Th.U. per cu. ft. at s.t.p.

∴ Heat supplied to the engine

$$= 4 \cdot 93 \frac{\text{ft.}^3}{\text{min.}} \times 497 \frac{\text{B.Th.U.}}{\text{ft.}^3} = 2{,}455 \text{ B.Th.U./min.}$$

Efficiencies.

Mechanical efficiency $= \frac{\text{b.h.p.}}{\text{i.h.p.}} = \frac{10 \cdot 6}{13 \cdot 7} = 77 \cdot 4$ per cent.

Thermal efficiency (b.h.p. basis)

$$= \frac{\text{Heat equivalent of b.h.p.}}{\text{Heat supplied to engine}}$$

$$= \frac{10 \cdot 6 \text{ h.p.} \left[\frac{33{,}000 \text{ ft.-Lb.}}{\text{h.p. min.}}\right]\left[\frac{\text{B.Th.U.}}{778 \text{ ft.-Lb.}}\right]}{2455 \frac{\text{B.ThU.}}{\text{min.}}} = 0 \cdot 183 \text{ or } 18 \cdot 3 \text{ per cent.}$$

Thermal efficiency (i.h.p. basis)

$$= \frac{\text{Heat equivalent of i.h.p.}}{\text{Heat supplied to engine}}$$

$$= \frac{13 \cdot 7 \text{ h.p.} \left[\frac{33{,}000 \text{ ft.-Lb.}}{\text{h.p. min.}}\right]\left[\frac{\text{B.Th.U.}}{778 \text{ ft.-Lb.}}\right]}{2{,}455 \frac{\text{B.Th.U.}}{\text{min.}}} = 0 \cdot 247 \text{ or } 24 \cdot 7 \text{ per cent.}$$

A standard with which the performance of internal combustion engines can be compared is known as the "Air Standard" efficiency given by the expression $1 - \left(\frac{1}{r_c}\right)^{\gamma - 1}$ (see page 366), where r_c is the ratio of compression,

$$= 1 - \left(\frac{1}{6 \cdot 32}\right)^{1 \cdot 4 - 1} = 0 \cdot 521 \text{ or } 52 \cdot 1 \text{ per cent.}$$

Relative efficiency (b.h.p. basis) $= \frac{\text{Brake thermal efficiency}}{\text{"Air Standard" efficiency}}$
or
Efficiency ratio

$$= \frac{18 \cdot 3}{52 \cdot 1} = 0 \cdot 352 \text{ or } 35 \cdot 2 \text{ per cent.}$$

Deductions.

Power absorbed in mechanical friction = i.h.p. − b.h.p.

$$= 13 \cdot 7 - 10 \cdot 6 = 3 \cdot 1 \text{ h.p.}$$

Gas used as recorded by meter

$$= 5 \cdot 24 \frac{\text{ft.}^3}{\text{min.}} \left[\frac{60 \text{ min.}}{\text{hour}} \right] = 314 \cdot 4 \text{ cu. ft./hour.}$$

or

$$\frac{314 \cdot 4 \dfrac{\text{ft.}^3}{\text{hour}}}{10 \cdot 6 \text{ h.p.}} = 29 \cdot 6 \text{ cu. ft. per brake h.p.-hour.}$$

Cost of running the engine per hour on gas at price of $8\frac{1}{2}$ pence per 100,000 B.Th.U. (one therm) is

$$2{,}455 \frac{\text{B.Th.U.}}{\text{min.}} \left[\frac{\text{therm}}{100{,}000 \text{ B.Th.U.}} \right] \left[\frac{60 \text{ min.}}{\text{hour}} \right] \frac{8\frac{1}{2} \text{ pence}}{\text{therm}}$$

$$= 12 \cdot 5 \text{ pence/hour.}$$

CRITICISMS AND CONCLUSIONS

It will be seen from the curve, fig. 4.2, showing gas consumption per b.h.p.-hour against b.h.p., that a minimum value is attained at about 10 b.h.p. and also from the efficiency curves that the brake thermal efficiency is a maximum at this power, and the mechanical efficiency is very nearly at its maximum. The trial, therefore, checks the makers' specification and rating of 10 b.h.p. at 225 r.p.m.

It will be noticed that the horse-power absorbed in overcoming the frictional resistances of the engine remains approximately the same over the whole range of power outputs. This is to be expected, since the engine speed remained nearly constant for all tests of the trial.

From the graph showing gas consumption per minute against b.h.p. it will be seen that the quantity of gas consumed by the engine per minute is proportional to the power developed—the law of the straight line being:

$$\text{cu. ft. of gas per minute} = 0 \cdot 344 \times b + 1 \cdot 5.$$

A criticism can be made against those conducting the trial in that the outlet temperature of the engine cooling water was not kept as constant as it might have been throughout the series of tests. This possible variable should have been kept the same for all tests, since the object of the trial implied treating the b.h.p. as the variable with the other possible variables kept constant so that the variation in gas consumption could be estimated against variation in b.h.p.

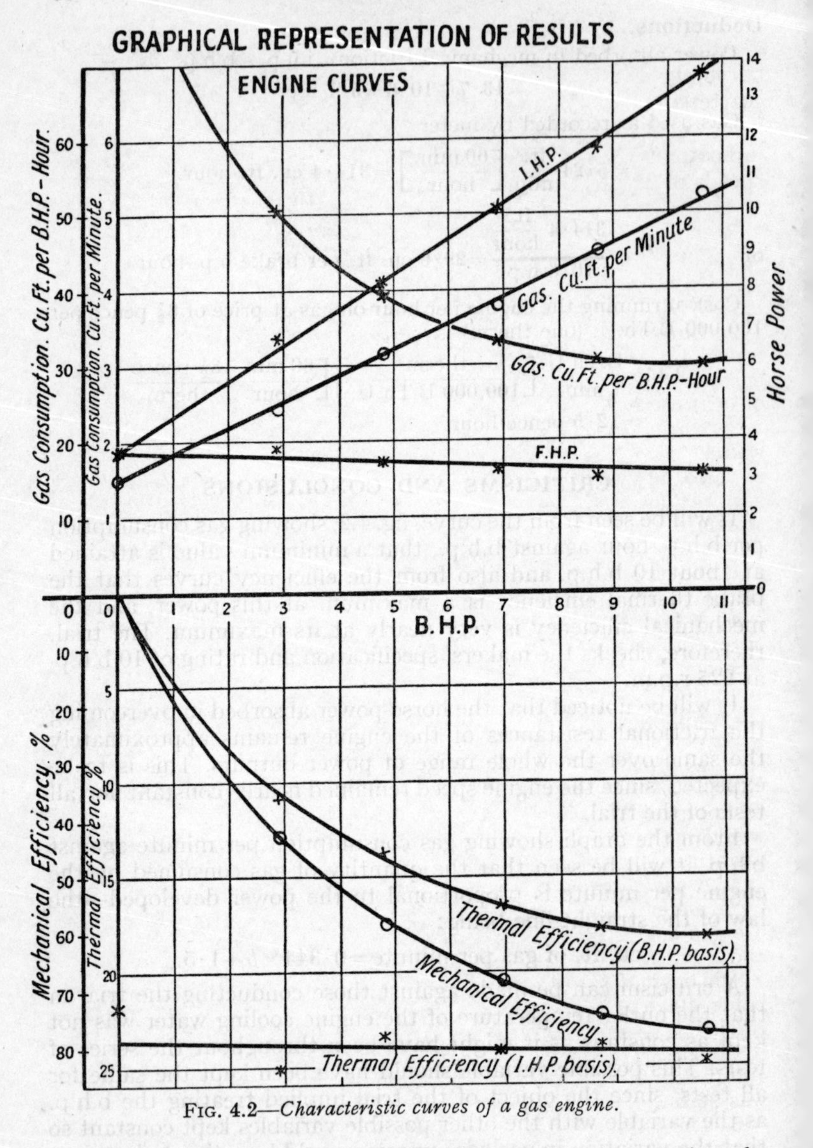

FIG. 4.2—*Characteristic curves of a gas engine.*

From the percentages given in the Heat Account another set of graphs can be drawn on a b.h.p. basis.

Also, with reference to the thermal efficiency (i.h.p. basis) curve, we may criticise again and say that those points are more scattered than they would have been if careful indicating had been carried out, though it may have been that the type of indicator was not quite suitable for an engine running between speeds of 225 and 240 r.p.m.

EXERCISES ON CHAPTER 4

(i)

1. What are the usual objects in view when engines are tested?

2. During the trial of an oil engine the cylinder of the engine was cooled by water circulating at the rate 450 lb. in 32 minutes. It entered the jacket at 50° F. and left at 95° C. Calculate the quantity of heat carried away by the cooling water per minute.

3. During a gas engine test the gas used, as recorded by the meter, was 87 cu. ft. in 52 minutes. The pressure of the gas above that of the atmosphere was 1·5 in. of water, and the temperature of the gas was 59° F. Calculate the quantity of gas used per hour at standard temperature and pressure if the height of the barometer during the test was 29·5 in. of mercury.

If the gas has a calorific value of 540 B.Th.U. per cu. ft. at s.t.p. calculate the heat supplied to the engine per minute.

4. A firm have supplied a gas engine specifying a certain power output for a certain fuel consumption. You are required to test whether their specification is correct; also to obtain a power-consumption curve together with thermal and mechanical efficiency curves for the engine. A heat balance sheet is also required showing what percentage of the heat applied flows along the various energy streams of the engine.

Make a diagrammatic sketch of the plant you would employ and describe your method of testing. Give a list of the observations you would make, and indicate how you would use them to obtain the quantities required.

5. A gas engine consumes 200 cu. ft. of gas per hour as measured by a meter in the supply pipe of the engine. The temperature of the gas and the pressure above atmospheric in the pipe are 17° C. and 2 in. of water respectively.

The engine is found to develop 7 b.h.p. when using gas of calorific value 400,000 ft.-Lb. per cu. ft. at s.t.p. Calculate the thermal efficiency (b.h.p. basis) and the consumption in lb. per b.h.p.-hour if the gas constant (R) in the characteristic equation $PV = RmT$ is 100 ft.-Lb. per lb. ° C. The height of the barometer during the test was 30 in. of mercury.

6. The following are the mean values of the observations made during a test of a four-stroke compression-ignition engine, the test being of 20 minutes' duration and the engine developing about three-quarters of the full power for which it is designed.

Revolutions per minute 260; m.e.p. of indicator diagrams 104 Lb. per sq. in.; brake dead load 74·5 Lb.; spring balance reading 18 Lb.; engine cooling water circulated at the rate of 6·4 lb. per min. with inlet and outlet temperatures 10·9° C. and 43·7° C., respectively; total weight of fuel used during the trial 1·294 Lb. of calorific value 17,640 B.Th.U. per lb. The piston diameter and stroke of the engine were $6\frac{1}{2}$ in. and $10\frac{5}{8}$ in. respectively and the diameter of the brake wheel+rope 5·4 ft.

Calculate: the i.h.p., b.h.p., f.h.p. of the engine; the heat carried away by the engine cooling water per minute; the heat supplied to the engine per minute; and draw up a heat account for the engine in B.Th.U. per minute and expressed as percentages of the heat supplied to the engine.

Calculate also the mechanical and thermal (b.h.p. basis) efficiencies, and express the consumption of fuel in lb. per b.h.p.-hour.

7. A four-stroke gas engine having a "hit and miss" governor has engine data: piston diameter 7 in.; stroke 15 in.; effective brake-wheel diameter 5 ft. This engine was tested for 16 minutes, and the following are the mean values of the observations made: r.p.m. 236·5; explosions per minute 110·8; mean effective pressure of indicator diagrams 79 Lb. per sq. in.; brake dead load 100 Lb.; spring balance reading 18 Lb.; engine cooling water flowed at the rate of 13·4 lb. per min.; inlet and outlet temperatures of cooling water 11·6° C. and 44·2° C., respectively; gas used per minute 3·74 cu. ft.; calorific value of gas, as used, 522 B.Th.U. per cu. ft.

Calculate: the i.h.p., b.h.p., f.h.p. of the engine; the heat carried away by the engine cooling water; the brake thermal efficiency of the engine and also the thermal efficiency on the i.h.p. basis; the mechanical efficiency; consumption of gas, as used, in cu. ft. per b.h.p.-hour; draw up a heat account for the engine in B.Th.U. per min., and as percentages of the heat supplied to the engine.

(ii)

8. A four-stroke gas engine having a "hit and miss" governor was tested for 1 hour under the following average conditions: r.p.m. 215; number of misses by the pecker of the governor in 2 minutes was 75; brake dead load 81 Lb.; spring balance reading 11·25 Lb.; m.e.p. of indicator diagrams 87·1 Lb. per sq. in.; total volume of gas used when reduced to 32° F. and 760 mm. of mercury, 160 cu. ft.; calorific value of gas at 32° F. and 760 mm. of mercury pressure, 620 B.Th.U. per cu. ft.; cooling water circulated at the rate of 13·64 lb. per minute; rise in temperature of cooling water from inlet to outlet of engine jacket 49·5° F. The engine had a piston diameter 6·69 in., a stroke of 1·187 ft., and the diameter of the brakewheel to the centre of the rope 4·72 ft.

Calculate: the i.h.p., b.h.p., and f.h.p. of the engine and the heat equivalent of these quantities in B.Th.U. per min.; the heat carried away per minute by the engine cooling water; the heat supplied to the engine per minute; the mechanical and thermal efficiencies of the engine; the gas consumption in cu. ft. at s.t.p. per b.h.p.-hour.

Also draw up a heat account in tabular form for the engine in B.Th.U. per minute and as percentages of the heat supplied.

9. The following are observations and results obtained from a series of six tests each of 16 minutes' duration during a trial of a four-stroke gas engine. Make out a complete Report Sheet for the test; give a specimen set of calculations; and draw the graphs and engine curves for the trial. Also draw conclusions and make criticisms from the curves and from the figures in the Report Sheet.

Number of Test.	1	2	3	4	5	6
Revolutions per minute.	236·5	237·5	241·1	244·9	248·0	250·0
Explosions per minute	110·8	97·5	80·2	63·2	52·4	37·4
M.e.p. Lb. per sq. in.	79·4	79·3	81·9	80·7	81·2	81·2
B.h.p. of engine.	9·26	7·45	5·36	3·16	1·82	0
Engine cooling water lb. per min.	13·4	12·73	10·47	8·35	5·24	4·83
Rise in temp. of cooling water °F.	58·6	55·5	56·0	55·5	69·2	65·2
Gas used per min. at meter cu. ft.	3·74	3·30	2·74	2·16	1·80	1·30
Temperature of gas at meter °F.	56	56·5	56·5	57	57	57
Pressure of gas above atmospheric in water	2·7	3·1	3·7	4·1	4·1	4·4
Atmospheric pressure.	29·64 in. mercury.					
Calorific value of gas.	520 B.Th.U. at 14·7 Lb. per sq. in. abs. and 60° F.					

Engine: Piston diameter, 7 in.; stroke, 15 in.; compression ratio, 5.

10. A four-stroke gas engine has a stroke of 1·25 ft. and a bore of 8 in. When the crank rotates at 250 r.p.m. and the brake torque is 360 Lb.-ft. the consumption of gas as metered is 5·5 ft.^{3}/min., the gas supply having a pressure of 5·2 in. of water above atmospheric and a temperature of 53·6° F. The calorific value of the gas is 486 B.Th.U. per ft.^{3} at s.t.p. Calculate the brake thermal efficiency of the engine.

If air is drawn from the atmosphere at the rate of 34·5 ft.^{3}/min. and the height of the barometer is 30·2 in. of mercury and the temperature of the atmosphere is 62·6° F., calculate the volume of gas and air at s.t.p. used per minute and the ratio of the sum of these volumes to the suction volume swept by the piston per minute, i.e. the s.t.p. volumetric efficiency of the engine.

11. Calculate the i.h.p., b.h.p., mechanical efficiency and indicated thermal efficiency of a single-cylinder four-stroke oil engine of 7·5 in. bore and 14·5 in. stroke which, when tested at a speed of 350 r.p.m. gave the following data: Net brake load 87·5 Lb. on a brake drum +rope diameter of 4·76 ft. Mean area and length of indicator cards 0·38 in.^{2} and 2·73 in., respectively. Indicator spring strength 500 Lb./in.^{2} per inch height of indicator diagram. Fuel oil, of calorific value 18,500 B.T.U./lb. was consumed at the rate of 2·25 lb. in 20 minutes. Cooling water flowed at the rate of 660 lb./hour and the mean inlet and outlet temperatures were 65° F. and 117° F., respectively. Air flowed into the engine at the rate of 4·52 lb./min. from the atmosphere at 72° F. and the exhaust gases of mean specific heat 0·24 B.Th.U. per lb. ° F. were rejected with a temperature of 460° F. Draw up a heat account in B.Th.U. per min. and as a percentage of the potential heat in the fuel supplied.

12 A swinging field electrical dynamometer has a torque arm of 1·75 ft. measured from the centre of the shaft to the line of action of a spring balance applying and measuring the load. Calculate the constant C in the numerical formula $\text{B.H.P.} = \frac{WN}{C}$ where W is the load in Lb. and N the number of r.p.m. of the armature shaft.

Use this formula to estimate the b.h.p. developed by a six-cylinder petrol engine of 3·5 in. bore and 3·75 in. stroke when the spring balance reads 81·8 Lb. and the shaft speed is 3,000 r.p.m. Also, estimate the f.h.p. and i.h.p. of the engine if, when motored at the same speed immediately after the b.h.p. test, the spring balance reading was 30·3 Lb.

Hence, deduce the mechanical efficiency of the engine.

13. A gas engine, of 10 in. bore, 15 in. stroke and compression ratio 6·2, with hit and miss governing, was tested at a speed of 210 r.p.m. with the following results:—Brake torque 533 Lb.-ft.; explosions per minute 99; i.m.e.p. 85 Lb. per sq. in.; gas consumption 444 cu. ft. per hour at 63° F. and 14·9 Lb. per sq. in. abs.; calorific value of gas 480 B.Th.U. per cu. ft. at 32° F. and 14·7 Lb. per sq. in. abs.; cooling water flowed at the rate of 13·2 lb. per min. with 67° F. rise of temperature.

Calculate the b.h.p., i.h.p., mechanical efficiency, indicated thermal efficiency and efficiency ratio based on air standard efficiency.

Draw up a heat balance in B.Th.U. per minute and state what happens to the energy used in overcoming engine friction.

[Part I., B.Sc., Lond.]

PART II

STEAM AND STEAM ENGINE PLANT

CHAPTER 5

GENERATION AND PROPERTIES OF STEAM

1. Steam and the Influence of Pressure.—Water is a compound substance of hydrogen and oxygen. One molecule of water is denoted by H_2O in the symbols of chemistry. Steam is water vapour, or water in the gaseous state, and has the same chemical composition as the water from which it is generated, the difference being in its physical condition or state.

The temperature at which water will boil or change into steam in a vessel depends upon the pressure in the vessel. *For every pressure there is a definite temperature at which steam will begin to form.* Water, therefore, together with all other liquids, has an infinite number of boiling-points, depending upon pressure.

The following figures, taken from Callendar's steam tables, show the temperatures at which steam forms at the various pressures:

Pressure Lb./sq. in. abs.	1	2	5	10	15	20
Temperature °F.	101·7	126·1	162·3	193·2	213·0	228·0

Pressure Lb./sq. in abs.	30	40	50	70	100	150
Temperature ·F.	250·3	267·2	281·0	302·9	327·8	358·4

Pressure Lb./sq. in abs.	200	300	450	600	800	1,000
Temperature °F.	381·8	417·3	456·3	486·2	518·2	544·6

These figures are plotted on fig. 5.4.

2. Pressure Gauges and Absolute Pressure.—Fig. 5.1 shows a diagram of Bourdon's pressure gauge. It consists of a tube BB, which is elliptical in cross-section as shown in the enlarged view at C. One end of the tube is closed and the other, through the cock A, can be put into communication with the fluid, the pressure of which is required to be measured. The closed end of the tube is attached to a sector D, the teeth of which gear with those of a small pinion rigidly fixed to the pointer EF. The effect of the fluid pressure within the tube BB is such that the tube tends to straighten itself and hence to move the sector D, which in turn moves the pointer EF over the graduated pressure scale. These gauges can be carefully graduated by means of the apparatus of fig. **3.18** or by means of a mercury gauge.

Gauges of this type indicate pressure above that of the atmosphere, *i.e.* they indicate a difference between two pressures. The absolute pressure of a fluid will therefore be equal to the sum of the gauge pressure and the atmospheric pressure.

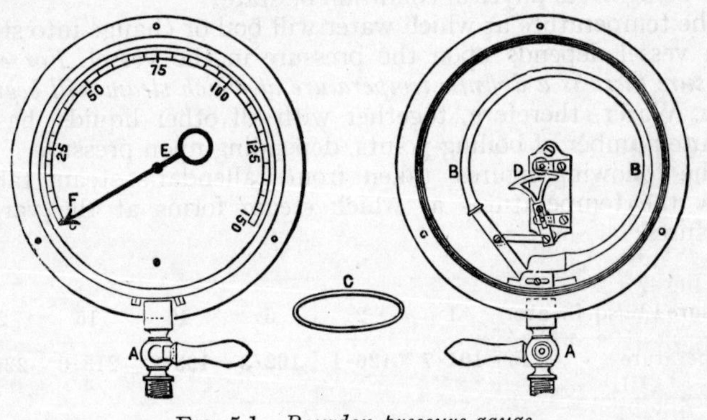

FIG. 5.1—*Bourdon pressure gauge.*

3. Atmospheric Pressure.—On the Earth's surface we live, as it were, at the bottom of an aerial sea which we call the atmosphere. Its weight causes a pressure in every direction of about **14·7** Lb. per sq. in., which is usually estimated by means of the accurate measurement of the height of a mercury column.

Suppose the exact height of the mercury column, as measured by means of the Vernier scale on Fortin's barometer shown in fig. 5.2, is H and that the tube is of uniform cross-sectional area A, then the pressure of the atmosphere acts on the surface of the well of mercury as does the pressure due to a height H of a mercury column. But since the pressure everywhere along the mercury surface must be the same, we can say that the pressure of the atmosphere is equal to the weight of the volume AH of mercury acting on an area A, or

$$P_{\text{atmos.}} = \frac{w_m AH}{A} = w_m H = \begin{pmatrix}\text{specific weight}\\ \text{of mercury}\end{pmatrix} \times \begin{pmatrix}\text{height of}\\ \text{mercury column}\end{pmatrix},$$

i.e. atmospheric pressure $P_{atmos.} = \left(\frac{w_m}{w_w}\right) w_w H = s_m \times w_w \times H$

$$= \begin{pmatrix}\text{specific gravity}\\ \text{of mercury}\end{pmatrix} \times \begin{pmatrix}\text{specific weight}\\ \text{of water}\end{pmatrix} \times \begin{pmatrix}\text{height of}\\ \text{mercury column}\end{pmatrix}$$

$$= 13 \cdot 6 \times 62 \cdot 3 \frac{\text{Lb.}}{\text{ft.}^3} \times \text{H}.$$

Thus, if H is measured in inches, as is usual in this country, the pressure of the atmosphere is

$$13 \cdot 6 \times 62 \cdot 3 \frac{\text{Lb.}}{\text{ft.}^3}\left(\frac{\text{H}}{\text{in.}}\right) \text{in.} \left[\frac{\text{ft.}^3}{1728 \text{ in.}^3}\right]$$

i.e.,
$$P_{atmos.} = \frac{13 \cdot 6 \times 62 \cdot 3}{1728}\left(\frac{\text{H}}{\text{in.}}\right)\frac{\text{Lb.}}{\text{in.}^2}$$

or
$$\left(\frac{\mathbf{P_{atmos.}}}{\mathbf{Lb./in.^2}}\right) = \mathbf{0 \cdot 49}\left(\frac{\mathbf{H}}{\mathbf{in.}}\right)$$

is the physical formula, and the corresponding numerical formula is

$$\boldsymbol{p_{atmos.} = 0 \cdot 49h},$$

where h is the height of the mercury barometer in inches and p is the number of Lb./in.^{2}

Therefore, absolute pressure of any fluid in Lb. per sq. in. = (gauge pressure $+0 \cdot 49h$), where h represents inches of mercury.

4. Temperature-Pressure Curve for Steam.—Fig. 5.3 illustrates a simple piece of apparatus by means

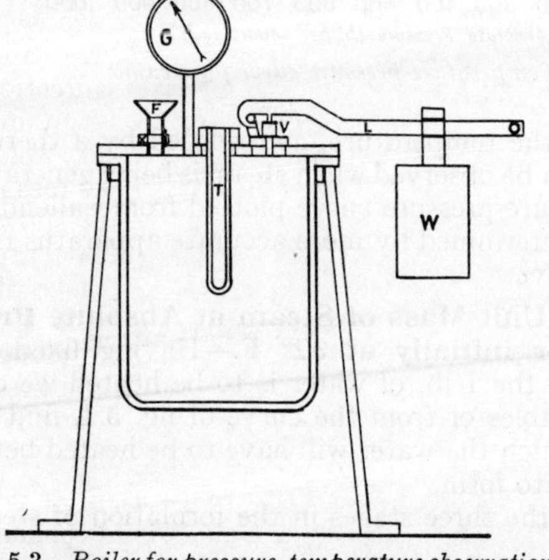

FIG. 5.3—*Boiler for pressure, temperature observations.*

FIG. 5.2—*Fortin's barometer.*

of which the temperature at which steam will form at various pressures can be found. A quantity of water is poured into the vessel through the valve F, which is afterwards closed. The water is then heated by placing a burner under the vessel. When the temperature of the water has reached a certain value, steam will begin to form and blow through the valve V, which will be lifted off its seat as steam is continuously generated. The pressure which the steam in the vessel must exert on the valve V before it will lift can be varied by altering the position of the weight W on the lever L. Thus, for a series of positions of W, the pressure, as recorded

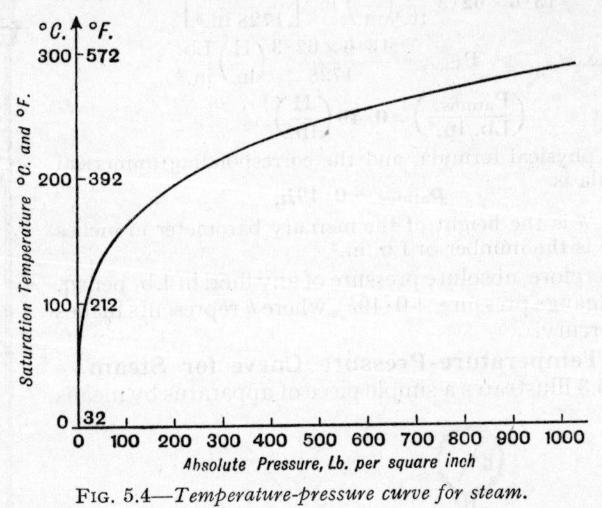

FIG. 5.4—*Temperature-pressure curve for steam.*

by the gauge G, and the temperature, as recorded by a thermometer in pocket T, can be observed when steam is being generated. Fig. 5.4 is a temperature-pressure curve plotted from Callendar's figures, which were determined by more accurate apparatus than the one described above.

5. Generation of Unit Mass of Steam at Absolute Pressure P from Water initially at 32° F.—Having fixed the pressure under which the 1 lb. of water is to be heated we can, by means of steam tables or from the curve of fig. 5.4, find the temperature (t_s) to which the water will have to be heated before steam will commence to form.

Fig. 5.5 illustrates the three stages in the formation of steam, namely:

(1) **The introducing stage,** during which 1 lb. of water at 32° F. is pumped into the cylinder against an absolute pressure P. This pressure is caused by weight W acting on the piston of area A together with the pressure of the atmosphere. The energy expended by the pump M in order to deliver 1 lb. of water of volume b at 32° F. is Pb. This energy appears as pressure energy of the water in the cylinder and could be made to do work, by virtue of its pressure alone, against the piston of an engine.

(2) **The warming stage,** during which heat is applied to the water to raise its temperature from 32° F. to t_s (the temperature at which steam will begin to form under abs. pressure P) and to increase the volume of the 1 lb. of water from b (the volume at 32° F. and abs. pressure P) to w (the volume at t_s and abs. pressure P). The heat supplied during this warming stage is called "sensible heat," because it can be detected by the sense of touch, and produces a rise in temperature (t_s—32° F.) to be seen on a thermometer. The sensible heat supplied in the warming stage is therefore used:

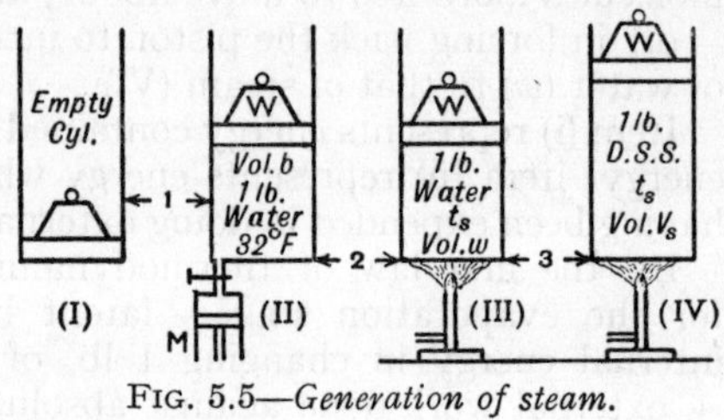

FIG. 5.5—*Generation of steam.*

(a) to increase the temperature of 1 lb. of water from 32° F. to t_s—this heat going into the water as internal energy and thus increasing the motion of its molecules; and

(b) to do external work=P(w—b) in increasing the volume of the water from b to w against the absolute pressure P which is constantly acting on the piston.

By the first law of thermodynamics, which, in this connection, states that the heat supplied=the increase in internal energy+the thermal equivalent of the external work done by the water, we can say, for the warming stage, that the sensible heat supplied to 1 lb. of water=increase in internal energy due to raising the temperature from 32° F. to t_s+external work done in increasing the volume from b to w under the absolute pressure P. That is,

$$S=(E_w-E_o)+P(w-b);$$

or, when changes in internal energy are reckoned from 32° F., as Callendar has done in his steam tables, E_o will be zero, the equation becomes:

$$\text{sensible heat}=S=E_w+P(w-b).$$

(3) **The evaporation stage,** during which further heat is applied to the 1 lb. of water at t_s and volume w to change it into 1 lb. of dry saturated steam at t_s and volume V_s. During this stage the heat is added at the constant temperature t_s and goes to change the water into steam absolute pressure P. The external work done during this evaporation stage is, therefore,

$$P(V_s - w)$$

Because the heat added during the evaporation stage does not make itself apparent by an increase in the temperature, it is called "latent heat" (*i.e.* hidden heat). The latent heat of evaporation is therefore used:—

(i) to overcome the internal molecular resistance of the water by changing it from water into steam and thus making the molecules more free to move about; and

(ii) in forcing back the piston to increase the volume from that of water (w) to that of steam (V_s).

Item (i) represents energy contained *in* the steam—*i.e.* internal energy; item (ii) represents energy which has passed out of it—having been expended in doing external work on the piston.

By the first law of thermodynamics we can, therefore, say for the evaporation stage:—latent heat supplied=increase in internal energy in changing 1 lb. of water to 1 lb. of steam + external work done against absolute pressure P in increasing the volume from that of water (w) to that of dry saturated steam (V_s),

$$\text{i.e.} \quad L = (E_s - E_w) + P(V_s - w).$$

Example.—(i) If 1 lb. of water at 32° F., having a volume $b = 0 \cdot 016$ cu. ft., is forced into a cylinder fitted with a movable piston of 25 sq. in. area and loaded by a dead weight of 100 Lb. in addition to the pressure of the atmosphere, find the work which must be done to get the whole of the water into the cylinder if the height of the barometer is 30 in. of mercury.

Atmospheric pressure $= 0 \cdot 49 \times 30 = 14 \cdot 7$ Lb. per sq. in.

$$\therefore \text{ Absolute pressure on piston} = \frac{100}{25} + 14 \cdot 7 = 18 \cdot 7 \text{ Lb. per sq. in.} = P.$$

∴ Energy required to pump 1 lb. of water at 32° F. into the cylinder

$$= Pb = 18 \cdot 7 \frac{\text{Lb.}}{\text{in.}^2} \times 0 \cdot 016 \text{ ft.}^3 \left[\frac{144 \text{ in.}^2}{\text{ft.}^2}\right]\left[\frac{\text{B.Th.U.}}{778 \text{ ft.-Lb.}}\right] = 0 \cdot 055 \text{ B.Th.U.}$$

(ii) If heat is now applied to the water in the cylinder until its volume has become $w = 0 \cdot 0165$ cu. ft., find the amount of heat which has gone to do external work.

Increase in volume $=0\cdot0165-0\cdot016=0\cdot0005$ cu. ft. against a constant absolute pressure of $18\cdot7$ Lb. per sq. in., and the energy required to do this $=P(w-b)$

$$=18\cdot7\ \frac{\text{Lb.}}{\text{in.}^2}\times0\cdot0005\ \text{ft.}^3\left[\frac{144\ \text{in.}^2}{\text{ft.}^3}\right]\left[\frac{\text{B.Th.U.}}{778\ \text{ft.-Lb.}}\right]=0\cdot0017\ \text{B.Th.U.}$$

(iii) If the volume of 1 lb. of steam at a pressure $P=18\cdot7$ Lb. per sq. in. absolute is $V_s=21\cdot39$ cu. ft., find the total external work done in changing 1 lb. of water at 32° F. and $18\cdot7$ Lb. per sq. in. abs. into 1 lb. of steam at the same pressure.

Increase in volume $=V_s-w=21\cdot374$ cu. ft.

∴ External work done

$$=P(V_s-w)=\frac{18\cdot7\times21\cdot374\times144}{778}\ \text{B.Th.U.}=74\ \text{B.Th.U.}$$

6. Saturated and Superheated Steam.—Steam in contact with the water from which it is being generated is called saturated steam, and the pressure of such vapour is called the "saturation vapour pressure" or simply the "vapour pressure" which is the pressure at which an equal number of molecules leave the liquid and enter it from the vapour phase in a given time.

The steam in the water-drum of a boiler is saturated steam, and the temperature at which steam forms is called the saturation temperature for the particular pressure in the boiler. Fig. 5.4 shows saturation temperatures of steam plotted against pressures. Different substances, however, have different characteristics.

Wet Steam.—Steam containing particles of moisture in suspension is called wet steam— that is, it contains particles of water which would, on further addition of heat, change into steam at the constant saturation temperature. Wet steam is saturated steam which has not received the whole of the latent heat.

Dry Saturated Steam.—If wet steam (which is always saturated steam) receives heat, the particles of moisture in suspension evaporate until a point is reached at which the last particle has just been changed into steam at the saturation temperature. At that point the steam is therefore "dry"—there being no particles of moisture left in the saturated steam. Because of this, it is called dry saturated steam when that particular point is reached. Dry saturated steam (abbreviated d.s.s.) is, therefore, steam which has received the whole of its latent heat, *i.e.* steam in which the last particle of moisture has been evaporated at the saturation temperature.

Superheated Steam.—If further heat is added to dry saturated steam, the temperature will commence to rise above the

ENERGY TABLE FOR THE GENERATING OF 1 LB. OF DRY SATURATED STEAM AT ABSOLUTE PRESSURE P FROM 1 LB. OF WATER INITIALLY AT 32° F.

The heat is reckoned from 32° F. as the datum.

Stage	Energy Supplied		Increase in Internal Energy		External Work done *by* the Fluid	
	During the Stage	Total Energy supplied	During the Stage	Total Internal Energy reckoned from 32° F.	During the Stage	Total External Work done *by* the fluid
(1) Introducing.	Pb	Pb	0	0	Pb	Pb
(2) Warming.	S	$Pb+S=h_w$	$S-P(w-b)$	$S-P(w-b)=E_w$	$P(w-b)$	Pw
(3) Evaporating.	L	$Pb+S+L$ $=H_s=h_w+L$	$L-P(V_s-w)$	$Pb+S+L-PV_s=E_s$ or $H_s-PV_s=E_s$	$P(V_s-w)$	PV_s

FIG. 5.6—*Generation of Steam.*

saturation temperature since there are no particles of moisture left to evaporate. The steam is then called superheated steam.

It will be seen that the first line of the table (fig. 5.6) represents the state at the end of the operation illustrated by (II) of fig. 5.5. The work done by the water in forcing back the piston during the introducing stage (1) is Pb. This energy has to be supplied by the pump M. During stage (1) the internal energy of the water is zero, since the arbitrary datum for reckoning heat energy has been chosen as 32° F.—the same as in Callendar's steam tables.

The second line in the table represents the state at the end of the operation illustrated by (III) of fig. 5.5. The sensible heat S has been added during the warming stage to increase the temperature from 32° F. to t_s, which is the saturation temperature at absolute pressure P. The energy supplied (S) during this stage minus the external work done $P(w-b)$ during the stage gives the increase in internal energy $[S-P(w-b)]$ during the warming stage (2). The latter quantity is also the total increase in internal energy up to the end of (III), since there was no internal energy at the end of the previous stage. The total energy supplied up to the end of (III) is $Pb+S$, and is called the "total heat" or "specific enthalpy" of water (h_w) at absolute pressure P, the word "specific" signifying per unit mass. That is,

$$h_w = Pb + S = E_w + Pw.$$

The third line of the table represents the state at the end of the operation illustrated by (IV) of fig. 5.5. The whole of the latent heat L has been added during the evaporation stage (3). Thus, all the particles of moisture have been evaporated resulting in the formation of 1 lb. of dry saturated steam of volume V_s. The total energy supplied from start to finish (that is, to get the water into the cylinder or "boiler," raise its temperature to t_s, and change it into dry saturated steam at t_s) is, therefore, equal to $Pb+S+L$. This quantity is called the "total heat" or "specific enthalpy" (H_s) of the dry saturated steam at absolute pressure P. Therefore, per unit mass (1 lb. say),

$$H_s = Pb + S + L = h_w + L = E_s + PV_s.$$

7. Pressure Energy, Internal Energy, and Total Heat.—Pressure Energy.—Pressure energy is energy stored in a fluid by virtue of its pressure and volume. If a volume V of any fluid be contained at absolute pressure P in the cylinder (II) fig. 5.5., then mechanical energy PV could, theoretically, be obtained from it by allowing it to do work in the cylinder of an engine—that is, the fluid contains pressure energy equal to PV, which can be converted into equivalent heat units by means of the Joule unity bracket $\left[\frac{\text{B.Th.U.}}{\text{778 ft. Lb.}}\right]$—see Example (i), page 102.

Internal Energy.—The internal energy (E) of steam is associated with the motion of its molecules. It is energy contained in the substance by virtue of the kinetic energy of its molecules. We have no means of measuring the total quantity of internal energy in a substance, and it is therefore always measured with reference to some standard state or datum, as, for instance, 32° F.

Total Heat (alternatively called **Enthalpy**).—We have seen that the total heat per unit mass of water is represented by $h_w = E_w + Pw$ and that the total heat (or enthalpy) per unit mass of dry saturated steam is represented by $H_s = E_s + PV_s$. These are two particular cases of **the general definition of enthalpy or total heat, namely, $H = E + PV$.** This definition applies to all fluids, liquid or gaseous, and here, in particular, to wet, dry and superheated steam, and in Callendar's steam tables is reckoned per unit mass of 1 lb.

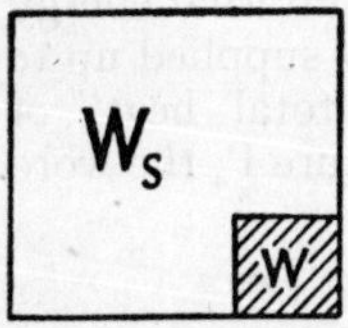

W_s W

FIG. 5.7—*Dryness fraction.*

8. Dryness Fraction (q).—The dryness fraction of wet steam is defined as the ratio of the weight of dry steam to the total weight of the wet steam containing it. For example, fig. 5.7 illustrates a weight $(W_s + W)$ of wet steam in which all the particles of moisture have been supposed collected in one corner and having weight W, the remaining weight W_s being dry saturated steam. The dryness fraction of this steam is, therefore,

$$q = \left(\frac{W_s}{W_s + W}\right) = \left(\frac{m_s}{m_s + m_w}\right)$$

since weight W is proportional to mass m.

Example.—A mass of 3 lb. of wet steam containing a mass of 0·15 lb. of moisture in suspension is made up of $3 - 0 \cdot 15 = 2 \cdot 85$ lb. of dry steam and 0·15 lb. of water.

The dryness fraction of the steam is, therefore, $\frac{2 \cdot 85}{3} = 0 \cdot 95$.

9. Wet Steam.—To produce 1 lb. of wet steam having dryness fraction q (fig. 5.7), the energy required for generation from water at 32° F. into wet steam at abs. pressure P would be

$$H = h_w + qL,$$

where h_w=total heat or enthalpy of water at abs. pressure P, L=latent heat of steam at abs. pressure P. These last two values can be obtained from Callendar's steam tables (drawn up for a mass of 1 lb.) by looking in the appropriate column opposite abs. pressure P.

The *volume* of 1 lb. of wet steam at this pressure is made up of the volume of q lb. of dry saturated steam and $(1-q)$ lb. of water, using symbol q to represent a number only. The volume of 1 lb. of wet steam is $V_q=qV_s+(1-q)V_w$, where V_s is the volume of 1 lb. of d.s.s. at abs. pressure P, and V_w is the volume of 1 lb. of water at abs. pressure P and at the saturation temperature t_s corresponding to that pressure.

If the steam is fairly dry, the term $(1-q)V_w$, which is the volume of the particles of moisture in the wet steam, is small compared with qV_s and is, therefore, often neglected. The equation for the volume of wet steam then reduces to:—$V_q=qV_s$.

Example 1.—Find the exact volume of 1 lb. of wet steam of dryness fraction 0·97 at 100 Lb. per sq. in. abs. pressure if the volumes of 1 lb. of dry saturated steam and of 1 lb. of water at this pressure and at the saturation temperature are 4·434 cu. ft. and 0·0178 cu. ft., respectively.

Find, also, the percentage error involved if the volume of the particles of moisture is neglected.

The formula for the exact volume of 1 lb. of wet steam is

$$\begin{aligned} V_q &= qV_s+(1-q)V_w \\ &= (0\cdot97\times4\cdot434+0\cdot03\times0\cdot0178)\ \text{ft.}^3 \\ &= (4\cdot30098+0\cdot00053)\ \text{ft.}^3 \\ &= 4\cdot30151\ \text{ft.}^3 \end{aligned}$$

If the volume of the particles of moisture in suspension $((1-q)V_w)$ is neglected, the volume of 1 lb. of wet steam 0·97 dry at 100 Lb. per sq. in. abs. pressure would be taken as 4·30098 ft.³ involving an error of $\frac{0\cdot00053}{4\cdot30151}\times100=0\cdot0123$ per cent.

Hence, except in cases where extreme accuracy is required, we are justified in neglecting the volume of moisture in fairly dry steam.

We may note that from the definition of total heat we can write for the total heat or enthalpy of wet steam:—$H=E+PV_q$, where E=internal energy, and V_q=volume of the wet steam of dryness fraction q at absolute pressure P.

Thus, the total heat or enthalpy of wet steam can be written:

$$H=h_w+qL=E+PV_q$$

from which can be calculated the internal energy of the wet steam, namely, $E=(h_w+qL)-PV_q$.

Example 2.—Find the internal energy of 1 lb. of the wet steam of the previous example.

The volume of wet steam of 0·97 dryness fraction at 100 Lb. per sq. in. abs. was calculated to be 4·301 cu. ft. per lb. From the steam tables we see that, at pressure 100 Lb. per sq. in. abs., $h_w=298{\cdot}5$ B.Th.U. per lb. and L=889·7 B.Th.U. per lb.

Therefore, the internal energy of the wet steam at 100 Lb. per sq. in. abs. and 0·97 dry is $E=(h_w+qL)-PV_q$.

$$=\left(298{\cdot}5\,\frac{\text{B.Th.U.}}{\text{lb.}}+0{\cdot}97\times889{\cdot}7\,\frac{\text{B.Th.U.}}{\text{lb.}}\right)$$

$$-100\,\frac{\text{Lb.}}{\text{in.}^2}\times4{\cdot}301\,\frac{\text{ft.}^3}{\text{lb.}}\left[\frac{144\text{ in.}^2}{\text{ft.}^2}\right]\left[\frac{\text{B.Th.U.}}{778\text{ ft.-Lb.}}\right]$$

$$=1161{\cdot}5\,\frac{\text{B.Th.U.}}{\text{lb.}}-79{\cdot}7\,\frac{\text{B.Th.U.}}{\text{lb.}}$$

$$=1081{\cdot}8\text{ B.Th.U./lb.}$$

10. Dry Saturated Steam.—It will easily be seen that the dryness fraction of dry saturated steam is 1, since there are no particles of moisture left in the steam. For dry saturated steam, the formula for total heat or enthalpy, therefore, becomes

$$H_s=h_w+L=E_s+PV_s$$

where the quantities h_w, L, H_s, V_s can be found in the steam tables on the line opposite abs. pressure P. We can, therefore, calculate the internal energy of dry saturated steam at abs. P from the equation:—$E_s=H_s-PV_s$.

11. Superheated Steam.—Superheated steam remains at the pressure of the boiler but increases in temperature as further heat is added. The specification of superheated steam is either by the actual temperature (t') after superheating, or by the degree of superheat ($t'-t_s$)—this being the temperature rise of the steam above the saturation temperature at the particular pressure at which the superheating has taken place.

The total heat (H′) of superheated steam is the sum of the total heat of dry saturated steam and the additional heat due to superheating. That is,

$$H'=H_s+s'(t'-t_s)=E'+PV'$$

where s' is the mean specific heat of the superheated steam ($s'=0{\cdot}45$ to $0{\cdot}65$ over the range of pressures used by engineers) and V′ is the volume of superheated steam at abs. pressure P and ($t'-t_s$) degrees of superheat. The volume V′ can be found from Callendar's steam tables or calculated from his formula for volume of 1 lb. of superheated steam (see the following example).

The internal energy of superheated steam can then be calculated from the equation:

$$E' = H' - PV' = h_w + L + s'(t' - t_s) - PV'.$$

It will be noticed that the symbols h_w, E_w, V_w have been used for water, the plain symbols H, E, V have been used for wet steam, the suffixed symbols H_s, E_s, V_s for dry saturated steam, and symbols H′, E′, V′ for superheated steam. This convention is adhered to throughout the book.

Example.—Find the total heat, the volume, and the internal energy of 1 lb. of superheated steam at 100 Lb. per sq. in. absolute pressure, the degree of superheat being 100° F. The mean specific heat of superheated steam over the range of temperature at this pressure may be taken as 0·536 B.Th.U. per lb. °F.

Total heat $H' = H_s + s'(t' - t_s)$

$$= 1188 \cdot 2 \frac{\text{B.Th.U.}}{\text{lb.}} + 0 \cdot 536 \frac{\text{B.Th.U.}}{\text{lb. °F.}} \times 100° \text{ F.}$$

$$= 1241 \cdot 8 \text{ B.Th.U./lb.}$$

From Callendar's numerical formula, $V' = \frac{1 \cdot 253(H - 835)}{p}$, for the volume of 1 lb. of superheated steam in cubic feet, where H is the enthalpy in B.Th.U./lb. and p is the absolute pressure in Lb./in.²

$$V' = \frac{1 \cdot 253(1241 \cdot 8 - 835)}{100}$$

$$= 5 \cdot 1 \text{ ft.}^3\text{/lb.}$$

The internal energy of the superheated steam is, therefore,

$$E' = H' - PV'$$

$$= 1241 \cdot 8 \frac{\text{B.Th.U.}}{\text{lb.}} - 100 \frac{\text{Lb.}}{\text{in.}^2} \times 5 \cdot 1 \frac{\text{ft.}^3}{\text{lb.}} \left[\frac{144 \text{ in.}^2}{\text{ft.}^2}\right] \left[\frac{\text{B.Th.U.}}{778 \text{ ft.-Lb.}}\right]$$

$$= (1241 \cdot 8 - 94 \cdot 4) \frac{\text{B.Th.U.}}{\text{lb.}} = 1147 \cdot 4 \text{ B.Th.U./lb.}$$

EXERCISES ON CHAPTER 5

(i)

1. What is the absolute pressure of steam in a boiler if the boiler gauge reads 152 Lb. per sq. in. and the height of a mercury barometer is 30 in.?

2. Draw a curve using figures in the steam tables to illustrate how the saturation temperature of steam depends upon pressure.

3. Find, in B.Th.U., the equivalent of the work done in pumping 10 cu. ft. of water into a boiler against a pressure of 140 Lb. per sq. in. abs.

4. Find the heat equivalent of the external work done in increasing the volume of 10 lb. of water contained in an engine cylinder from 0·16 cu. ft. to 0·17 cu. ft. when under a pressure of 140 Lb. per sq. in. abs. Also find the total external work done in changing it into steam having a volume 32·2 cu. ft. at that pressure.

5. What is saturated steam? Give an explanation of the difference between wet, dry saturated, and superheated steam.

6. Find the internal energy at 140 Lb. per sq. in. abs. of 1 lb. of water which has a total heat 324·9 B.Th.U. and a volume of 0·018 cu. ft. Find also the internal energy at this pressure of 1 lb. of dry saturated steam having a total heat 1194·0 B.Th.U. and a volume 3·222 cu. ft.

7. Define dryness fraction. If the dryness fraction of 5 lb. of wet steam is 0·98, find the weight of the particles of water.

8. If the barometric height due to atmospheric pressure is 30 in. of mercury find the barometric height of a column of water supported by the atmosphere. Take 13·6 as the ratio of the density of mercury to that of water and the latter to have a specific weight of 62·3 Lb. per cu. ft. Thus calculate the atmospheric pressure in Lb. per sq. ft.

9. Describe how the condition of water is affected by the addition of: (*a*) sensible heat, (*b*) latent heat. Explain the significance of the first law of thermodynamics in this connection.

10. Find the increase in internal energy when 1 lb. of water at 140 Lb. per sq. in. abs. is changed into dry saturated steam by the addition of the latent heat 869·1 B.Th.U. if the volume increases from 0·018 cu. ft. to 3·222 cu. ft.

(ii)

11. Find the total heat of 1 lb. of steam 0·98 dry at 140 Lb. per sq. in. abs. from data given in the steam tables.

If the volume of 1 lb. of water at the saturation temperature corresponding to this pressure is 0·018 cu. ft., find the volume of the wet steam if the volume of the particles of water in the steam is taken into account. What is the percentage error involved if the volume of the particles of water is neglected?

12. Find the internal energy of the 1 lb. of steam of the previous exercise.

13. If the total heat of 1 lb. of superheated steam at 140 Lb. per sq. in. abs. and 100° F. of superheat is 1249·9 B.Th.U., find its volume by means of Callendar's formula, and also the internal energy of the 1 lb. of superheated steam.

14. (*a*) Find at what pressure 1 lb. of dry saturated steam occupies exactly 10·5 cu. ft. and find the total heat (enthalpy) and internal energy of the steam at this pressure.

(*b*) How many B.Th.U. must be abstracted from this steam to reduce its pressure to 20 Lb. per sq. in. abs. without change of volume or weight, and what will be the dryness fraction of the steam in its final state?

15. Calculate the internal energy of 1 lb. of steam at 10 Lb. per sq. in. abs. and dryness 0·9. If this steam is compressed to 100 Lb. per sq. in. abs. according to the law $PV^{1\cdot1}$=constant, calculate the final dryness of the steam and the change of internal energy, stating whether the latter is an increase or a decrease.

[Part I, B.Sc. Lond.]

16. Explain the terms (*a*) latent heat, (*b*) sensible heat, (*c*) total heat, (*d*) dryness fraction, (*e*) saturation temperature, (*f*) specific volume, as applied to steam.

Calculate the weight of steam of dryness fraction 0·96 required to move a piston of diameter 18 in. through a distance of 3 ft. at a constant pressure of 200 Lb. per sq. in. abs.

[I.Mech.E., Sec. A.]

CHAPTER 6

THE STEAM TABLES AND THEIR USE

1. Callendar's Steam Tables.—It has already been mentioned in the previous chapter that Callendar's steam tables are drawn up for the unit mass 1 lb., and that heat and energy are reckoned from 32° F. as the datum of temperature.

In the tables there are separate columns for absolute pressure, P; for saturation temperature, t_s; for total heat or enthalpy of water, tabulated in the column headed h (given the symbol h_w throughout this book); for latent heat, L; for total heat or enthalpy of dry saturated steam in the column headed H_s, and which will be seen to be the sum $h_w + L$; for the volume of 1 lb. of dry saturated steam, V_s, at the various pressures. There are other columns in the tables, such as φ_w and φ_s, giving the entropy of 1 lb. of water at the saturation temperature and the specific entropy of dry saturated steam, but which, being of no immediate use here, will not be dealt with until later (see Chapter 20).

Other tables drawn up on similar lines dealing with superheated steam are included in Callendar's steam tables.

2. Graphical Representation of Data on Steam.—A graph showing how the saturation temperature, or the temperature at which steam forms under various pressures, has been shown in fig. 5.4.

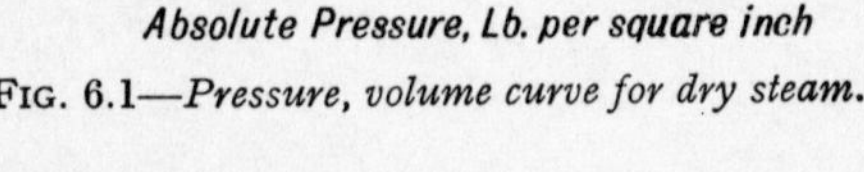

FIG. 6.1—*Pressure, volume curve for dry steam.*

Volume of steam depends, in a like manner, on pressure; fig. 6.1 is a graph plotted from figures in the steam tables showing how the volume of 1 lb. of dry saturated steam varies with pressure.

The critical points in the changes of state from liquid to wet steam and from dry saturated steam to superheated steam can be shown graphically, as in fig. 6.2, which shows pressure and saturation temperature plotted against total heat—the figures being for 1 lb., and taken from the steam tables. The point A represents the state of 1 lb. of water at 32° F. and at low pressure. Point B

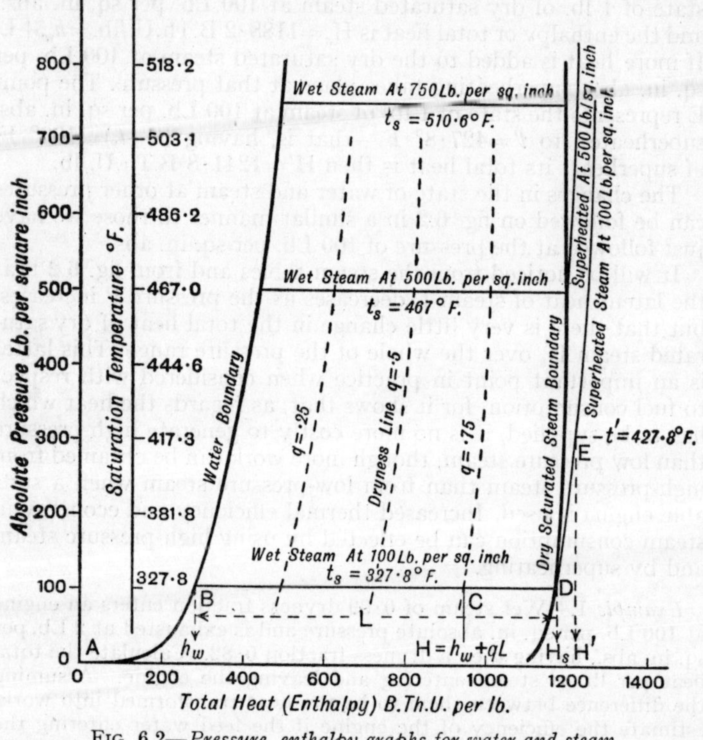

FIG. 6.2—*Pressure, enthalpy graphs for water and steam.*

represents the state of 1 lb. of water at 100 Lb. per sq. in. abs. and at the saturation temperature t_s=327·8° F. for that particular pressure. The total heat of the water at B is h_w=298·5 B.Th.U. per lb. Further application of heat to water at the state B under 100 Lb. per sq. in. abs. would commence to change it into steam at that pressure—the steam having the saturation temperature t_s. The point C represents the state of 1 lb. of wet steam at 100 Lb. per sq. in. abs. of dryness fraction $q=0{\cdot}75$, the total heat or enthalpy being

$$H=h_w+qL=298{\cdot}5+0{\cdot}75\times 889{\cdot}7=965{\cdot}8 \text{ B.Th.U./lb.}$$

When the whole of the latent heat $L=889{\cdot}7$ B.Th.U. per lb. has been added at 100 Lb. per sq. in. abs., the state of the steam is represented by the point D. Thus, the point D represents the state of 1 lb. of dry saturated steam at 100 Lb. per sq. in. abs., and the enthalpy or total heat is $H_s=1188{\cdot}2$ B.Th.U./lb. $=h_w+L$. If more heat is added to the dry saturated steam at 100 Lb. per sq. in. abs., superheating takes place at that pressure. The point E represents the state of 1 lb. of steam at 100 Lb. per sq. in. abs. superheated to $t'=427{\cdot}8°$ F.—that is, having $(t'-t_s)=100°$ F. of superheat; its total heat is then $H'=1241{\cdot}8$ B.Th.U./lb.

The changes in the state of water and steam at other pressures can be followed on fig. 6.2 in a similar manner to those we have just followed at the pressure of 100 Lb. per sq. in. abs.

It will be noticed from the steam tables and from fig. 6.2 that the latent heat of steam L decreases as the pressure P increases, but that there is very little change in the total heat of dry saturated steam H_s over the whole of the pressure range. This latter is an important point in practice when considered with respect to fuel consumption, for it shows that, as regards the heat which has to be supplied, it is no more costly to generate high-pressure than low-pressure steam, though more work can be obtained from high-pressure steam than from low-pressure steam when a suitable engine is used. Increased thermal efficiency and economy in steam consumption can be effected by using high-pressure steam and by superheating.

Example 1.—Wet steam of $0{\cdot}99$ dryness fraction enters an engine at 100 Lb. per sq. in. absolute pressure and is exhausted at 2 Lb. per sq. in. abs., having then a dryness fraction $0{\cdot}82$. Calculate the total heat per lb. of steam entering and leaving the engine. Assuming the difference between them to be the heat transformed into work, estimate the efficiency of the engine if the feed water entering the boiler takes in with it 90 B.Th.U. per lb.

Total heat of steam entering the engine

$$=H_1=h_{w1}+q_1L_1=298{\cdot}5+0{\cdot}99\times 889{\cdot}7=1179{\cdot}3 \text{ B.Th.U./lb.}$$

Total heat of steam leaving the engine

$$=H_2=h_{w2}+q_2L_2=94{\cdot}0+0{\cdot}82\times 1022{\cdot}2=932{\cdot}2 \text{ B.Th.U./lb.}$$

$$\therefore \text{ Heat transformed into work}=247{\cdot}1 \text{ B.Th.U./lb.}$$

Heat supplied to 1 lb. of steam by the boiler = Heat in 1 lb. of steam leaving the boiler (taken the same as that entering engine) minus the heat in 1 lb. of feed water entering the boiler $=1179\cdot3-90$ $=1089\cdot3$ B.Th.U./lb.

$$\therefore \text{ Thermal efficiency of engine} = \frac{\text{Work done per lb. of steam}}{\text{Heat supplied per lb. of steam}}$$

$$= \frac{247\cdot1}{1089\cdot3} = 22\cdot6 \text{ per cent.}$$

Example 2.—A steam boiler working at 550 Lb. per sq. in. absolute pressure is supplied with feed water at $141\cdot5°$ F. Find the total heat of 1 lb. of feed water as it is entering the boiler through the check valve at 550 Lb. per sq. in. abs. and $141\cdot5°$ F.

Total heat or Enthalpy $=\text{H}=\text{E}+\text{PV}$ by definition

or, for water, $h_w = \text{E}_w + \text{PV}_w$.

That is, total heat of water at 550 Lb. per sq. in. abs. and $141\cdot5°$ F. =internal energy of water at $141\cdot5°$ F.+pressure energy of water at 550 Lb. per sq. in. abs. and $141\cdot5°$ F.

The internal energy of water at $141\cdot5°$ F. is

$$\text{E}_{w2} = (h_{w2} - \text{P}_2\text{V}_{w2}),$$

where P_2 is the pressure corresponding to the saturation temperature $141\cdot5°$ F., and, on looking in the steam tables, is found to be 3 Lb. per sq. in. abs., V_{w2} is the volume of water at $141\cdot5°$ F. and is $0\cdot0163$ cu. ft./lb., and h_{w2} is the total heat of water at pressure P_2 and found in the tables to be $109\cdot4$ B.Th.U./lb.

Hence, the total heat of feed water at 550 Lb. per sq. in. abs. and $141\cdot5°$ F. is

$h_f = \text{E}_{w2} + \text{P}_1\text{V}_{w2}$ (where P_1 is the boiler pressure $=550$ Lb./in.² abs.)

$$\therefore\ h_f = h_{w2} + (\text{P}_1 - \text{P}_2)\text{V}_{w2} = \left(109\cdot4 + \frac{144(550-3)\times0\cdot0163}{778}\right)\text{B.Th.U./lb.}$$

$$= 109\cdot4 + 1\cdot65 = 111\cdot05 \text{ B.Th.U./lb.}$$

Example 3.—If the boiler pressure in the above example had been 150 Lb. per sq. in. abs., how would this have affected the total heat of the feed water?

It will be seen that the only difference would be in the pressure energy term $(\text{P}_1 - \text{P}_2)\text{V}_{w2}$, the value of which would be

$$(150-3)\frac{\text{Lb.}}{\text{in.}^2}\left[\frac{144\text{ in.}^2}{\text{ft.}^2}\right]\times0\cdot0163\frac{\text{ft.}^3}{\text{lb.}}\left[\frac{\text{B.Th.U.}}{778\text{ ft.-Lb.}}\right] = 0\cdot44\frac{\text{B.Th.U.}}{\text{lb.}}$$

and making a total heat $h_f = (109\cdot4 + 0\cdot44)$ B.Th.U./lb.
$= 109\cdot84$ B.Th.U./lb.

It is common practice to read h_{w2} from the steam tables $=109\cdot4$ B.Th.U./lb. corresponding to $141\cdot5°$ F. at 3 Lb. per sq. in. abs., and to take this as the total energy of the ingoing feed water. Others may consider the numerical value of the temperature of the feed water above 32° F. to be good enough to take for the numerical value of h_f, or

$$(141\cdot5-32)^\circ\ \mathrm{F.}\left[\frac{\mathrm{B.Th.U.}}{\mathrm{lb}_w.\ ^\circ\mathrm{F.}}\right]=109\cdot5\ \frac{\mathrm{B.Th.U.}}{\mathrm{lb.}}$$

It will be seen from the above two calculations that the pressure energy term can make an appreciable difference, and becomes more and more important as the pressures get higher. This would certainly have to be taken into account if accurate estimations were required for modern high-pressure boilers working at pressures over 1,000 Lb. per sq. in.

Example 4.—0·5 lb. of steam 0·95 dry at atmospheric pressure is blown into an open vessel containing 5 lb. of water at 68° F. Find the resulting temperature if losses are neglected.

Heat lost by steam = Heat gained by water.

If t is the final temperature:

$$\text{mass of steam}\times[q\mathrm{L}+\text{sp. ht.}(212^\circ\ \mathrm{F.}-t)]$$
$$=\text{mass of water}\times\text{sp. ht.}\times(t-68^\circ\ \mathrm{F.})$$

i.e. $$0\cdot5\ \mathrm{lb.}\left\{0\cdot95\times970\cdot6\ \frac{\mathrm{B.Th.U.}}{\mathrm{lb.}}+\frac{1\ \mathrm{B.Th.U.}}{\mathrm{lb.}\ ^\circ\mathrm{F.}}(212^\circ\ \mathrm{F.}-t)\right\}$$

$$=5\ \mathrm{lb.}\times\frac{1\ \mathrm{B.Th.U.}}{\mathrm{lb.}\ ^\circ\mathrm{F.}}\times(t-68^\circ\ \mathrm{F.})$$

$$\therefore\ 921+212-\frac{t}{^\circ\mathrm{F.}}=10\frac{t}{^\circ\mathrm{F.}}-680$$

$$\therefore\ 11\frac{t}{^\circ\mathrm{F.}}=1813,\ \text{hence}\ t=164\cdot8^\circ\ \mathrm{F.}$$

Example 5.—Wet steam is exhausted into a condenser working at 2 Lb. per sq. in. abs. pressure at the rate of 10 lb. per min. and leaves as water at 104° F. Cooling water is circulated through the condenser tubes at the rate of 230 lb. per min. with a rise in temperature from inlet to outlet of from 64·4° F. to 100° F. Calculate the dryness fraction of the steam entering the condenser.

Heat lost by steam and condensate = Heat gained by cooling water.

$$\therefore\ m_s\{q_2\mathrm{L}_2+\mathrm{C}_w(t_{s2}-t_w)\}=m_w\times\mathrm{C}_w(t_o-t_i)$$

is the physical equation, (i.e. in which symbols represent numbers × units).

i.e. $$10\ \frac{\mathrm{lb.}}{\mathrm{min.}}\left\{q_2\times1022\cdot2\ \frac{\mathrm{B.Th.U.}}{\mathrm{lb.}}+\frac{1\ \mathrm{B.Th.U.}}{\mathrm{lb.}\ ^\circ\mathrm{F.}}(126\cdot1^\circ\ \mathrm{F.}-104^\circ\ \mathrm{F.})\right\}$$

$$=230\ \frac{\mathrm{lb.}}{\mathrm{min.}}\times\frac{1\ \mathrm{B.Th.U.}}{\mathrm{lb.}\ ^\circ\mathrm{F.}}(100\cdot4^\circ\ \mathrm{F.}-64\cdot4^\circ\ \mathrm{F.})$$

or $1022\cdot2\ q_2+22\cdot1=23(36)$. Hence, $q_2=0\cdot783$.

Example 6.—A steam engine exhausts 240 lb. of steam per hour of dryness fraction 0·8 into a condenser working at 1·5 Lb. per sq. in. abs. Cooling water enters the condenser at 64° F. and leaves at 118° F. Calculate (*a*) the mass of cooling water required per hour in order just to condense the steam, and (*b*) the mass per hour which is circulated if the temperature of the condensate leaving the condenser is 95° F. What amount of under-cooling is there in the latter case, and what is the amount of heat abstracted per hour reckoned from the saturation temperature as datum?

(*a*) If the steam is just condensed to water at absolute pressure P_2, then q_2L_2 will be abstracted from the steam, and the temperature of the resulting condensate will be the saturation temperature t_{s2} corresponding to P_2.

Thus, $m_s(q_2L_2) = m_w \times C_w(t_o - t_i)$.

$\therefore$ Mass of cooling water required per hour is

$$m_w = \frac{240\ \frac{\text{lb}_s.}{\text{hr.}}\left(0\cdot8\times1028\cdot1\ \frac{\text{B.Th.U.}}{\text{lb}_s.}\right)}{\frac{1\ \text{B.Th.U.}}{\text{lb}_w.\ ^\circ\text{F.}}\times54^\circ\ \text{F.}}$$

$$=3{,}550\ \text{lb. per hour.}$$

(*b*) If the steam is condensed at $P_2 = 1\cdot5$ Lb. per sq. in. abs. to water at $t_{s2} = 115\cdot7°$ F. and then the resulting condensate cooled still further or "undercooled" from 115·7° F. down to 95° F., the mass of cooling water required is

$$m_w = m_s\frac{[q_2L_2 + C_w(t_{s2} - t_w)]}{C_w(t_o - t_i)}$$

$$=\frac{240}{54}\left\{0\cdot8\times1028\cdot1+(115\cdot7-95)\right\}\frac{\text{lb.}}{\text{hr.}}$$

$$=3{,}642\ \text{lb. per hour.}$$

The amount of "undercooling" in reducing the temperature from t_{s2} to t_w

$$=240\frac{\text{lb.}}{\text{hr.}}\times\frac{1\ \text{B.Th.U.}}{\text{lb. }^\circ\text{F.}}\times(115\cdot7-95)^\circ\ \text{F.}=4{,}970\ \text{B.Th.U. per hour.}$$

The total amount of cooling in the latter case in condensing the steam and cooling the condensate to t_w

$$=240\left\{0\cdot8\times1028\cdot1+(115\cdot1-95)\right\}\frac{\text{B.Th.U.}}{\text{hr.}}$$

$$=202{,}000\ \text{B.Th.U. per hour.}$$

Reckoned from t_{s2} as a datum, the heat abstracted in condensing the steam to water at $t_{s2} = 202{,}000 - 4{,}970 = 197{,}030$ B.Th.U. per hour.

Example 7.—A reciprocating engine is supplied with superheated steam, and information per lb. of steam relating to two points in the expansion is given in fig. 6·3. If the expansion is assumed to

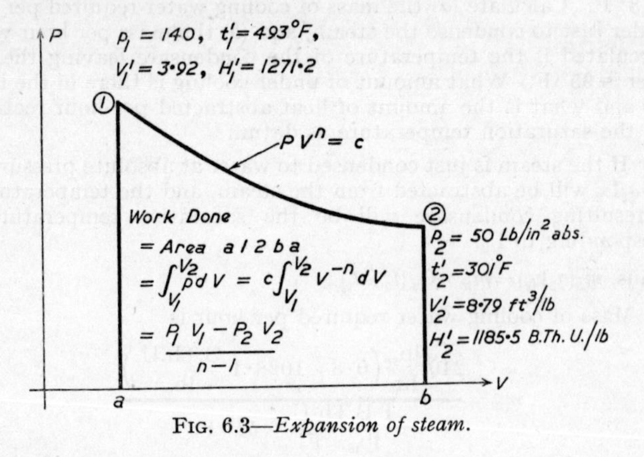

Fig. 6.3—*Expansion of steam.*

obey the law PV^n=constant, find the value of n, the work done and the amount of the heat interchange per lb. of steam between the steam and the cylinder walls.

Referring to fig. 6.3,

$$P_1V_1{}^n = P_2V_2{}^n, \text{ hence } \frac{140}{50} = \left(\frac{8\cdot79}{3\cdot92}\right)^n$$

and $$n = \frac{\log 2\cdot8}{\log 2\cdot24} = 1\cdot277.$$

$$\text{Work done} = \frac{P_1V_1 - P_2V_2}{n-1} = \frac{144(140\times3\cdot92 - 50\times8\cdot79)}{0\cdot277} \text{ ft.-Lb./lb.}$$

$$= 56{,}500 \text{ ft.-Lb./lb.}$$

Internal energy $E_1' = H_1' - P_1V_1'$

$$= 1271\cdot2 \frac{\text{B.Th.U.}}{\text{lb.}} - 140 \frac{\text{Lb.}}{\text{in.}^2} \times 3\cdot92 \frac{\text{ft.}^3}{\text{lb.}} \left[\frac{144 \text{ in.}^2}{\text{ft.}^2}\right]\left[\frac{\text{B.Th.U.}}{778 \text{ ft.-Lb.}}\right]$$

$$= 1169\cdot7 \text{ B.Th.U. per lb.}$$

Similarly, $$E_2' = \left(1185\cdot5 - \frac{144\times50\times8\cdot79}{778}\right) = 1104\cdot2 \text{ B.Th.U./lb.}$$

∴ Gain in internal energy, $\delta E = E_2' - E_1' = -65\cdot5$ B.Th.U./lb.

External work done by expanding steam, δW, is

$$56{,}500 \frac{\text{ft.-Lb.}}{\text{lb.}} \left[\frac{\text{B.Th.U.}}{778 \text{ ft.-Lb.}}\right] = 72\cdot5 \text{ B.Th.U./lb.}$$

Hence, by the first law of thermodynamics as stated on page 17, $\delta Q = \delta E + \delta W$, the heat gained by the steam during expansion between points ① and ②

$$= -65 \cdot 5 + 72 \cdot 5 = 7 \text{ B.Th.U. per lb.}$$

3. Estimation of Dryness Fraction.—An apparatus for estimating the dryness fraction of steam is illustrated in fig. 6.4. It is a combined separating and throttling calorimeter, D being

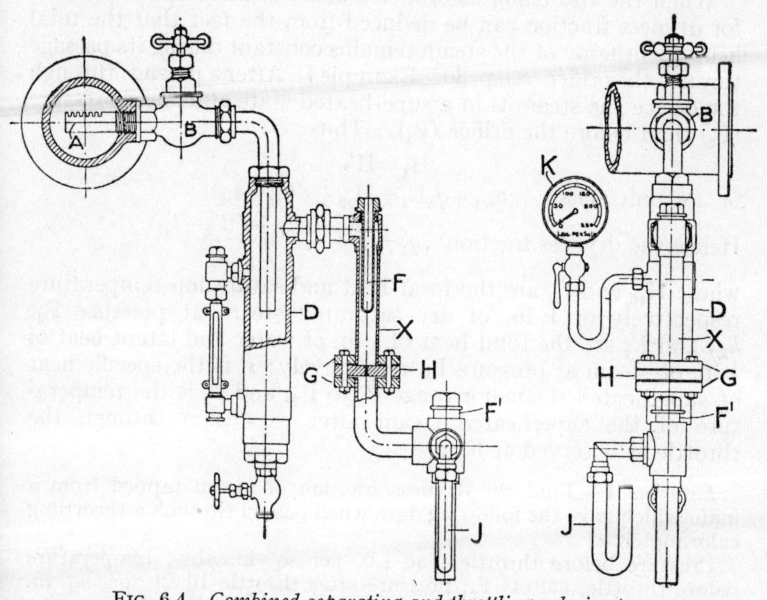

FIG. 6.4—*Combined separating and throttling calorimeter.*

the separator and X the throttle calorimeter. The combined calorimeter is only necessary when very wet steam is being tested. When the steam is fairly dry the throttling calorimeter X can be used alone without the separator D. The method of using the combined calorimeter is to allow steam, picked up by the sampler A, to flow through the valve B into the separator D, where the greater part of any moisture in the steam is collected. The steam then flows through the orifice plate H of the throttle calorimeter. The temperature and pressure before the orifice are observed on a thermometer placed in F and pressure gauge K, respectively (the temperature recorded at F should be the saturation temperature corresponding to the pressure in X). After the orifice the temperature and pressure of steam are obtained from the thermometer placed in F′ and manometer tube J, respectively. The outlet from the throttling-calorimeter is connected to a condensing coil open to the atmosphere, and the condensed steam is collected and weighed. The water collected in the separator is also weighed, and from the data it is possible to calculate the dryness fraction of the steam sampled (see Example 2).

When the throttling calorimeter alone is used, the expression for dryness fraction can be deduced from the fact that the total heat or enthalpy of the steam remains constant during its passage through the orifice (see p. 302, Example 1). After a passage through the orifice the steam is in a superheated state at a lower pressure (P_2) than before the orifice (P_1). Thus

$$H_1 = H'_2$$

or, for unit mass, $$h_{w1} + q_1 L_1 = H_{s2} + s'(t'_2 - t_{s2}).$$

Hence the dryness fraction $$q_1 = \frac{H_{s2} - h_{w1} + s'(t'_2 - t_{s2})}{L_1},$$

where H_{s2} and t_{s2} are the total heat and saturation temperature respectively of 1 lb. of dry saturated steam at pressure P_2; h_{w1} and L_1 are the total heat of 1 lb. of water and latent heat of 1 lb. of steam at pressure P_1, respectively; s' is the specific heat of superheated steam for range P_1 to P_2; and t'_2 is the temperature of the superheated steam after expansion through the throttle as observed at F′.

Example 1.—Find the dryness fraction of steam tapped from a main which gave the following data when passed through a throttling calorimeter:—

Pressure before throttle, 150 Lb. per sq. in. abs.; temperature before throttle, 358·4° F.; pressure after throttle 16 Lb. per sq. in. abs.; temperature after throttle, 239° F. Take the mean specific heat of the superheated steam to be 0·5 B.Th.U. per lb. ° F.

From the steam tables we find that at $P_1 = 150$ Lb. per sq. in. abs., $h_{w1} = 330 \cdot 6$ B.Th.U./lb., and $L_1 = 864 \cdot 5$ B.Th.U./lb.; and that at $P_2 = 16$ Lb. per sq. in. abs. $H_{s2} = 1152 \cdot 4$ B.Th.U./lb. and $t_{s2} = 216 \cdot 3°$ F.

Hence $$q_1 = \frac{1152 \cdot 4 - 330 \cdot 6 + 0 \cdot 5(239 - 216 \cdot 3)}{864 \cdot 5} = 0 \cdot 96.$$

It should be noticed that the observation of temperature before expansion through the throttle, namely, 358·4° F., has not been used in the calculation. The reason for taking this temperature is that it serves as a check on the observed pressure P_1, in that the observed temperature should correspond to the saturation temperature as given in the steam tables. It is usually more accurate in finding h_{w1} and L_1 from the tables, if any discrepancy arises between P_1 and the temperature, to look opposite the temperature figure rather than the pressure (though the two should correspond) because a thermometer observation is likely to be more accurate than an observation on a close-scale pressure gauge.

When the combined separator and throttling calorimeter is used it is necessary to weigh the amount of water collected in the separator (W_D), and also to condense and weigh the steam which flows through the throttle (W_T), besides making temperature and pressure observations before and after the throttle. From these data a calculation for dryness fraction of the steam entering the apparatus can be made in the following way:—

Total weight of steam entering the sampling tube$=(W_D+W_T)$
Moisture collected in the separator from the sample steam$=W_D$
Weight of steam passing through the throttling calorimeter$=W_T$

From the observations made on the throttling calorimeter we find that the dryness fraction of the steam which enters the throttling calorimeter is

$$q_T=\frac{H_{s2}-h_{w1}+s'(t'_2-t_{s2})}{L_1}$$

Hence the ratio of the weight w_T of moisture (water) to the weight W_T of wet steam entering the *throttle* is $\frac{w_T}{W_T}=(1-q_T)$, i.e. the weight w_T of water in a weight of steam W_T which flows through the throttle is $w_T=W_T(1-q_T)$ and the weight w of water in the weight of steam $W=(W_D+W_T)$ which enters the combined separating and throttling calorimeter through the *sampling tube* is $w=W_D+(1-q_T)W_T$.

Hence the ratio of the weight w of water in the steam to the weight W of steam sampled is

$$\frac{w}{W}=\frac{W_D+(1-q_T)W_T}{W_D+W_T}=1-\frac{q_TW_T}{W_D+W_T}$$

and the ratio of the weight W_s of dry saturated steam to the weight of steam entering the sampling tube is the dryness fraction of the sampled steam, namely,

$$q=\frac{W_s}{W}=\frac{W_s}{w+W_s}=1-\frac{w}{W}=\frac{q_TW_T}{W_D+W_T}$$

i.e. the dryness fraction of the steam entering the sampling tube is

$$\boldsymbol{q=\frac{q_T}{1+\frac{W_D}{W_T}}}$$

Example 2.—Steam at 120 Lb. per sq. in. abs. was passed through a combined separating and throttling calorimeter and the following data were obtained:

Weight of moisture collected in separator: $1 \cdot 5$ Lb. $= W_D$
Weight of steam condensed after throttle: 23 Lb. $= W_T$
Pressure after throttling: 15 Lb. per sq. in. abs.
Temperatures before and after throttling: $341 \cdot 3°$ F. and $257°$ F. respectively.
Find the dryness fraction q of the steam entering the apparatus.
Total weight of steam entering the apparatus $= W_D + W_T = 24 \cdot 5$ Lb.
Dryness fraction of steam passing through the throttle is

$$q_T = \frac{H_{s2} - h_{w1} + s'(t'_2 - t_{s2})}{L_1} = \frac{1151 \cdot 2 - 312 \cdot 5 + 0 \cdot 5(257 - 213)}{878 \cdot 9} = 0 \cdot 98.$$

Hence the dryness fraction of the steam sampled is

$$q = \frac{q_T W_T}{W_D + W_T} = 0 \cdot 98 \times \frac{23}{24 \cdot 5} = 0 \cdot 92.$$

EXERCISES ON CHAPTER 6

(i)

1. Plot graphs from figures given in the steam tables showing how:

(*a*) Volume of dry saturated steam varies with pressure.
(*b*) Latent heat varies with pressure.
(*c*) Total heat of water and total heat of dry saturated steam vary with pressure; and indicate dryness lines where $q = 0 \cdot 25$, $0 \cdot 5$, and $0 \cdot 75$.

2. A boiler working at a pressure 100 Lb. per sq. in. abs. generates steam of dryness fraction $0 \cdot 98$. Calculate, with the aid of steam tables, the total heat per lb. of steam leaving the boiler.

3. If feed water is supplied to the above boiler at a temperature $141 \cdot 5°$ F., calculate the heat supplied by the boiler to each lb. of steam generated:

(i) Accurately, by taking pressure energy into account.
(ii) By reading h_{w2} direct from the tables.
(iii) By taking the temperature of the feed water minus 32 to represent the numerical value of the total heat of the water entering the boiler.

What is the error due to using the methods (ii) and (iii) rather than the accurate result of (i)?

4. Repeat question (3) when the boiler is such that dry saturated steam is generated at 2,000 Lb. per sq. in. abs., and note the extent of the errors for this high-pressure steam.

5. One lb. of steam of $0 \cdot 95$ dryness fraction is blown, at 15 Lb. per sq. in. abs., into 50 lb. of water of temperature $65°$ F. Find the final temperature of the water.

6. The inlet and outlet temperatures of the cooling water which circulates through a surface condenser are 60° F. and 100° F., respectively. The condenser works at a pressure 1 Lb. per sq. in. abs. and condenses 12 lb. of steam per min. which enters the condenser 0·8 dry and leaves it as water with a temperature 90° F. Find the quantity of cooling water circulating per minute through the condenser tubes.

7. Data obtained from a throttling calorimeter were:—pressures and temperatures before throttle 200 Lb. per sq. in. abs. and 381·8° F., and after throttling 15 Lb. per sq. in. abs. and 233° F., respectively. With the aid of steam tables calculate the dryness fraction of the steam entering the calorimeter, assuming the numerical value of the specific heat of superheated steam to be 0·5.

8. It is required to change 1 lb. of water at 32° F. into 1 lb. of dry saturated steam at 150 Lb. per sq. in. abs. by:—

(i) Introducing it at 32° F. into the boiler against a pressure 150 Lb. per sq. in. abs. (volume of 1 lb. of water at 32° F. is $b=0·016$ cu. ft.).

(ii) Warming it from 32° F. to the saturation temperature at 150 Lb. per sq. in. abs. (volume of 1 lb. of water at 358·4° F. is $w=0·018$ cu. ft.).

(iii) Evaporating it at 150 Lb. per sq. in. abs. by adding the corresponding latent heat (volume of 1 lb. of dry saturated steam at this pressure is $V_s=3·015$ cu. ft.).

Calculate in B.Th.U.:—

(*a*) The energy required to introduce the water into the boiler.

(*b*) The external work done during the warming stage in changing the volume of the water from b to w at 150 Lb. per sq. in. abs.

(*c*) The external work done during the evaporation stage in changing the volume (w) of water into dry saturated steam of volume V_s at 150 Lb. per sq. in. abs.

9. Find from the steam tables the numerical values of the total heat of water (h_w) and the latent heat of steam (L) for the pressure 150 Lb. per sq. in. abs., and use these figures together with the results of question (8), to make an energy table similar to that shown in Paragraph 6 of Chapter 5.

(ii)

10. Calculate with the aid of steam tables the total heat or enthalpy of 1 lb. of steam at 115 Lb. per sq. in. abs. when the dryness fraction of the steam is $q=1$, $0·7$, and $0·3$.

Find the volume of 1 lb. of steam in each case, taking into account that the volume of 1 lb. of water at 115 Lb. per sq. in. abs. and a 338·1° F. is $w=0·0179$ cu. ft. Compare this accurately calculated volume with the approximate value as calculated when the volume of water (w) is neglected.

For each dryness fraction calculate the external work done and the increase in internal energy during the process of evaporation. Tabulate the sets of results.

11. Steam at 200 Lb. per sq. in. abs. is throttled down to 2 Lb. per sq. in. abs., the total heat remaining constant during the process. It is known that the dryness fraction of the steam before the throttle is 0·8. Find the dryness fraction of the steam after throttling.

12. If the dryness fraction of the steam before throttling had been 0·98 in the previous question, what would be the degree of superheat of the throttled steam? The specific heat of superheated steam may be taken as 0·5 B.Th.U. per lb. °F.

13. Find the dryness fraction of steam entering a combined separating and throttling calorimeter if, of the 20 lb. of steam entering the apparatus, 1·2 lb. is collected as moisture in the separator, and data obtained from the throttling calorimeter are:—temperatures of steam before and after throttle 341·3° F. and 253° F., respectively, and pressure after throttle 15 Lb. per sq. in. abs. Take the specific heat of superheated steam to be 0·5 B.Th.U. per lb. ° F.

14. Define the term " total heat " or " enthalpy " in words and in symbols. Estimate, with the aid of steam tables, the total heat of (*a*) 1 lb. of superheated steam at 1,000 Lb. per sq. in. abs. pressure and 400° F. of superheat, (*b*) 1 lb. of water at 100° F. and 1,000 Lb. per sq. in. abs., assuming the volume of the water to remain constant at 0·016 cu. ft. per lb.

Calculate the efficiency of a boiler which generates 8·5 lb. of steam in condition (*a*) per 1 lb. of coal fired if feed water enters the boiler in condition (*b*).

15. Describe with the aid of sketches how a combined separating and throttling calorimeter is used.

The steam is in a main at 100 Lb. per sq. in. abs. pressure and its dryness is q. The temperature and pressure after the throttle are 250° F. and 18 Lb. per sq. in. abs. respectively. At the separator, 2·52 lb. of water are trapped while 8·1 lb. of steam pass the throttle. Find the value of q, taking C_p for superheated steam as 0·48 B.Th.U. per lb. ° F. [Part I, B.Sc. Lond.]

16. Steam from a main in which the pressure is 105 Lb. per sq. in. gauge is passed into a heat insulated copper calorimeter containing 5 lb. of water at 79·6° F., the calorimeter itself weighs 2 Lb. When the total weight has become 7·386 Lb. the temperature has risen to 160·6° F. What is the condition of the steam in the main?

Barometer 30·5 inches; specific heat of copper, 0·0928. [I.Mech.E., Sec. A.]

17. Prove that when steam passes through a throttle valve from a region of constant pressure to a region of lower constant pressure without any gain of kinetic energy the *total heat* remains constant.

Steam at a pressure of 100 Lb. per sq. in. abs. dryness 0·96 pasess through such a throttle valve and emerges just dry and saturated. Determine the lower pressure. [I.Mech.E., Sec. A.]

18. At a point just after cut-off in a steam-engine cylinder the steam pressure was 150 Lb. per sq. in. abs. and the dryness 0·85. After expansion, at a point just before release, the pressure was 60 Lb. per sq. in. abs. and the dryness 0·80. Assuming that expansion obeys a law PV^n=a constant, determine the heat exchange per lb. between the steam and the cylinder walls, and state whether it is a gain or a loss by the steam. [Part I, B.Sc. Lond.]

19. An engine is supplied with steam from a boiler through a long pipe-line. The steam leaving the boiler is at 200 Lb. per sq. in. abs. and 400° F. Some of the steam at the engine end of the pipe-line is bled off and passed through a throttling calorimeter: the steam temperature entering the calorimeter is 381·8° F., while the pressure and temperature of the steam after passing through the calorimeter are respectively 15 Lb. per sq. in. abs. and 240° F.

Determine:—

(*a*) the heat-loss per lb. of steam during passage through the pipe;
(*b*) the steam dryness at the engine;
(*c*) the change in volume per lb. of steam during passage through the pipe. [Part I, B.Sc. Lond.]

20. A quantity of steam at 300 Lb. per sq. in. abs., and of dryness fraction 0·98, is throttled until the pressure falls to 120 Lb. per sq. in. abs. It is now mixed at this pressure with an equal weight of new steam supplied at 120 Lb. per sq. in. abs. and 500° F. The mixture is then expanded adiabatically until the pressure falls to 1 Lb. per sq. in. abs. Using the steam tables, calculate:—

(*a*) the state of the high pressure steam after throttling;
(*b*) the state of the steam after mixing;
(*c*) the state of the steam mixture after reversible adiabatic expansion;
(*d*) the heat drop during this expansion.

[Part I, B.Sc. Lond.]

21. Steam flows into a reducing valve with a pressure 200 Lb. per sq. in abs. and dryness fraction 0·98; it leaves the valve with a pressure of 20 Lb. per sq. in. abs.

What diameters of inlet and outlet pipes would be required for a flow of 5,000 pounds per hour with a velocity of 50 ft. per second at both positions? State the condition of the steam at the outlet.

[I.Mech.E., Sec. A.]

CHAPTER 7

THE STEAM ENGINE PLANT AND RANKINE'S CYCLE OF COMPARISON

1. The Steam Engine Plant.—We have seen in Chapter 2 that the essentials for the working of a steam engine, as for all other engines, are:—

(i) *a source of heat*;
(ii) *a working agent*; and
(iii) *a sink or receiver* into which heat can be rejected;

and that these three essentials operate and function through the three main organs of a steam engine plant—the boiler, the engine, and the condenser.

In all steam engine plant, whether it be for a reciprocating engine or steam turbine, it will be found that there are three distinct circuits necessary for the working and successful operation of the three essentials as illustrated in fig. 7.1. They are:—

(i) A gas circuit, which enters the boiler furnace as air fresh from the atmosphere, and supplies the oxygen necessary for the combustion of the combustible elements in the fuel. The resulting products of combustion, after transmitting a part of their heat into the water and steam of the boiler while they are passing through the heating tubes, flow up the chimney-stack out into the atmosphere carrying with them the remainder of the heat of combustion and any unburnt fuel particles there may be. Thus we have a gas circuit—fresh air entering the combustion chamber from the atmosphere and the products of combustion leaving via the chimney to flow out into the atmosphere again.

The furnace and the products of combustion thus form the source of heat which is the first of the three essentials and which depends for its production on the gas circuit.

(ii) A circuit of "water-stuff" taking alternately the forms of water and steam. It flows in the state of steam from the boiler to do work in the engine, and from the engine it is exhausted into the condenser, where it is condensed into water. The water is then extracted from the condenser and pumped back into the boiler, where it is again changed into steam.

The "water-stuff" (H_2O) forms the working-agent, and is the second of the three essentials necessary for the working of a steam engine.

(iii) A circuit of cooling water flowing through the condenser to carry away the heat abstracted from the stream which enters from the exhaust pipe of the engine or turbine. The function of the cooling water is to abstract heat from the exhaust steam in order to condense it to water ready for pumping back into the boiler again.

The cooling water circuit of the condenser forms the sink or receiver into which heat is rejected from the working agent. It is the third of the three essentials of a steam engine plant.

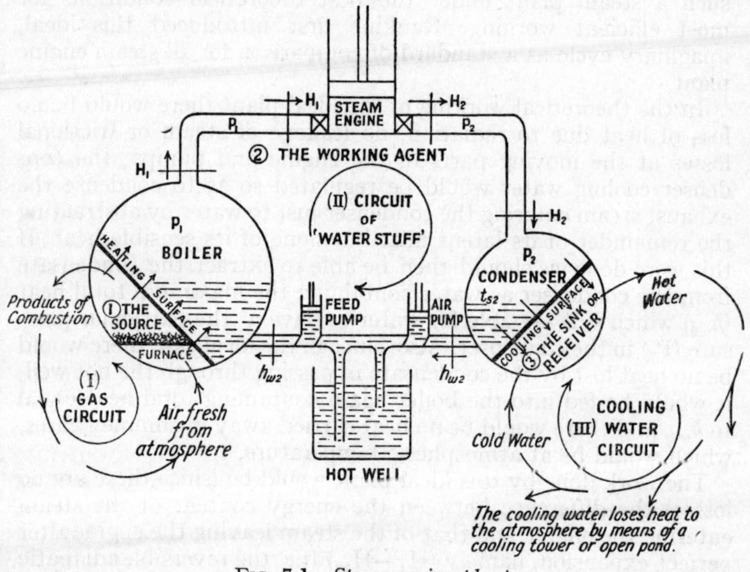

FIG. 7.1—*Steam engine plant.*

The three circuits can be seen in fig. 7.1, which is a diagrammatic sketch of a steam engine plant. It will be seen that after the steam has passed from the boiler through the engine into the condenser, where it is condensed into water, a pump, whose function is to maintain the vacuum (or absolute pressure P_2) in the condenser and to extract the condensate, delivers it into the hot well which is open to the atmosphere. From the hot well the water is pumped by means of a feed pump into the boiler again for re-evaporation into steam.

All steam plant can be represented in some such diagrammatic ways as in figs. 7.1 and 7.2 in order to show the heat transferences and energy streams and to indicate the cycle of states through which the working agent passes. It is the aim of the engineer to perform the cycle of operations in any plant with a minimum waste or loss of energy. An ideal cycle for steam engine plant—known as the Rankine Cycle introduced in 1854, is set up as a criterion with which to compare the working of actual steam plant.

2. The Rankine Cycle of Comparison.—The Rankine Cycle can be thought of with reference to fig. 7.1 as the operation of such a steam plant under the best theoretical conditions for most efficient working. Rankine first introduced this ideal, imaginary cycle as a standard of comparison for all steam engine plant.

In the theoretical working of the ideal plant there would be no loss of heat due to radiation, no leakage of steam or frictional losses at the moving parts of the engine and pumps; the condenser cooling water would be regulated so as to condense the exhaust steam entering the condenser just to water by abstracting the remainder of its latent heat but none of its sensible heat. If this were done we should then be able to extract the condensate from the condenser as water containing the maximum total heat (h_{w2}) which it is possible for water to have at the particular pressure (P_2) in the condenser. Also, since in the ideal case there would be no heat lost by the condensate in passing through the hot well, it would be fed into the boiler again containing total heat equal to h_{w2}, and there would be no heat carried away in chimney gases, which would be at atmospheric temperature.

The work done by this ideal plant would be (since there are no losses) the difference between the energy content of the steam entering the engine and that of the steam leaving the engine after perfect expansion, namely ($H_1 - H_{2a}$) (*i.e.* the reversible adiabatic "heat drop"—H_{2a} being the total heat of the steam after an ideal expansion during which there are no eddies, friction, or transfers of heat).

The heat supplied by the furnace and flue gases to the water and steam in the boiler will be the difference between the total heat of the steam leaving the boiler and that of the feed water entering the boiler, namely ($H_1 - h_{w2}$).

Thus, the ratio: $\dfrac{\text{thermal equivalent of output}}{\text{thermal equivalent of input}}$, or **the thermal efficiency of the Rankine Cycle, is** $\dfrac{H_1 - H_{2a}}{H_1 - h_{w2}}$ (neglecting the small pump term), where H_1 is the total heat or enthalpy of steam at absolute pressure P_1, and which may be wet, dry, or superheated.

H_{2a} is the total heat or enthalpy of steam at pressure P_2 after reversible adiabatic expansion (see p. 292).

h_{w2} is the total heat or enthalpy of water at P_2 which will be seen from the tables to be numerically very nearly equal to the temperature of the condensate minus 32, *i.e.* $(t_{s2}-32)$, the temperature of the condensate in the Rankine Cycle being t_{s2}.

[It should be noted that if q_{2a} is not known so as to find H_{2a} from the sum $h_{w2}+q_{2a}L_2$, the formula $H_{2a}=T_{s2}\varphi_{2a}-G_2$ can be used (see page 494), where T_{s2} and G_2 are tabulated in the steam tables opposite the pressure P_2; and $\varphi_{2a}=\varphi_1=\varphi_{w1}+q_1\frac{L_1}{T_{s1}}$, where φ_{w1}, L_1 and T_{s1} are to be found in the tables opposite pressure P_1.]

Although, as will be seen later, the Carnot Cycle gives the best possible efficiency any heat engine can (theoretically) have, we shall see that this cycle is impracticable, and therefore the Rankine Cycle, being based on a set of operations which are practicable, is taken as the standard of comparison for steam engine plant. Thus, it is usual after trials on steam engines and steam turbines to give a relative efficiency or efficiency ratio

$$=\frac{\text{thermal efficiency of the actual plant}}{\text{thermal efficiency of the ideal Rankine cycle}}$$

Example.—A steam engine admits steam 0·99 dry at 100 Lb. per sq. in. abs. and exhausts at 2 Lb. per sq. in. abs. into a condenser. Find the efficiency of the Rankine cycle.

Total heat of 1 lb. of steam entering the engine $=H_1=h_{w1}+q_1L_1$, which, with the aid of tables, gives $H_1=298\cdot5+0\cdot99\times889\cdot7=1179\cdot3$ B.Th.U./lb. Total heat of the steam after perfect (i.e. reversible) adiabatic expansion $=H_{2a}=T_2\varphi_{2a}-G_2$, or since, in the ideal Rankine engine,

$$\varphi_1=\varphi_{2a}, \text{ we have } H_{2a}=T_{s2}\left(\varphi_{w1}+q_1\frac{L_1}{T_1}\right)-G_2.$$

Hence, with the aid of Callendar's steam tables,

$$H_{2a}=585\cdot8\left(0\cdot4742+\frac{0\cdot99\times889\cdot7}{787\cdot5}\right)-8\cdot5=922\cdot4 \text{ B.Th.U./lb.}$$

The total heat of water at the saturation temperature corresponding to 2 Lb. per sq. in. abs. is $h_{w2}=94\cdot0$ B.Th.U./lb.

$$\therefore \text{ Rankine Efficiency}=\frac{H_1-H_{2a}}{H_1-h_{w2}}=\frac{1179\cdot3-922\cdot4}{1179\cdot3-94\cdot0}=\frac{256\cdot9}{1085\cdot3}$$
$$=23\cdot7 \text{ per cent.}$$

Alternatively the reversible adiabatic heat drop (see page 494) can be calculated from the formula $H_1 - H_{2a} = \varphi_1(T_{s1} - T_{s2}) - (G_1 - G_2)$.

3. Energy Streams of a Steam Turbine Plant.—The energy streams flowing in a simple steam turbine plant can be shown diagrammatically as in fig. 7.2, from which it is seen that the circuit of the working agent is closed except for the free surface of the hot well.

The complete plant has been enclosed within an outer boundary and the individual units of the plant are enclosed within inner boundaries. The letters attendant on the arrows represent, per unit mass of working agent, the quantities of energy flowing along

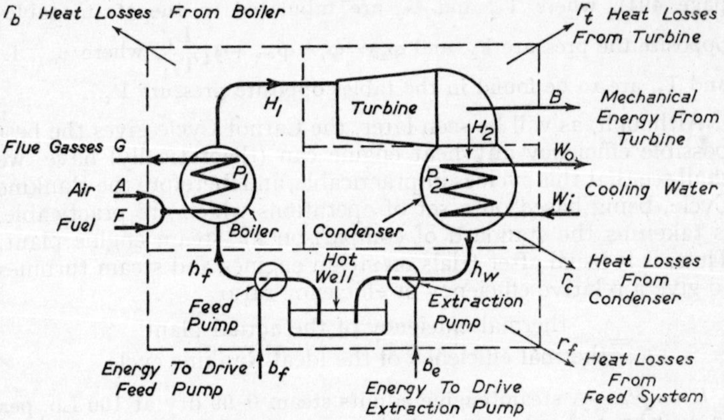

FIG. 7.2—*Steam turbine plant.*

the various energy streams entering and leaving the boundaries. These enable energy equations to be deduced for the individual units and for the plant as a whole, based on the fact that, when the plant is running under steady conditions, the energy per unit mass of working agent (or per unit of time, whichever is the more convenient) entering any particular boundary must, by the law of conservation of energy, be equal to the rate at which energy is leaving the boundary.

For the boiler unit:

$$F + A + h_f = H_1 + G + r_b;\ \text{hence, } F + A = G + H_1 - h_f + r_b.$$

For the turbine unit:

$$H_1 = B + H_2 + r_t;\ \text{hence, } 0 = B - H_1 + H_2 + r_t.$$

For the condenser unit:

$$W_i + H_2 = W_o + h_w + r_c;\ \text{hence, } W_i = W_o + h_w - H_2 + r_c.$$

For the feed water system:

$$h_w + b_e + b_f = h_f + r_f;\ \text{hence, } b_e + b_f = -h_w + h_f + r_f.$$

The four equations on the right may be added to give the equation: $F + A + W_i + b_e + b_f = G + B + W_o + \Sigma r$ which, on referring again to fig. 7.2, will be seen to be the same as the energy equation for the whole plant as deduced from the outer boundary.

Since energy equations form the basis of energy stream diagrams and energy balance sheets (as on p. 82), the latter can be drawn up without any danger of error as regards the items which should compose the balance sheets of individual units, combinations of units, or the whole plant. Thus, the mechanical energy (B) available from the turbine is represented by the equation: $B = (H_1 - H_2) - r_t$, as deduced from the above equation for the turbine unit. When translated into words this last equation states that the mechanical energy (B) available from the turbine per lb. of steam supplied is equal to the actual heat drop $(H_1 - H_2)$ less the radiation losses (r_t) from the turbine.

The energy equation for the whole plant may be rearranged as:

$$F = [B - (b_e + b_f)] + [G - A] + [W_o - W_i] + \Sigma r,$$

which, when translated into words, states that, per unit mass of working agent, the potential energy (F) of the fuel is equal to the sum of the mechanical energy $[B - (b_e + b_f)]$ available from the turbine less that required by the pumps, the energy $[G - A]$ leaving in the chimney gases reckoned from the air temperature as datum, the heat $[W_o - W_i]$ gained by the water circulating through the condenser, and the heat (Σr) gained by the air surrounding the plant.

The overall thermal efficiency of an actual working plant can, therefore, be represented by the ratio of the net mechanical energy available to the potential energy of the fuel supplied, i.e. by the expressions:

$$\eta_o = \frac{B - (b_e + b_f)}{F} = 1 - \frac{[(G - A) + (W_o - W_i) + \Sigma r]}{F}.$$

If, as in the imaginary Rankine cycle, the plant represented in fig. 7.2 could work without loss of heat in chimney gases and losses due to radiation, and also achieve perfect or reversible adiabatic expansion in the turbine and the minimum of heat carried away by the condenser cooling water, the Rankine cycle would be operating, i.e. $(G-A)=0$, $\Sigma r=0$, (H_1-H_{2a})=reversible adiabatic heat drop, and $(W_o-W_i)=q_{2a}L_2$. Thus, the efficiency of the Rankine cycle would be:

$$\eta_R = 1 - \frac{q_{2a}L_2}{F_R}$$

or

$$\eta_R = \frac{B_R-(b_e+b_f)}{F_R} = \frac{(H_1-H_{2a})-(P_1-P_2)V_{w2}}{(H_1-h_{w2})-(P_1-P_2)V_{w2}},$$

where the "pump term," $(b_e+b_f)=(P_1-P_2)V_{w2}$, represents the energy required to increase the pressure per lb. of water from P_2, the condenser pressure, to P_1, the pressure in the boiler, and V_{w2} represents the volume of 1 lb. of water at the saturation temperature, t_{s2}, corresponding to the condenser pressure, P_2. The pump term is, however, usually so small relatively that it is neglected, thus leaving the expression

$$\eta_R = \frac{H_1-H_{2a}}{H_1-h_{w2}}$$

to represent the efficiency of the Rankine Cycle, as developed in a different way on page 128.

4. Efficiency of Steam Engine Plant.—A steam engine or a steam turbine plant is, at best, inefficient. Even the most efficient power stations working with high boiler pressures and high degrees of superheat, high vacua in condensers, reheating of steam and multi-stage heating of feed water, only approach overall efficiencies of about 30 per cent.

The chief cause of this low efficiency is the fact that, as the working agent or "water stuff" travels round its circuit, most of the heat received from the boiler furnace is needed to convert water into steam and at a much lower temperature than that of the furnace. *A fundamental defect of the orthodox boiler is that it permits a large irreversible temperature drop between the flame and the highest temperature of the working agent used in the engine.*

e.g. The furnace temperature in the boiler of a steam engine or turbine plant is very high, say, $T_1=3{,}200°$ abs. F. Assuming the vacuum in the condenser is such that a sink temperature of $T_2=540°$ abs. F. is possible for abstraction of heat during the condensation process, the maximum efficiency of transformation of heat into work between these two temperatures of source and receiver is that of the Carnot cycle (page 348), namely,

$$\eta_c = \frac{T_1-T_2}{T_1} = 1-\frac{T_2}{T_1} = 1-\frac{540}{3200} = 0\cdot83 \text{ or 83 per cent.}$$

In practice, however, the furnace is used to generate and superheat steam to a temperature of about 1,500° abs. F. and this reduces the upper limit of efficiency even in the most efficient power stations to $1-\frac{540}{1500}=0\cdot 64$ or 64 per cent. This represents a very large wastage of high quality heat which practical considerations make inevitable.

The greater part of the latent heat (say, 90 per cent.) is still retained in the steam exhausted from the engine or turbine. A small proportion of this heat can be prevented from entering the condenser by "bleeding" partially expanded steam from the turbine or between stages of a compound steam engine in order to heat the feed water on its way to the boiler, but most of the heat is inevitably carried away and wasted in the cooling water flowing from the condenser.

Having seen that all steam engine plant is made up of three main units, namely: (i) the engine, (ii) the boiler, (iii) the condenser, succeeding chapters deal in turn with each of these units.

Example 1.—A steam turbine consumes 10 lb. of steam per horse-power-hour when developing 100 horse-power. The condenser vacuum is equivalent to 27 inches of mercury when the atmospheric pressure is 14·7 Lb. per sq. in. abs. The temperature of the condensate extracted from the condenser is 104° F., and 490 lb. of cooling water per minute circulate through the condenser tubes with a rise of temperature of 30° F. Calculate the dryness fraction of the steam entering the condenser and the total heat of the steam entering the turbine.

If the efficiency of the steam boiler is 80 per cent. estimate the overall thermal efficiency of the plant allowing 4° F. reduction in temperature during the transference of the condensate from the condenser to the boiler. Neglect pump terms and loss of heat to surrounding air.

The pressure in the condenser is $P_2=14\cdot 7-0\cdot 49\times 27=1\cdot 5$ Lb. per sq. in. abs. Referring to fig. 7.2 and to the energy equation for the condenser, namely $(W_o-W_i)=(H_2-h_w)-r_c$, we get

$$\frac{490\,\frac{\text{lb}_w.}{\text{min.}}\times\frac{1\text{ B.Th.U.}}{\text{lb}_w.\ ^\circ\text{F.}}\times 30^\circ\text{ F.}}{10\,\frac{\text{lb}_s.}{\text{h.p.-hr.}}\times 100\text{ h.p.}\left[\frac{\text{hr.}}{60\text{ min.}}\right]}=882\,\frac{\text{B.Th.U.}}{\text{lb}_s.}=(q_2L_2+h_{w2})-h_w,$$

neglecting, r_c, the small loss of heat to surrounding air.

$$882=q_2\times 1028\cdot 1+83\cdot 7-(104-32)$$

$$\therefore\ q_2=\frac{882-11\cdot 7}{1028\cdot 1}=0\cdot 847.$$

Similarly, for the turbine unit: $B=(H_1-H_2)-r_t$
or, neglecting r_t,

$$B=\frac{\text{h.p.-hr.}}{10\ \text{lb}_s.}\left[\frac{33{,}000\ \text{ft. Lb.}}{\text{h.p.-min.}}\right]\left[\frac{60\ \text{min.}}{\text{hr.}}\right]\left[\frac{\text{B.Th.U.}}{778\ \text{ft.-Lb.}}\right]$$

$$=254\cdot5\ \frac{\text{B.Th.U.}}{\text{lb}_s.}=H_1-H_2$$

i.e. $$254\cdot5\ \frac{\text{B.Th.U.}}{\text{lb}_s.}=H_1-(83\cdot7+0\cdot847\times1028\cdot1)\ \frac{\text{B.Th.U.}}{\text{lb}_s.}$$

Hence, $H_1=1{,}209$ B.Th.U. per lb. of steam supplied.

Reference to the boiler unit shows that the boiler efficiency is given by the ratio $\frac{H_1-h_f}{F}=\eta_B$, hence the potential heat in the fuel supplied to the boiler per lb. of steam delivered is

$$F=\frac{H_1-h_f}{\eta_B}=\frac{1209-(100-32)}{0\cdot8}=1{,}470\ \text{B.Th.U. per lb. of steam.}$$

Thus, the overall efficiency of the plant, neglecting pump terms, is

$$\eta_P=\frac{B}{F}=\frac{254\cdot5}{1470}=0\cdot173\ \text{or}\ 17\cdot3\ \text{per cent.}$$

Example 2.—Find the efficiency of the Rankine cycle of comparison for the previous example and the efficiency ratio if the entropy of the steam entering the engine is $\varphi_1=1\cdot57$ B.Th.U./lb. °F. Neglect the pump term.

The pressure in the condenser is $P_2=1\cdot5$ Lb. per sq. in. abs., hence, from steam tables, $T_{s2}=575\cdot4°$ abs. F., $G_2=6\cdot7$ B.Th.U./lb., and $h_{w2}=83\cdot7$ B.Th.U./lb. After perfect (i.e. reversible) adiabatic expansion the total heat per lb. of steam leaving the Rankine engine would be $H_{2a}=T_{s2}\varphi_{2a}-G_2=T_{s2}\varphi_1-G_2$ since $\varphi_1=\varphi_{2a}$ for reversible adiabatic expansion (see page 474). Thus,

$$H_{2a}=575\cdot4\times1\cdot57-6\cdot7=896\cdot3\ \text{B.Th.U./lb.}$$

and the Rankine efficiency $$=\frac{H_1-H_{2a}}{H_1-h_{w2}}=\frac{1209-896\cdot3}{1209-83\cdot7}=0\cdot278.$$

$$\text{Efficiency ratio}=\frac{17\cdot3}{27\cdot8}=\cdot627\ \text{or}\ 62\cdot7\ \text{per cent.}$$

Example 3.—With the help of steam tables estimate the Rankine efficiency of a plant supplying dry and saturated steam to an engine at 300 Lb. per sq. in. abs. pressure, and condensing at 1 Lb. per sq. in. abs. Show that the "pump term" makes a negligible difference to the answer.

Reversible adiabatic heat drop from the dry and saturated state (see page 494)

$$\left.\right\}\begin{aligned}&=H_{s1}-H_{2a}=\varphi_{s1}(T_{s1}-T_{s2})-(G_1-G_2)\\&=1\cdot6031(877-561\cdot4)-(121\cdot7-4\cdot7)\\&=506-117=389\ \text{B.Th.U. per lb.}\end{aligned}$$

Rankine efficiency (neglecting the pump term)

$$=\frac{H_{s1}-H_{2a}}{H_{s1}-h_{w2}}=\frac{389}{1203\cdot 8-69\cdot 7}=0\cdot 343 \text{ or } 34\cdot 3 \text{ per cent.}$$

The pump term, namely,

$$(P_1-P_2)V_{w2}=(300-1)\frac{\text{Lb.}}{\text{in.}^2}\times 0\cdot 016\,\frac{\text{ft.}^3}{\text{lb.}}\left[\frac{144\text{ in.}^2}{\text{ft.}^2}\right]\left[\frac{\text{B.Th.U.}}{778\text{ ft.-Lb.}}\right]$$

$$=0\cdot 9 \text{ B.Th.U. per lb. of fluid.}$$

$$\text{Rankine efficiency}=\frac{(H_{s1}-H_{2a})-(P_1-P_2)V_{w2}}{(H_{s1}-h_{w2})-(P_1-P_2)V_{w2}}$$

$$=\frac{389-0\cdot 9}{1134\cdot 1-0\cdot 9}=0\cdot 342 \text{ or } 34\cdot 2 \text{ per cent.}$$

CHAPTER 8

THE STEAM ENGINE—SIMPLE AND COMPOUND

1. Energy of a Working Fluid.—We have seen on p. 106 that the "total heat" or enthalpy of any fluid is defined by the equation

$$H=E+PV$$

where E represents the internal energy of the fluid and depends n temperature and molecular kinetic energy, and PV represents nergy contained in the fluid by virtue of its pressure.

Fluid under pressure can be made to do work by virtue of its pressure energy (PV) alone irrespective of any internal energy (E) which it contains by virtue of its temperature. If a fluid contains both pressure energy and internal energy it can be made to do work by giving up parts of both these forms of energy, as, for instance, when steam is used expansively in the cylinder of an engine.

The total energy of a fluid is the sum of the energy due to its total heat, velocity, and height above a datum (see also pp. 251, 305), but changes in the two latter are often negligible in steam plant.

2. Work by Virtue of Pressure Energy Alone.—If, into the cylinder of an engine in which clearance volume is neglected, fluid at pressure P_A be admitted through port A of fig. 8.1 for the full stroke-volume V_K, and then exhausted through the port B at pressure P_B, we have seen on p. 52 that the net work done by the steam per cycle is represented by the area *abcda* on the P,V diagram. That is, in such an engine the fluid, due to its pressure energy alone, will do work $(P_A-P_B)V_K$ per cycle, irrespective of whether or not it possesses any heat energy.

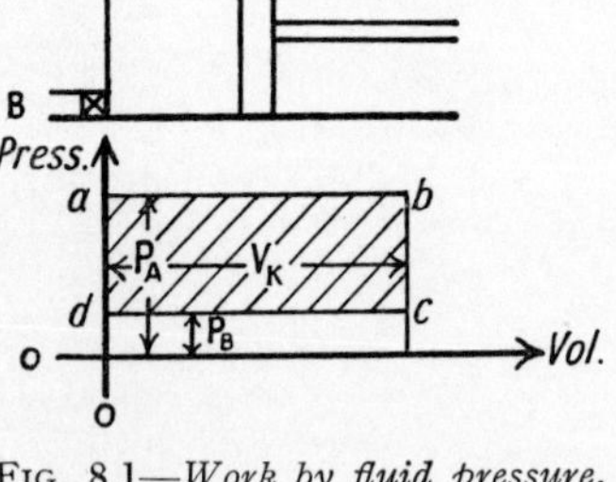

FIG. 8.1—*Work by fluid pressure.*

If the fluid used in this way is steam, the work it will do by virtue of its pressure alone is only a small fraction of the total energy contained in the steam. For example, taking dry saturated steam as the working fluid in the above case (fig. 8.1) with admission pressure P_A=250 Lb. per sq. in. abs. and back pressure P_B=15 Lb. per sq. in. abs., then in a cylinder of volume 1·844 cu. ft. (being the volume of 1 lb. of dry saturated steam at 250 Lb. per sq. in. abs.) the value of

$$(P_A-P_B)V_K \text{ is } (250-1)\frac{\text{Lb.}}{\text{in.}^2}\times 1\cdot 844 \text{ ft.}^3\left[\frac{144 \text{ in.}^2}{\text{ft.}^2}\right]\left[\frac{\text{B.Th.U.}}{778 \text{ ft. Lb.}}\right]$$
$$=80\cdot 21 \text{ B.Th.U.}$$

That is, the work done by the steam due to its pressure energy alone=80·21 B.Th.U. per lb. or 62,402 ft.-Lb. per lb. But the minimum heat which would have to be supplied by the boiler to raise 1 lb. of dry saturated steam at 250 Lb. per sq. in. abs. from feed water only just condensed and pumped from a condenser working at 15 Lb. per sq. in. abs. would be

$$(H_{s1}-h_{w2})=1202\cdot 1-181\cdot 2=1020\cdot 9 \text{ B.Th.U. per lb.}$$

Thus, of the 1020·9 B.Th.U. supplied only 80·2 B.Th.U. are changed into work, *i.e.* the energy utilised is only 7·8 per cent. of the energy required to raise the steam. This is a very low percentage, and shows that the obtaining of work from steam by virtue of its *pressure energy alone* is a very inefficient way of working. A means is therefore sought whereby some of the heat energy as well as the pressure energy of the steam can be utilised.

3. Expansive Working.—If, instead of steam being admitted for the full length of the stroke, the admission steam (*af* of fig. 8.2) is cut off early in the stroke (at *f*) and the steam so enclosed in the cylinder allowed to expand for the remainder (*fr*) of the outstroke until release (at *r*) occurs, and then exhausted for the full instroke (*eb*), the work done by the steam admitted will be represented by the area *afreba*. The area *afmoa* under the admission line *af* is the work done by virtue of the pressure energy of the admission steam; the area *frnmf* under expansion curve *fr* is the work done by the steam at the expense of its internal energy; and the area *nebon* under the exhaust line *eb* is the work done *on* the steam in exhausting it from the cylinder.

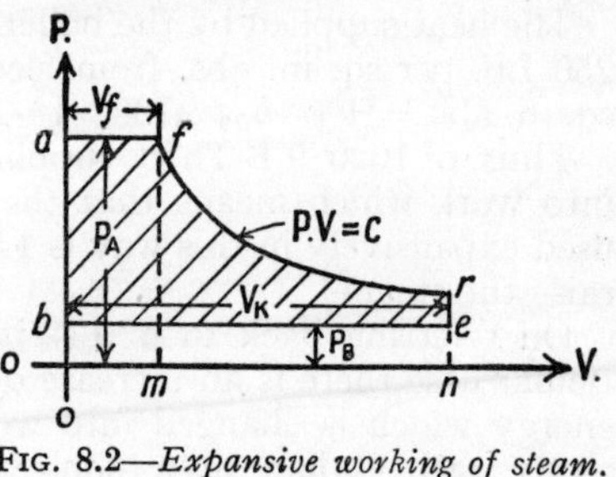

FIG. 8.2—*Expansive working of steam.*

By using steam expansively in this way considerable economy in steam consumption and increase in efficiency are obtained For example, taking the same case as in Paragraph 2, where the admission steam is dry saturated steam at a pressure of 250 Lb. per sq. in. abs. and the exhaust pressure 15 Lb. per sq. in abs. working in a cylinder of volume 1·844 cu. ft. (clearance neglected), suppose cut-off occurs at 0·4 of the stroke, then $V_f = 0{\cdot}4 \times V_K = 0{\cdot}74$ cu. ft. Therefore, the mass of dry saturated steam admitted =mass of volume V_f of dry saturated steam=0·4 lb. The work done by the admission steam up to the point of cut-off (f)=area of $afmoa = P_A V_f = (144 \times 250 \text{ Lb./ft.}^2)\ (0{\cdot}74 \text{ ft.}^3) = 26{,}640$ ft.-Lb. which is the work done by virtue of pressure energy alone. The work done by the steam in expanding (fr) according to the law $PV = c$ from the point of cut-off to the point of release

$$=\text{area } frnmf = P_f V_f \log_e\left(\frac{V_r}{V_f}\right) \text{ (proved on p. 292)}$$

$$=(144 \times 250)\ \frac{\text{Lb.}}{\text{ft.}^2} \times (0{\cdot}74) \text{ ft.}^3 \times \log_e\left(\frac{1}{0{\cdot}4}\right) = 24{,}410 \text{ ft.-Lb.}$$

which is mostly done at the expense of the internal energy of the steam. Thus, the total work done *by* the steam during the outstroke (afr)=area $afrnoa = 26{,}640 + 24{,}410 = 51{,}050$ ft.-Lb. Work done *on* the steam during the instroke or exhaust stroke (eb)

$$=\text{area } nebon = P_B V_K = (144 \times 15)\ \frac{\text{Lb.}}{\text{ft.}^2} \times 1{\cdot}844 \text{ ft.}^3 = 3{,}983 \text{ ft.-Lb.}$$

Thus, the resultant work done by 0·4 lb. of steam admitted =47,067 ft.-Lb. Therefore, the work done by steam working expansively in this way=117,688 ft.-Lb./lb.=151·29 B.Th.U./lb.

The heat supplied by the boiler to raise dry saturated steam at 250 Lb. per sq. in. abs. from feed just condensed at 15 Lb. per sq. in. abs. $= H_{s1} - h_{w2} = 1202{\cdot}1 - 181{\cdot}2 = 1020{\cdot}9$ B.Th.U./lb.

Thus, of 1020·9 B.Th.U. supplied, 151·29 B.Th.U. are changed into work which means that the energy utilised when steam is used expansively in this way is 14·8 per cent. of that required to raise the steam.

On referring back to p. 137 it will be seen that in this particular case there is an increase of 14·8−7·8=7 per cent. in the energy which is changed into work by using the steam expansively rather than in a non-expansive way. Because of this increase in efficiency, steam engines are always worked expansively. There are various valve gears in use for giving an early cut-off of admission steam. Variable cut-off mechanisms are often used, and particularly on locomotives which may be required to develop great powers for short periods, as happens when mounting inclines—the steam then being admitted to the cylinder at full pressure for the greater part of the stroke without regard to efficiency or economy in consumption of steam and fuel. But this is not the way in which steam is used for any length of time in well-managed engines, for although more work per cycle is obtained (though less is done per lb.) by using steam non-expansively, it is being dearly paid for because the efficiency is low. The difference in work per cycle and in thermal efficiency can be seen by comparing the example worked in this paragraph and in paragraph 2. It will be found that 88 per cent. more work per lb. of steam is obtained by using steam expansively.

4. Hypothetical and Actual Indicator Diagrams of a Steam Engine.—*Hypothetical Indicator Diagrams.*—If the critical events in the cycle of a steam engine took place instantaneously, the resulting P,V diagrams would have sharp corners at cut-off, release, exhaust, and admission. Figs. 8.2 and 8.3 illustrate two such diagrams without compression curves. These are known as hypothetical diagrams—being diagrams we get by hypothesis or from theoretical considerations. Such diagrams are never obtained in practice, for actual indicator diagrams differ from theoretical diagrams in that they have rounded corners at the critical points and also have compression curves before admission as in fig. 8.5.

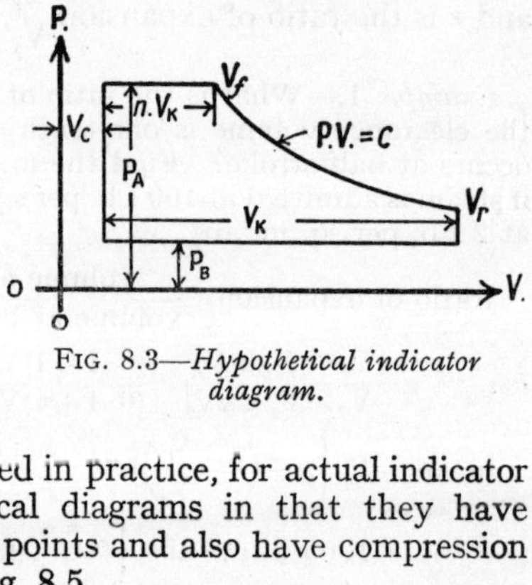

FIG. 8.3—*Hypothetical indicator diagram.*

The m.e.p. of the theoretical or hypothetical indicator diagram shown in fig. 8.2 which neglects the effect of clearance volume,

$$=\frac{\text{area of diagram}}{\text{length of diagram}}$$

$$\textit{i.e.}\ \textbf{m.e.p.}=\frac{P_AV_f+P_AV_f\log_\varepsilon\left(\dfrac{V_r}{V_f}\right)-P_BV_K}{V_K}=\mathbf{P_A}\left(\frac{\mathbf{1+\log_\varepsilon}\ r}{r}\right)-\mathbf{P_B}$$

where r is the ratio of expansion $\dfrac{V_K}{V_f}$ of fig. 8.2.

A probable m.e.p. for an actual engine is sometimes estimated from this hypothetical m.e.p. by multiplying the latter by a "diagram factor" which takes into account the rounding-off of the corners and the effect of compression, all of which appear on actual diagrams. The numerical value taken for the diagram factor in any particular case is based on experience from tests made on actual plant.

The m.e.p. of the hypothetical diagram of fig. 8.3, which takes clearance volume into account, will be:

$$\frac{P_A n V_K + P_A(V_C + nV_K)\log_\varepsilon\left(\frac{V_r}{V_f}\right) - P_B V_K}{V_K}$$

$$i.e.\quad \textbf{m.e.p.} = P_A\left\{n + \left(n + \frac{V_C}{V_K}\right)\log_\varepsilon r\right\} - P_B$$

where n is the fraction of the stroke at which cut-off takes place, and r is the ratio of expansion $\frac{V_r}{V_f}$, or $\frac{V_C+V_K}{V_C+nV_K}$.

Example 1.—What is the ratio of expansion in an engine in which the clearance volume is one-tenth the stroke volume when cut off occurs at half stroke? Find the m.e.p. of the hypothetical diagram if steam is admitted at 100 Lb. per sq. in. abs. and exhaust takes place at 2 Lb. per sq. in. abs.

$$\text{Ratio of expansion} = \frac{\text{volume at end of expansion}}{\text{volume at beginning of expansion}}$$

$$i.e.\qquad r = \frac{V_r}{V_f} = \frac{V_c+V_k}{V_c+nV_k} = \frac{(0\cdot1+1)V_k}{(0\cdot1+n)V_k} = \frac{1\cdot1}{0\cdot1+0\cdot5} = \frac{11}{6}$$

$$\text{m.e.p.} = P_A\left\{n + \left(n + \frac{V_c}{V_k}\right)\log_\varepsilon r\right\} - P_B$$

$$= 100\ \text{Lb./in.}^2\ \text{abs.}\left\{0\cdot5 + (0\cdot5+0\cdot1)\log_\varepsilon\frac{11}{6}\right\} - 2\ \text{Lb./in.}^2\ \text{abs.}$$

$$= 84\cdot36\ \text{Lb. per sq. in.}$$

Actual Indicator Diagrams.—Fig. 8.4 shows an actual indicator diagram superimposed on a hypothetical diagram. It will be seen that admission occurs slightly before inner dead centre at *a*, after which the pressure in the cylinder rises rapidly to *b*. From *b* to the cut-off point *f* there is usually a slight fall in pressure, depending on the speed at which the engine is running and on the restriction of the port opening which throttles the steam in a way known as "*wire-drawing.*" The points of cut-off and release cannot be instantaneous in an actual engine, hence there is a rounding-off of the corners at *f* and *r*. It will be seen from the diagram that release occurs before outer dead centre, so that there is a fall in pressure during the remainder of the stroke *re* before the exhaust period *ec* is commenced. The point of compression *c* occurs well before inner dead centre in order to trap the "cushion steam" in the cylinder which, as it is compressed, helps to bring the reciprocating parts to rest at the dead centre point. Also the pressure, and therefore the temperature, of the steam in the cylinder during the compression period from *c* to *a* are raised due to compression before high-pressure steam, of high temperature, is again admitted at *a*.

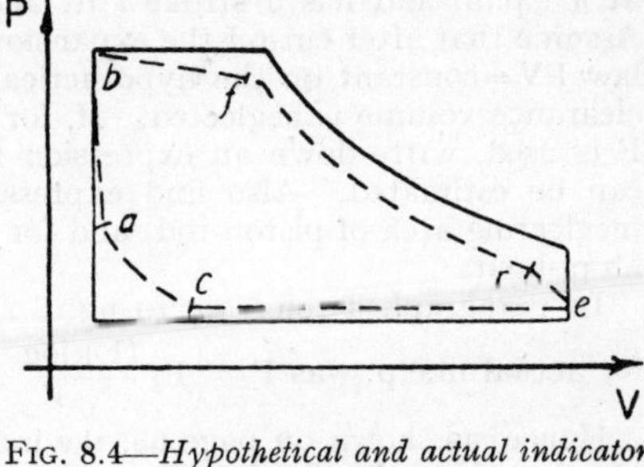

Fig. 8.4—*Hypothetical and actual indicator diagrams.*

It is evident from fig. 8.4 that the actual indicator diagram is less than the hypothetical one. **The diagram factor will be:**

$$\frac{\textbf{area of actual diagram}}{\textbf{area of hypothetical diagram}} \text{ or } \frac{\textbf{actual m.e.p.}}{\textbf{hypothetical m.e.p.}}$$

Fig. 8.5 shows an actual indicator diagram taken from a vertical double-acting steam engine, both ends of the cylinder being

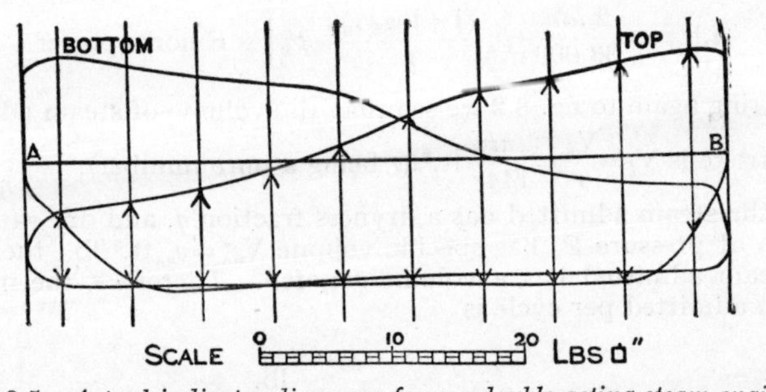

Fig. 8.5—*Actual indicator diagrams from a double acting steam engine.*

indicated on the same card by the same indicator. The m.e.p.s of the two diagrams are found by the mid-ordinate method in which the atmospheric line AB is divided into ten equal strips and then the mean height of the mid-ordinates (shown in fig. 8.5) of these strips is found. From the mean height and the scale of the diagrams, the m.e.ps. are found to be 10·85 Lb. per sq. in. for the diagram recorded from the top of the cylinder and 11·18 Lb. per sq. in. for the bottom diagram.

Example 2.—A single-cylinder double-acting steam engine runs at n r.p.m. and has a stroke l ft. and an area of piston a sq. in. Assume that after cut-off the expansion curve follows the hyperbolic law PV=constant on the hypothetical indicator diagram on which clearance volume is neglected. If, for this engine, a diagram factor F is used, write down an expression from which the actual m.e.p. can be estimated. Also find expressions for the i.h.p. developed (neglecting area of piston rod) and for steam consumption in lb. per i.h.p.-hour.

In paragraph 4 referring to fig. 8.2 we saw that the expression for actual m.e.p. was $P=\left\{P_A\dfrac{(1+\log_\varepsilon r)}{r}-P_B\right\}\times F.$

Hence, as shown on page 63, the indicated power is given by the physical formula $\mathcal{P}_i$=PLAC, and the indicated horse-power by the numerical formula $i=\dfrac{plac}{33{,}000}=2\dfrac{plan}{33{,}000}$ where symbols in the latter formula represent numbers only—

p being the number of Lb./in.^{2};
l the number of ft. in the stroke;
a the number of in.^{2} of piston area;
and n the number of revs./min. of the crank.

Thus, for this steam engine the

$$\text{i.h.p.}=\frac{2\,lan}{33{,}000}\left\{p_A\frac{(1+\log_\varepsilon r)}{r}-p_B\right\}\times F \text{ horse-power.}$$

Referring again to fig. 8.2 we see that the volume of steam admitted per stroke is $V_f=\dfrac{V_K}{r}=\dfrac{al}{144r}$ ft.^{3} (r being a pure number).

If the steam admitted has a dryness fraction q, and dry saturated steam at pressure P_A has specific volume $V_{SA}=v_{SA}$ft.^{3}/lb., then 1 lb. of steam admitted has a volume qv_{SA} ft.^{3}. Therefore, the mass of steam admitted per cycle is

$$\frac{V_f}{qV_{SA}}=\frac{al}{144rqv_{SA}}\text{ lb.}$$

Hence, the theoretical rate at which steam is used by the engine, which traces cycles with a frequency C=2n/min. or 120n/hour is

$$\frac{V_fC}{qV_{SA}}=\frac{120aln}{144rqv_{SA}}\text{ lb./hour.}$$

and, since the number of indicated horse-power is $i=\dfrac{2plan}{33{,}000}$, the

the theoretical consumption of steam may be expressed in a physical or numerical formula as

$$\frac{V_f C}{q V_{SA} P_i} \text{ or } \frac{120aln}{144irqv_{SA}} \text{ lb./h.p.-hour} = \frac{120aln \times 33{,}000}{144 \times 2planrqv_{SA}} \text{ lb./h.p.-hour}$$

$$= \frac{13{,}750}{prqv_{SA}} \text{ lb./h.p.-hour, respectively.}$$

It is found from steam tables that the product $P_A V_{SA}$, and therefore the numerical value pv_{SA} remains nearly constant over a range of pressure used in ordinary reciprocating steam engines and, therefore, we deduce that the consumption of steam per i.h.p.-hour remains nearly constant in engines of fixed expansion ratio, r.

Willans demonstrated the truth of this by testing steam engines of constant cut-off and governed by throttling the incoming steam. The straight line resulting from plotting weight of steam consumed per hour against i.h.p. is known as the Willans Line.

Example 3.—The dimensions of the above engine are: stroke 18 in., piston diameter 12 in., and the speed is 150 r.p.m. Calculate the actual m.e.p. if the admission pressure is 100 Lb. per sq. in. abs. and exhaust pressure 15 Lb. per sq. in. abs., when cut-off takes place at half stroke and the diagram factor is 0·75. Calculate also the i.h.p. of the engine and the consumption in lb. per i.h.p.-hour if the dryness fraction of the steam admitted to the engine is 0·98.

$$\text{M.e.p.} = \left\{P_A\left(\frac{1+\log_\varepsilon r}{r}\right) - P_B\right\} \times F = \left\{100\left(\frac{1+\log_\varepsilon 2}{2}\right) - 15\right\} \times 0 \cdot 75$$

$$= (69 \cdot 66) \times (0 \cdot 75) = 52 \cdot 25 \text{ Lb. per sq. in.}$$

$$\text{Hence, } i = \frac{2(\text{m.e.p.})lan}{33{,}000} = \frac{2(52 \cdot 25)\frac{18}{12}\left(\frac{\pi}{4}144\right)150}{33{,}000} = 80 \cdot 6$$

and thus, i.h.p. = 80·6 h.p.

$$\text{Steam consumption} = \frac{13{,}750}{rqv_{SA}(\text{m.e.p.})} = \frac{13{,}750}{2 \times 0 \cdot 98 \times 4 \cdot 429 \times 52 \cdot 25}$$

$$= 30 \cdot 3 \text{ lb. per i.h.p.-hour.}$$

Example 4.—Describe the hypothetical diagram used in determining the dimensions of reciprocating steam engine cylinders and state the assumptions made in the construction of the diagram.

A double-acting single-cylinder steam engine has a piston 30 in. diameter and a stroke of 3 ft. 3 in. The engine runs at 100 r.p.m. and develops 550 i.h.p. If the initial steam pressure is 155 Lb. per sq. in. abs. and exhaust is at 2 Lb. per sq. in. abs., cut-off taking place at one-twelfth of the stroke, determine the diagram factor. The effect of the diameter of the piston rod may be neglected.

[Part I, B.Sc. Lond.]

$$\text{Hypothetical m.e.p.} = P_A\left(\frac{1+\log_\varepsilon r}{r}\right) - P_B$$

$$\text{or } P = p\text{ Lb. per sq. in.} = 155\left(\frac{1+\log_\varepsilon 12}{12}\right) - 2 = 43 \text{ Lb. per sq. in.}$$

Hence, $$i = \frac{2(Fp)lan}{33{,}000} = 550$$

∴ The diagram factor

$$F = \frac{33{,}000i}{2plan} = \frac{33{,}000 \times 550}{2 \times 43 \times 3\cdot25 \times \pi \times 225 \times 100} = 0\cdot917.$$

Example 5.—Steam is admitted to an engine for 0·3 of the stroke with a pressure 100 Lb. per sq. in. abs.; the law of expansion which it follows is $PV^{1\cdot15}$=constant. Compression commences at 0·6 of the return stroke and follows the law $PV^{1\cdot3}$=constant. The clearance volume is 20 per cent. of the displacement, and the back pressure 25·9 in. vacuum (barometer 30·0 in.). Estimate the mean effective pressure and the indicated horse-power of a double-acting engine with cylinder diameter 12 in., stroke 18 in., and speed 200 r.p.m.

[I.Mech.E., Sec. A.]

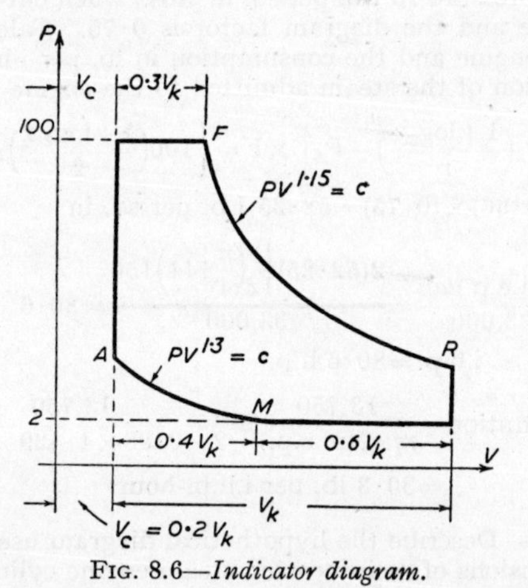

FIG. 8.6—*Indicator diagram.*

$$\text{Back pressure} = (30\cdot0 - 25\cdot9)\text{ in. Hg}\left[\frac{0\cdot49 \text{ Lb./in.}^2}{1 \text{ in. Hg}}\right]$$

$$= 2 \text{ Lb. per sq. in. abs.}$$

Referring to fig. 8.6, the pressure at release is

$$P_R = P_F\left(\frac{V_F}{V_R}\right)^{1\cdot15} = 100\left(\frac{0\cdot5\,V_K}{1\cdot2\,V_K}\right)^{1\cdot15} = 36\cdot5 \text{ Lb. per sq. in. abs.,}$$

and the pressure at the end of compression is

$$P_A = P_M\left(\frac{V_M}{V_A}\right)^{1\cdot3} = 2\left(\frac{0\cdot6\,V_K}{0\cdot2\,V_K}\right)^{1\cdot3} = 8\cdot34 \text{ Lb. per sq. in. abs.}$$

$$\text{m.e.p.} = \frac{\text{area of indicator diagram}}{V_K} = P$$

$$= \left\{(100\times0\cdot3) + \left(\frac{100\times\cdot5 - 36\cdot5\times1\cdot2}{0\cdot15}\right)\right\} - \left\{(2\times0\cdot6+)\left(\frac{8\cdot34\times0\cdot2 - 2\times0\cdot6}{0\cdot3}\right)\right\}$$

$$= [30+41\cdot3] - [1\cdot2+1\cdot57] \text{ Lb./in.}^2$$

i.e. $P = 68\cdot53$ Lb. per sq. in. $= p$ Lb. per sq. in.

$$\text{Hence,} \quad i = \frac{2plan}{33{,}000} = \frac{2\times68\cdot53\times1\cdot5\times(\pi\times36)\times200}{33{,}000}$$

$= 141$, *i.e.* indicated power $= 141$ h.p. $= \mathcal{P}_i$

Alternatively, indicated power is $\mathcal{P}_i = PLAC$

$$= 68\cdot53\,\frac{\text{Lb.}}{\text{in.}^2}\times1\cdot5\text{ ft.}\times\pi\times36\text{ in.}^2\times\frac{400}{\text{min.}}\left[\frac{\text{h.p. min.}}{33{,}000\text{ ft.-Lb.}}\right] = 141\text{ h.p.}$$

5. REPORT ON SIMPLE STEAM ENGINE TRIAL

Object of Trial

To obtain a power-consumption curve, thermal and mechanical efficiency curves for the engine when tested over the range of power output from no load to full load. Also to draw up a heat account or heat balance sheet for the engine.

The Plant

(*a*) *Diagrammatic Sketch or Line Diagram.*—This is shown in fig. 8.7, from which the energy equation and energy stream diagram for the engine can be deduced.

The engine under test has been enclosed within an imaginary boundary. Assuming that the plant has been running long enough for conditions to have become steady, the rate at which energy flows into the boundary must equal the rate at which energy flows out of the boundary.

(*b*) *Energy Equation and Energy Stream Diagram for the Plant.*—The energy streams flowing into and out of the boundary of fig. 8.7 are indicated by means of arrows with attendant letters representing the rate at which energy flows along the respective

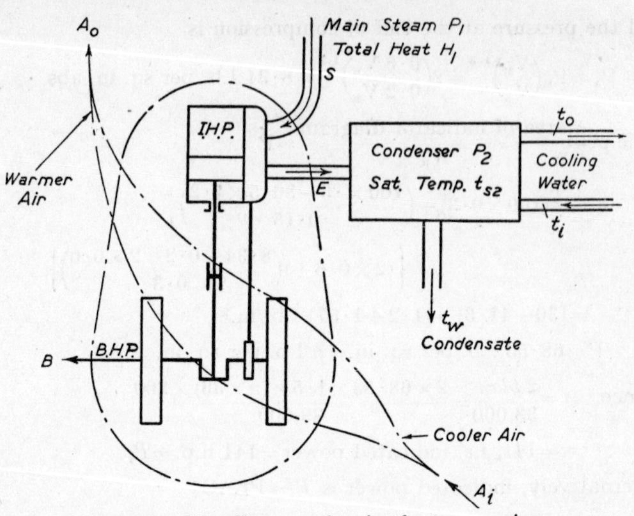

FIG. 8.7—*Line diagram of a simple steam engine.*

streams and from which the following energy equation can be deduced:—

$$S+A_i=B+E+A_o$$

Rearranged, the energy equation can be written:

$$S=B+E+(A_o-A_i)$$

and, if the total heat (h_{w2}) per. lb. of water at the condenser pressure (P_2) is taken as the datum from which to reckon the energy in the stream, the energy diagram can be drawn up as follows:—

HEAT SUPPLIED TO ENGINE PER MINUTE

(Stream S)

[lb. of steam per min. $\times (H_1-h_{w2})$]

HEAT TRANSFORMED INTO WORK PER MIN.	HEAT CARRIED AWAY PER MIN. BY EXHAUST STEAM	HEAT LOST PER MIN. TO SURROUNDING AIR
(Stream B)	(Stream E)	(Stream (A_o-A_i))
[Heat equivalent of b.h.p.]	[Mass of cooling water/min. $\times (t_o-t_i)$ − mass of condensate/min. $\times (t_{s2}-t_w)$]	[Obtained by difference]

Also, since indicated horse-power splits into brake horse-power and friction horse-power, we may write:—

$$\text{i.h.p.} = \left(\frac{\{p_o A + p_i(A - a)\}ln}{33{,}000}\right)\text{h.p.}$$

b.h.p.

$$\left(\frac{2\pi(w-s)\left(r+\frac{d}{2}\right)n}{33{,}000}\right)\text{h.p.}$$

f.h.p.

(i.h.p. − b.h.p.)

(c) *Description of Plant and Method of Testing.*—The engine tested was a vertical single-cylinder double-acting steam engine actuated by a simple D slide valve similar to that illustrated by fig. 2.2. Steam was supplied direct from a Lancashire boiler and the exhaust was led into a condenser working at atmospheric pressure. The mass of steam used per minute was obtained by weighing the condensate as it was rejected from the condenser. The rate at which cooling water flowed through the condenser, together with temperatures at inlet and outlet, were noted. Indicated horse-power was estimated from diagrams which were taken with a spring and piston indicator, and the brake horse-power was obtained by means of a rope brake. The dryness fraction of the main steam was taken as unity. Five tests were made over the range from 5 b.h.p. to no load, each of 20 minutes' duration, and simultaneous observations were made on all the instruments every 2 minutes.

REPORT SHEET FOR TRIAL ON SIMPLE STEAM ENGINE

Engine Data:—Piston Diameter, 8·47 in. Stroke, 1·01 ft. Piston Rod Diameter, 1·45 in. Brake Weight Radius, 1·95 ft.

DATE OF TRIAL

Number of Test.		1	2	3	4	5
Duration of Test.	min.	20	20	20	20	20
Power.						
Revolutions per minute, n		120	119·5	120	119·5	120
Mean effective pressure (outstroke), po,	Lb. per sq. in.	15·1	12·1	7·9	5·4	2·5
Mean effective pressure (instroke), pi,	Lb. per sq. in.	14·0	11·3	7·4	5·6	2·4
I.h.p. $=\dfrac{(poA+pi(A-a))ln}{33,000}$ h.p.		5·92	4·74	3·14	2·22	1·01
Brake weight—Spring balance, $(w-s)$,	Lb.	111·4	78·06	44·46	26·9	0
B.h.p. $=\dfrac{2\pi(w-s)\left(r+\dfrac{d}{2}\right)n}{33,000}$ h.p.		4·98	3·47	1·98	1·19	0
Heat equivalent of b.h.p.	B.Th.U. per min.	211·5	147·0	84·0	50·5	0
Heat to Exhaust.						
Weight of cooling water per minute,	Lb.	105	99	99·5	100	100
Inlet temperature of cooling water, t_i,	°C.	6·76	6·81	6·99	7·10	7·05
Outlet temperature of cooling water, t_o,	°C.	33·34	31·20	27·06	24·29	19·66
Rise in temperature of cooling water, $(t_o-t_i)\times\frac{9}{5}$	°F.	47·8	43·8	36·2	30·9	22·7
Heat given to cooling water per minute,	B.Th.U.	5,019	4,336	3,602	3,090	2,270
Weight of condensate per minute	Lb.	5·65	4·78	3·85	3·19	2·41
Temperature of condensate leaving condenser, tw,	°F.	154·5	148	143·2	140·2	136·3
Saturation temperature t_{s2} corresponding to condenser pressure,	°F.	212	212	212	212	212
Undercooling of condensate $=(t_{s2}-tw)$.		57·5	64	68·7	71·8	75·7
Heat given to cooling water per minute in undercooling from ts_2 to tw	B.Th.U.	325	306	264	229	183
Heat to exhaust per minute reckoned from hw_2 (*i.e.* temperature t_{s2})	B.Th.U.	4,694	4,030	3,338	2,861	2,087

Heat Supplied.						
Mass of steam used per minute,	lb.	5·65	4·78	3·85	3·19	2·41
Gauge pressure of steam in valve chest,	Lb. per sq. in.	26·1	20·8	15·7	12·5	10·1
Atmospheric pressure (30 in. Hg),	Lb. per sq. in.	←		14·7		→
Absolute steam pressure, p_1,	Lb. per sq. in.	40·8	35·5	30·4	27·2	24·8
Absolute pressure in condenser, p_2,	Lb. per sq. in.	14·7	14·7	14·7	14·7	14·7
Total heat of 1 lb. dry saturated steam at p_1, (Hs_1).	B.Th.U.	1170·9	1167·9	1164·8	1162·7	1160·8
Total heat of 1 lb. water at p_2, (hw_2),	B.Th.U.	180·1	180·1	180·1	180·1	180·1
Heat supplied to 1 lb. dry saturated steam, reckoned from $hw_2 = (Hs_1 - hw_2)$,	B.Th.U.	990·8	987·8	984·7	982·6	980·7
Heat supplied to engine per minute, reckoned from hw_2 = mass of steam per minute × ($Hs_1 - hw_2$),	B.Th.U.	5,600	4,725	3,785	3,135	2,365
Heat Account (in B.Th.U. per minute reckoned from hw_2 as datum).						
Heat supplied to engine.		5,600	4,725	3,785	3,135	2,365
Heat equivalent of b.h.p.		211·5	147	84	50·5	0
Heat to exhaust.		4,694	4,030	3,338	2,861	2,087
Heat to surrounding air (by difference).		694·5	548	363	223·5	278
		5,600	4,725	3,785	3,135	2,365
Efficiencies.						
Mechanical efficiency,	per cent.	84·2	73·2	63·5	53·6	0
Thermal efficiency (b.h.p. basis),	per cent.	3·78	3·12	2·21	1·62	0
Thermal efficiency (i.h.p. basis),	per cent.	4·48	4·25	3·48	3·00	1·82
Rankine Efficiency $\left(\frac{H_{s1} - H_{a2}}{H_{s1} - h_{w2}}\right)$,	per cent.	7·4	6·5	5·39	4·64	3·8
Relative efficiency (b.h.p. basis),	per cent.	51	48·1	41·0	34·9	0
Relative efficiency (i.h.p. basis),	per cent.	60·5	65·4	64·5	64·6	47·8
Deductions.						
Horse-power absorbed in friction.		0·94	1·27	1·14	1·03	1·01
Proportion of heat supplied absorbed in friction,	per cent.	0·71	1·14	1·27	1·39	1·81
Steam used per b.h.p.-hour,	lb.	68·1	82·7	116·5	161·0	∞
Steam used per i.h.p.-hour,	lb.	57·3	60·6	74·0	86·2	143·0

SPECIMEN SET OF CALCULATIONS FOR TEST I

Indicated Horse-power.

Piston diameter $= 8 \cdot 47$ in.

$\therefore$ piston area (A) $= \frac{\pi}{4}(8 \cdot 47)^2 = 56 \cdot 1$ sq. in.

Piston rod diameter $= 1 \cdot 45$ in.

$\therefore$ piston rod area (a) $= \frac{\pi}{4}(1 \cdot 45)^2 = 1 \cdot 65$ sq. in.

M.e.p. (outstroke) $= 15 \cdot 1$ Lb. per sq. in. $= P_o$. Stroke $= 1 \cdot 01$ ft. $=$ L. M.e.p. (instroke) $= 14 \cdot 0$ Lb. per sq. in. $= P_i$. R.p.m. $= 120$.

$\therefore$ Indicated power $= \mathcal{P}_i = \{P_o A + P_i(A - a)\} LN$

(which is a physical formula) or using the corresponding numerical formula we get

$$i = \left\{ \frac{15 \cdot 1 \times 56 \cdot 1 + 14 \cdot 0(56 \cdot 1 - 1 \cdot 65)}{33{,}000} \right\} \times 1 \cdot 01 \times 120$$

$= 5 \cdot 92$. Hence, indicated power $= \mathcal{P}_i =$ i.h.p. $= 5 \cdot 92$ h.p.

Brake Horse-power.

Net brake load $= 111 \cdot 4$ Lb. acting at radius $1 \cdot 95$ ft. Hence, using the numerical formula for the number of brake horse-power b, we get

$$b = \frac{2\pi t n}{33{,}000} = \frac{2\pi \times (111 \cdot 4 \times 1 \cdot 95) \times 120}{33{,}000} = 4 \cdot 98$$

$\therefore$ Heat equivalent of b.h.p. $= 4 \cdot 98$ h.p. $\left[\frac{33{,}000 \text{ ft.-Lb.}}{\text{h.p. min.}}\right]\left[\frac{\text{B.Th.U.}}{778 \text{ ft.-Lb.}}\right]$

$= 211 \cdot 5$ B.Th.U./min.

Heat of Exhaust.

Heat given to cooling water per minute $=$ mass of cooling water flowing per minute $\times$ specific heat $\times$ rise in temperature

$$= 105 \frac{\text{lb.}}{\text{min.}} \times \frac{1 \text{ B.Th.U.}}{\text{lb.}^\circ \text{ F.}} \times 47 \cdot 8^\circ \text{ F.} = 5{,}019 \frac{\text{B.Th.U.}}{\text{min.}}$$

Weight of condensate leaving condenser per minute $= 5 \cdot 65$ Lb. at temperature $t_w = 154 \cdot 5^\circ$ F.

Saturation temperature corresponding to pressure $14 \cdot 7$ Lb. per sq. in. abs. in condenser $= 212^\circ$ F. $= t_{s2}$ $\therefore$ undercooling of condensate $= (t_{s2} - t_w) = 212 - 154 \cdot 5 = 57 \cdot 5^\circ$ F.

$\therefore$ Heat given to cooling water in undercooling the condensate from 212° F. to $154 \cdot 5^\circ$ F. $= 5 \cdot 65 \times 57 \cdot 5 = 325$ B.Th.U. per min.

$\therefore$ Heat to exhaust reckoned from datum t_{s2} or h_{w2} is $5{,}019 - 325 = 4{,}694$ B.Th.U. per min.

Heat Supplied.

Total heat of dry saturated steam at $P_1 = 40 \cdot 8$ Lb. per sq. in. abs., is $H_{s1} = 1170 \cdot 9$ B.Th.U./lb.

Total heat of water at $P_2 = 14 \cdot 7$ Lb. per sq. in. abs. is $h_{w2} = 180 \cdot 1$ B.Th.U./lb.

$\therefore$ Heat supplied to dry saturated steam reckoned from $h_{w2} = 1170 \cdot 9 - 180 \cdot 1 = 990 \cdot 8$ B.Th.U./lb. $= H_{s1} - h_{w2}$

Mass of steam supplied $= 5 \cdot 65$ lb./min.

$\therefore$ Heat supplied to engine reckoned from $h_{w2} = 5 \cdot 65 \times 990 \cdot 8 = 5{,}600$ B.Th.U./min.

Efficiencies.

$$\text{Mechanical efficiency} = \frac{\text{b.h.p.}}{\text{i.h.p.}} = \frac{4 \cdot 98}{5 \cdot 92} = 84 \cdot 2 \text{ per cent.}$$

$$\text{Thermal efficiency (b.h.p. basis)} = \frac{\text{heat equivalent of b.h.p.}}{\text{heat supplied}}$$

$$= \frac{117 \cdot 4}{3{,}120} = 3 \cdot 78 \text{ per cent.}$$

Thermal efficiency (i.h.p. basis)

$$= \frac{\text{heat equivalent of i.h.p.}}{\text{heat supplied}} = \frac{5 \cdot 92 \times \frac{33{,}000}{778}}{5{,}600} = 4 \cdot 48 \text{ per cent.}$$

Reversible Adiabatic Heat Drop, $H_{s1} - H_{2a}$.

Using the formula $H_{2a} - T_{s2}\varphi_{2a} - G_2$, we first find from the steam tables for dry saturated steam at $P_1 = 40 \cdot 8$ Lb. per sq. in. abs. that $\varphi_{s1} = 1 \cdot 6792$ B.Th.U./lb. °F. $= \varphi_{2a}$ after reversible adiabatic expansion. At $P_2 = 14 \cdot 7$ Lb. per sq. in. abs.; $T_{s2} = 671 \cdot 7$ abs. °F. and $G_2 = 29 \cdot 4$ B.Th.U./lb.

$\therefore$ $H_{2a} = (671 \cdot 7 \times 1 \cdot 6792 - 29 \cdot 4)$B.Th.U./lb. $= 1098 \cdot 1$ B.Th.U./lb.

H_{s1} (at $P_1 = 40 \cdot 8$ Lb. per sq. in. abs.) $= 1170 \cdot 9$ B.Th.U./lb.

$\therefore$ Reversible adiabatic heat drop $= 1170 \cdot 9 - 1098 \cdot 1 = 72 \cdot 8$ B.Th.U./lb.

$$\therefore \text{Rankine efficiency} = \frac{H_{s1} - H_{2a}}{H_{s1} - h_{w2}} = \frac{72 \cdot 8}{990 \cdot 8} = 7 \cdot 4 \text{ per cent.}$$

$\therefore$ Relative thermal efficiency (b.h.p. basis) or efficiency ratio $= \dfrac{3 \cdot 78}{7 \cdot 4} = 51$ per cent.

and relative thermal efficiency (i.h.p. basis) $= \dfrac{4 \cdot 48}{7 \cdot 4} = 60 \cdot 5$ per cent.

GRAPHICAL REPRESENTATION OF RESULTS

(a) Engine Curves

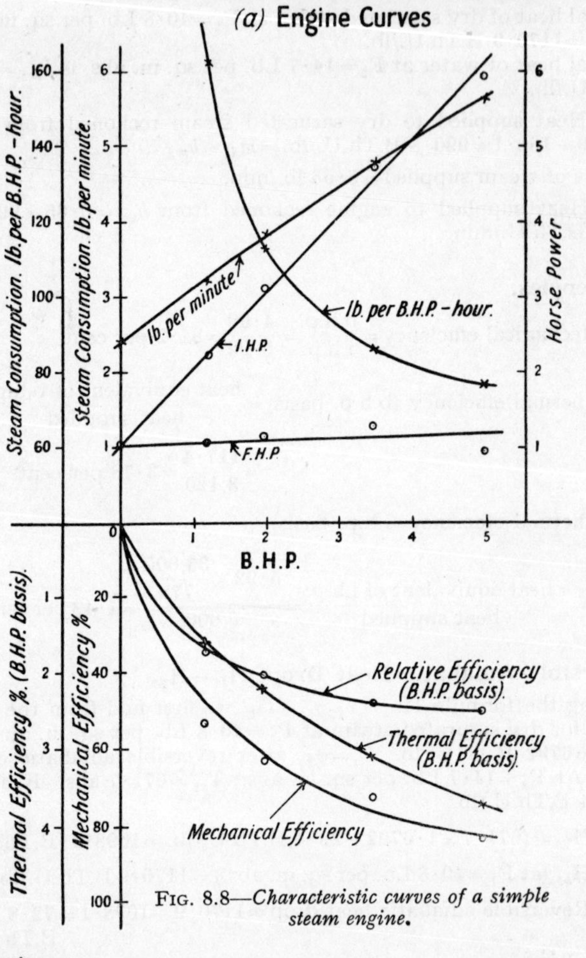

FIG. 8.8—*Characteristic curves of a simple steam engine.*

Deductions.

Horse-power absorbed in friction $=5\cdot92-4\cdot98=0\cdot94$.

Percentage of heat supplied absorbed in friction

$$=\frac{0\cdot94\text{ h.p.}\left[\dfrac{33{,}000\text{ ft.-Lb.}}{\text{h.p. min.}}\right]\left[\dfrac{\text{B.Th.U.}}{778\text{ ft.-Lb.}}\right]\times100}{5{,}600\ \dfrac{\text{B.Th.U.}}{\text{min.}}}=0\cdot71\text{ per cent.}$$

$$\text{Steam used} = 5\cdot 65\ \frac{\text{lb.}}{\text{min.}}\left[\frac{60\ \text{min.}}{\text{hour}}\right] = 339\ \text{lb./hr.}$$

$$\therefore\ \text{Steam used per b.h.p.-hour} = \frac{339}{4\cdot 98} = 68\cdot 1\ \text{lb.}$$

$$\therefore\ \text{Steam used per i.h.p.-hour} = \frac{339}{5\cdot 92} = 57\cdot 3\ \text{lb.}$$

CONCLUSIONS AND CRITICISMS

It will be seen from the engine curves, fig. 8.8, that at about 5 b.h.p. the consumption of steam per b.h.p.-hour is approaching a minimum value—that is, at this power the engine requires a less amount of steam to do the definite amount of work 1 b.h.p.-hour (1,980,000 ft.-Lb.) than at any other power. To run the engine at about 5 b.h.p. will therefore be the most economical power. It should be noticed that at this power the relative thermal efficiency is a maximum and also the thermal efficiency curve on the b.h.p. basis would reach a maximum at about 5 b.h.p.

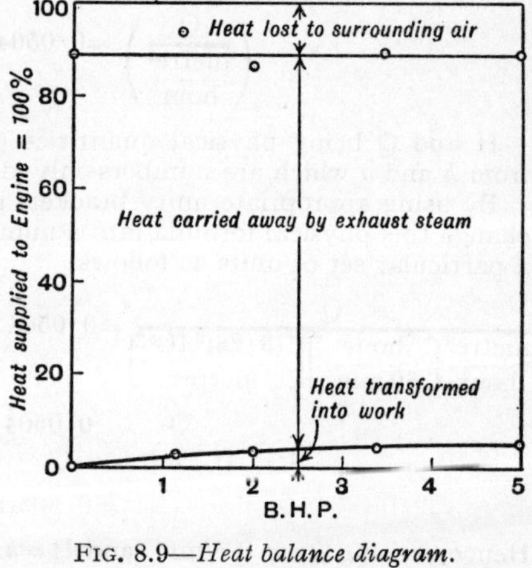

FIG. 8.9—*Heat balance diagram.*

The low thermal efficiency that results from this trial should be particularly noticed, e.g. as shown in fig. 8.9. The reasons for this can be seen when reference is made to figures on the report sheet. There it will be seen that the trial was run at low steam pressures and that exhaust took place at atmospheric pressure—thus not making use of the advantage of the vacuum that can be obtained in a condenser. Also it should be noticed that the valve was a simple D slide valve. These three factors are the reasons for the low thermal efficiency and high steam consumption of the engine.

In steam plant the rate of flow of cooling water through condensers is relatively large, and in many cases may be estimated by measuring the head of water flowing over a notch.

Example.—The empirical formula for a 90 degree Vee notch was found, in metric units, to be $\boldsymbol{q=0\cdot0504h^{5/2}}$ where q is the number of cubic metres of water flowing per hour when h is measured in centimetres. Convert this formula to one in which the head h may be measured in inches and q represents the number of cubic ft. of water flowing over the notch per minute.

The given empirical formula (which is a numerical formula) can be converted into a physical formula in which Q and H represent rate of volumetric flow and head, unrestricted by any system of units. Thus, in the particular metric units used $Q=q\,\frac{\text{metre}^3}{\text{hour}}$ and $H=h$ cm., and the given empirical formula may be re-written as

$$\left(\frac{Q}{\frac{\text{metre}^3}{\text{hour}}}\right)=0\cdot0504\left(\frac{H}{\text{cm.}}\right)^{5/2}$$

—H and Q being physical quantities (numbers × units) as distinct from h and q which are numbers only (dependent on the units used).

By using appropriate unity brackets it is now a simple process to change this physical formula into a numerical formula dependent on a particular set of units as follows:

$$\frac{Q}{\frac{\text{metre}^3}{\text{hour}}\left[\frac{\text{hour}}{60\text{ min.}}\right]\left[\frac{(3\cdot28)^3\text{ ft.}^3}{\text{metre}^3}\right]}=0\cdot0504\left(\frac{H}{\text{cm.}\left[\frac{\text{inch}}{2\cdot54\text{ cm.}}\right]}\right)^{5/2}$$

i.e.

$$\frac{Q}{\text{ft.}^3/\text{min.}}=\frac{0\cdot0504\times(2\cdot54)^{5/4}\times(3\cdot28)^3}{60}\left(\frac{H}{\text{inch}}\right)^{5/2}$$

$$=0\cdot305(H/\text{inch})^{5/2}$$

Hence, writing $Q=q$ ft.^{3}/min. and $H=h$ inch, the empirical formula in f.p.s. units is $\boldsymbol{q=0\cdot305\,h^{5/2}}$, where q is the number of cubic ft. of water flowing per minute when the number of inches of head of water flowing over the notch is h.

6. Apparent Dryness of Steam during Expansion, and the Missing Quantity.—If a known mass of steam in the cylinder of an engine expands from cut-off (F) to release (R) along a P,V curve FR, as shown on the indicator diagram fig. 8.10, and the dryness line (DL) for that steam is plotted on the same diagram (*i.e.* the P,V curve which would be traced out if the steam remained dry and saturated throughout the expansion), then the dryness of the steam at any pressure P_x during expansion

$$=\frac{\text{actual volume of the mass of expanding steam}}{\text{volume of the same mass of dry saturated steam}}=\frac{xm}{xn}$$

It will be noticed that the volume represented by mn is the lack of volume due to the steam not remaining dry and saturated during expansion. This lack of volume is usually known as the "*missing quantity*."

If we assume that all the steam supplied to the engine actually enters and expands in the cylinder before flowing along the exhaust pipe to the condenser, from which it is pumped out as condensate, then the mass of steam entering the cylinder per expansion stroke is

$$m_s = \frac{\text{mass of condensate pumped from the condenser per minute}}{\text{number of expansion strokes per minute}}.$$

The stroke steam m_s enters the cylinder during the admission

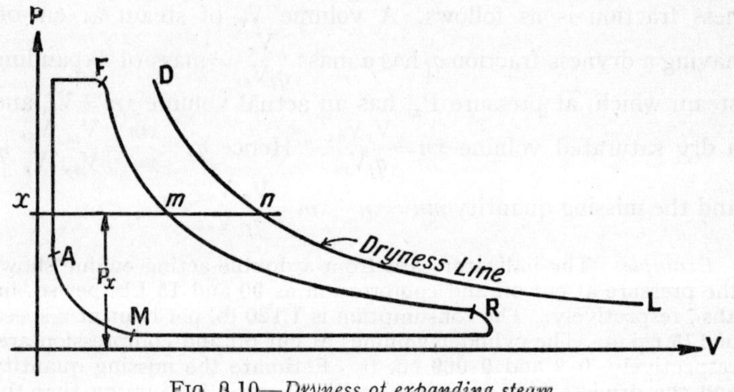

FIG. 8.10—*Dryness of expanding steam.*

period AF and is rejected during the exhaust period RM. Hence the mass of steam expanding during period FR is $m_s + m_c$, where m_c is the mass of steam in the cylinder during the compression period MA, and which never leaves the cylinder. The steam present in the cylinder during compression is known as the "cushion steam," and its mass can be calculated (assuming dry saturated steam at A, the end of compression) from $m_c = \frac{V_A}{V_{SA}}$, where V_A is the actual volume of steam in the cylinder at the end of compression as scaled from the P,V diagram, and V_{SA} is the specific volume of dry saturated steam at the pressure P_A. This latter volume can be found in the steam tables.

Thus, having found the total weight $(m_s + m_c)$ expanding in the cylinder, the dryness line DL can be plotted and the apparent dryness at any point in the expansion found from the ratio of the lengths xm and xn.

The dryness fraction as estimated from the indicator diagram in the above way is, however, only correct if there is no leakage of steam past the valve. Such leakage steam would go straight to exhaust and into the condenser without ever entering the cylinder. Since leakage steam does not expand in the cylinder, the dryness fraction, as calculated from the diagram, is, in this case, apparent rather than real. The real dryness fraction

$$=\frac{xm}{\left[\begin{array}{c}\text{dry saturated vol. of the mass of steam}\\ m_s+m_c-\text{mass of leakage steam per expansion stroke.}\end{array}\right]}$$

A more usual way of estimating the missing quantity and dryness fraction is as follows. A volume V_F of steam at cut-off having a dryness fraction q_f has a mass $\frac{V_F}{q_f V_{SF}}$ = mass of expanding steam which, at pressure P_x, has an actual volume $xm = V_m$ and a dry saturated volume $xn = \frac{V_F V_{SX}}{q_f V_{FS}}$. Hence $q_x = \frac{xm}{xn} = \frac{V_m}{V_{SX}} \frac{V_{SF}}{V_F} q_f$ and the missing quantity $mn = xn - xm = \frac{V_F}{q_f} \frac{V_{SX}}{V_{SF}} - V_m$.

Example.—The indicator card from a double-acting engine shows the pressure at cut-off and compression as 90 and 15 Lb. per sq. in. abs., respectively. The consumption is 1,120 lb. per hour at a speed of 175 r.p.m. The cylinder volumes at cut-off and compression are, respectively, 0·2 and 0·069 cu. ft. Estimate the missing quantity and the dryness fraction of the steam at cut-off assuming that the steam at the beginning of compression is dry and saturated and that there is no leakage.

Referring to fig. 8.10 we deduce that at the point M the mass of steam being compressed is: $m_c = \frac{V_M}{V_{SM}} = \frac{0 \cdot 069}{26 \cdot 28} = 0 \cdot 00262$ lb.

The mass of steam admitted to the engine per cycle is

$$m_s = 1120\,\frac{\text{lb.}}{\text{hr.}} \times \frac{1}{2 \times 175\,\frac{\text{cycles}}{\text{min.}}} \times \left[\frac{\text{hour}}{60\text{ min.}}\right]$$

$$= 0 \cdot 0533 \text{ lb./cycle.}$$

Hence, the mass of steam expanding from F to $R = m_c + m_s = 0 \cdot 05592$ lb. At cut-off the pressure is 90 Lb. per sq. in. abs., and the volume of 0·05592 lb. of dry and saturated steam at this pressure would be $0 \cdot 05592 \times 4 \cdot 896 = 0 \cdot 2735$ cu. ft., but the actual volume of this steam at cut-off is given as 0·2 cu. ft. Hence, the missing quantity at cut-off is $0 \cdot 2735 - 0 \cdot 2 = 0 \cdot 0735$ cu. ft., and the dryness fraction $= \frac{0 \cdot 2}{0 \cdot 2735} = 0 \cdot 732$.

7. Ways of Reducing the "Missing Quantity."—The missing quantity may be due to:—

(i) Initial condensation of the admission steam coming into contact with the relatively cold walls of the cylinder and piston which have just completed exhausting steam at a lower pressure and temperature.

(ii) Heat leaving the expanding steam through the cylinder walls.

(iii) Leakage steam, which gets under the valve seating and flows straight to exhaust without ever entering the cylinder.

Ways of reducing the missing quantity are therefore:—

(i) By superheating the admission steam so as to allow of a certain amount of superheat being abstracted from the steam when it comes into contact with the colder cylinder walls and piston, and so perhaps avoid altogether the condensation which results in a sudden reduction of volume. Separate steam and exhaust valves are also fitted in order to reduce initial condensation. It is found that superheating also reduces leakage under the seating of a slide valve. Thus, besides reducing initial condensation, superheating also reduces leakage.

(ii) By compressing a portion of steam (the "cushion steam") the temperatures of the cylinder cover and piston are raised before fresh high-pressure steam at high temperature is admitted, although this reduces the area of the indicator diagram.

(iii) By jacketing the cylinder with hot steam. This stops heat from flowing out through the walls and keeps the expanding steam dryer than it otherwise would be. Jacket steam, if hot enough, will actually give heat to the expanding steam through the walls of the cylinder. The consumption of jacket steam is relatively very small, but from the point of view of cost of manufacture of the jacket it is seldom considered worth while.

(iv) By compounding, *i.e.* by completing the expansion in two or more cylinders. For if the expansion be done in two cylinders—called high-pressure and low-pressure cylinders—instead of in one cylinder, the pressure difference, and therefore the temperature difference, between the admission steam and exhaust steam in each cylinder is less than if one larger cylinder only were used, although initial condensation depends not only upon temperature range but also upon the amount of metal surface exposed to the steam.

Since the temperature difference between the walls and the steam admitted to the cylinders of compound engines is less than if the expansion were done in one cylinder, initial condensation will be less in the compound engine. This is one advantage of compounding when high-pressure steam is being used. Other advantages of compounding are:—

(*a*) Leakage steam is not wholly lost, for if steam leaks under the slide valve of the high-pressure cylinder it may do work in a later cylinder, say an intermediate cylinder or in the low-pressure cylinder.

(*b*) By spacing the cranks at 90° in the case of two-cylinder engines or at 120° in triple-expansion engines, a more even turning moment can be exerted on the crankshaft.

(*c*) Moving parts of the cylinders can be more easily balanced, for they can be balanced against one another.

8. Elementary Work on Compounding.—Compound steam engines have two or more cylinders of successively increasing diameters so arranged that the exhaust steam from the first cylinder is passed on to do the work in a second, and to a third in triple-expansion engines, before being finally exhausted into a condenser.

In multiple-expansion steam engines it is desirable in the first place to aim at designing so that:—

(*a*) *each cylinder does the same amount of work*; and also, if possible, for

(*b*) *the pistons to have the same initial load.*

It is easy to achieve the one or the other, but seldom possible to achieve both.

In the case of working engines, indicator diagrams are taken from each cylinder on separate cards. A composite or combined diagram can then be plotted showing the diagrams from the individual cylinders drawn on a common scale for easy comparison.

Different cases of an introductory nature will now be considered with reference to hypothetical indicator diagrams in which the receiver pressures are assumed to remain constant.

(I) **Compound Engine with Full Expansion.**—Taking first the simplest hypothetical case, where clearance volume is neglected and hyperbolic expansion is assumed, the hypothetical indicator diagram would be as shown in fig. 8.11. It should be noted, however, that "full" expansion is never obtained in an actual engine because of the relatively large increase in cylinder volume that would be necessary in order to obtain the relatively small amount of work at the "toe" of the diagram. In an actual engine the "toe" is always cut off as in Case II (fig. 8.12).

In fig. 8.11 the overall ratio of expansion is $\frac{V_2}{V_1}=\frac{V_2}{V_3}\times\frac{V_3}{V_1}$

$$\text{or } R=r_L\times r_H \quad . \quad . \quad . \quad . \quad . \quad (1)$$

where r_H is the ratio of expansion in the h.p. cylinder, and r_L is the ratio of expansion in the l.p. cylinder, which is equal to the ratio of the cylinder volumes, *i.e.* $\frac{V_2}{V_3}=r_L=\frac{V_L}{V_H}$.

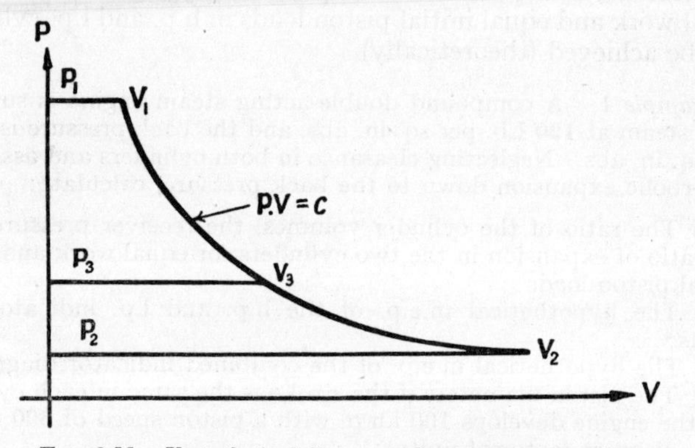

Fig. 8.11—*Hypothetical diagram of a compound engine.*

(a) For equal work done in each cylinder.

$$P_1V_1+P_1V_1\log_e r_H-P_3V_3=P_3V_3+P_3V_3\log_e r_L-P_2V_2.$$

Hence, since $\quad P_1V_1=P_2V_2=P_3V_3 \quad \therefore r_H=r_L \quad . \quad . \quad . \quad (2)$

Thus the ratio of expansion must be the same in each cylinder.

i.e. $$\frac{V_3}{V_1}=\frac{V_2}{V_3} \text{ or } \frac{P_1}{P_3}=\frac{P_3}{P_2} \text{ or } P_3=\sqrt{P_1P_2} \quad . \quad . \quad (2a)$$

(b) For equal initial piston loads.

$$(P_1-P_3)A_3=(P_3-P_2A)_2$$

where A_3 and A_2 are the piston areas, the piston rod areas being neglected.

Hence, if the stroke is the same in each cylinder

$$\frac{A_2}{A_3}=\frac{V_2}{V_3}=\frac{V_L}{V_H}=\left(\frac{P_1-P_3}{P_3-P_2}\right) \quad . \quad . \quad . \quad . \quad (3)$$

From (3),

$$\frac{V_2}{V_3}=\frac{P_3}{P_2}=\frac{P_1-P_3}{P_3-P_2} \quad \therefore P_3{}^2= \quad \therefore P_3=\sqrt{P_1P_2} \quad . \quad . \quad (3a)$$

It will be noticed that in this particular case of full expansion, the calculations for equal work done and equal initial piston loads give, independently, the result $P_3=\sqrt{P_1P_2}$ in equations (2*a*) and (3*a*). Hence, if the intermediate pressure P_2 is given this value, equal work and equal initial piston loads in h.p. and l.p. cylinders will be achieved (theoretically).

Example 1.—A compound double-acting steam engine is supplied with steam at 120 Lb. per sq. in. abs. and the back pressure is 3 Lb. per sq. in. abs. Neglecting clearance in both cylinders and assuming hyperbolic expansion down to the back pressure, calculate:

(*a*) The ratio of the cylinder volumes, the receiver pressure, and the ratio of expansion in the two cylinders for equal work and equal initial piston loads;

(*b*) The hypothetical m.e.p. of the h.p. and l.p. indicator diagrams;

(*c*) The hypothetical m.e.p. of the combined indicator diagram;

(*d*) The piston diameters if the stroke is the same in each cylinder and the engine develops 100 i.h.p. with a piston speed of 500 ft. per min. (diagram factor of unity);

(*e*) Check the results to see if equal work is done and equal initial piston loads occur in h.p. and l.p. cylinders.

(*a*) Referring to fig. 8.11, $P_1=120$, $P_2=3$, both in Lb. per sq. in. abs. $\therefore$ for equal work and equal initial piston loads the receiver pressure $P_3=\sqrt{P_1P_2}=\sqrt{360}=19$ Lb. per sq. in. abs. Overall ratio of expansion $R=\frac{120}{3}=40=r_H\times r_L=r^2$, since r_H and r_L have been proved equal for this hypothetical indicator diagram.

$\therefore$ ratio of expansion in each cylinder $=\sqrt{40}=6\cdot 3$.

The ratio of the cylinder volumes will be $\frac{V_L}{V_H}=\frac{V_2}{V_3}=r_L=6\cdot 3$.

(*b*) Hypothetical m.e.p. in h.p. cylinder $=P_1\left(\frac{1+\log_\varepsilon r_H}{r_H}\right)-P_3$

$$=120\left(\frac{1+\log_\varepsilon 6\cdot 3}{6\cdot 3}\right)-19=35\cdot 2 \text{ Lb. per sq. in.}$$

Hypothetical m.e.p. in l.p. cylinder $=P_3\left(\frac{1+\log_\varepsilon r_H}{r_H}\right)-P_2$

$$=19\left(\frac{1+\log_\varepsilon 6\cdot 3}{6\cdot 3}\right)-3=5\cdot 6 \text{ Lb. per sq. in.}$$

(*c*) Hypothetical m.e.p. of the combined indicator diagram

$$=P_1\left(\frac{1+\log_\varepsilon R}{R}\right)-P_3$$

$$=120\left(\frac{1+\log_\varepsilon 40}{40}\right)-3=3\log_\varepsilon 40$$

$$=11\cdot 07 \text{ Lb. per sq. in.}$$

(*d*) Since the piston speed in ft. per min. $=2ln$, the total i.h.p. calculated from the combined diagram will be given by the numerical formula

$i=\frac{2(\text{m.e.p.})lan}{33{,}000}$; *i.e.* in the particular units quoted on p. 64.

$$i=\frac{(\text{m.e.p. of combined diagram})\times\text{area of l.p. piston}\times\text{piston speed}}{33{,}000}$$

$$\therefore\ 100=\frac{11\cdot 07\times a_2\times 500}{33{,}000}\quad \therefore\ a_2=596,$$

i.e. the area of the l.p. piston is $A_2=a_2$ sq. in. $=596$ sq. in.

$\therefore$ Diameter of l.p. piston $=27\cdot 6$ in.

The ratio of cylinder volumes was calculated in (*a*) to be $6\cdot 3$, which is also equal to the ratio of the piston areas if the stroke is the same in both cylinders. Therefore the area of the h.p. piston is

$A_3=\frac{A_2}{6\cdot 3}=\frac{596 \text{ in.}^2}{6\cdot 3}=94\cdot 5 \text{ in.}^2$ and the diameter of the h.p. piston is $\sqrt{\frac{4\times 94\cdot 5 \text{ in.}^2}{\pi}}=11$ in.

(*e*) The power developed in the high pressure cylinder is given by the physical formula ${}_H\mathcal{P}_i=P_H L A_3 C$, or by the numerical formula

$i=\frac{2(\text{m.e.p.})\times l\times a_3\times n}{33{,}000}$; i.e., in particular units,

$$i=\frac{(\text{m.e.p. in h.p. cylinder})\times\text{area of h.p. piston}\times\text{piston speed}}{33{,}000}$$

$$=\frac{35\cdot 2\times 94\cdot 5\times 500}{33{,}000}=50\cdot 5.$$

Hence, the indicated horse-power of the high-pressure cylinder is ${}_H\mathcal{P}_i=$ i.h.p. $=50\cdot 5$ h.p.

6

Initial piston load on h.p. piston $=(P_1-P_3)\times A_3$

$$=(120-19)\,\frac{\text{Lb.}}{\text{in.}^2}\times 94\cdot 5\ \text{in.}^2=9550\ \text{Lb.}\left[\frac{\text{Ton}}{2240\ \text{Lb.}}\right]=4\cdot 25\ \text{Tons.}$$

Similarly, the indicated power developed in the l.p. cylinder is given by the physical formula ${}_{L}\mathcal{P}_i=P_L A_2 LC$ and since, in a double-acting engine, LC is the piston speed, the value is

$${}_{L}\mathcal{P}_i=5\cdot 6\,\frac{\text{Lb.}}{\text{in.}^2}\times 596\ \text{in.}^2\times 500\,\frac{\text{min.}}{\text{ft.}}\left[\frac{\text{h.p. min.}}{33{,}000\ \text{ft.-Lb.}}\right]=50\cdot 5\ \text{h.p.}$$

Also, the initial load on the l.p. piston is

$$(P_3-P_2)A_2=(19-3)\,\frac{\text{Lb.}}{\text{in.}^2}\times 596\ \text{in.}^2=9550\ \text{Lb.}=4\cdot 25\ \text{Tons.}$$

Thus it will be seen that the results satisfy the conditions of equal work done and equal initial piston loads for the two cylinders.

(II) **Compound Engine with Incomplete Expansion.**—It will have been noticed in Case I that to get the maximum amount of work out of a volume of steam V_1 admitted at P_1 by expanding it fully (*i.e.* completely) down to the back pressure P_2, a large l.p. cylinder volume V_2 is needed and a large overall $R=\frac{P_1}{P_2}$.

In practice it is not worth making such a large l.p. cylinder in order to obtain the comparatively small amount of work from the "toe" of the l.p. diagram. Hence, the overall ratio of expansion, R, is usually limited to 10 or 15, according to the initial pressure, The "toe" of the diagram is thus cut off, leaving a hypothetical

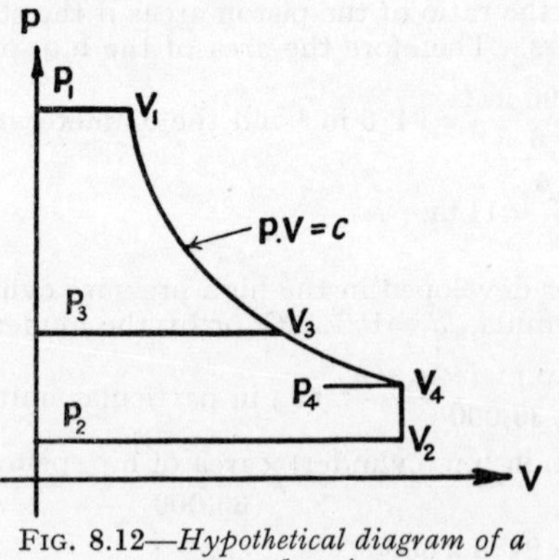

FIG. 8.12—*Hypothetical diagram of a compound engine.*

diagram as shown in fig. 8.12 which also neglects clearance volume and assumes hyperbolic expansion $PV=c$.

The overall ratio of expansion $=\frac{V_4}{V_1}=\frac{V_4}{V_3}\times\frac{V_3}{V_1}$

or

$$R=r_L\times r_H \quad . \quad . \quad . \quad . \quad . \quad . \quad (1)$$

(a) For equal work done in h.p. and l.p. cylinders.

$$P_1V_1+P_1V_1\log_\varepsilon r_H-P_3V_3=P_3V_3+P_2V_2\log_\varepsilon r_L-P_2V_2$$

$$\therefore \log_\varepsilon r_H=1+\log_\varepsilon r_L-\frac{P_2V_2}{P_1V_1}$$

$$\log_\varepsilon\left(\frac{r_H}{r_L}\right)=1-\frac{P_2}{P_1}R \quad . \quad . \quad . \quad . \quad . \quad (2)$$

From (1) $\frac{r_H}{r_L}=\frac{r_H^2}{R}$, which, when substituted in (2), gives

$$r_H=\frac{P_1}{P_3}=\sqrt{R\text{ antilog}_\varepsilon\left(1-\frac{P_2}{P_1}R\right)}$$

i.e. the intermediate pressure for equal work done is given by the expression

$$P_3=\frac{P_1}{\sqrt{R\text{ antilog}_\varepsilon\left(1-\frac{P_2}{P_1}R\right)}} \quad . \quad . \quad . \quad . \quad (2a)$$

(b) For equal initial piston loads.

$(P_1-P_3)A_3=(P_3-P_2)A_2$ [piston rod areas being neglected].

$\therefore$ If the stroke is the same in both cylinders,

$$\frac{A_2}{A_3}=\frac{V_2}{V_3}=\frac{V_4}{V_3}=\frac{V_L}{V_H}=r_L=\frac{P_1-P_3}{P_3-P_2} \quad . \quad . \quad . \quad (3)$$

From (1), $r_L=\frac{R}{r_H}=R\frac{P_3}{P_1}$, which, when substituted in (3), gives

$$R\frac{P_3}{P_1}=\frac{P_1-P_3}{P_3-P_2}$$

$$\therefore RP_3^2-(RP_2-P_1)P_3-P_1^2=0.$$

$$\therefore P_3=\frac{(RP_2-P_1)\pm\sqrt{(RP_2-P_1)^2+4RP_1^2}}{2R} \quad . \quad (3a)$$

It will be noticed that equations (2*a*) and (3*a*), giving the intermediate pressure for equal work done and equal initial loads respectively, are entirely different. They are only the same when $R=\frac{P_1}{P_2}$, which is Case I, where there is full expansion. Hence, with the theoretical indicator diagram of fig. 8.12 it is not possible to fulfil both conditions of equal work and equal initial loads. A compromise is therefore made in the choice of R for any particular admission pressure, P_1, and exhaust pressure, P_2, both of which are usually quite definite and fixed by boiler and condenser conditions. The overall ratio of expansion, R, however, can be chosen by the designer, and a compromise is therefore possible between equations (2*a*) and (3*a*) which give the intermediate pressure P_3 for equal work done in h.p. and l.p. cylinders and equal initial piston loads, respectively.

Example 2.—Calculate the ratio of the cylinder volumes and the receiver pressure in the previous example (Case I) when the overall ratio of expansion is limited to 10: (*a*) for equal work in the two cylinders; (*b*) for equal initial piston loads.

(*a*) Referring to fig. 8.12, Case II, we get from equation (1)

$$R = r_L \times r_H = 10,$$

and from equation (2)

$$r_L = \frac{V_L}{V_H} = \frac{R}{r_H} = \frac{R}{\sqrt{R \operatorname{antilog}_\varepsilon\left(1 - \frac{P_2}{P_1}R\right)}}$$

$$= \frac{10}{\sqrt{10 \operatorname{antilog}_\varepsilon\left(1 - \frac{3 \times 10}{120}\right)}} = 2 \cdot 175.$$

From equation (2*a*) we get

$$P_3 = \frac{120 \text{ Lb. per sq. in. abs.}}{\sqrt{10 \operatorname{antilog}_\varepsilon\left(1 - \frac{3 \times 10}{120}\right)}} = \frac{120}{\sqrt{21 \cdot 17}} = 26 \cdot 1 \text{ Lb. per sq. in. abs.}$$

Hence, for equal work done in each cylinder, the ratio of the cylinder volumes must be $2 \cdot 175$ and the intermediate pressure in the receiver $26 \cdot 1$ Lb. per sq. in. abs.

(*b*) For equal initial piston loads we get from equation (3*a*) that the receiver pressure

$$P_3 = \frac{(RP_2 - P_1) \pm \sqrt{(RP_2 - P_1)^2 + 4RP_1^2}}{2R}$$

$$= \frac{-90 \pm \sqrt{8{,}100 + 576{,}000}}{20} = 33 \cdot 75 \text{ Lb. per sq. in. abs.}$$

∴ From equation (3) we get the cylinder volume ratio for equal initial loads piston $r_L = \frac{V_L}{V_H} = \frac{P_1 - P_3}{P_3 - P_2} = \frac{120 - 33 \cdot 75}{33 \cdot 75 - 3} = 2 \cdot 8.$

It will be noticed that the two conditions give different results for receiver pressure and also for cylinder volume ratio. A compromise would therefore have to be made.

(III) **Compound Engine with Incomplete Expansion in Both Cylinders.**—A further attempt is made at fulfilling the conditions of equal work done and equal initial piston loads for both h.p. and l.p. cylinders by having incomplete expansion in both cylinders as shown in fig. 8.13.

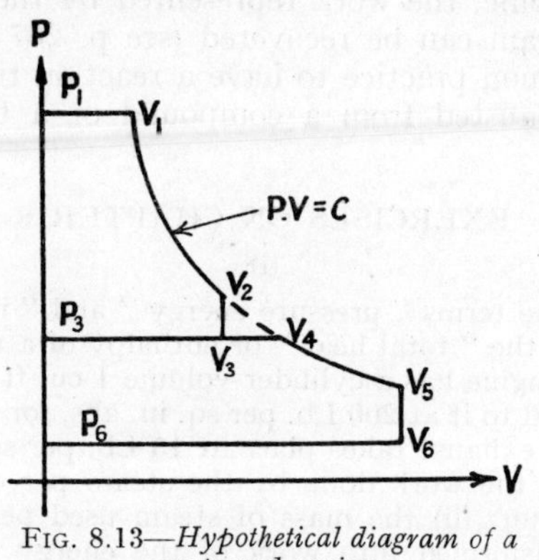

FIG. 8.13—*Hypothetical diagram of a compound engine.*

If V_1, V_2, V_4, V_5 are on the same hyperbola $PV=c$, then the ratio of the cylinder volumes

$$\frac{V_L}{V_H}=\frac{V_6}{V_3}=\frac{V_5}{V_2}=\frac{V_5}{V_1}\times\frac{V_1}{V_2}=R\times\frac{1}{r_H},$$

or overall ratio of expansion

$$R=r_H\times\frac{V_L}{V_H} \quad . \quad . \quad . \quad . \quad . \quad (1)$$

(a) **For equal work done in h.p. and l.p. cylinders.**

$$P_1V_1+P_1V_1\log_\varepsilon r_H-P_3V_3=P_3V_4+P_3V_4\log_\varepsilon r_L-P_6V_6$$

or
$$\left[P_1\frac{(1+\log_\varepsilon r_H)}{r_H}-P_3\right]V_H=\left[P_3\frac{(1+\log_\varepsilon r_L)}{r_L}-P_6\right]V_L \quad (2)$$

(b) **For equal initial piston loads.**

$$(P_1-P_3)V_3=(P_3-P_6)V_6\left[\begin{array}{c}\text{if the strokes are the same and}\\ \text{piston rod areas neglected}\end{array}\right]$$

$$\therefore \frac{V_L}{V_H}=\frac{P_1-P_3}{P_3-P_6} \quad . \quad . \quad . \quad . \quad . \quad (3)$$

The three equations must be satisfied to fulfil the condition for equal work and equal initial piston loads.

At the commencement of Case (I) it has been stated that the hypothetical case of full expansion is never realised in an actual reciprocating engine. The "toe" of the low-pressure indicator diagram is always cut off owing to incomplete expansion in order to reduce the dimensions of the l.p. cylinder. If, however, the steam which is exhausted from the l.p. cylinder is admitted to a reaction turbine, the work represented by the toe of the l.p. indicator diagram can be recovered (see p. 267 and fig. 12.14). It is now common practice to have a reaction turbine receiving the steam exhausted from a compound or a triple expansion engine.

EXERCISES ON CHAPTER 8

(i)

1. Explain the terms "pressure energy" and "internal energy" with respect to the "total heat" or enthalpy of a working fluid.

2. A steam engine has a cylinder volume 1 cu. ft. Dry saturated steam is supplied to it at **200** Lb. per sq. in. abs. for the full length of the stroke, and exhaust takes place at **15** Lb. per sq. in. abs.

Calculate: (i) the work done by the steam per cycle (neglecting clearance volume); (ii) the mass of steam used per cycle; (iii) the percentage transformed into work of the energy supplied by the boiler in generating steam from feed water containing 181·2 B.Th.U. per lb.

3. What is meant by the expression "expansive working of steam"? If the steam in the engine of Question 2 is cut off at half stroke, calculate: (i) the mass of steam (d.s.s.) admitted per cycle; (ii) the work done by the steam per cycle assuming the expanding steam to follow the law PV=constant (see pages **138** and **292**; (iii) the thermal efficiency.

4. (i) A single-cylinder double-acting steam engine has a piston diameter 24 in. and a stroke 3 ft. When running at **60** r.p.m. the m.e.p. was found to be **40** Lb. per sq. in. Calculate the i.h.p. developed.

(ii) If the engine is required to develop **250** i.h.p., what must be the m.e.p. if the engine is running at the same speed?

(iii) If, instead of increasing the m.e.p. to obtain **250** i.h.p., this was done by increasing the speed, calculate the value of the increased speed.

5. Find the tractive horse-power of a locomotive which draws a train, including its own weight, of **100** Tons along a level track at **30** m.p.h. when the resistance is **10** Lb. per ton.

6. Steam at **60** Lb. per sq. in. gauge pressure is used to drive two engines of the same piston diameter and stroke, one a non-condensing and the other a condensing engine. In both engines the steam is

cut off at one-third of the stroke and in the non-condensing engine the back pressure is 15 Lb. per sq. in. abs. while in the condensing engine it is 3 Lb. per sq. in. abs. Atmospheric pressure may be taken as 15 Lb. per sq. in. abs. and the stroke volume 1 cu. ft.

Calculate: (i) the work done per cycle in each case, assuming $PV=c$ during expansion (neglect clearance); (ii) the mass of steam used per cycle if it is dry saturated steam; (iii) the theoretical thermal efficiencies of the engines if the dry saturated steam is generated from feed water containing total heat corresponding to the respective back pressures; (iv) the ideal Rankine efficiencies of the two engines (see page 128); (v) the relative efficiencies of the two engines—that is, the ratio of actual to the Rankine efficiency in each case.

7. Define clearly, with sketched indicator diagrams, what you understand by the term " diagram factor."

During a test of a double-acting single-cylinder steam engine running at 200 r.p.m. the indicated horse-power was 120. The cylinder diameter was 12 in., the piston rod $2\frac{1}{2}$ in., and the stroke 15 in. Cut-off was at $\frac{1}{3}$ stroke, the initial pressure 150 Lb. per sq. in. abs., and exhaust was to 26 in. vacuum (30 in. barometer). Find the diagram factor. (Assume hypothetical m.e.p. is the same in head and crank ends of cylinder.) [I.Mech.E., Sec. A.]

8. The following are the mean values of the observations made on a single-cylinder double-acting steam engine when running on light load: Duration of trial 20 minutes. Barometer 30 in. of mercury. Total steam used 112·8 lb. Gauge pressure of steam in valve chest 26·1 Lb. per sq. in. The engine rejected exhaust steam into a condenser at the pressure of the atmosphere. The state of the steam in the valve chest was found to be dry and saturated. Mean engine speed 120 r.p.m. M.e.p. outstroke 15·1 Lb. per sq. in. M.e.p. instroke 14 Lb. per sq. in. Piston diameter 8·47 in. Stroke 1·01 ft. Piston rod diameter 1·45 in. Net brake load $(W-S)$ 111·4 Lb. Brake wheel radius + rope radius 1·95 ft. Cooling water flowed through the condenser at the rate of 6,300 lb. per hour with a rise in temperature of 47·8° F. Temperature of the condensate leaving the condenser 154·6° F. Put this data on a diagrammatic sketch, and calculate the consumption in lb. per i.h.p.-hour and lb. per b.h.p.-hour, the mechanical and brake thermal efficiencies of the engine. Also draw up a heat account or heat balance sheet for the plant, reckoning from a datum, $h_{w2}=180\cdot1$ B.Th.U./lb.—this being the total heat of 1 lb. of water at the saturation temperature corresponding to the pressure ($P_2=14\cdot7$ Lb./in.^{2} abs.) in the condenser.

9. The clearance volume of a steam engine is one-tenth of the stroke volume. Find the ratio of expansion if cut-off takes place at 0·4 of the stroke.

If steam is admitted to the cylinder at 150 Lb. per sq. in. abs. and exhaust takes place at 3 Lb. per sq. in. abs., find the m.e.p. of the hypothetical indicator diagram. Prove any formula used.

10. The piston diameter and stroke of the engine of Question 9 are 8 in. and 12 in. respectively. Find the i.h.p. developed if the

engine is double-acting and runs at 120 r.p.m. Take a diagram factor on the hypothetical indicator diagram of 0·7.

11. Find the diameter and stroke of a double-acting steam engine to develop 30 i.h.p. at 180 r.p.m. on steam admitted (dry saturated) to the engine at 100 Lb. per sq. in. gauge and exhaust taking place at atmospheric pressure 15 Lb. per sq. in. abs. Cut-off takes place at 0·4 of the stroke; clearance volume is 10 per cent. of the swept volume; the stroke is 1·5 times the cylinder diameter; the diagram factor may be taken as 0·8, and the expansion hyperbolic, *i.e.* $PV=c$.

(ii)

12. (*a*) Assuming hyperbolic expansion $PV=$constant and a diagram factor of unity for the hypothetical indicator diagram which neglects clearance volume, calculate the indicated horse-power of a single-cylinder double-acting steam engine of piston diameter 12 in., stroke 18 in., when running at 150 r.p.m., if:

(i) The admission pressure of the steam is kept constant at 100 Lb. per sq. in. abs., and the back pressure constant at atmospheric pressure 15 Lb. per sq. in. abs., and the ratio of expansion r takes values 2, 3, 4, 5, 6, 8, 10, 15 in turn.

(ii) The ratio of expansion is kept constant at $r=3$ and the back pressure constant at 15 Lb. per sq. in. abs., but the inlet pressure takes values of 100, 90, 80, 70, 60, 50, 40, 30 Lb. per sq. in. abs. in turn.

(*b*) Plot curves on an i.h.p. base showing the steam consumption per hour and also per horse-power hour.

13. A steam engine is supplied with 635 lb. of dry saturated steam per hour at a pressure of 200 Lb. per sq. in. abs. The condenser into which the engine exhausts works at a pressure 1 Lb. per sq. in. abs., and after the steam has been just condensed by the abstraction of the remainder of its latent heat, the condensate is pumped as feed water into the boiler again:

(i) Find the amount of energy supplied by the boiler per hour in changing the feed water into dry saturated steam.

(ii) Find the indicated thermal efficiency if the i.h.p. of the engine is 35·6.

(iii) Show that the work done per lb. of steam admitted to the ideal Rankine engine as given by the formula $H_1-H_{2a}=\varphi_1(T_{s1}-T_{s2})-(G_1-G_2)$ is 336·1 B.Th.U. per lb., and hence, calculate the Rankine efficiency of the engine.

(iv) Find the relative efficiency (i.h.p. basis) or efficiency ratio.

14. A compound double-acting steam engine is to develop 350 i.h.p. when taking steam at 125 Lb. per sq. in. abs. and exhausting at 2 Lb. per sq. in. abs. The rotational speed is 140 r.p.m. and the mean piston speed is 500 ft. per min. Cut-off in the h.p. cylinder is to be 0·4 and the ratio of the l.p. and h.p. cylinder volumes is to be 3·7 Allowing a diagram factor of 0·83 for the combined indicator diagram, determine suitable cylinder dimensions. Assume hyperbolic expansion, a common stroke, and neglect clearance volume.

15. Find the horse-power developed in the h.p. and l.p. cylinders of Question 14 and the initial piston loads taking a diagram factor of 0·83 for both diagrams.

16. The following data were obtained during a trial of a compound double-acting steam engine with cylinders 11·5 in. and 27·5 in. bore and stroke 26 in.: Steam pressure at stop valve 170 Lb. per sq. in. abs.; temperature at stop valve 368·4° F.; condenser vacuum 25·92 in.; barometer 30 in. Cut-off in h.p. cylinder at one-third stroke. I.h.p. = 260; b.h.p. = 235; r.p.m. = 140. Steam used per hour 4,700 lb. Circulating water per hour 66,000 lb. Inlet and outlet temperatures of circulating water 54·5° F. and 122° F. respectively.

Find: (*a*) the overall diagram factor; (*b*) the thermal efficiency (i.h.p. basis); the Rankine efficiency and relative efficiency; (*c*) draw up a heat account for the test in B.Th.U. per minute reckoned from h_{w2} as datum which corresponds to the condenser pressure. The hot-well temperature was observed to be 113° F.

17. A compound double-acting steam engine is required to obey the following particulars: inlet steam pressure 120 and exhaust 4 Lb. per sq. in. abs.; r.p.m. 300; ratio of cylinder volumes 1 to 4; h.p. cut-off 0·5; i.h.p. 60, with a diagram factor of 0·7, assuming hyperbolic expansion and no clearance volume. Determine (*a*) suitable cylinder diameters, if the common stroke is 1 ft.; (*b*) the maximum thrust on the piston rod of the h.p. cylinder, if the discharge pressure of the h.p. cylinder is 27 Lb. per sq. in. abs. [Part I, B.Sc. Lond.]

18. In passing to an engine, steam is wire-drawn at the stop valve from 180 Lb. per sq. in. abs., and 473° F. to 150 Lb. per sq. in. abs. Find from the steam tables the condition of the steam inlet to the engine and the reversible adiabatic heat drop to 2·0 Lb. per sq. in. abs. from the condition after the stop valve. [I.Mech.E., Sec. A.]

19. A triple-expansion engine is designed to work with steam admitted and exhausted at 250 and 4 Lb. per sq. in. abs., respectively—the overall ratio of expansion being 12. It is later decided to obtain a reduction in steam consumption by adding a low-pressure turbine and a more efficient condensing plant in order that continuous expansion may be obtained down to 1 Lb. per sq. in. abs. Neglecting receiver losses, estimate the probable percentage saving of steam for the same output of power. Assume hyperbolic expansion throughout and neglect the effect of clearance volumes.

20. Calculate the brake thermal and the Rankine efficiency reckoned from the saturation temperature in the condenser as datum, and draw up a heat balance sheet for the reciprocating steam-engine and condenser, which gave the following data on test :—

Power.—Brake horse-power, 24.

Steam supply.—Pressure, 125 Lb. per sq. in. abs. Dryness fraction 0·98.

Condenser.—Vacuum, 27 in. of mercury. Barometer, 30·06 in. of mercury. Condensate, 390 lb. per hour. Temperature of condensate, 104° F. Cooling water, 100 lb. per min. Rise in temperature of cooling water, 61° F.

CHAPTER 9

BOILERS: TYPES OF BOILERS; COMBUSTION; AIR SUPPLY; DRAUGHT; STOKING; BOILER AUXILIARIES; AND BOILER TRIAL

1. The Function of Boilers.—The objects of a boiler or steam generator may be stated as: (*a*) to produce large quantities of heat by combustion of fuel in the combustion chamber: and (*b*) to transmit heat of combustion into the water and steam contained in the boiler drum.

The efficiency of process (*a*) is known as **the combustion efficiency,** and is given by the ratio

$$\frac{\textbf{heat liberated by combustion}}{\textbf{potential heat in the fuel}}.$$

The efficiency of process (*b*) is known as **the transmission efficiency**

$$=\frac{\textbf{heat transmitted to water and steam in the boiler}}{\textbf{heat liberated by combustion}}.$$

The overall efficiency of the boiler, or **the boiler efficiency**

$$=\frac{\text{thermal output of boiler}}{\text{thermal input to boiler}}$$

$$=\frac{\textbf{heat transmitted to water and steam in the boiler}}{\textbf{potential heat in the fuel}}.$$

From this it will be seen that *the boiler efficiency is the product of the combustion efficiency and the transmission efficiency.*

If water is heated in a closed vessel such as a steam boiler, then, as heat is continuously added, the temperature, the pressure, and the density (i.e. mass per cu. ft.) of the steam generated will all increase indefinitely so long as the strength of the boiler is not exceeded; and the relation between temperature, pressure, and density (of dry saturated steam) is always interrelated as shown in the steam tables or by the curves of figs. 5.4 and 6.1.

If the rate at which heat is supplied is just sufficient to maintain the temperature constant, the pressure and density remain constant also, and evaporation ceases. But if, now, a communication be opened between the boiler and, say, an engine, steam will

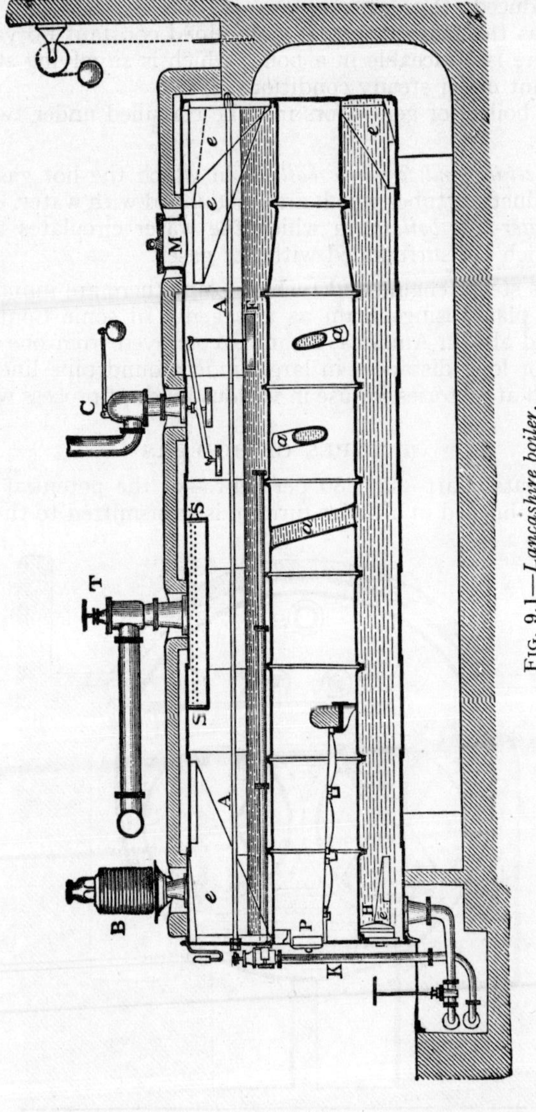

FIG. 9.1—*Lancashire boiler.*

flow from the boiler, and the pressure in the drum will be momentarily reduced, thus causing evaporation to commence again. So long as the temperature is maintained constant no variation of pressure is noticeable in a boiler which is supplying steam to other plant under steady conditions.

Steam boilers or generators may be classified under two main headings:

(i) *Flue-tube and fire-tube boilers,* in which the hot gases flow through ducts or tubes which are surrounded with water.

(ii) *Water-tube boilers,* in which the water circulates through tubes which are surrounded with hot gases.

Besides steam engine and turbine plant there are innumerable types of plant using steam as an agent. In some Continental cities, and also in America, steam is conveyed from one central station for long distances in large underground pipe lines to be tapped off at factories for use in various kinds of process work.

(i) TYPES OF BOILERS

The greater part—say, 80 per cent.—of the potential energy in the fuel burned in a boiler furnace is transmitted to the water

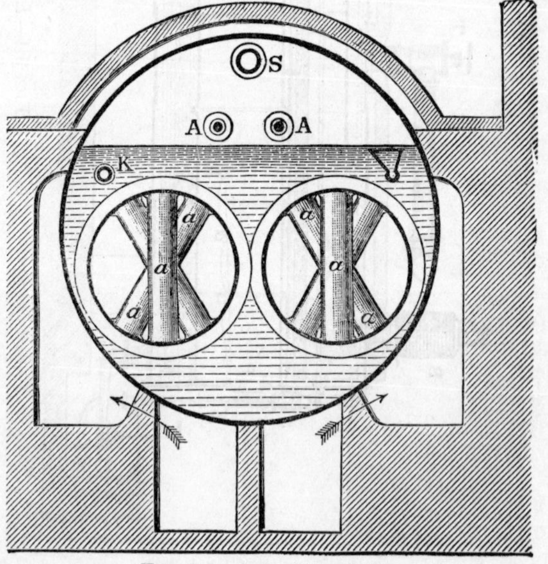

FIG. 9.2—*Lancashire boiler.*

and steam in the boiler, the rest of the heat being either carried up the chimney stack to waste, or lost, by conduction, convection and radiation from the hot surfaces of the exterior of the boiler, to the air surrounding the boiler.

A small fraction of the steam generated is usually used to drive the auxiliaries of the boiler, such as the feed pump, air ejectors, de-aerating plant, water softening plant or evaporators. The steam available from boilers is, therefore, somewhat less than the total amount generated.

2. The Lancashire Boiler.—Figs. 9.1 and 9.2 illustrate the Lancashire type of boiler. It has two internal furnace tubes and the separate furnaces are intended to be fired alternately. "Galloway" tubes *a, a, a* can be seen across the furnace tubes along which the flue gases first pass. The gases return from the back of the boiler by the underneath flue and then along the side flues (fig. 9.2) to the chimney stack.

The steam is conducted from the boiler through the dryer S (fig. 9.1), which is perforated with holes along the top and allows the steam to pass through to the stop valve T. Two safety valves are shown, one a dead-weight safety valve B, and the other a lever safety valve C. The float F is balanced so as to float on the surface of the water, and, should the water fall below a safe level, the float causes a small supplementary valve to open by means of levers and allows steam to escape, which gives the warning of insufficient water.

Access to the interior of the boiler for inspection, repairs or cleaning purposes can be made through the manhole M. Sediment can be removed from the boiler through the mudhole H. A blow-off cock is shown at the bottom front end of the boiler in fig. 9.1.

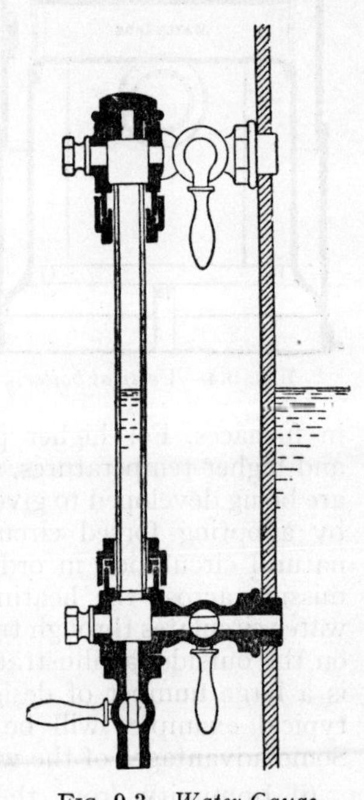

FIG. 9.3—*Water Gauge.*

Fig. 9.3 illustrates a water gauge fitted to the front of the boiler to indicate the water level. The feed pipe K will be seen on fig. 9.1 to continue half way into the boiler.

3. Vertical Boilers.—Fig. 9.4 illustrates a type of vertical boiler used for small powers and where space is limited. Water tubes pass across the internal fire-box and increase the heating surface as well as improve the circulation.

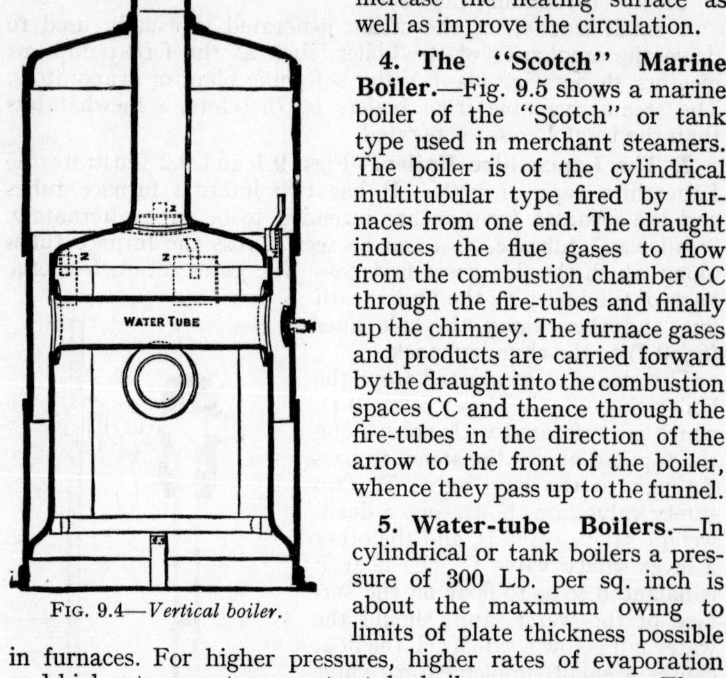

Fig. 9.4—*Vertical boiler.*

4. The "Scotch" Marine Boiler.—Fig. 9.5 shows a marine boiler of the "Scotch" or tank type used in merchant steamers. The boiler is of the cylindrical multitubular type fired by furnaces from one end. The draught induces the flue gases to flow from the combustion chamber CC through the fire-tubes and finally up the chimney. The furnace gases and products are carried forward by the draught into the combustion spaces CC and thence through the fire-tubes in the direction of the arrow to the front of the boiler, whence they pass up to the funnel.

5. Water-tube Boilers.—In cylindrical or tank boilers a pressure of 300 Lb. per sq. inch is about the maximum owing to limits of plate thickness possible in furnaces. For higher pressures, higher rates of evaporation and higher temperatures, water-tube boilers are necessary. These are being developed to give higher and higher rates of evaporation by adopting forced circulation or designs allowing of a rapid natural circulation in order to increase the rate of heat transmission across the heating surfaces. In water-tube boilers the water circulates through tubes which are in contact with hot gases on the outside, as illustrated diagrammatically in fig. 9.6. There is a large number of designs of water-tube boilers. One or two typical examples will be described in succeeding paragraphs. Some advantages of the water-tube type of boiler are:

(i) Immunity from the occasional disastrous explosions of cylindrical boilers.
(ii) Space is saved.
(iii) Capable of rapid steam-raising.
(iv) Easy of transportation.

Some disadvantages are:

(i) They require treated (and often pure) feed water; for, with certain kinds of feed water, the material of the tubes is not so

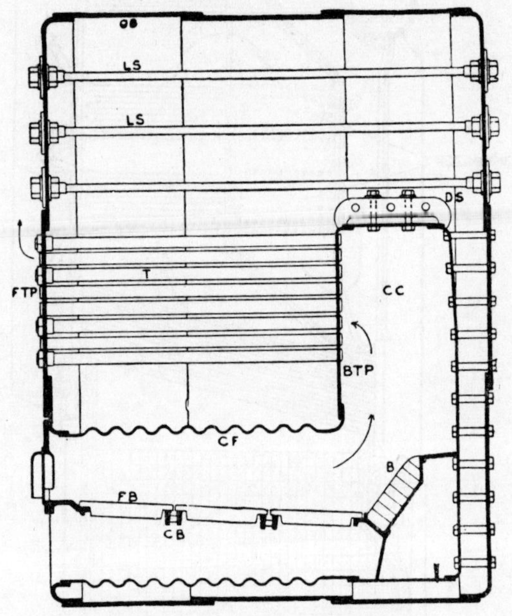

FIG. 9.5—"*Scotch*" *marine boiler.*

durable as the thicker plates used in boilers of, say, the Lancashire type. If there are salts in the water, then, on evaporation, solids may be deposited on the tubes to form a more or less solid incrustation which is a bad conductor of heat. Since, also, the incrustation keeps the water from contact with the hot tubes there is danger of the tubes getting red hot and bursting. It is necessary, therefore, to supply water-tube boilers with treated water or, best of all, with the distilled water from a condenser.

FIG. 9.6—*Water tubes.*

(ii) Water-tube boilers consist of

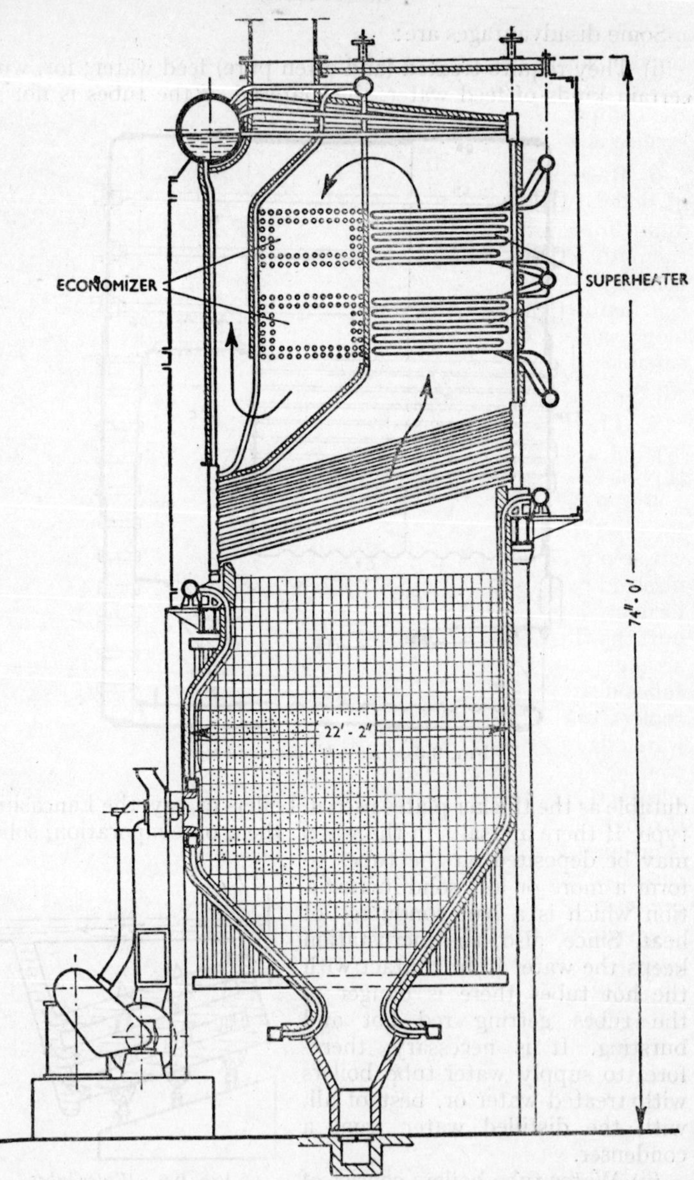

FIG. 9.7—*Water-tube boiler.*

many separate parts and are therefore more liable to minor breakdowns.

(iii) They cannot function as steam reservoirs, and, because of the comparatively small water content, carefully controlled feed service is essential.

6. Babcock and Wilcox Water-tube Boiler.—One type of boiler is illustrated in fig. 9.7 and has water-tubes placed in an inclined position fitted into headers at each end which connect them to the boiler drum. A set of U-shaped tubes fixed horizontally constitutes the superheater through which steam from the main drum is passed before going through the stop valve along the pipe line to the engine plant. The boiler is oil-fired and capable of delivering 80 tons of steam per hour at 675 Lb. per sq. in.

7. The Yarrow Boiler.—Of the small-tube or "express" type of water-tube boiler, probably the best known is the Yarrow type used extensively in marine work.

Fig. 9.8 illustrates the type of Yarrow boiler of which twenty-four are fitted in S.S. *Queen Mary*. It consists of an upper cylindrical steam and water drum into the lower portion of which are inserted three sets of straight tubes spread at the bottom so as to form a combustion space. The bottom ends of the tubes are fixed into the three water drums. Circulation of the water in the tubes arranges itself—the current flowing upwards through the hottest tubes nearest the furnace and downwards through the outer and cooler tubes. The superheater will be seen fitted between two water drums on one side of the boiler. The flow of gases is, of course, controlled by baffle plates so as to make the gases sweep across the tubes the required number of times before passing through the air heater and economiser to the chimney. The boiler is oil-fired and the pre-heated air is forced into the furnace with the oil-spray. This particular boiler was designed for a working pressure of 400 Lb. per sq. in.

8. Waste-heat Boilers.—A waste-heat boiler utilising the exhaust gases from internal combustion engines should be capable of absorbing heat from gases at relatively low temperatures. An advantage (apart from heat regained in using waste-heat boilers with internal combustion engines) is that the boiler replaces the usual silencer and itself acts as a muffle in reducing the noise of the exhaust, without causing too high a back pressure at the exhaust valve of the engine.

Fig. 9.9 shows a waste-heat boiler which is designed so as to permit of separate firing by means of an oil burner situated

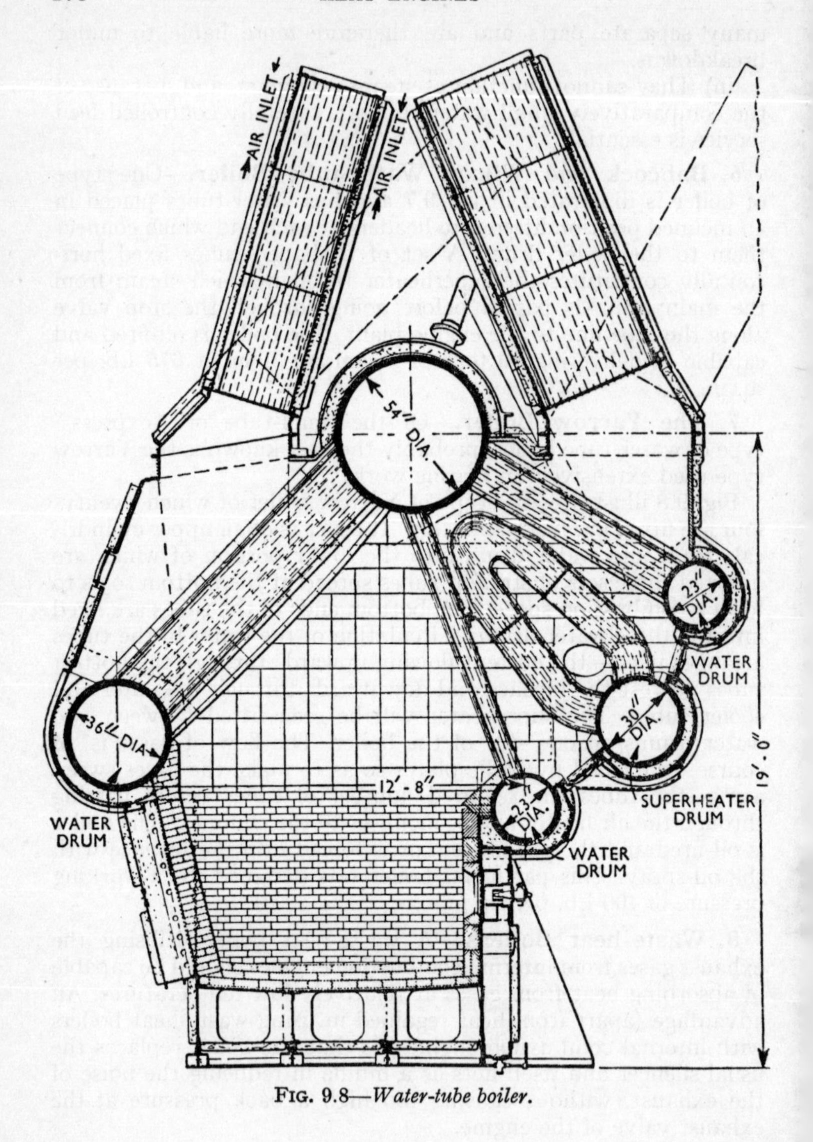

Fig. 9.8—*Water-tube boiler.*

beneath the heating surface for the purpose of raising steam when the internal combustion engine is not in use. Also the materials of design are such that no harm is done when the hot exhaust gases are passed through the empty boiler—steam not being required. When steam is being raised, approximately 2,000 B.Th.U. can be absorbed per sq. ft. of heating surface by this

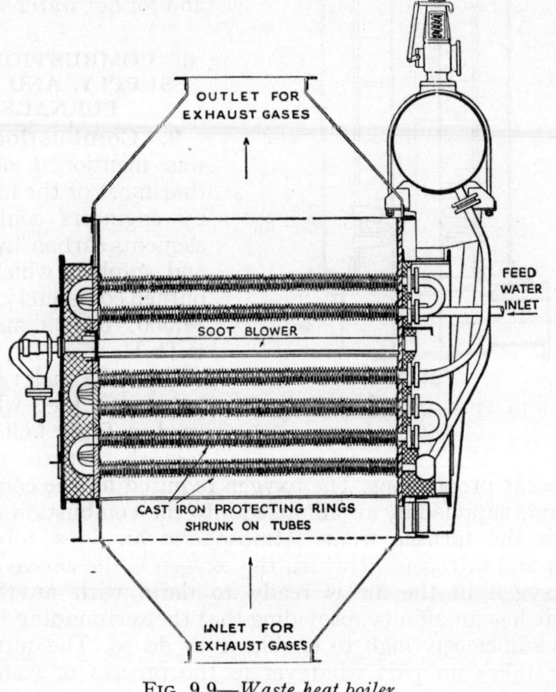

FIG. 9.9—*Waste heat boiler.*

type of boiler, and about 3,000 lb. of steam per hour raised at 40 Lb. per sq. in. pressure.

Fig. 9.10 shows a section through a " thimble tube " exhaust gas boiler which can be fitted on the exhaust near the engine to take the place of a silencer. The boiler consists essentially of a number of thimble tubes fitted round a cylindrical plate acting as the partition between the gas and water circuits.

By means of these boilers hot water and low-pressure steam can be produced from the heat in the exhaust gases, which may be of the order of 30 per cent. of the potential heat in the fuel supplied to the engine. A considerable fraction of this waste heat can thus be recovered for use in radiator heating systems and for hot water services.

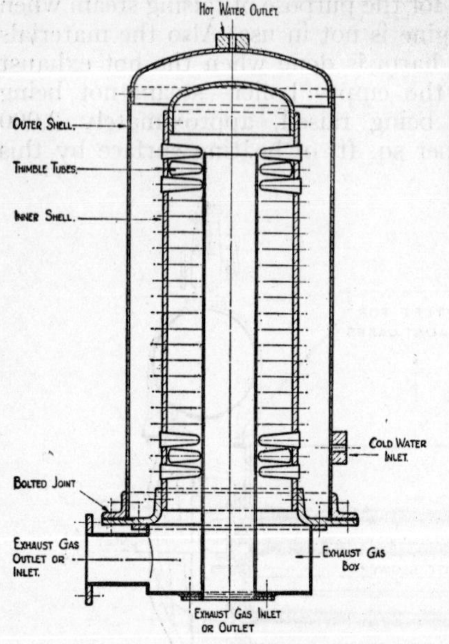

FIG. 9.10—*Thimble tube exhaust gas boiler.*

(ii) COMBUSTION, AIR SUPPLY, AND THE FURNACE

9. Combustion. — It was mentioned on p. 12 that most of the fuels used by engineers contain the elements carbon, hydrogen, and sulphur, which, when burned completely, liberate 14,550, 62,000 and 4,000 B.Th.U. per lb., respectively. The fuels: coal, oil, pulverised fuel, which are used in firing boilers, contain these three elements in different proportions. The oxygen required for the combustion of them is supplied by air admitted into the combustion chamber through the furnace front. Atmospheric air is a mixture of oxygen and nitrogen, of which the oxygen is the active element. The oxygen in the air is ready to unite with anything for which it has an affinity, providing that the surrounding temperature is sufficiently high to enable it to do so. The nitrogen in the air takes no part whatever in the process of combustion. Merely to bring the oxygen of the air into the presence of combustible elements does not mean that combustion will necessarily follow. The combustible substances must have temperatures at least equal to their individual ignition temperatures before they will unite with oxygen. The approximate ignition temperature of carbon is 840° F., of hydrogen 1,110° F., sulphur 480° F., carbon monoxide and methane 1,200° F.

Given unlimited air and unlimited time and the necessary temperature it is a simple matter to liberate completely the heat available in any fuel. In boiler plant, however, fuel must be burnt at a high rate in order to limit the size and cost, and burning must be accomplished with a minimum of air in order to minimise the amount of heat which is finally rejected up the chimney and wasted.

With ordinary hand stoking or mechanical chain-grate stoking it is necessary, owing to the small surface of coal in contact with the oxygen of the air, to admit excess air in order to achieve complete combustion. This excess air has to be heated up to the temperature of the flue gases, and heat is thus lost in the excess air which flows up the chimney stack.

Thus, once the ignition temperatures of the individual combustible substances have been reached, the problem of efficient combustion resolves itself into one of the proper introduction of the smallest amount of air necessary for complete combustion of the fuel. As about three-quarters of air is nitrogen serving no useful purpose in the combustion process but is responsible for a large proportion of the heat which goes to waste up the chimney stack, a minimum of excess air is desired.

With oil firing, the oil is sprayed from a jet into the combustion chamber in the form of a mist, and thus it can be thoroughly mixed with the air which flows in through the swirling vanes on the air director of the burner. Better mixing is obtained and a minimum of excess air is required, and therefore less heat is carried up the chimney stack and wasted.

Pulverised fuel also lends itself to good mixing, and it is claimed that pulverised coal firing is as flexible as oil firing. Its greatest advantage is that low-grade fuels can be burned.

Combustion may be thought of as the chemical combination of the inflammable constituents of a fuel with oxygen, resulting in the evolution of heat and usually accompanied by light.

When coal is burned in a furnace there are three stages in the process of its combustion:

(i) gases are distilled from the coal [methane (CH_4), hydrogen (H_2), and tar];

(ii) these gases are either burnt or pass along the flues unburnt;

(iii) the residue of the coal is burnt.

Air has to be admitted above the coal in order to burn the distilled gases, but if a large excess is allowed to enter, the furnace temperature may be so much reduced that combustion will not take place. When this is the case (and also when the distilled gases have insufficient air for combustion), clouds of finely divided carbon are disengaged from the gas and pass along the flues towards the chimney in the form of smoke—part of which is deposited in the flues as soot.

The remaining solid residue of coke or carbon burns either to carbon monoxide (CO) or carbon dioxide (CO_2) according to whether there is a deficiency or sufficiency, respectively, of oxygen present at a sufficiently high temperature during the process of combustion. The air which passes through the fuel may supply sufficient oxygen to form CO_2 with the lower layers of carbon, but on reaching the upper layers it may only burn the carbon to CO because of a reduction in available oxygen. If, however, a sufficient quantity of air is supplied over the top of the coal, the CO will burn and liberate heat, but if this secondary air is not allowed to enter, the CO will pass up the chimney unburnt and there will be the consequent loss of heat owing to incomplete combustion.

Carbon and hydrogen form the major combustibles in fuels; sulphur, being present in small quantities only, is of minor importance in its contribution to the heating value of a fuel.

The combustion of carbon can be represented by the chemical equation:

$C+O_2=CO_2$, liberating 14,550 B.Th.U. per lb. of carbon burnt if the resulting CO_2 is cooled to 60° F.

or, we can say, 12 lb. of carbon + 32 lb. of oxygen produce 44 lb. of carbon dioxide;

or, 1 lb. of C requires $\frac{32}{12}$ lb. of O_2 to produce $\frac{44}{12}$ lb. of CO_2 and to liberate 14,550 B.Th.U.

If carbon is burnt only to carbon monoxide (CO) instead of to carbon dioxide (CO_2), considerably less heat is liberated. The chemical statement is:

$2C+O_2=2CO$, liberating 4,360 B.Th.U. per lb. of C burnt if the resulting CO is cooled to 60° F.

or, 24 lb. of carbon + 32 lb. of oxygen produce 56 lb. of carbon monoxide;

or, 1 lb. of C requires $\frac{32}{24}$ lb. of O_2 to produce $\frac{56}{24}$ lb. of CO and liberate 4,360 B.Th.U.

Thus, incomplete combustion of carbon to CO instead of to CO_2 results in a loss of heat 14,550 − 4,360 = 10,190 B.Th.U. per lb. of C. Hence, the importance of not having any CO in the chimney flue gases of a boiler.

The combustion of hydrogen can be represented by the chemical equation:

$2H_2+O_2=2H_2O$, liberating 62,000 B.Th.U. per lb. of H_2 burnt if the H_2O is cooled to 60° F.

or, 4 lb. of hydrogen + 32 lb. of oxygen produce 36 lb. of steam;
or, 1 lb. of H_2 requires 8 lb. of O_2 to produce 9 lb. of H_2O and liberate 62,000 B.Th.U.

The combustion of sulphur can be represented by the chemical equation:

$S+O_2=SO_2$, liberating 4,000 B.Th.U. per lb. of S burnt if the SO_2 is cooled to 60° F.
or, 32 lb. of sulphur + 32 lb. of oxygen produce 64 lb. of sulphur dioxide;
or, 1 lb. of S requires 1 lb. of O_2 to produce 2 lb. of SO_2 and liberate 4,000 B.Th.U.

10. Air Supply.—*The theoretical air required* for the combustion of 1 lb. of fuel can be calculated, since:

$\bar{c}$ lb. carbon requires $\frac{32}{12}\bar{c}$ lb. oxygen for complete combustion
$\bar{h}$ lb. hydrogen ,, $8\bar{h}$,, ,, ,, ,, ,,
$\bar{s}$ lb. sulphur ,, $1\bar{s}$,, ,, ,, ,, ,,

1 lb. fuel therefore requires $\left(\frac{32}{12}\bar{c}+8\bar{h}+1\bar{s}\right)$ lb. oxygen for complete combustion.

Air contains 23 per cent. of oxygen and 77 per cent. of nitrogen by weight—that is, 0·23 lb. of oxygen is contained in 1 lb. of air. Therefore, the air theoretically required for the combustion of 1 lb. of fuel is

$$\frac{1}{0\cdot 23}\left[\frac{32}{12}\bar{c}+8\bar{h}+1\bar{s}\right]\text{lb.}$$

Example 1.—The analysis of 1 lb. of oil gave carbon 0·8525, hydrogen 0·130, sulphur 0·0125, ash 0·005. Find the weight of air theoretically required for complete combustion. Calculate also the volume of air required if its pressure and temperature are 14·7 Lb. per sq. in. abs. and 60° F. respectively.

Mass of oxygen required for complete combustion

$$=\frac{32}{12}(0\cdot 8525)+8(0\cdot 13)+(0\cdot 0125)\text{ lb.}$$

$$\therefore \text{Air theoretically required}=\frac{1}{0\cdot 23}\left[\frac{8}{3}\times 0\cdot 8525+8\times 0\cdot 13+0\cdot 0125\right]$$
$$=14\cdot 46\text{ lb.}$$

From the characteristic equation, $PV=RmT$, the volume of air for complete combustion of 1 lb. of oil will be

$$V=\frac{RmT}{P}=\frac{53\cdot 3\text{ ft.-Lb.}}{\text{lb. °F.}}\times\frac{14\cdot 46\text{ lb.}\times 520°\text{ F. ft.}^2}{14\cdot 7\times 144\text{ Lb.}}=189\text{ ft.}^3$$

Excess air is usually necessary in all combustion processes, for we have seen that if there is incomplete combustion of carbon to carbon monoxide instead of to carbon dioxide there is a loss of 10,190 B.Th.U. per lb. of carbon burnt. This is a serious loss (70 per cent.), and in order to avoid it air, in excess of that theoretically required for combustion, is always admitted to the combustion chamber so as to ensure that there is sufficient oxygen present to burn the carbon before the products of combustion leave the flue tubes for the chimney stack.

The actual air admitted to the combustion chamber of a boiler can be estimated from an analysis of the flue gases leaving the boiler. Such an analysis gives an indication of the completeness of combustion of the carbon content of the fuel.

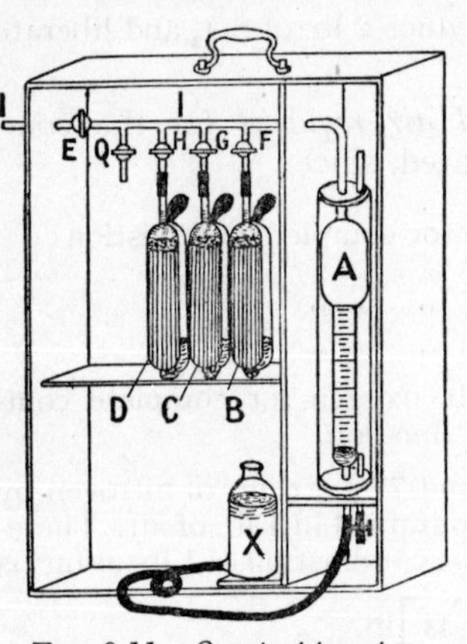

FIG. 9.11—*Orsat apparatus.*

If a sample of flue gas is drawn from the exit flue of a boiler and fed into an Orsat apparatus, fig. 9.11, most of the steam contained in the sample will condense and drop out before the gas enters the reservoir of the apparatus, which is therefore filled with 100 c.c. of *dry* flue gas except for the water vapour above the surface of the water in A. Allowing for this it can be shown that the Orsat apparatus determines the percentage composition on a dry gas basis—i.e. even though the sample is saturated with water vapour in the sample vessel of the apparatus, the resulting analysis is that of the dry gases in the flue gas or exhaust gas mixture. The sample is first passed a few times through the caustic potash solution contained in the first bottle to absorb the CO_2. The percentage of CO_2 in the sample can thus be read directly on the reservoir scale after the liquid levels have been adjusted to the same height. The remainder of the sample is then passed several times through the pyrogallic acid solution in the next bottle to absorb the O_2. The percentage O_2 contained in the sample is obtained by subtracting the previous CO_2 reading from the scale reading after the oxygen has been absorbed as well.

Similarly, by passing what remains of the sample through the cuprous chloride solution contained in the third bottle, the percentage of CO contained in the sample of flue gas can be found. After the absorption of CO_2, O_2, and CO, from the sample, we shall be left with a remainder of N_2.

The analysis of flue gas should always be complete since a

high percentage of CO_2 appearing in dry flue gas analysis is not, by itself, a sufficient indication of good combustion, as it may be offset by an appreciable percentage of CO which will remain unknown if analysis for CO_2 only is made.

The analysis made with an Orsat apparatus is by volume:

Carbon dioxide	CO_2	per cent. by volume
Oxygen	O_2	,, ,, ,, ,,
Carbon monoxide	CO	,, ,, ,, ,,
Nitrogen (by diff.)	N_2	,, ,, ,, ,,
		100 per cent.

It is then necessary to convert this into a weight or mass analysis, or percentage analysis by weight. This is done by multiplying the volumetric analysis by the molecular weights of the respective components and, converting the resulting products into percentages of the total.

The reason for multiplying by molecular weights is a result of Avogadro's Law, which states that, at the same temperature and pressure, equal volumes of different gases contain the same number of molecules. Thus all gases have the same volume per molecule at the same temperature and pressure, but they have different weights per molecule.

One molecule of CO_2 can be represented as weighing 44
,, ,, ,, O_2 ,, ,, ,, ,, ,, 32
,, ,, ,, CO ,, ,, ,, ,, ,, 28
,, ,, ,, N_2 ,, ,, ,, ,, ,, 28
} but each have the same volume at s.t.p. (see page 280).

Example 2.—The analysis of the flue gases from a coal-fired boiler gave, by volume, 12 per cent. CO_2, 1 per cent. CO, 7 per cent. O_2, and 80 per cent. N_2. Calculate the amount of air entering the combustion chamber per lb. of coal burnt if the composition of the coal by weight is 86 per cent. C, 4 per cent. H_2, ash and undetermined 10 per cent. Calculate also the air theoretically required and the excess air.

Dry Flue Gas	Analysis by Vol. per cent. N	Molecular Wt. M	Product NM	Dry Flue Gas Analysis by Wt. and by Mass per cent.
CO_2	12	44	528	17·5
O_2	7	32	224	7·4
CO	1	28	28	0·9
N_2	80	28	2,240	74·2
	100		3,020	100·0

From the table we see that 1 lb. of dry flue gas contains 0·175 lb. of CO_2 and 0·009 lb. of CO—that is, it contains:

$$\left[\frac{12}{44}\times 0\cdot 175+\frac{12}{28}\times 0\cdot 009\right]=0\cdot 051 \text{ lb. of C.}$$

$$\therefore \text{ 1 lb. of carbon is contained in } \frac{1}{0\cdot 051}=19\cdot 6 \text{ lb. of dry flue gas.}$$

But 1 lb. of coal contains 0·86 lb. of C, which (assuming that it all burns to appear in the flue gas analysis) therefore produces $0\cdot 86 \times 19\cdot 6=16\cdot 9$ lb. of dry flue gas. 1 lb. of coal also contains 0·04 lb. of H_2, which on burning produces $9\times 0\cdot 04=0\cdot 36$ lb. of water vapour.

Hence, 1 lb. of coal burns to produce $16\cdot 9+0\cdot 36=17\cdot 26$ lb. of flue gas.

Of this 17·26 lb. of flue gas $(0\cdot 86+0\cdot 04)=0\cdot 9$ lb. comes from the carbon and hydrogen of the coal, and hence $(17\cdot 26-0\cdot 9)=16\cdot 36$ lb. is air entering the furnace per lb. of coal burnt.

Air theoretically required for complete combustion

$$=\frac{1}{0\cdot 23}\left(\frac{32}{12}\times 0\cdot 86+8\times 0\cdot 04\right)=11\cdot 3 \text{ lb. per 1 lb. of coal.}$$

Therefore, excess air is $(16\cdot 4-11\cdot 3)=5\cdot 1$ lb. $=45$ per cent.

$$\text{Ratio } \frac{\text{air actually used}}{\text{air theoretically required}}=\frac{16\cdot 36}{11\cdot 3}=1\cdot 45.$$

Example 3.—During a boiler trial coal was burned at the rate of 1,527 lb. per hour. The coal had a calorific value 15,000 B.Th.U. per lb. and contained 87 per cent. of carbon by weight. Ashes and cinders were collected at the rate of 221 lb. per hour containing 37 per cent. of carbon by weight. The volumetric analysis of the dry flue gas was CO_2, 12·1; CO, 0·6; O_2, 6·2; N_2, 81·1. Find the combustion efficiency, *i.e.*, what percentage of the calorific value of the coal was actually produced by burning, given that 1 lb. of carbon burning completely to CO_2 evolves 14,550 B.Th.U. and when burning to CO only, 4,350 B.Th.U.

$$\text{Potential heat in fuel fired per second}=\frac{1{,}527\times 15{,}000}{60\times 60}$$
$$=6{,}360 \text{ B.Th.U}$$

Carbon fired per hour $=1{,}527\times 0\cdot 87=1{,}328$ lb.

Carbon in ashes per hour $=221\times 0\cdot 37=81\cdot 8$ lb.

Hence, the carbon burned per hour $=1246\cdot 2$ lb. of which part burns to CO_2 and the rest to CO calculated as follows:

$$133\cdot 1 \text{ lb of } CO_2 \text{ are produced from } \frac{12}{44}\times 133\cdot 1=36\cdot 4 \text{ lb. of carbon}$$

$$4\cdot 2 \text{ lb. of CO are produced from } \frac{24}{56}\times 4\cdot 2=1\cdot 8 \text{ lb. of carbon.}$$

Constituent	Analysis of Dry Flue Gas by Volume (N)	Factor proportional to Molecular Weight $\left(\frac{M}{4}\right)$	Product (N) $\left(\frac{M}{4}\right)$ gives the Analysis by Weight
CO_2	12·1	$\frac{44}{4}=11$	133·1
CO	0·6	$\frac{28}{4}=7$	4·2
O_2	6·2	$\frac{32}{4}=8$	49·6
N_2	81·1	$\frac{28}{4}=7$	567·7
Totals .	100·0		754·6

Hence, of 38·2 lb. of carbon burned, 36·4 lb. burn to CO_2 and 1·8 lb. burn to CO

Therefore, of 1246·2 lb. of carbon burned per hour
1187·6 lb. burn to CO_2 and 58·6 lb. burn to CO.

The heat per second unreleased owing to 58·6 lb of carbon per hour burning to CO instead of to $CO_2 = \frac{58 \cdot 6}{3600}(14{,}550-4{,}350)=166$ B.Th.U. per second.

The heat per second unreleased owing to 81·8 lb. of carbon per hour remaining in ashes and cinders $=\frac{81 \cdot 8 \times 14{,}550}{3{,}600}=331$ B.Th.U. per second.

Thus, of 6,360 B.Th.U. per second potentially available in fuel fired, 497 B.Th.U. remain unreleased owing to CO in the flue gas and unburnt carbon in the ashes and cinders. Hence, the heat actually released $=6{,}360-497=5{,}863$ B.Th.U. per second, and, therefore, the

$$\text{combustion efficiency} = \frac{\text{heat actually produced by combustion}}{\text{potential heat in fuel}}$$

$$=\frac{5863}{6360}=0 \cdot 92 \text{ or } 92 \text{ per cent.}$$

11. Temperature of Combustion.—In the furnace of a boiler we must distinguish between *quantity* of heat produced and the *intensity* of heat, for it is upon the latter that the transmission efficiency depends. The transmission of heat from the furnace gases depends on the differences of temperature across the boiler heating surfaces. The same *quantity* of heat is evolved by the complete combustion of 1 ton of fuel whether it is burned with no excess air or with a large amount of excess air, also whether the time of burning is 1 hour or 1 day, but the *intensity* of heat or temperature due to combustion will be very different, and so, therefore, will the rate of steam generation.

If 1 lb. of carbon yielding 14,550 B.Th.U. is burned completely in 12 lb. of air (which is almost the theoretical minimum) initially at 60° F. to produce 13 lb. of products having a specific heat of numerical value 0·24, then the calculated maximum temperature will be

$$13 \text{ lb.} \times 0 \cdot 24 \frac{\text{B.Th.U.}}{\text{lb. °F.}}(t-60° \text{ F.})=14{,}550 \text{ B.Th.U., or } t=4{,}720° \text{ F.}$$

This temperature is never realised in actual practice because of excess air which is usually present, and also because of imperfect combustion owing to the cooling action of the comparatively cold surfaces of the water-tubes or furnace plates. Combustion is, however, assisted by the large quantity of heat which is stored in the brickwork of furnaces. Pre-heating of air by means of heat from flue gases also assists combustion and reduces waste of heat.

The achieving and maintaining of the highest practicable temperature within the combustion chamber should be the primary aim of the combustion engineer and stoker, provided that this temperature is below that at which furnace materials and superheater tubes begin to deteriorate.

A low furnace temperature can result from a deficiency of air, since incomplete combustion would result and about 70 per cent. of the heat due to combustion of carbon would be lost if the carbon burned to carbon monoxide only instead of completely to carbon dioxide. A large amount of excess air also results in a low furnace temperature and, therefore, a compromise is necessary between excess air and incomplete combustion in order to achieve the highest temperature possible with complete combustion of the fuel in the furnace. The ratio of the quantity of air actually supplied in order to achieve complete combustion in a boiler furnace to the quantity of air theoretically required is a measure of the efficiency of the combustion process.

12. Heating Surface.—The heating surfaces of a boiler have hot gases on one side and comparatively cold water on the other. Heat passes freely from the plate to the water if there is good circulation, but not so easily from the gases to the plate. This latter is probably due to a layer of non-conducting gas being imposed between the plate and the hot gases by the cooling action of the comparatively cold plate on the gas in contact with it. The layer of stagnant and comparatively cold gas can, however, be removed in water-tube boilers by baffling, so that the gas flow is transverse and across the tubes, thus disturbing and sweeping away any gas tending to remain around the tubes.

The quantity of heat which a given area of heating surface will transfer depends not only on the extent of the area but also on the way in which it is arranged relative to the flow of gases.

Once the heat is taken up by a furnace plate or tube it is so quickly given up to the water that the difference in temperature between the two sides of the plate or tube is very small, the plate being practically no hotter than the water unless it is excessively thick, in which case the surface on the fire side will be burnt. It is for this reason that the furnace plates and water-tubes for transmitting are kept as thin as possible consistent with strength.

It will be obvious from the above how essential it is, if efficiency is to be maintained, to keep the heating surfaces free from soot. It is equally important to keep the surfaces and tubes free from scale on the water side, otherwise the rate of transmission of heat is reduced, and the heating surfaces or tubes will get red hot, then soften, blister, and the pressure in the boiler will eventually cause a tube to burst.

13. Evaporative Capacity of Boilers.—The evaporative capacity or mass of water evaporated per lb. of fuel burned does not vary greatly in different types of boilers if fired efficiently with the same quality of fuel in clean boilers. (10 lb. of water evaporated per lb. of fuel is an average figure in clean boilers.) It does vary, however, according to the quality of the fuel used and according to the conditions of the heat-absorbing surfaces, both on the flame side and on the water side. Soot on the flame sides or a deposit of scale on the water sides greatly diminishes the evaporative capacities of boilers, which also vary with the amount of excess air admitted into the combustion chambers.

In attempting a comparison between the evaporative capacities of different boilers it is common practice for the results to be stated so that they are approximately comparable irrespective of the variation in feed water temperatures and boiler pressures which may exist in the different boiler installations. Thus the evaporative capacities of boilers "from and at 212° F." at atmospheric pressure are calculated, and the result called the equivalent evaporation from and at 212° F.

Examples.—(i) A boiler evaporated 8 lb. of water per lb. of coal into dry saturated steam when working at 100 Lb. per sq. in. abs. from feed water at 90° F. Find the equivalent evaporation "from and at 212° F."

Heat required to evaporate 8 lb. of water at 90° F. into dry saturated steam at 100 Lb. per sq. in. abs.

$$=8 \text{ lb.} \times (1188 \cdot 2 - 59) \text{ B.Th.U./lb.} = 9041 \cdot 6 \text{ B.Th.U.}$$

Heat required to evaporate 1 lb. of water at 212° F. into dry saturated steam at 212° F. = L at atmospheric pressure

$$=970 \cdot 6 \text{ B.Th.U.}$$

$$\therefore \text{ Equivalent evaporation from and at } 212° \text{ F.} = \frac{9041 \cdot 6 \text{ B.Th.U.}}{970 \cdot 6 \text{ B.ThU./lb.}}$$

$$=9 \cdot 3 \text{ lb. of water per lb. of coal.}$$

(ii) The evaporative capacity of a Lancashire boiler with two furnaces each of grate area of 16·5 sq. ft. burning 18 lb. of coal per hour per sq. ft. of grate area and evaporating 9 lb. of water per lb. of coal, will be $2 \times 16 \cdot 5 \times 18 \times 9 = 5{,}346$ lb. of steam per hour. If this steam drives an engine requiring 15 lb. of steam per i.h.p.-hour, then the capacity of the boiler may be said to be equivalent to

$$\frac{5346 \frac{\text{lb.}}{\text{hr.}}}{15 \frac{\text{lb.}}{\text{i.h.p.-hr.}}} = 356 \cdot 4 \text{ horse-power when working that particular engine.}$$

(iii) DRAUGHT AND STOKING

14. Natural Draught.—Natural draught is created by means of a chimney alone. It is caused by the difference in temperature, and therefore in density, between a hot column of gas in the chimney and a similar column of cold air outside the chimney.

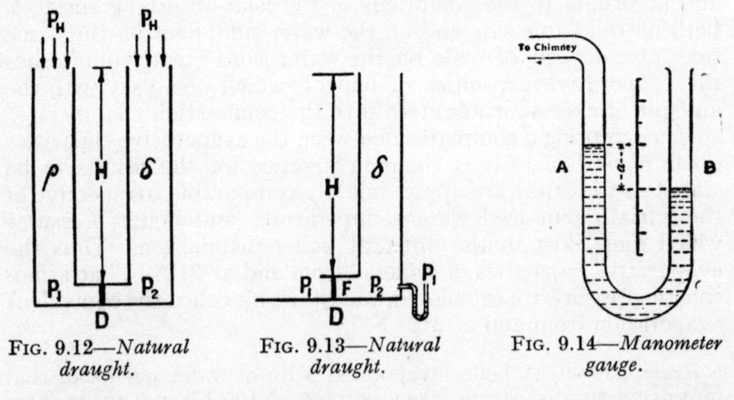

FIG. 9.12—*Natural draught.*

FIG. 9.13—*Natural draught.*

FIG. 9.14—*Manometer gauge.*

Fig. 9.12 shows two columns of different gases equal in height but of different densities ρ and δ (lb. per cu. ft.). In this particular case the densities are taken to be constant throughout the whole of the height H. A duct connects the two columns at the base which is shown closed by means of the partition D. If the pressure of the outer air at a height H is P_H, which acts at the top of both columns, then the pressures at the base of the columns will be $P_1 = P_H + w_1H$ and $P_2 = P_H + w_2H$, where w_1 and w_2 are the specific weights (Lb. per cu. ft.).

Therefore, the static difference of pressure on the two sides of the partition will be $(P_1 - P_2) = (w_1 - w_2)H = g(\rho - \delta)H$, this being a physical formula, i.e. symbols represent numbers × units.

That is, the pressure difference is due to the difference in density $(\rho - \delta)$ of the two columns, and which, in the case of a chimney stack, is caused by a difference in temperature.

If the gas ρ is the cold air of the atmosphere, then the state of the air inside that chimney is exactly the same as the air outside it, and therefore the chimney on the left is unnecessary. Remove that chimney and we are left with one chimney, fig. **9.13**, containing hot flue gases of density δ—which is less than the density of the outside air ρ, and results in a pressure difference at the base of the chimney equal to $P_1 - P_2$. This means that on opening the partition or door D there will be a flow of air from the atmosphere into the furnace F. The air will supply the oxygen necessary for combustion and lead to the production of further hot chimney gases which, in turn, will maintain the draught and inflow of air at the furnace front.

Draught is usually measured in inches of water head. A manometer containing water, fig. 9.14, placed at the base of a chimney will indicate the draught or pressure difference between the gases at the base of the chimney and the outer atmosphere. The height $A = a$ in. measures the draught as a head of water. The draught or pull of an ordinary chimney produces a very small amount of pressure difference.

For example, if in fig. 9.13 the difference in water head is A representing a pressure difference of $(P_1 - P_2)$ between the atmosphere and the chimney, then $P_1 = P_2 + WA$, where W is the specific weight of water $= 62{\cdot}3$ Lb. per cu. ft.

$\therefore \left(\frac{P_1 - P_2}{W}\right) = A$, the head of water which also $= \left(\frac{w_1 - w_2}{W}\right)H$ as deduced from the previous equation.

We can also express draught as a head in inches of water by the numerical formula $(p_1 - p_2) = \frac{a}{27{\cdot}7}$, where $p_1 - p_2$ is the number of Lb./in.^{2} pressure difference and a is the number of inches of water head.

This latter formula is deduced from the general physical formula $P_1-P_2=WA$ by imposing definite units on it,

$$\text{e.g.}\quad \frac{P_1-P_2}{\text{Lb./in.}^2}=62\cdot 3\,\frac{\text{Lb.}}{\text{ft.}^3}\times\frac{A}{\text{in.}}\left\{\frac{\text{in.}^3}{\text{Lb.}}\right\}$$

is the physical formula re-written so as to be able to write

$$(P_1-P_2)=(p_1-p_2)\ \text{Lb./in.}^2 \text{ and } A=a \text{ in.}$$

$$\text{Hence,}\quad p_1-p_2=62\cdot 3\,\frac{\text{Lb.}}{\text{ft.}^3}\times a\left\{\frac{\text{in.}^3}{\text{Lb.}}\right\}\left[\frac{\text{ft.}^3}{1728\ \text{in.}^3}\right]$$

$$\text{i.e.}\quad p_1-p_2=\left(\frac{62\cdot 3}{1728}\right)a=\frac{a}{27\cdot 7}.$$

Thus a draught of 1 in. of water head represents a difference of pressure of 0·0361 Lb. per sq. in.; and in ordinary chimneys, where the draught is less than ½ in. of water, the pressure difference between the outside air and the gases at the base of the chimney will be less than 0·018 Lb. per sq. in. This pressure difference is responsible for the inflow of air to the combustion chamber.

Example.—Take chimney stacks of different heights containing flue gas at different average temperatures and calculate the average density of the flue gas, the draught at the base of the stack, and the pressure difference in Lb. per sq. ft.

From the characteristic gas equation, $PV=RmT$, we see that the density of a gas (taking R as for air) is

$$\delta=\frac{m}{V}=\frac{P}{RT}=\frac{14\cdot 7\times 144}{53\cdot 3\times|T|}\,\frac{\text{lb.}}{\text{ft.}^3}$$

$$=\frac{39\cdot 7}{|T|}\,\frac{\text{lb.}}{\text{ft.}^3}$$

and the specific weight is $w=\dfrac{39\cdot 7}{|T|}$ Lb./ft.³, where $|T|$ is the number of ° abs. F.

From the physical formula $\dfrac{P_1-P_2}{W}=A=\left(\dfrac{w_1-w_2}{W}\right)H$, we see that the draught may be expressed in inches by water and the height of the chimeny in feet by imposing these units on the physical formula:

$$\left(\frac{A}{\text{in.}}\right)=\left(\frac{39\cdot 7}{|T_a|}-\frac{39\cdot 7}{|T|}\right)\frac{\text{Lb.}}{\text{ft.}^3}\left(\frac{1\ \text{ft.}^3}{62\cdot 3\ \text{Lb.}}\right)\left(\frac{H}{\text{ft.}}\right)\left\{\frac{\text{ft.}}{\text{in.}}\right\}\left[\frac{12\ \text{in.}}{\text{ft.}}\right]$$

which may be re-written as a numerical formula, namely,

$$a=\frac{12\times 39\cdot 7}{62\cdot 3}\left(\frac{1}{|T_a|}-\frac{1}{|T|}\right)h$$

$$\text{or}\qquad a=7\cdot 64\left(\frac{1}{|T_a|}-\frac{1}{|T|}\right)h,$$

where a is the number of inches of water, $|T_a|$ and $|T|$ the number of degrees absolute Fahrenheit of atmospheric air and of the average chimney gases, respectively, and h is the number of ft. in the height of the chimney.

Also the pressure difference created is given by the physical formula $P_1-P_2=WA$=specific weight×height of water, and which can be changed into a numerical formula in which the pressure difference is in Lb./ft.² and the draught in inches of water head, as follows:

$$\frac{P_1-P_2}{\text{Lb./ft.}^2}=W\left(\frac{A}{\text{in.}}\right)\left\{\frac{\text{ft.}^2\text{ in.}}{\text{Lb.}}\right\}$$

i.e.
$$p_1-p_2=a\times 62\cdot 3\,\frac{\text{Lb.}}{\text{ft.}^3}\left\{\frac{\text{ft.}^2\text{ in.}}{\text{Lb.}}\right\}\left[\frac{\text{ft.}}{12\text{ in.}}\right]$$

or
$$p_1-p_2=5\cdot 2a,$$

where p_1-p_2 is the number of Lb./ft.² pressure difference and a is the number of inches of water head.

Height of Chimney Stack (H=h ft.)	Average Temperature of Gas in Stack		Average Density of Gas in Stack, $\delta=\frac{39\cdot 7}{\|T\|}$	Draught at Base of Stack, taking air temp. 60° F. $a=7\cdot 64\left(\frac{1}{520}-\frac{1}{\|T\|}\right)h$	Pressure Difference at Base of Stack, $(P_1-P_2)=5\cdot 2a$ Lb. per sq. ft.
ft.	t° F.	|T|abs. °F.	lb. per cu. ft.	in. of water	
250	800	1,260	0·0314	2·15	11·20
	600	1,060	0·0374	1·86	9·66
	400	860	0·0461	1·45	7·55
200	800	1,260	0·0314	1·72	8·95
	600	1,060	0·0374	1·49	7·75
	400	860	0·0461	1·16	6·03
150	800	1,260	0·0314	1·29	6·71
	600	1,060	0·0375	1·12	5·82
	400	860	0·0461	0·87	4·52
100	800	1,260	0·0314	0·86	4·47
	600	1,060	0·0374	0·75	3·90
	400	860	0·0461	0·58	3·02

15. Forced and Induced Draught.—A chimney is a costly structure, and when considered as a means of producing draught, it is by no means the best way of doing it. Fans are much more effective. But a tall chimney of some kind is necessary in any case to emit the gaseous products of combustion at a reasonable height. It is, therefore, also convenient to utilise the chimney as a means of producing natural draught which may be sufficient for ordinary boilers. When a bigger draught is required, some mechanical system for producing draughts is adopted to give induced or forced draught as shown in fig. 9.28.

One of the earliest examples of induced draught is in a locomotive, where the exhaust steam blast is directed up the chimney.

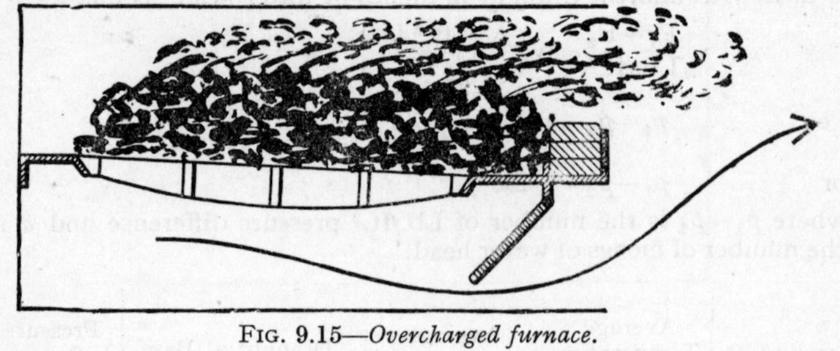

FIG. 9.15—*Overcharged furnace.*

By this means a comparatively small and light boiler can be made to generate steam at a high rate.

Forced draught is usually obtained by means of fans, which deliver air to the furnace under pressures varying from 1 to about 3 in. of water.

FIG. 9.16—*Correctly charged furnace.*

Draught can also be induced by placing a fan, capable of dealing with the products of combustion, near the base of the chimney, as in fig. 9.28. Air is thus drawn through the fires or into the combustion chamber making it possible to burn a larger amount of fuel in a limited combustion space.

16. Stoking.—The most common cause of serious loss of efficiency in a boiler is the flow of cold air to the chimney other than through or over the fire. This may happen in several ways:

(i) By allowing air to flow along the ashpit to the back of the bridge, fig. 9.15, instead of through the firebars. This is usually done to prevent excessive smoke. The damper should, however,

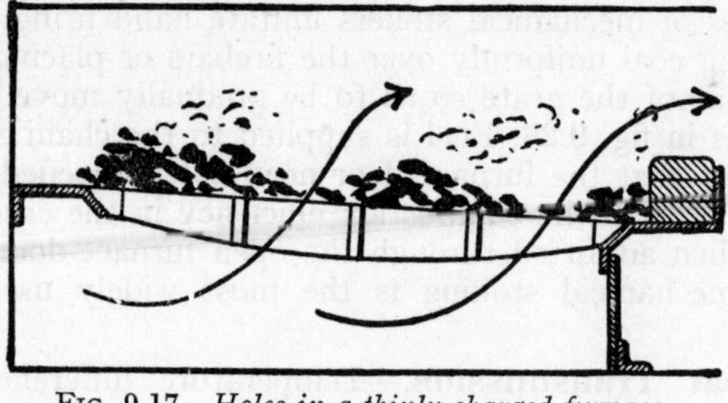

FIG. 9.17—*Holes in a thinly charged furnace.*

only be open for a few moments after firing when black smoke is produced; fig. 9.15 shows a furnace overcharged with coal.

(ii) By air leaks in the brickwork. The motion of the flame of a lighted candle will reveal air leaks if moved over a suspected area of brickwork.

(iii) By the rapid flow of air through badly stoked fires, as shown in figs. 9.17 and 9.18.

FIG. 9.18—*Under-charged furnace near the bridge.*

Fig. 9.16 illustrates good stoking, *i.e.* there is good combustion on a minimum of excess air. This produces the maximum furnace temperature and, therefore, maximum transmission of heat across the heating surfaces and only a trace of smoke at the top of the chimney stack.

When a furnace is not evenly charged with fuel the air flows quicker through the thin parts with the result that the fire soon burns into holes (fig. 9.17). If the furnace is not charged thickly near the bridge air flows straight to the flues as in fig. 9.18, without first having been through or over the fire. Excessive smoke may, however, be prevented in this way.

Mechanical stokers may be used to do away with hand firing. Most types of mechanical stokers imitate hand firing either by distributing coal uniformly over the firebars or placing the coal at the front of the grate so as to be gradually moved into the furnace, as in fig. 9.28. Fuel is supplied to the chain grate from a hopper so that the furnace door need not be opened and cold air which reduces the combustion efficiency in the case of hand stoking when admitted through the open furnace-door. Forced-draught mechanical stoking is the most widely used in this country.

17. Heat Transmission.—Temperature difference is the cause of transfer of heat, which can occur by *convection, conduction* and *radiation*. These three modes of transference of heat occur together in most practical cases, *e.g.* in a boiler furnace the heat released by the combustion of coal reaches the heating surfaces by direct radiation from the fire bed and by reflected radiation from the refractories lining the combustion chamber, and also by convection from the gases due to the contact of the moving gases with the heating surfaces. The heat then passes through the heating surface of the tubes by conduction, and the water in the boiler is heated by convection. Also, the largest part of the heat transferred in condensers, economisers, and air heaters is by convection. The rate at which heat is transferred by conduction and convection depends on temperature difference, whereas radiation of heat depends on the level of temperature of the radiating body. *Conduction of heat is a result of molecular exchange of energy*. The kinetic energy which molecules of a solid may have in excess of that of adjacent molecules results in a transference of heat by conduction, and the quantity of heat which can be so transmitted through a plate is given by the physical formula

$$Q=\frac{kA(T_1-T_2)t}{x} \text{ or } \frac{dQ}{dt}=-kA\frac{dT}{dx},$$

where Q=quantity of heat transmitted; A=area of plate; t=time; (T_1-T_2)=temperature difference; x=thickness; k=coefficient of thermal conductivity.

In the second equation, which states Fourier's law for unidirectional transfer of heat by conduction, the minus sign is introduced in order that the positive direction of flow of heat shall be in the positive direction of x, *the temperature gradient* $\frac{dT}{dx}$ *in the direction of flow of heat being negative always.*

Example 1.—If the temperature difference on two sides of an iron plate $\frac{5}{16}$ in. thick is 17° F., and the coefficient of conductivity of iron is 500 B.Th.U. in. per sq. ft.-hour °F., the heat transmitted per hour per sq. ft. of plate will be

$$Q=\frac{kA(T_1-T_2)t}{x}=\left(500\ \frac{\text{B.Th.U. in.}}{\text{ft.}^2\ \text{°F. hour}}\right)\left(\frac{1\ \text{ft.}^2\times 17°\ \text{F.}\times 1\ \text{hour}}{\frac{5}{16}\ \text{in.}}\right)$$

$$=27{,}200\ \text{B.Th.U.},$$

$$\text{or}\quad \frac{Q}{At}=\frac{k(T_1-T_2)}{x}=\left(\frac{500\ \text{B.Th.U. in.}}{\text{ft.}^2\ \text{°F. hour}}\right)\left(\frac{17°\ \text{F.}}{\frac{5}{16}\text{in.}}\right)=27{,}200\ \frac{\text{B.Th.U.}}{\text{ft.}^2\text{-hr.}}$$

Example 2.—Change the units of the coefficient of conductivity from the British to the c.g.s. system in the following case:

The coefficient of conductivity of lagging is often written $k=0\cdot4$ B.Th.U. per sq. ft. per hour per ° F. per inch of thickness. The interpretation of the " pers " has to be such as to comply with the equation involving the coefficient of conductivity, namely,

$$Q=\frac{kA(T_1-T_2)t}{x}\quad\text{or}\quad k=\frac{Qx}{tA(T_1-T_2)}.$$

Hence, the value of k for the lagging in question is

$$k=\frac{0\cdot4\ \text{B.Th.U. inch}}{\text{hour-ft.}^2\ \text{°F.}}$$

which can be converted into c.g.s. units by means of appropriate unity brackets as follows:

$$k=\frac{0\cdot4\ \text{B.Th.U. in.}}{\text{hour-ft.}^2\ \text{°F.}}\left[\frac{\text{hour}}{3600\ \text{sec.}}\right]\left[\frac{5\ \text{C.H.U.}}{9\ \text{B.Th.U.}}\right]\left[\frac{9°\ \text{F.}}{5°\ \text{C.}}\right]\times$$

$$\left[\frac{453\cdot6\ \text{cal.}}{\text{C.H.U.}}\right]\left[\frac{\text{ft.}^2}{144\ \text{in.}^2}\right]\left[\frac{\text{in.}}{2\cdot54\ \text{cm.}}\right]$$

$$=\frac{0\cdot4\times453\cdot6}{3600\times144\times2\cdot54}\ \frac{\text{cal.}}{\text{sec. cm. °C.}}=\frac{0\cdot1375}{10^3}\ \frac{\text{cal.}}{\text{sec. cm. °C.}}$$

$$\text{or}\ 0\cdot1375\times10^{-3}\ \frac{\text{cal. cm.}}{\text{sec. cm.}^2\ \text{°C.}}$$

which would (unfortunately) often be written as $k=0\cdot1375\times10^{-3}$ calories per sq. cm. per sec. per °C. per cm. of thickness.

Example 3.—A furnace wall consists of 9 in. of firebrick and $4\frac{1}{2}$ in. of insulating brick having thermal conductivities of $0\cdot4$ and $0\cdot15$

$$\frac{\text{B.Th.U.}}{\text{hour-ft. °F.}}\quad\text{or}\quad\frac{\text{B.Th.U. ft.}}{\text{hour-ft.}^2\ \text{°F.}}$$

Calculate the heat transmitted per sq. ft. per hour when the difference in temperature between the inner and outer surface is 900° F.

If $T_1 - T_2 = 900$ °F. and T_3 is the temperature of the surface joining the firebrick and insulating brick, then, since $T_1 - T_3 = \frac{Qx_f}{Atk_f}$ for the firebrick and $T_3 - T_2 = \frac{Qx_i}{Atk_i}$ for the insulating brick, we deduce, by addition, that

$$T_1 - T_2 = \frac{Q}{At}\left(\frac{x_f}{k_f} + \frac{x_i}{k_i}\right)$$

and

$$\frac{Q}{At} = \frac{T_1 - T_2}{\left(\frac{x_f}{k_f} + \frac{x_i}{k_i}\right)}.$$

Hence, replacing each symbol in this physical formula by its value, namely, by a number and its unit or measure, we get

$$\frac{Q}{At} = \frac{900° \text{ F.}}{\left(\frac{9}{0\cdot4} + \frac{4\cdot5}{0\cdot15}\right)\frac{\text{in. hour-ft.}^2\ °\text{F.}}{\text{B.Th.U.} \times 12 \text{ in.}}}$$

$$= \left(\frac{900 \times 12}{22\cdot5 + 30}\right)\frac{\text{B.Th.U.}}{\text{hour-ft.}^2}$$

$$= 205\cdot5 \text{ B.Th.U. per sq. ft. per hour.}$$

Example 4.—Deduce an expression for the rate at which heat flows radially through a thick cylinder of coefficient of thermal conductivity k, and whose inner and outer radii and temperatures are R_i, T_i and R_o, T_o, respectively.

Rate of heat transfer by conduction is given by

$$\boldsymbol{q = \frac{dQ}{dt} = -kA\frac{dT}{dx}}$$

Thus, for a tube of the material of inner radius r, thickness dr and length l within the thick cylinder and across which there is a temperature rise of dT, the rate at which heat flows radially outwards is

$$q = -k(2\pi rl)\frac{dT}{dr} = \text{constant for all such tubes imagined in the thick cylinder.}$$

Hence,

$$q\int_{R_i}^{R_o}\frac{dr}{r} = -2\pi lk\int_{T_i}^{T_o} dT$$

and

$$q = \frac{dQ}{dt} = \frac{2\pi lk(T_i - T_o)}{\log_\varepsilon \frac{R_o}{R_i}}.$$

Example 5.—A pipe of 6 in. outside diameter carries dry saturated steam at 200 Lb./in.^{2} abs. The pipe is lagged with a 2 in. thickness of material of thermal conductivity $0 \cdot 12 \frac{\text{B.Th.U.}}{\text{ft.-hour °F.}}$ The temperature of the exposed surface of the lagging was found to be 169° F. Neglecting any drop in temperature through the wall of the pipe, estimate the amount of steam condensed per hour for each foot length of pipe.

From the formula of Example 4, we deduce that the rate at which heat flows through the surface of 1 ft. length of lagging is

$$q = \frac{2\pi \times 1 \text{ ft.} \times 0 \cdot 12 \frac{\text{B.Th.U.}}{\text{ft.-hour °F.}} (382 - 169) \text{ °F.}}{\log_\varepsilon \frac{5}{3}}$$

$$= 314 \text{ B.Th.U./hour.}$$

From the steam tables the latent heat of steam at 200 Lb./in.^{2} abs. is found to be 844 B.Th.U./lb. Hence, the mass of steam condensed per hour in each foot length of pipe is $\frac{314 \text{ B.Th.U./hour}}{844 \text{ B.Th.U./lb.}} = 0 \cdot 373$ lb./hour.

Because of the difficulty of generalising where turbulent motion is concerned, a complete analysis of convection has not yet been accomplished. In the case of radiant heat, it is known to travel at the rate of 186,000 miles per second and is in the same category as wireless waves, light, and X-rays. The rate at which radiant energy is emitted, absorbed or reflected depends on the nature of the body, the state and extent of its surface, and on its temperature. Polished surfaces reflect thermal radiation according to the laws of optics, but **a body which absorbs all the radiation falling upon it, *i.e.* has a non-reflecting surface, is said to be a "black" body.** Experiment shows that a high or low absorber of radiant heat is a high or low emitter of radiation. Also, **a "black" body emits the maximum amount of radiation possible at a given temperature, and the amount is proportional to the fourth power of the absolute temperature.** In general, the emissivity of a real body is defined as the ratio of the thermal radiation actually emitted from the body to that which would be emitted in the same time from the same area of a black body at the same temperature. The exact nature of the process of emission and absorption of radiation are still unknown, although they are accompanied by changes which are believed to occur in the outer parts of atoms. Certain laws of radiation have, however, been discovered, *e.g.* different surfaces at the same temperature emit radiant energy at different rates. The low emissivities and absorptivities of polished metals are made use of in apparatus used in tests and trials, *e.g.* the external surfaces of throttling and other forms of calorimeters are brightly polished to reduce loss of heat by radiation.

The amount of heat transmitted to boiler heating surfaces by radiation can be estimated from the Stefan-Boltzmann formula

$$Q = K(T_1^4 - T_2^4),$$

where Q = heat transmitted per unit area of hot surface in unit time.
K = a constant depending on the unit of heat used and on the condition of the surface.
T_1 = absolute temperature of the furnace.
T_2 = absolute temperature of the heating surface.

Experimental results led Planck to the view that emission and absorption of radiation was not a perfectly continuous process, but occurred in small amounts or quanta of energy as given in his quantum theory. Since the quantity of heat radiated depends upon the fourth power of the absolute temperature, it will be obvious that a small increase in the temperature of the furnace is responsible for a comparatively large increase in the heat transmitted across the boiler heating surfaces. *Hence the importance of achieving as high a temperature as is practically possible in boiler furnaces.*

Improvements in design and construction of boilers have been such that efficiencies of over 90 per cent. are now possible, and steam generating plant in some power stations are capable of delivering over a quarter of a million pounds of steam per hour.

More efficient economisers and air pre-heaters have been fitted, both of which abstract heat from the flue gases before rejection up the chimney stack (see fig. 9.28). Combustion chambers have been designed to yield 13 to 14 per cent. CO_2 without CO in the gases at the base of the chimney, and water-cooled furnace walls or "water walls" absorb heat from the fuel bed and also reduce the space into which large boilers can be installed.

(IV) BOILER AUXILIARIES

18. Steam Regulating Valves.—The *stop valve* is fitted in order to open or close the communication between the boiler and engine or other steam-using plant. Fig. 9.19 shows in section a common type of stop valve which may be opened or closed by means of a screwed spindle when turned by a hand wheel.

Fig. 9.20 shows the section of an equilibrium valve which consists of two disc-valves, A and B, on one spindle, each of which

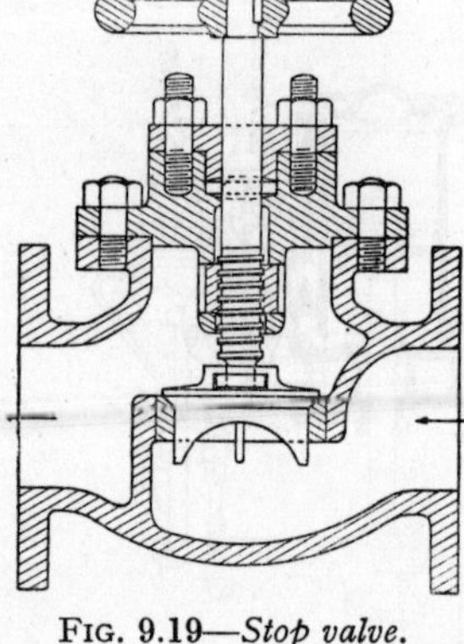

Fig. 9.19—*Stop valve.*

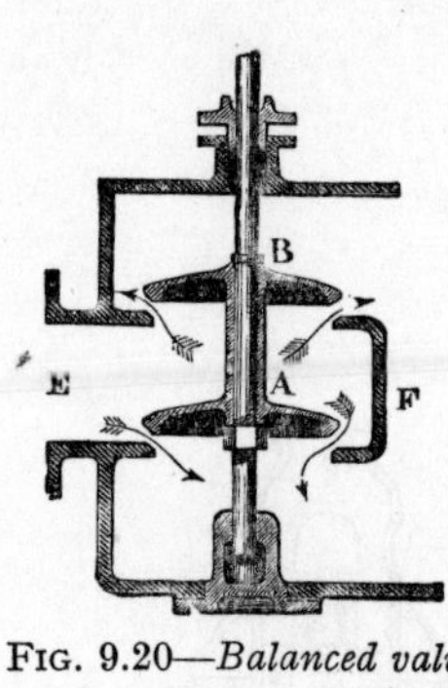

Fig. 9.20—*Balanced valve.*

has its own seating. The arrows show the direction of the steam on entering the valve box F from the passage E. The valve B is made a little larger than A to enable the lower valve A to be put in its place from the top. The pressure of the steam acts on the top side of valve A and on the under side of valve B, hence the two valves, being nearly in equilibrium, may easily be lifted from their seating when under pressure. This design of double-beat valve provides a large opening to steam in valves of comparatively small diameter.

The Spring-loaded Safety Valve for Locomotives.—This type of safety valve, otherwise known as Ramsbottom's valve, is illustrated in fig. 9.21. It consists of two separate valves and seatings, having one lever which acts on the two valves and which is loaded by a spring placed between them. To be sure that the valves are not sticking, the pressure on either valve can be reduced by movement of the lever.

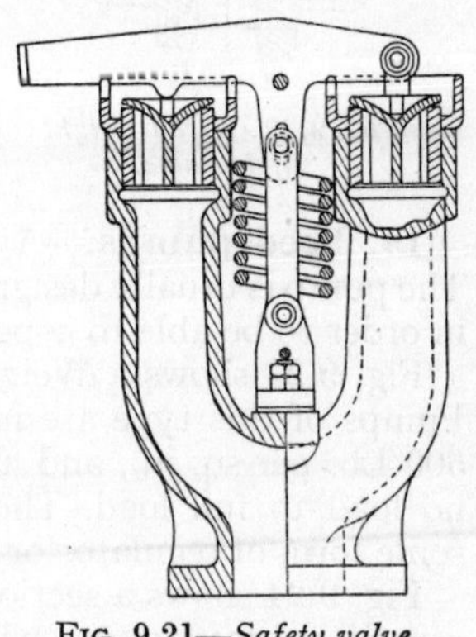

Fig. 9.21—*Safety valve.*

The Dead-weight Safety Valve.—Fig. 9.22 shows a type of dead-weight safety valve for stationary boilers. The valve *a* rests on the seating *b*, which is situated on the top of a length of pipe. The valve is fastened to the casting A, which fits over the pipe like a sleeve. Weights W rest on the casting and form the dead-load.

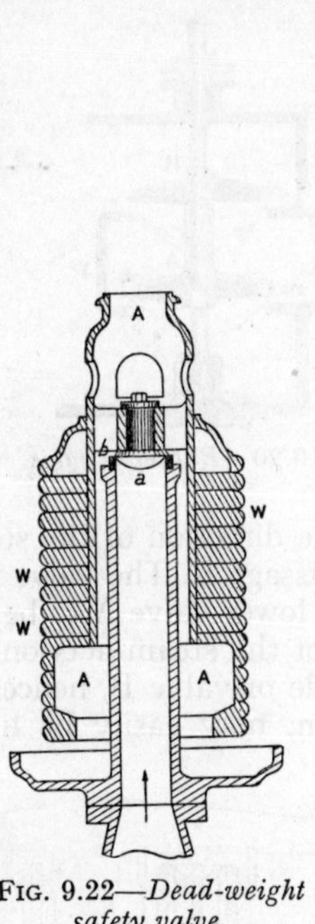

FIG. 9.22—*Dead-weight safety valve.*

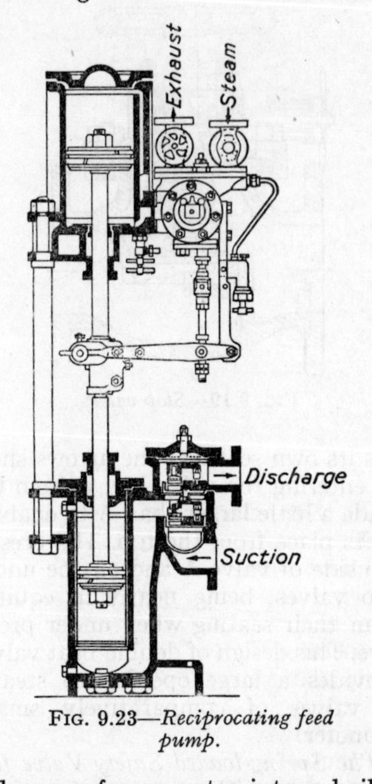

FIG. 9.23—*Reciprocating feed pump.*

19. Feed pumps.—A feed pump forces water into a boiler. The pump is usually designed larger than for the full load quantity in order to be able to cope with emergencies.

Fig. 9.23 shows a Weir direct-acting steam-driven feed pump. Pumps of this type are in operation with steam pressures up to 500 Lb. per sq. in., and are extremely flexible in operation from no load to full load. They can be controlled automatically by some form of regulator or by hand.

Fig. 9.24 shows a section through a turbine-driven single-stage centrifugal-feed pump whose speed ranges from 8,000 r.p.m. in small pumps to 5,000 r.p.m. in large pumps. Such pumps will discharge into boilers working at pressures up to 400 Lb. per sq. in., and two-stage pumps can be used for higher pressures.

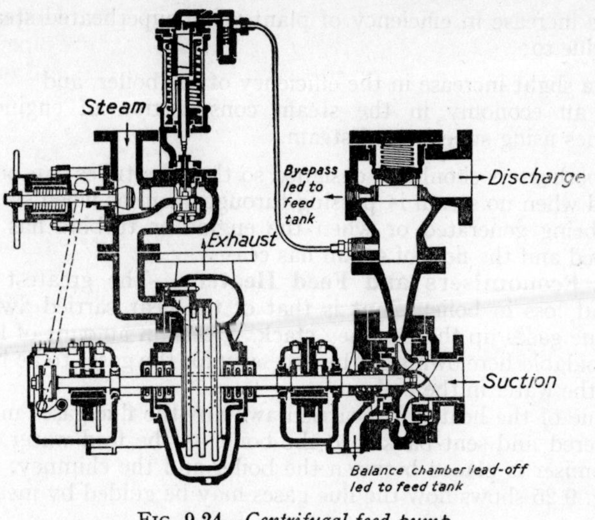

FIG. 9.24—*Centrifugal feed pump.*

20. Superheaters.—The steam generated from water in a boiler drum is saturated steam never quite reaching unity dryness fraction. We have seen that the temperature of saturated steam depends upon the pressure and that by the further application of heat to dry saturated steam it becomes *superheated*, that is, its temperature is raised above the saturation temperature at the particular pressure at which the steam is generated. The degree of superheat is $(t'-t_s)$, where t' is the actual temperature of the superheated steam and t_s is the saturation temperature at the particular pressure of the steam. The increase in efficiency obtained by the use of superheated steam has led to its increasing use in steam engines and turbines.

The usual method of producing superheated steam is that of leading saturated steam from the boiler drum through a series of tubes which form the superheater situated where the hottest gases of combustion are flowing. If steam is highly superheated by the hot products of combustion, the boiler efficiency will most probably be only slightly increased, because the heat which is used for superheating the steam would otherwise have been used in producing saturated steam; but an increase in the overall efficiency of steam plant is obtained because of the reduced steam consumption of an engine or turbine using superheated steam.

The increase in efficiency of plant using superheated steam is thus due to:

(i) a slight increase in the efficiency of the boiler, and

(ii) an economy in the steam consumption of engines or turbines using superheated steam.

Superheaters should be designed so that the tubes can be protected when no steam is passing through them as when steam is first being generated or when the engine or turbine has been stopped and the flow of steam has ceased.

21. Economisers and Feed Heaters.—The greatest item of heat loss in boiler plant is that of the heat carried away in the flue gases up the chimney stack. A certain amount of loss is unavoidable here owing to the necessity for the gases to be hotter than the water in the boiler.

Some of the heat being carried away by the flue gases may be recovered and sent back into the boiler in the feed water, if an economiser is placed between the boiler and the chimney.

Fig. 9.25 shows how the flue gases may be guided by means of

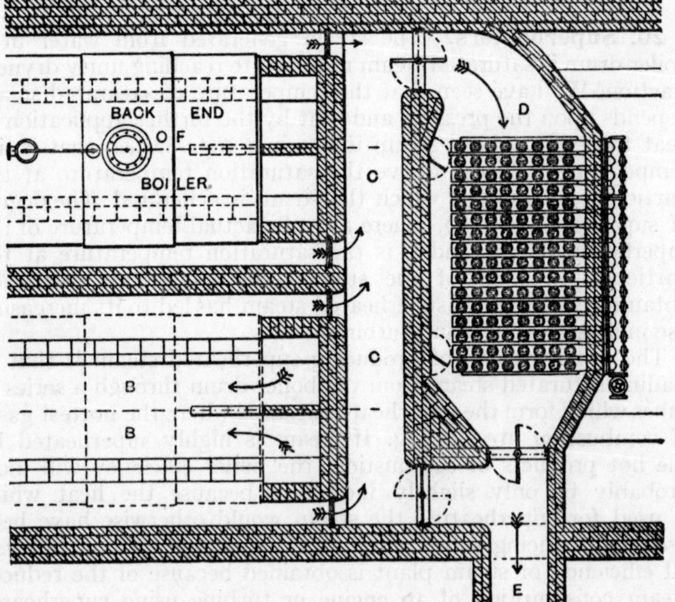

FIG. 9.25—*Economiser and gas flow.*

dampers so as to pass through an economiser on their way to the chimney, or direct to the chimney without passing through the economiser.

There are many different designs of economisers to suit the many designs of boilers, but they all work on the same principle. A saving of over 10 per cent. is often achieved by their use.

Example 1.—Feed water enters an economiser at 90° F. and leaves at 200° F. If the pressure in the boiler is 135 Lb. per sq. in. abs., find the percentage saving by use of the economiser, assuming the steam to be dry and saturated.

If no economiser is used the heat required to raise 1 lb. of dry saturated steam at 135 Lb. per sq. in. abs. from feed water at 90° F. will be $(H_{s1} - h_f) = 1193 \cdot 4 - 58 = 1135 \cdot 4$ B.Th.U.

If the economiser is used the heat required to raise 1 lb. of dry saturated steam at 135 Lb. per sq. in. abs. from feed water at 200° F will be $1193 \cdot 4 - 168 = 1025 \cdot 4$ B.Th.U.

There is therefore a saving of 110 B.Th.U. per lb. or

$$\frac{110}{1135 \cdot 4} \times 100 = 9 \cdot 7 \text{ per cent.}$$

Example 2.—The amount of feed water passing through the economiser of a Lancashire boiler is 5,000 lb. per hour. The temperature of the water entering the economiser is 100° F. and on leaving is 220° F. If the temperature of the flue gases entering the economiser is 600° F. and estimated to flow at the rate of 10,000 lb. per hour, find the temperature of the gases which finally pass up the chimney stack. The specific heat of flue gases may be taken as 0·24 B.Th.U. per lb. ° F.

Heat lost by flue gases of final temperature t_f = heat gained by water.

$$10{,}000\,\frac{\text{lb}_g.}{\text{hour}} \times 0 \cdot 24\,\frac{\text{B.Th.U.}}{\text{lb}_g\,°\text{F.}} \times \left(600 - \frac{t_f}{°\text{F.}}\right)°\text{F.}$$

$$= 5000\,\frac{\text{lb}_w}{\text{hour}} \times \frac{1\ \text{B.Th.U.}}{\text{lb}_w\,°\text{F.}}\,(220 - 100)°\ \text{F.}$$

$$\text{i.e.} \qquad \frac{t_f}{°\text{F.}} = 600 - \frac{5000 \times 120}{2400} = 600 - 250$$

$$\text{or} \qquad t_f = 350°\ \text{F.}$$

Feed heaters are also used for supplying boilers with hot feed water, and an important advantage which they possess is that most of the dissolved gases, such as air and carbon monoxide, are separated out and liberated from the water. Any calcium bi-carbonate present can be removed before the water is pumped into the boiler. The modern development of high-capacity, high-pressure boilers would never have been possible without feed-water chemists and equipment for feed-water treatment. Modern feed-water treatment eliminates the formation of scale on boiler tubes, and de-aerating feed-water heaters eliminate corrosion difficulties.

Fig. 9.26 shows a section through a feed heater in which the feed water is pumped through the U-tubes which are exposed to steam brought from one or more points in the turbine expansion or from a receiver between the cylinders of a multiple expansion steam engine. The steam condenses in the heater in raising the temperature of the feed water. The heater condensate is passed into the main condensate system. It is found that by heating the boiler feed water with partly expanded steam an increase in thermal efficiency of turbine and engine plant is obtained.

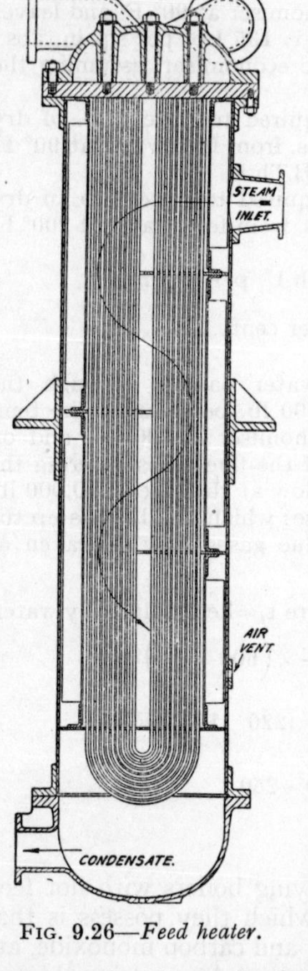

Fig. 9.26—*Feed heater.*

22. De-aerating Plant. — Boiler feed water is often de-aerated before being passed on to the economiser and boiler in order to prevent corrosion, and also to avoid passing air with steam into the condenser and thus reducing the vacuum.

Fig. 9.27 illustrates a de-aerator. It is of the spray type consisting of a de-aerating vessel A which is evacuated by a steam-operated ejector B.

Hot feed water enters through the inlet pipe C and is sprayed into the vacuum space through the special spray-nozzle valve D. The supply of water is regulated by the bucket-float E operating on the water level in the vessel. The extraction pump F withdraws the water from the de-aerator and discharges it into the boiler feed-pump suction range. A loaded non-return valve G may be fitted between the de-aerator inlet and extraction pump discharge, which will operate automatically and admit feed water direct from the feed tank to the boiler feed pump in the event of the extraction pump motor being stopped. This de-aeration can be used without any form of feed heating provided

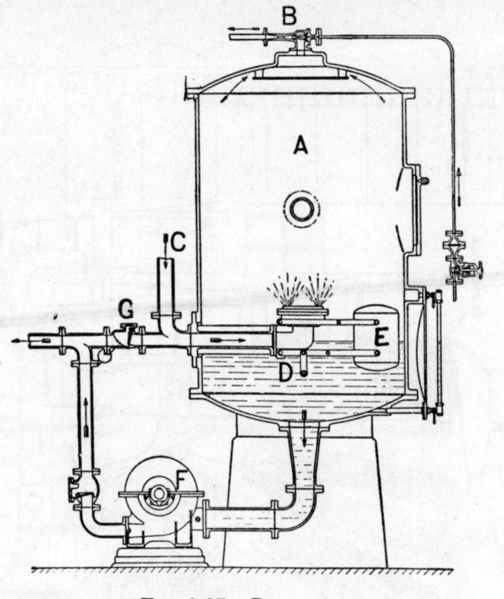

Fig. 9.27—*De-aerator.*

that the water inlet temperature is not less than 130° F.—the de-aeration then being effective owing to the fine spray. A full spraying effect is obtained at all duties by the special arrangement of control, which opens up groups of nozzles in sequence according to the demand on the plant. Where the temperature of water is slightly less than 130° F. a separate exhaust steam feed heater may be fitted in the pipe-line C, or, if more convenient, exhaust steam may be blown into the hot-well to bring the water up to the required temperature.

Fig. 9.28 shows a section through a boiler plant in which solid fuel is fed into the furnace by means of a mechanical chain-grate stoker.

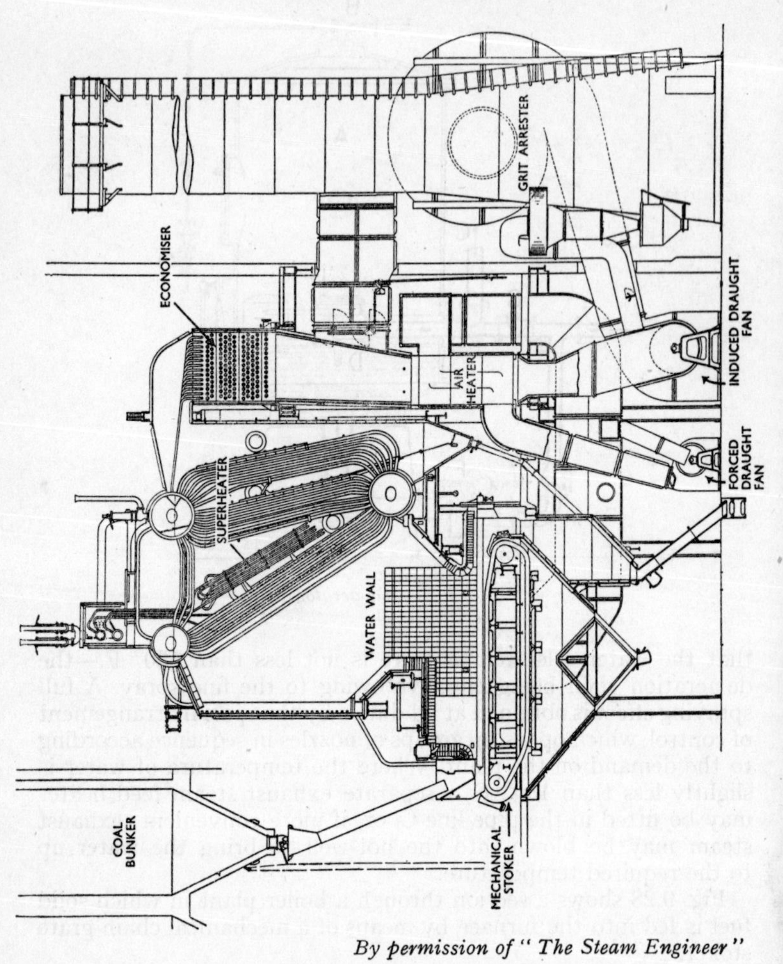

By permission of "The Steam Engineer"

FIG. 9.28—*Section through a boiler plant.*

23. (v) Report on a Boiler Trial

I. OBJECT OF TRIAL

To estimate the steam raising capacity and efficiency of the boiler when working at a definite pressure; also to draw up a heat account or heat balance sheet for the boiler.

II. THE PLANT

(*a*) *Diagrammatic Sketch or Line Diagram of Plant.*—From fig. 9.29 the energy equation and energy stream diagram can be deduced as follows.

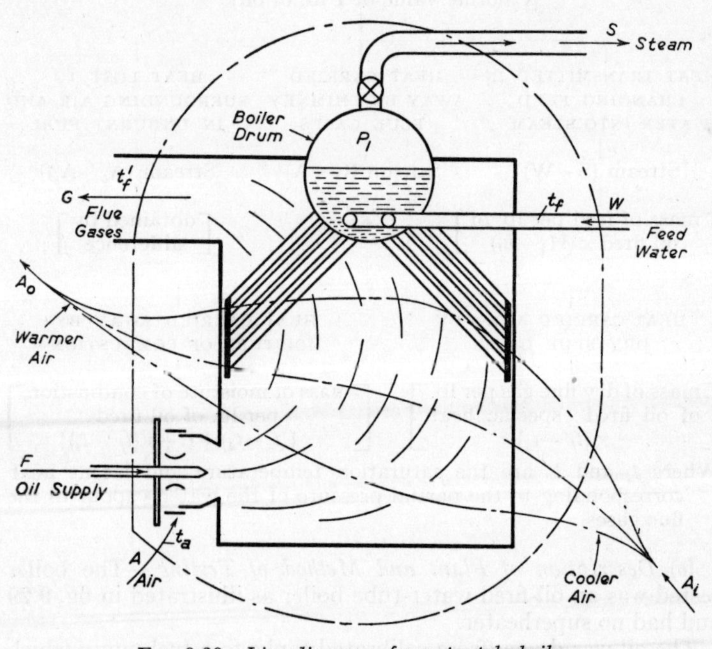

FIG. 9.29—*Line diagram of a water-tube boiler.*

(*b*) *Energy Equation and Energy Stream Diagram.*—When the boiler has been running long enough for steady conditions to have been reached, the rate of flow of energy into the boundary must be equal to the rate at which energy flows out of the boundary. Thus:—

$$F+A+W+A_i=S+G+A_o$$

or $$F=(S-W)+(G-A)+(A_o-A_i)$$

where the letters represent the amounts of energy flowing along the energy streams per lb. of oil fired.

From the latter equation the following energy stream diagram can be deduced:—

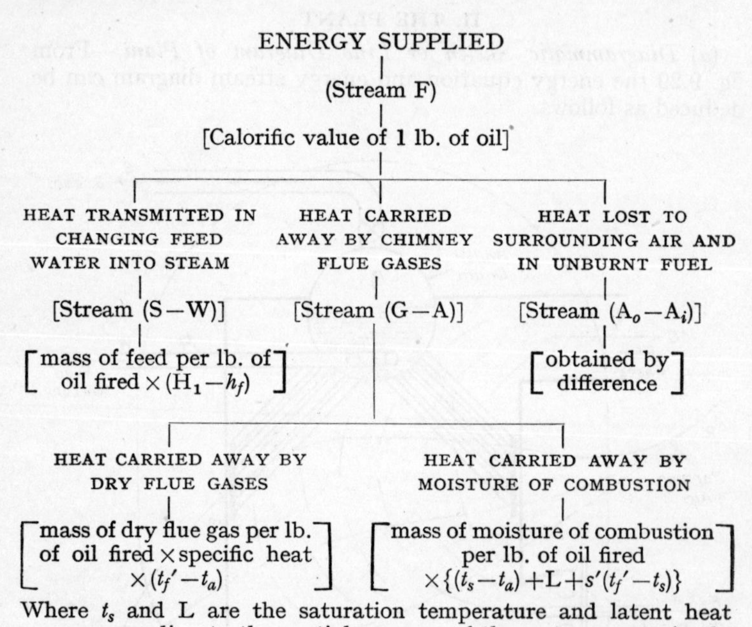

Where t_s and L are the saturation temperature and latent heat corresponding to the partial pressure of the water vapour in the flue gases.

(c) *Description of Plant and Method of Testing.*—The boiler tested was an oil-fired water-tube boiler as illustrated in fig. 9.29 and had no superheater.

The oil was drawn from calibrated tanks to a fuel pump which delivered the oil under pressure to the burner at the furnace front. The quantity of oil fired was obtained from observations made on the calibrated tanks.

The feed water was passed through a water-softener into calibrated tanks from which it was drawn by the feed pump for delivery into the boiler drum. The rate at which feed water was pumped into the boiler was, therefore, estimated from observations made on the calibrated feed tanks. The dryness fraction of the steam delivered from the boiler was estimated by means of a throttling calorimeter.

The gases passing along the flue to the chimney were analysed by means of an Orsat apparatus.

Simultaneous observations were made on all the instruments and apparatus every 10 minutes.

III. REPORT SHEET ON

BOILER DATA : Total heating surface 205 sq. ft.
DATE OF TRIAL :
DURATION OF TRIAL : 8 hours.

Oil Supply.		
Temperature of oil supplied at burner,	°F.	90
Pressure of oil supplied at burner,	Lb. per sq. in. gauge	134
Oil used was Shell " Domestic,"	specific gravity	0·89
Percentage composition (by wt.)	Carbon	85·25
	Hydrogen	13·0
	Sulphur	1·25
	Undetermined	0·5
		100·0
Higher calorific value of oil,	B.Th.U. per lb.	19,250
Oil fired per hour,	lb.	112
Heat Transmitted to Feed Water.		
Feed water pumped per hour,	lb.	1,390
Temperature of feed water entering boiler,	°F.	165
Boiler pressure,	Lb. per sq. in. gauge	124
Absolute pressure in boiler,	Lb. per sq. in. abs.	139
Throttling calorimeter temperature at inlet, t_1,	°F.	352·4
Throttling calorimeter temperature at outlet, t_2',	°F.	230
Dryness fraction of steam delivered.		0·96
Total heat of steam delivered.	B.Th.U. per lb.	1159·4
Total heat of feed water entering boiler,	B.Th.U. per lb.	133
Heat transmitted to 1 lb. of steam,	B.Th.U.	1026·4
Steam raised per lb. of oil fired,	lb.	12·4
Heat transmitted to steam per lb. of oil fired,	B.Th.U.	12,735

Heat to Flue Gases.	% by Volume.	% by Weight.
Dry flue gas analysis : CO_2	12·4	18·1
O_2	4·3	4·6
CO	0	0
N_2	83·3	77·3
	100·0	100·0

BOILER TRIAL

Mass of dry flue gases per lb. of oil fired,	lb.	17·3
Specific heat of dry flue gases,		0·24
Temperature of flue gases leaving boiler,	°F.	645
Chimney draught,	inches of water	0·075
Temperature of air in boiler house, t_a,	°F.	70
Heat carried away by dry flue gases per lb. of oil fired,	B.Th.U.	2,385
Moisture of Combustion.		
Moisture of combustion from 1 lb. of oil fired,	lb.	1·17
Heat carried away by moisture of combustion per lb. of oil fired,	B.Th.U.	1,550
Total heat carried away by flue gases per lb. of oil fired,	B.Th.U.	3,935
Heat Account per lb. of Oil Fired.	B.Th.U.	%
Heat supplied to the boiler (H.C.V.)	19,250	100
Heat transmitted to water and steam	12,735	66·2
Heat carried away by dry flue gases.	2,385 }	
Heat carried away by moisture of combustion.	1,550 }	20·4
Heat lost to surrounding air, and in unburnt fuel.	2,580	13·4
	19,250	100
Efficiency.		
Boiler efficiency (H.C.V. basis),	per cent.	66·2
Deductions.		
Equivalent evaporation from and at 212° F. per lb. of oil fired,	lb.	13·1
Equivalent evaporation per hour,	lb.	1,470
Equivalent evaporation per sq. ft. of heating surface,	lb.	7·17
Theoretical air required to burn completely 1 lb. of oil,	lb.	14·46
Actual air entering combustion chamber per lb. of oil,	lb.	17·42
Ratio of actual to theoretical air.		1·2
Excess air.	per cent.	20·4

IV. SPECIMEN SET OF CALCULATIONS

Dryness Fraction of Steam Delivered.

Inlet and outlet temperatures observed on throttling calorimeter were $t_1 = 352 \cdot 4°$ F. and $t_2' = 230°$ F. respectively.

$$\text{Dryness fraction} \quad q_1 = \frac{H_{s2} + 0 \cdot 48(t_2' - t_{s2}) - h_{w1}}{L_1},$$

$$\text{which from steam tables} = \frac{1151 \cdot 2 + 0 \cdot 48(230 - 213) - 324 \cdot 3}{869 \cdot 6}$$

$$= \frac{835 \cdot 1}{869 \cdot 6} = 0 \cdot 96.$$

Heat Transmitted.

Total heat of 1 lb. of steam delivered at 139 Lb. per sq. in. abs. and $0 \cdot 96$ dryness fraction

$$= H_1 = h_{w1} + q_1 L_1 = 324 \cdot 3 + 0 \cdot 96 \times 869 \cdot 6 = 1159 \cdot 4 \text{ B.Th.U.}$$

Total heat of feed water entering boiler = 133 B.Th.U.

∴ Heat transmitted to 1 lb. of steam $1159 \cdot 4 - 133 = 1026 \cdot 4$ B.Th.U

Feed water pumped per hour = 1,390 lb.

Oil fired per hour = 112 lb.

$$\therefore \text{ Steam raised per lb. of oil fired} = \frac{1390}{112} = 12 \cdot 4 \text{ lb}$$

∴ Heat transmitted to steam per lb. of oil fired

$$= 12 \cdot 4 \times 1026 \cdot 4 = 12{,}735 \text{ B.Th.U.}$$

Dry Flue Gases.

Dry Flue Gases, % by Volume N	Factor $\left(\frac{M}{4}\right)$ Proportional to Molecular Weight	Product $N \times \frac{M}{4}$ i.e. analysis by weight	Dry Flue Gases % by Weight
Dry flue gas analysis:			
CO_2 12·4	11	136·4	18·1
O_2 4·3	8	34·4	4·6
CO 0	7	0	0
N_2 83·3	7	583·1	77·3
100·0		753·9	100·0

Mass of dry flue gases per lb. of oil fired

$$=\left\{\frac{C}{\frac{3}{11}CO_2}\right\}=\frac{0\cdot8255}{\frac{3}{11}\times0\cdot118}=17\cdot25 \text{ lb. of which} \begin{cases} 3\cdot12 \text{ lb. is } CO_2 \\ 0\cdot80 \text{ lb. is } O_2 \\ 13\cdot33 \text{ lb. is } N_2 \end{cases}$$

where C = mass of carbon in 1 lb. of oil fired, and CO_2 = mass of CO_2 in 1 lb. of dry flue gas.

Specific heat of dry flue gases taken as 0·24 B.Th.U. per lb. °F.
Temperature of flue gases leaving boiler $= t_f' = 645$ °F.
Temperature of air entering furnace $= t_a = 70°$ F.

∴ Heat carried away by dry flue gas per lb. of oil fired = $\{\text{mass} \times \text{sp. heat} \times (t_f' - t_a)\} = 17\cdot25 \times 0\cdot24 \times (645-70) = 2385$ B.Th.U.

Moisture of Combustion.

Mass of hydrogen present in 1 lb. of oil = 0·13 lb.

∴ Moisture produced by the combustion of 1 lb. of oil $= 9 \times 0\cdot13 = 1\cdot17$ lb.

Thus, the burning of 1 lb. of oil produces a total mass of flue gases $= 17\cdot25 + 1\cdot17 = 18\cdot42$ lb., composed of 3·12 lb. CO_2, 0·80 lb. O_2, 13·33 lb. N_2, and 1·17 lb. H_2O, from which the following table can be drawn up for the total flue gases.

Constituent	Total Flue Gases by Weight or by Mass		Molecular Weight of Constituent	Total Flue Gases by Volume		Partial Pressure of Constituent (Lb. per sq. in. abs.)
	per lb. of Oil Fuel	Per cent.		Volumetric Analysis	Per cent.	
		m	M	m/M	v	15 × v/100
H_2O	1·17	6·3	18	0·353	10·3	1·55
CO_2	3·12	16·9	44	0·385	11·1	1·66
O_2	0·80	4·3	32	0·136	3·9	0·58
N_2	13·33	72·5	28	2·588	74·7	11·21
Total	18·42	100·0	—	3·462	100·0	15·00

Thus the pressure of the water vapour in the flue gases is 1·55 Lb. per sq. in. abs., the corresponding saturation temperature and latent heat at this pressure being 117° F. and 1027·5 B.Th.U. per lb., respectively (see also Example 4 on page 281).

Taking an average temperature of oil and air in the boiler-house as 75° F., the heat required to change 1·17 lb. of moisture at 75° F. into superheated steam at 645° F.

$= 1\cdot17 \times \{(117-75) + 1027\cdot5 + 0\cdot48(645-117)\} = 1{,}550$ B.Th.U.

which is carried away in addition to that of the dry flue gases.

$\therefore$ Heat carried away by flue gases per lb. of oil fired

$$=2{,}385+1{,}550=3{,}935 \text{ B.Th.U.}$$

Efficiencies.

Boiler efficiency $=\dfrac{\text{heat transmitted}}{\text{heat supplied}}$, which, on the basis of higher or gross calorific value $=\dfrac{12{,}735}{19{,}250}=66\cdot 2$ per cent.

Deductions.

Equivalent evaporation from and at 212° F.

$$=\frac{12{,}735}{970\cdot 6}=13\cdot 1 \text{ lb. of steam per lb. of oil fired.}$$

Equivalent evaporation per hour $=13\cdot 1\times 112=1{,}470$ lb.

Equivalent evaporation per sq. ft. of heating surface

$$=\frac{1{,}470}{205}=7\cdot 17 \text{ lb.}$$

Excess Air.

The theoretical air required for the complete combustion of 1 lb. of this oil was worked out in Example 1, page 183, to be 14·46 lb.

From the flue gas analysis we get that 1 lb. of dry flue gas contains $0\cdot 181$ lb. of CO_2, i.e. $\frac{12}{44}\times 0\cdot 181$ lb. of C.

$\therefore$ 1 lb. of C is contained in $\dfrac{44}{12\times 0\cdot 181}$ lb. of dry flue gas.

But 1 lb. of oil contains 0·8525 lb. of C and therefore produces

$$\frac{44}{12}\times\frac{0\cdot 8525}{0\cdot 181}=17\cdot 25 \text{ lb. of dry flue gas.}$$

Also 1 lb. of oil contains 0·13 lb. of H_2, which produces

$$0\cdot 13\times 9=1\cdot 17 \text{ lb. of moisture.}$$

$\therefore$ 1 lb. of oil produces $(17\cdot 25+1\cdot 17)=18\cdot 42$ lb. of flue gases. Of this mass 1 lb. comes from the oil (assuming all burnt). Therefore, the amount of air entering the combustion chamber per lb. of oil fired $=17\cdot 42$ lb.

$$\therefore \text{Ratio of } \frac{\text{air entering combustion chamber}}{\text{theoretical air required}}=\frac{17\cdot 42}{14\cdot 46}=1\cdot 2.$$

Mass of excess air per lb. of oil $=17\cdot 42-14\cdot 46=2\cdot 96$ lb.

$$\text{Per cent. excess air}=\frac{2\cdot 96}{14\cdot 46}=20\cdot 4 \text{ per cent.}$$

V. GRAPHICAL REPRESENTATIONS OF RESULTS

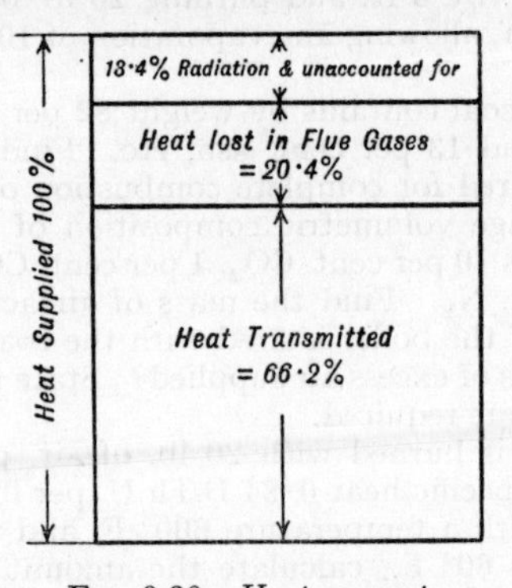

Fig. 9.30—*Heat account.*

VI. CONCLUSIONS AND CRITICISMS

We may criticise the report on this trial by saying that no account has been taken of the power required to drive the pump which delivers the oil under pressure to the burner. Also, the feed-water softener delivered water to the boiler feed pump at 165° F. without any heat being given by the boiler steam to the softening plant. The temperature of the softening plant was maintained by a neighbouring boiler; hence, during the test here reported, a benefit was derived from the softener without any contribution to the heat required by that plant being made from the boiler under test. Also, the moisture in the air supplying the oxygen has been neglected.

A more complete test on this boiler would take into account the above items which would appear on the heat account of fig. 9.30.

EXERCISES ON CHAPTER 9

(i)

1. What is meant by the expression " equivalent evaporation from and at 212° F."?

A boiler evaporates 7·5 lb. of water per lb. of coal fired from feed water entering at 100° F. when working at a pressure 150 Lb. per sq. in. gauge. Find the equivalent evaporation from and at 212° F., assuming unity dryness fraction and an absolute atmospheric pressure of 15 Lb. per sq. in.

2. Find the evaporative capacity of a marine boiler having three furnaces each 3 ft. by 6 ft. and burning 20 lb. of coal per hour per sq. ft. of grate area, allowing an evaporation of 10 lb. of water per lb. of coal.

3. A sample of coal contains by weight 82 per cent. carbon, 5 per cent. hydrogen, and 13 per cent. ash, etc. Find the amount of air theoretically required for complete combustion of 1 lb. of coal.

4. The percentage volumetric composition of dry flue gas taken from a boiler flue is 10 per cent. CO_2, 1 per cent. CO, 8·5 per cent. O_2, and 80·5 per cent. N_2. Find the mass of air actually supplied per lb. of coal burnt if the boiler is fired with the coal of Question 3.

What is the mass of excess air supplied? State this as a percentage of the theoretical air required.

5. 1 lb. of coal is burned with 20 lb. of air, producing 21 lb. of flue gases having specific heat 0·24 B.Th.U. per lb. ° F. If the gases leave the boiler with a temperature 600° F. and the temperature in the boiler-house is 60° F., calculate the amount of heat flowing to waste up the chimney-stack per lb. of coal burned. If the calorific value of 1 lb. of coal is 14,600 B.Th.U., calculate the percentage of waste heat flowing up the chimney.

6. The analysis of a light fuel oil gave carbon 85·25 per cent., hydrogen 12·75 per cent., sulphur 1·5 per cent., ash and undetermined 0·5 per cent. Calculate the mass of air theoretically required for complete combustion.

7. (i) A sample of coal contains 87 per cent. C, 4 per cent. H_2, and 9 per cent. ash. Calculate the mass of air theoretically required to burn it completely.

(ii) If the above coal is used to fire a boiler and a sample of dry flue gas taken from the base of the chimney gives an analysis by volume of 12·5 per cent. CO_2, 0·5 per cent. CO, 7 per cent. O_2, 80 per cent. N_2, calculate the mass of air actually entering the furnace.

(iii) Find the quantity of excess air as a percentage of the theoretical air, and the ratio of air actually used to the theoretical air required.

8. 1 lb. of fuel oil is composed of 0·8525 lb. carbon, 0·13 lb. hydrogen, 0·0125 lb. sulphur, and 0·005 undetermined. Calculate the mass of air theoretically required for complete combustion. Also calculate the percentage composition of the resulting dry products of combustion by weight and by volume.

9. Describe three methods by which draught may be created in the furnace of a boiler.

(ii)

10. Prove that a chimney of height H containing flue gases which have an average density δ, produces a draught measured by a water manometer head of $A=\left(\frac{\rho-\delta}{w}\right)H$, where ρ is the average density of the outside air and w is the density of water. Prove also that the

draught a in. of water produces a pressure difference in Lb. per sq. in. between the atmosphere and chimney base of

$$(p_1-p_2)=\frac{a}{27\cdot 7} \text{ or } (P_1-P_2)=(p_1-p_2) \text{ Lb./in.}^2$$

11. A chimney of height 250 ft. produces a draught of 2·15 in. of water as recorded by a manometer at the base of the chimney stack. Find the difference in pressure between the gases at the base of the chimney and the outside air.

12. Study the Example on page 192 of the text and check a few of the figures given in the table of that example.

13. (*a*) The following are the mean values of the observations made on an oil-fired water-tube boiler: duration of trial 8 hrs.; oil fired per hour 101·5 lb.; feed water pumped into boiler per hour 1,150 lb. at a temperature 150° F.; pressure in boiler 125 Lb. per sq. in. by gauge; atmospheric pressure 15 Lb. per sq. in. Dryness fraction of steam leaving boiler calculated to be 0·955 from data obtained from a throttling calorimeter. Higher or gross calorific value of oil 19,250 B.Th.U. per lb. Calculate the efficiency of the boiler.

(*b*) The temperature of the flue gases leaving the boiler was 700° F. and the dry flue gas analysis 12·2 per cent. CO_2; 4·6 per cent. O_2; 0 per cent. CO. The oil contained 0·8525 lb. C and 0·13 lb. H_2 per lb. Calculate the heat carried away by the dry flue gases, the partial pressure of the water vapour in the total flue gases, and the heat carried away by the moisture of combustion. Temperature of the air in the boiler-house 75° F., the specific heat of dry flue gases 0·24, and the specific heat of superheated steam 0·5 B.Th.U./lb. ° F.

(*c*) Draw up a heat balance sheet for the trial per lb. of oil fired, obtaining, by difference, the "heat to surrounding air and unaccounted for." Criticise the magnitude of this latter quantity and suggest possible explanations, or point out where there may be possible errors in the testing, to account for this comparatively large quantity.

14. Coal with a percentage analysis by weight: carbon 73·0, hydrogen 5·0, oxygen 4·0, moisture and ash 18·0, is burnt in a furnace, with 70 per cent. excess air, at the rate of 400 lb. per min. For what volume of air (in cu. ft. per min.) at 60° F. and 14·7 Lb. per sq. in. abs. should the ducts leading the air to the furnace be designed? [I.Mech.E., Sec. A.]

15. The coal used in a boiler furnace contains, by weight, 15 per cent. moisture and the percentage analysis of the dry coal by weight is: carbon 77, hydrogen 5, oxygen 8, and ash 10. The air supplied is twice that theoretically necessary for combustion. The temperature of the atmosphere and boiler-house is 70° F. and of the flue gases is 610° F. Estimate the partial pressure of the water vapour in the products of combustion the total pressure of which is 15 Lb. per sq. in. abs. Estimate, per lb. of moist fuel, (i) the heat carried away by the dry flue gases of mean specific heat 0·24; (ii) the heat carried away by the water vapour in the flue gases assuming the mean specific heat of the water vapour to be 0·48. [Part I, B.Sc. Lond.]

16. Briefly describe the ways by which heat may be transmitted. Write down an expression giving the rate at which heat is transmitted by conduction. Calculate the rate at which heat will leak per foot length of pipe through lagging 2 in. thick placed round the pipe of 6 in. external diameter conveying steam at a temperature of 650° F. The temperature drop through the metal pipe may be neglected and the temperature on the exposed surface of the lagging taken as 150° F. The thermal conductivity per ° F. of temperature difference through 1 in. thickness of lagging is 0·46 B.Th.U. per sq. ft. per hour, i.e. the coefficient of conductivity is $k=0 \cdot 46 \dfrac{\text{B.Th.U. in.}}{\text{ft.}^2\text{-hour °F.}}$

17. The boiler of a central heating system uses liquid fuel, $C_{12}H_{26}$, of higher calorific value 19,600 B.Th.U. per lb. Ten per cent. excess air is used, and the energy required to drive the oil pump and the air blower amounts to one horse-power hour for every 20 lb. of oil supplied. The oil and dry air enter the burner at 60° F. and the products of combustion leave the boiler at 440° F. The specific heat of the dry products may be assumed to be 0·24 and the steam in the products carries away 1,250 B.Th.U. per lb. Water at 170° F. is supplied to the boiler in which dry saturated steam is raised at 20 Lb. per sq. in. abs. pressure. Assuming 3 per cent. of the energy supplied in the fuel is lost by radiation to the surrounding air, estimate the amount of steam delivered by the boiler per lb. of fuel supplied. Also draw up an energy balance sheet for the boiler plant. Air contains 21 per cent. of oxygen and 79 per cent. of nitrogen by volume.

18. (*a*) With the aid of a line diagram of a boiler unit briefly describe the functions of an economizer, a superheater, an air heater and a reheater.

(*b*) The boiler of a power station uses 20 tons of coal per hour, of calorific value 12,400 B.Th.U. per lb. as fired. Steam is generated at the rate of 170 tons per hour at 650 Lb. per sq. in. abs. and delivered to the turbine set with a temperature of 854·7° F. After expansion in the high-pressure turbine, dry saturated steam is taken back to the boiler and reheated at 160 Lb. per sq. in. abs. and supplied to the intermediate pressure turbine with a temperature of 763·6° F. Estimate the efficiency of the boiler unit, if the feed water enters the economizer with a temperature of 352° F. If the turbo-alternator set generates 50 million watts of useful power, calculate the overall efficiency of the plant.

19. A furnace wall consists of 9 in. of firebrick and 4½ in. of insulating brick having thermal conductivities of 0·4 and 0·15 B.Th.U. per ft.-hour ° F., respectively. Calculate the rate of heat loss per sq. ft. when the temperature difference between inner and outer surfaces is 900° F.

20. Calculate the temperature difference required to cause the transfer of 18,700 B.Th.U. per hour per sq. ft. of tube surface between the gas in the flue and the water in a boiler, if the heat is transferred by conduction only. The metal thickness is ¾ in. and

you may assume that there is a layer of scale on the water side 0·05 in. thick and a gas film 0·005 in. thick on the flue side; neglect any other resistances to heat flow.

The conductivity of the metal is		38 B.Th.U. per foot-hour °F.	
,, ,, ,,	scale is	1·02	,, ,, ,, ,,
,, ,, ,,	gas is	0·012	,, ,, ,, ,,

[I.Mech.E., Sec. A]

21. (i) What is meant by "the equivalent evaporation from and at 212° F." of a boiler? Calculate its value for a boiler which receives feed-water at 140° F. and delivers 35,000 lb. per hour of steam at 250 Lb. per sq. in. abs. with 120° F. of superheat.

(ii) If the coal consumption under these conditions is $1\frac{1}{2}$ tons per hour of coal of calorific value 15,000 B.Th.U. per lb., find the efficiency of the boiler.

(iii) What considerations govern the supply of air to a boiler, and what should one aim at in this respect? [Part I, B.Sc. Lond.]

22. Show that the heat flow per unit time across the lagging of a cylindrical pipe is given by:

$$q = \frac{2\pi k l(\theta_1 - \theta_2)}{\log_e r_2/r_1}.$$

where k = conductivity of the lagging.
r_2, r_1 = the outer and inner radii of the lagging.
θ_2, θ_1 = the corresponding surface temperatures.
l = the axial length involved.

Calculate the heat lost per hour from a steam pipe 4·5 inches outside diameter and 20 ft. long if the temperature difference across the lagging is 300° F. and the lagging thickness is 2 inches. Take

$$k = 0\cdot 04 \frac{\text{B.Th.U.}}{\text{ft.-hour °F.}}$$

[I.Mech.E., Sec. A.]

CHAPTER 10

CONDENSERS

1. Vacuum.—A perfect vacuum would be an absolutely empty space. This has never been achieved and probably never will be.

Vapours above their liquids exert what is known as vapour pressure, which depends upon temperature. The minimum pressure attainable in a condenser depends on the temperature of the condensate or condensed steam, and on the air present in the condenser. It is found in large turbine plant that by increasing the vacuum from 28 to 29 in. of mercury the steam consumption can be reduced by about 5 per cent. for the same power output. Hence the importance of high vacua in steam turbine and engine plant.

2. Types of Condensers.—A condenser is a vessel into which steam is exhausted and condensed instead of being rejected into the atmosphere after doing work in an engine cylinder or turbine. Another object of condensers is to remove, as far as possible, the effect of atmospheric pressure on steam engines and turbines. They do this by receiving the exhaust steam and condensing it to water at a pressure less than atmospheric. At 1 Lb. per sq. in. abs. the reduction in volume, due to condensation of dry steam to water, is about 20,000 to 1; hence, a partial vacuum is created in the exhaust pipe which can be maintained if air and condensate are pumped out. The steam acting on the piston in the cylinder of an engine can thus be expanded down to a lower pressure and made to do more work than would be the case if the steam were exhausted into the atmosphere. Another important advantage with some types of condensers is that the condensate pumped from the condenser is distilled water, and hence a boiler drawing its feed from this condensate is supplied with pure water free from salts and foreign matter.

Two types of condensers will be mentioned: (i) the jet condenser which employs a jet of cold water to condense the steam; and (ii) the surface condenser, which employs cold metallic surfaces to condense the steam. The latter is the most important type of condenser.

Jet Condenser Fitted with an Air Ejector.—Fig. 10.1 shows a section through a jet condenser A fitted with an air ejector H, and fig. 10.2 shows a section through the air ejector. This condenser plant is suitable where conditions permit condensation of exhaust steam by direct contact with the cooling water. It can maintain a pressure less than 1 Lb. per sq. in. abs. and condense over 24,000 lb. of steam per hour. The condenser shown in fig. 10.1 is of the multiple jet type and of vertical cylindrical form. The injection water is drawn by the vacuum into a closed annulus B, and through the spray nozzles C into the main condensing

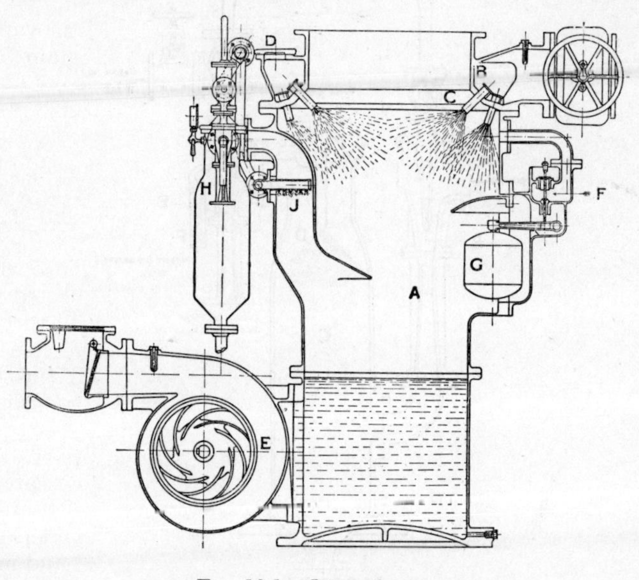

FIG. 10.1—*Jet condenser.*

chamber A, where finely divided water meets the steam. The steam condenses and falls to the bottom of the condenser with the injection water. From there the water is withdrawn by means of the centrifugal extraction pump E which, in addition to withdrawing the water from the vacuum space, can be made to impart pressure head to the water sufficient to raise it to the height of a cooling tower, hence obviating the necessity of an additional lift pump. To avoid any possibility of the condenser flooding, a vacuum breaker F is fitted and actuated by the float G, which opens the valve to admit atmospheric air if the water should rise to a dangerous level.

The air and other gases which enter with the steam and injection water are extracted by the air ejector H, the air being cooled on its way to the ejector by the auxiliary jet J. This reduces the volume of the air and hence reduces the work to be performed by the ejector.

Fig. 10.2 illustrates the air ejector, which embodies two steam

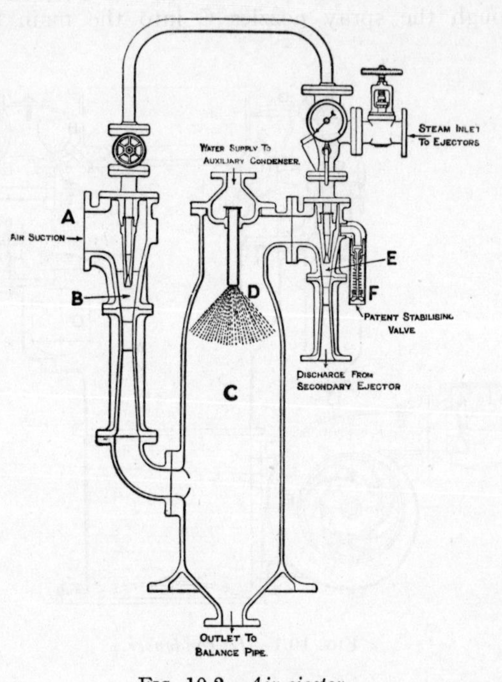

FIG. 10.2—*Air ejector.*

ejectors working in series with an intermediate cooling chamber C. Air is drawn from the condenser through A and is compressed by the primary jet B, through which steam is flowing with a comparatively high velocity. The steam and air mixture flows into the intermediate condenser C. The jet of cold water D condenses the steam coming from B and also cools the air before it gets to the secondary jet E. The jet E withdraws the air from C and discharges the mixture of air and jet-steam into the hot-well. The water from the intermediate condenser is drained away by passing it back to the main condenser through a balance pipe.

The whole heat of evaporation of the steam used in the jets is recovered; that of the first jet is added to the condensate withdrawn from the main condenser by passing it through the drain balance pipe from the intermediate condenser, while the heat from the second jet is absorbed in either a feed heater or feed tank.

Example 1.—Find the mass of condenser water required in a jet condenser to condense 1 lb. of exhaust steam having a dryness fraction 0·8 at 2 Lb. per sq. in. abs. if the initial and final temperatures of the water are 68° F. and 113° F., respectively. Neglect radiation.

Heat gained by jet water=heat lost by steam and condensate.

$$m_w \times \frac{1 \text{ B.Th.U.}}{\text{lb}_w.° \text{ F.}} \times (113-68)° \text{ F.}$$

$$=1 \text{ lb}_s.\left(0 \cdot 8 \times 1022 \cdot 2 \frac{\text{B.Th.U.}}{\text{lb}_s.}\right)+1 \text{ lb}_c. \times \frac{1 \text{ B.Th.U.}}{\text{lb}_c.° \text{ F.}} (126 \cdot 1-113)° \text{ F.}$$

i.e. $45\left(\frac{m_w}{\text{lb}_w.}\right)=817 \cdot 8+13 \cdot 1=830 \cdot 9.$

or $m_w=18 \cdot 5 \text{ lb}_w.$

Thus, 18·5 lb. of jet water are required to condense 1 lb. of steam.

The surface condenser is the most important type of condenser in use to-day. Its main functions are to condense the low-pressure steam exhausted from steam engines and turbines, and to maintain the vacuum at the exhaust end of the turbines and in the exhaust pipes of engines. It is designed such that the condensate and the cooling water are kept separate. The condensate is thus delivered by the extraction pump as distilled water into the hot-well and at a much higher temperature than it would be if mixed with large quantities of cold water, as happens in the jet condenser. Fig. 10.3 illustrates a surface condenser in which cold water circulates through a series of tubes as shown by the arrows. This type of condenser provides a large cooling surface within a relatively small volume. The steam is passed into the condenser and comes into contact with the cold external surfaces of the tubes, and is thus condensed as it flows to the bottom. From there it is extracted by the pump and delivered into the hot-well.

The heat transfer in surface condensers is such that (neglecting radiation): heat lost by steam=heat gained by circulating water.

$$S\{q_2 L_2+s(t_{s2}-t_w)\}=Ws(t_o-t_i),$$

i.e. the ratio of the mass of the circulating water to that of the steam condensed is

$$\frac{W}{S}=\frac{q_2 L_2+s(t_{s2}-t_w)}{s(t_o-t_i)},$$

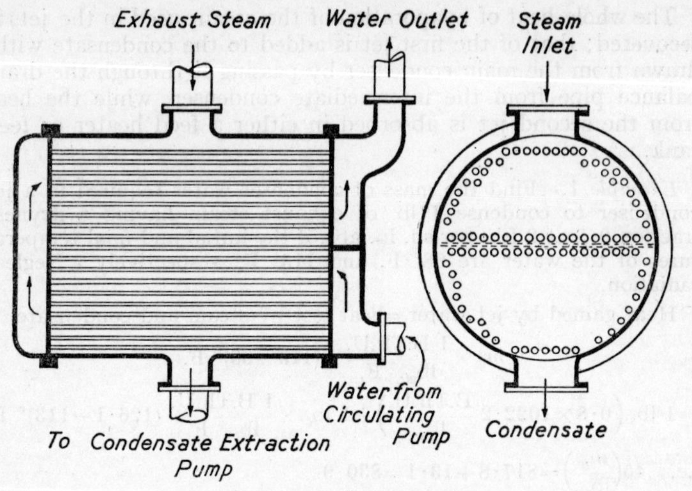

FIG. 10.3—*Surface condenser.*

where q_2, L_2, and t_{s2} refer to the steam entering the condenser, t_w=temperature of condensate leaving condenser, t_o and t_i are the outlet and inlet temperatures of the water circulating through the condenser, and s is the specific heat of water.

Figs. 10.4 and 10.5 show the steam paths in central-flow and downflow surface condensers.

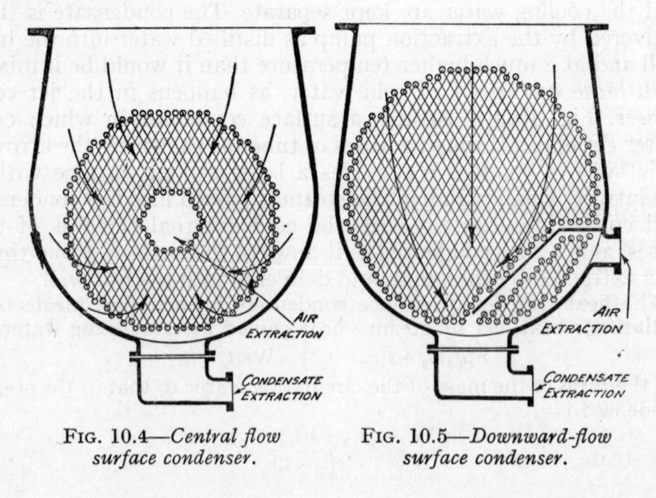

FIG. 10.4—*Central flow surface condenser.*

FIG. 10.5—*Downward-flow surface condenser.*

It is claimed that the central-flow type is more efficient than the older downflow type because there is less pressure drop between the steam inlet and extraction pump suction in the former than in the latter.

By careful regulation of the flow of cooling water through the condenser tubes it can be arranged that the condensate leaves the condenser at a temperature within about half a degree of the saturation temperature of the exhaust steam.

The air, with accompanying water vapour, is drawn away from the centre of the condenser (fig. 10.4), causing the steam to flow from the periphery into the nest of tubes. It will be seen that the path of flow for the steam in the central-flow type is considerably less than in the downflow type, and also that the area of steam admission to the nest of tubes is larger.

Example 2.—A surface condenser working at 1·5 Lb. per sq. in. abs. receives steam having dryness fraction 0·8. The inlet and outlet temperatures of the cooling water circulating through the condenser tubes are 62° F. and 98° F., respectively. If the temperature of the condensate leaving the condenser is 100° F., calculate the quantity of cooling water circulating per lb. of steam condensed.

$$\text{Heat lost by 1 lb. of steam} = 0\cdot 8\times 1028\cdot 1+(115\cdot 7-100) = 838\cdot 2 \text{ B.Th.U.}$$

$$\text{Heat gained by circulating water} = \text{W}s(98-62)^\circ \text{ F.} = 36\text{W B.Th.U./lb}_w.$$

$$\therefore\quad \text{W}=\frac{838\cdot 2}{36}\ \text{lb}_w.=23\cdot 2 \text{ lb. of water per lb. of steam.}$$

3. The Effect of Air in Condensers.—The absolute pressure in a condenser depends upon the temperature of the condensate and upon the amount of air present in the condenser. The mixture of air and water vapour in a condenser may be regarded as an atmosphere which is always saturated. Each is responsible for part of the pressure.

Dalton's Law of Partial Pressures.—This law, thought of with reference to a mixture of air and steam in a condenser, states that, at a common temperature, the mixture will exert on the sides of the vessel a total pressure equal to the sum of the pressures which each constituent would exert separately if it alone occupied the vessel.

Assuming there is a small amount of water in the condenser so that the steam is in contact with its liquid, the pressure p_s, which the steam exerts, depends upon the temperature only, as given in the steam tables.

The pressure of the air present in the condenser depends upon the temperature and upon the mass of air present, and is given by $p_a = \frac{RmT}{V}$.

The total absolute pressure in the condenser is $p = p_s + p_a$. This can be estimated by means of a vacuum gauge and barometer. Thus, if the temperature remains constant and the steam remains in contact with its liquid, the removal of all the air would reduce the total pressure in the condenser to p_s, the value of which is settled by the temperature of the condensate in the condenser.

The presence of air in surface condensers not only spoils the vacuum but also reduces the rate of condensation of steam, since the abstraction of heat by water circulating through the tubes is then partly from steam and partly from the air. The evacuation of the air from condensers is, therefore, of importance on both accounts. Air ejectors (fig. 10.2) are used to remove air from condensers, and de-aerating plant (fig. 9.27) is used to remove dissolved air from the feed water before pumping through the economiser into the boiler.

The higher the vacuum (*i.e.* the lower the back pressure) in engines and turbines the larger is the work done. There is, however, an economic limit to the vacuum which can be maintained because of the extra pumping power required. A vacuum of 29 in. of mercury, which corresponds to a pressure of about 0·5 Lb. per sq. in. abs., is considered to be the economical limit in surface condensers fitted to large turbine plant.

Example 3.—(i) Neglecting the volume of condensed steam appearing as water in the bottom of a surface condenser, calculate the quantity of air present in a condenser of 10 cu. ft. capacity in which the temperature is assumed uniform at 87·8° F. and the total pressure in the condenser is $p = 2 \cdot 65$ Lb. per sq. in. abs.

(ii) Find the mass of air per lb. of exhaust steam present in the condenser.

At a temperature 87·8° F. steam in contact with its liquid would have a pressure $p_s = 0 \cdot 65$ Lb. per sq. in. abs. as given in the steam tables. Hence, by the law of partial pressures, the pressure exerted by the air present $= p_a = p - p_s = 2 \cdot 65 - 0 \cdot 65 = 2$ Lb. per sq. in. abs.

Thus, the air present in a volume of 10 cu. ft. at 87·8° F. and 2 Lb. per sq. in. abs. is

$$m = \frac{P.V}{R.T} = \frac{(144 \times 2) \times 10}{53 \cdot 3 \times (87 \cdot 8 + 460)} = 0 \cdot 0985 \text{ lb.}$$

The mass of steam (assumed dry and saturated) in 10 cu. ft. of condenser volume

$$=\frac{\text{Volume of steam in the condenser at } 0\cdot65 \text{ Lb. per sq. in. abs.}}{\text{Volume of 1 lb. dry saturated steam at } 0\cdot65 \text{ Lb. per sq. in. abs.}}$$

$$=\frac{10}{499\cdot8}=0\cdot02001 \text{ lb.}$$

$$\therefore \text{ Ratio } \frac{\text{mass of air}}{\text{mass of steam}}=\frac{0\cdot0985}{0\cdot02001}=4\cdot92.$$

It will be seen that of the absolute pressure 2·65 Lb. per sq. in. in the condenser 2 Lb. per sq. in. is due to the presence of air and only 0·65 Lb. per sq. in. due to steam. Hence the necessity, where low condenser pressures or high vacua are required, of providing for the removal of air from condensers.

4. Air Pumps and Extraction Pumps.—There are several types of air and extraction pumps of the reciprocating type and also of the rotary type. The Edward's pump, illustrated in fig. 10.6, is of the reciprocating type. Vertical ports cut in the cylinder allow the air and condensate to pass when the plunger uncovers them near the end of its downward stroke. The water in the bottom cone is thus forced through the specially designed passages on to the top side of the plunger, where there is a partial vacuum because the head valves remain water-sealed during the downward stroke of the valveless plunger. The upward stroke of the plunger delivers the water into the hot-well. This type of pump requires little attention and seldom goes wrong. Fig. 10.7 shows a section through one of the automatic disc valves.

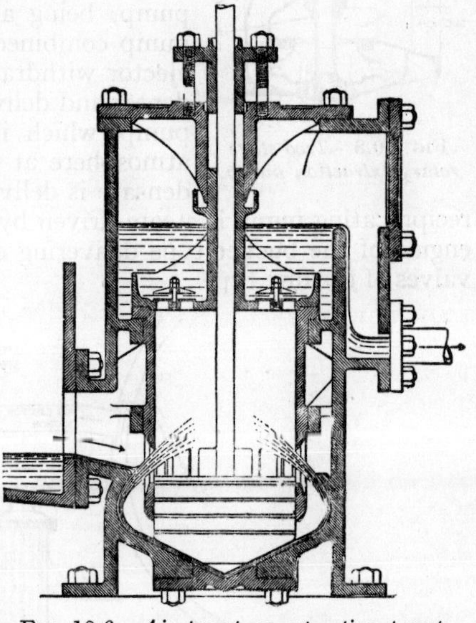

FIG. 10.6—*Air pump or extraction pump.*

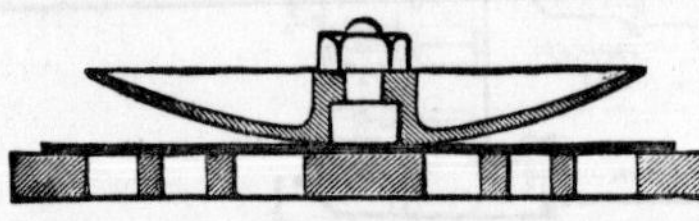

FIG. 10.7—*Automatic disc valve.*

In cases where high vacua are required it is necessary to have separate pumps for the air and for the condensed steam.

Fig. 10.8 illustrates a Weir rotary two-stage extraction pump. The condensate is drawn from the condenser through the suction pipe A and delivered from the impeller B through the passage C to the eye of the second impeller D, from which it is finally delivered to the discharge pipe E. The rotating shaft is of stainless steel running in two bearings F and G, the former designed to work with water lubrication.

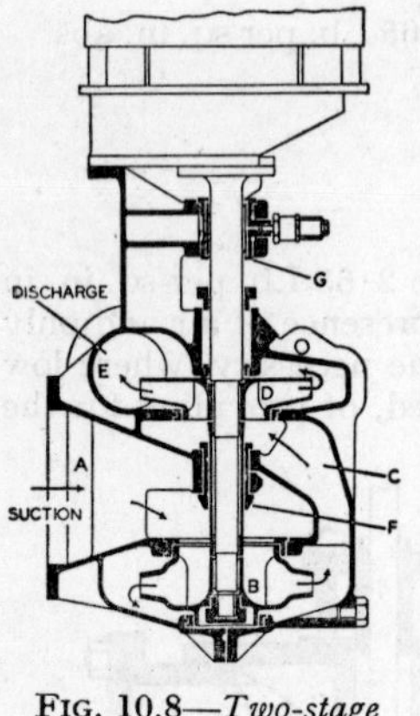

Fig. 10.8—*Two-stage rotary extraction pump.*

Fig. 10.9 shows another Weir extraction pump, being a reciprocating condensate pump combined with an air ejector. The ejector withdraws the air from the condenser and delivers it to the reciprocating pump, which in turn delivers it to the atmosphere at the same time as the condensate is delivered to the hot-well. The reciprocating pump is steam driven by means of a double-acting engine of the bucket type delivering every two strokes through valves of the disc type.

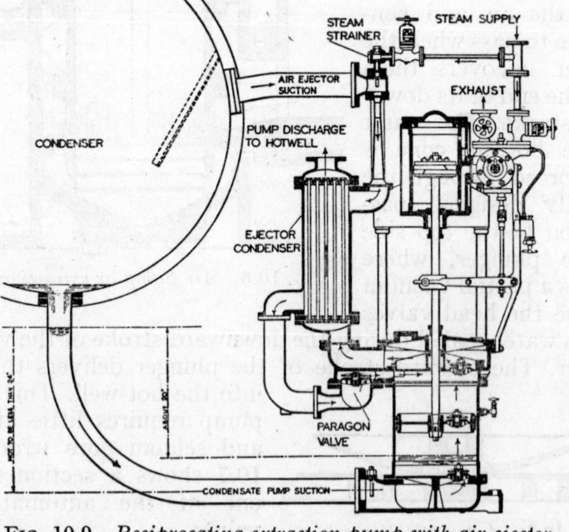

Fig. 10.9—*Reciprocating extraction pump with air ejector.*

5. Arrangement of a Condensing Plant Operating with Cooling Towers.—Most large power stations are built adjacent to rivers or the seaboard where water is available in great quantity for the purpose of circulating through condenser tubes. Fig. 10.10 shows an arrangement of a condensing plant for power stations operating with cooling towers which can be built to heights up to 350 ft. and capable of cooling several million gallons of water per hour for repeated use when the supply of water for circulating through condensers is limited as is the case in many inland towns. A represents the ground level and B the floor of the engine room. D represents a surface condenser which is served

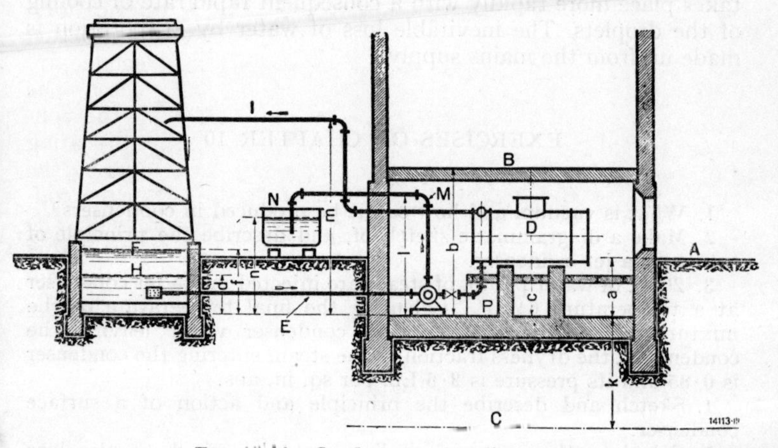

FIG. 10.10—*Condenser and cooling tower.*

by means of an intake pipe E and a pump with cooling water from the channel in which F represents the highest water level and H the lowest water level. After passing through the condenser the cooling water is led by the delivery pipe I to a cooling tower, where it is split up into small particles by a network of laths or splash-bars which also reduce the rate of fall of water and so increase the time of contact between the hot water droplets and the cooler upflowing air. Thus, the water is cooled in dropping through the air towards the well and intake channel again. The warmer column of air in the tower is displaced by cooler air which flows in from the outer atmosphere at the base, and a continuous upward motion is maintained by the creation of natural draught as in a chimney (p. 190). Forced draught has to be used in hot climates and entails expenditure of energy to drive fans which, if used in cooler climates, make it possible to reduce the size of tower for the same duty. The main condensate is delivered by the condenser extraction-pump into the pipe M, which delivers into the condensate tank or hot-well N from which feed water for the boiler is taken. The cooling of the droplets of condenser cooling-water while falling and, later, while in the well or pond, is due mainly to the process of evaporation, though conduction, convection, and radiation of heat from the water to the air also take place. The more water vapour there is in the atmosphere the slower will be the rate of cooling of the falling droplets, whereas if the atmosphere is dry, *i.e.* of low relative humidity, evaporation takes place more rapidly with a consequent rapid rate of cooling of the droplets. The inevitable loss of water by evaporation is made up from the mains supply.

EXERCISES ON CHAPTER 10

(i)

1. What is vacuum and how can it be produced in condensers?

2. Make a diagrammatic sketch of, and describe the principle of action of, a jet condenser.

3. 20 lb. of water per lb. of steam are injected into a jet condenser at a temperature 64° F. Calculate the final temperature of the mixture of condensed steam and condenser water leaving the condenser if the dryness fraction of the steam entering the condenser is 0·85 and its pressure is 2·6 Lb. per sq. in. abs.

4. Sketch and describe the principle and action of a surface condenser.

5. Calculate the mass of cooling water required to circulate per minute through a surface condenser per lb. of steam which enters 0·8 dry if the pressure of the steam in the condenser is 1·7 Lb. per sq. in. abs. and the inlet and outlet temperature of the cooling water are 68° F. and 113° F., respectively. The temperature of the condensed steam leaving the condenser is 104° F.

6. Make a sketch and describe the action of an air pump or extraction pump.

(ii)

7. State Dalton's law of partial pressures and make a brief statement with reference to its application to the air and steam present in condensers of steam plant.

8. The total pressure in a condenser as recorded by a gauge is 1 Lb. per sq. in. abs. and the uniform temperature 92·3° F. Find, from the steam tables, the pressure exerted by the steam at this temperature. Deduce the pressure exerted by the air present in the condenser and calculate from the formula $PV=RmT$ the volume

occupied by 1 lb. of air at this temperature and pressure. Estimate, using steam tables, the mass of dry saturated steam occupying this volume under the above conditions, and find the ratio of air to steam by weight contained in the mixture occupying the volume of the condenser.

9. Steam enters a jet condenser in which the pressure is 2 Lb. per sq. in abs. with a dryness fraction 0·85, and is condensed by water entering at 50° F. At what temperature does the condensed steam and water mixture leave the condenser, and how much water will be required per lb. of steam? The air present may be assumed to be 34·6 per cent. of the mass of air and vapour.

[I.Mech.E., Sec. A.]

10. A closed vessel containing water and air is heated until the water changes into dry saturated steam at 312° F. The total pressure in the vessel is then 86 Lb. per sq. in. abs. With the aid of steam tables estimate the mass of air present per lb. of steam.

11. The vacuum in a condenser and the height of the barometer were 28·1 and 30·2 in. of mercury respectively. The condensation temperature in the condenser was 82·5° F. and the temperature of the condensate extracted from the condenser at the rate of 3,930 lb. per hour was 51·7° F. Cooling water was supplied at the rate of 12,660 gallons per hour and its temperature rise in passing through the condenser tubes was 32° F. Calculate the dryness fraction of the steam entering the condenser and the mass of air present per cu. ft. of condenser volume. Neglect radiation.

12. Steam is condensed at 0·5 Lb. per sq. in. abs. in a condenser at the rate of 7,500 lb. per hour, and the condensate enters the extraction pump at a temperature of 80° F. If the volume swept by the pump is 72 cu. ft. per minute, estimate the mass of air removed per minute from the condenser, neglecting water vapour. Specific volume of condensate is 0·016 cu. ft. per lb.

13. A mixture of steam, 0·9 dry, and air at 180° F. and 20 Lb. per sq. in. abs. is compressed to one-fifth of the original volume when the temperature becomes 273·1° F.

Calculate the final pressure of the mixture and the dryness fraction of the steam. Neglect the volume of water.

14. With the aid of a sketch, briefly describe a modern surface condenser. How and why is air extracted from such a condenser?

The vacuum in the condenser of a large steam-turbine generating set may be assumed to have the mean value of 28·98 in. of mercury when the barometer stands at 30 in. of mercury. Cooling water flows through the condenser tubes at the rate of 27,000 gallons per minute and rises in temperature from 50·8° F. to 68·9° F. Wet steam is condensed at the rate of 378,000 lb. per hour and the temperature of the condensate is 78·6° F. Estimate the dryness fraction of the steam entering the condenser, stating the assumptions made. By how much is the condensate undercooled and why is this necessary?

15. In a particular steam power plant air is believed to leak into the condenser. To check whether this is so, the plant is run until

8*

conditions are steady, whereupon the steam supply from the engine is shut off; simultaneously, the air and condensate extraction pumps are closed down, so that the condenser is isolated. At shut down the temperature and vacuum in the condenser are observed to be 101·7° F. and 27·3 inches of mercury. After five minutes the values are 82·5° F. and 19·25 inches. The barometer reading is 29·70 inches. The effective volume of the condenser is 12 cu. ft.

Determine from these data:—

(*a*) the weight of air leakage into the condenser during the observed period:

(*b*) the weight of water vapour condensed in this same period.

Assume R for air is 53·3 ft.-Lb. per lb. °F. and steam is dry and saturated. [Part I, B.Sc. Lond.]

CHAPTER 11

VALVES AND VALVE DIAGRAMS FOR STEAM ENGINES

1. Simple Steam Engine Valves.—On p. 25 brief mention was made of the simple slide valve (fig. 2.2) for steam engines. We shall now add to this, and analyse the simple D slide valve by means of valve diagrams.

Fig. 11.1 illustrates a piston slide valve—consisting of two pistons each working in a barrel in which there are openings round the circumference (seen in section AA) acting as the steam ports. Such a piston valve is an equilibrium valve. It is not pressed against the sliding surface as is an ordinary D slide valve. It is used for the high-pressure cylinder in triple-expansion and compound engines. The face of each piston is of the same length as that of the D slide valve; the steam and exhaust laps are the same as in a D slide valve. Steam is admitted at the two ends of the valve alternately and flows to the cylinder of the engine along the ports S. The exhaust steam flows into the space between the two pistons and thence along the port E into the receiver before entering the next cylinder.

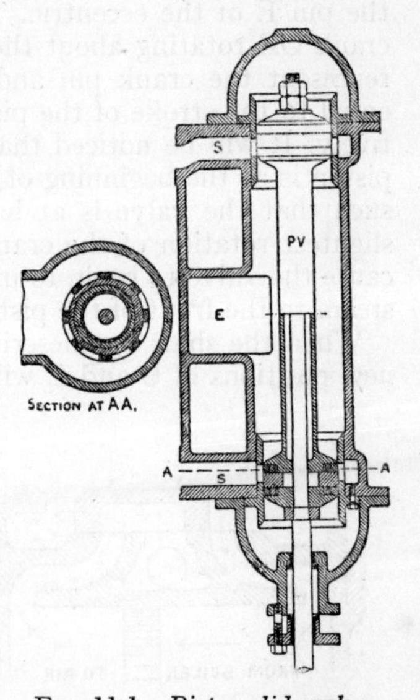

FIG. 11.1—*Piston slide valve.*

2. The Action of the Simple D Slide Valve.—First consider the simple form of slide valve shown in fig. 11.2, in which the valve is shown in its mid-position completely closing both ports and having edges of the valve exactly the same width as that of the steam ports. The piston is at inner dead-centre ready to commence the outstroke. The piston in an actual engine is connected by means of a piston rod and connecting rod to the crank OC

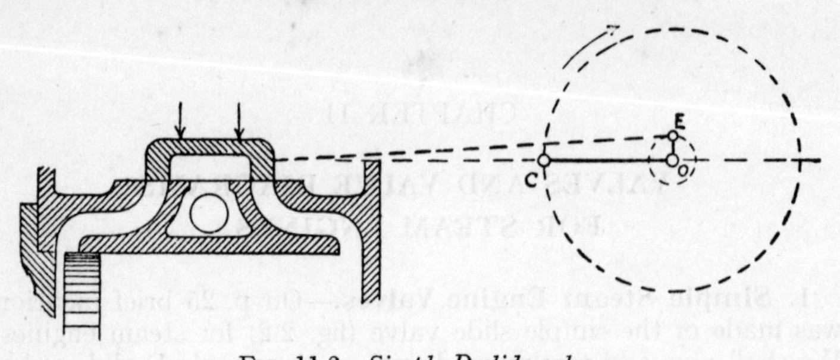

FIG. 11.2—*Simple D slide valve.*

which rotates about the centre O, and the valve is connected to the pin E of the eccentric. The eccentric is, in effect, a smaller crank OE rotating about the same centre O. The dotted circles represent the crank pin and eccentric circles having diameters equal to the stroke of the piston and stroke of the valve respectively. It will be noticed that the position of C is such that the piston is at the beginning of the outstroke and the position of E such that the valve is at half stroke, *i.e.* in mid-position. The slightest rotation of the crankshaft in a clockwise direction will cause the valve to begin to uncover the left-hand port and admit steam to the front of the piston.

When the shaft has described one-quarter of a revolution the new positions of C and E will be as shown in fig. 11.3, with the

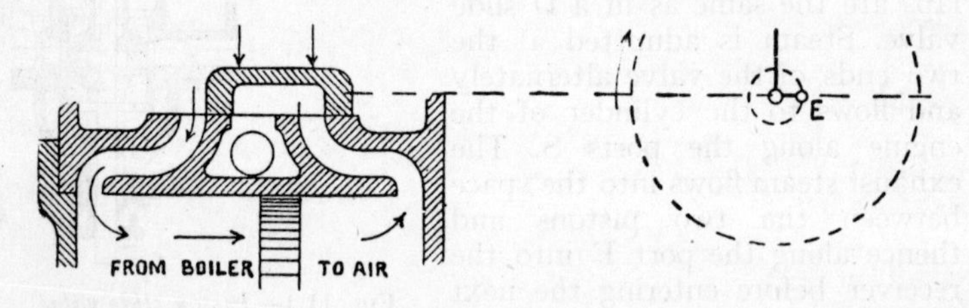

FIG. 11.3—*Simple D slide valve.*

piston and valve in the positions shown. The arrows on the figure show the way the steam flows from the valve-chest and also to exhaust. As the piston travels towards outer-dead-centre it will be seen that the valve returns to its mid-position and just closes the ports as the piston reaches outer-dead-centre. On continuing the rotation of the crankshaft the valve begins to uncover the right-hand port and the steam flows in directions opposite to those indicated by the arrows on the figure, until the piston has travelled to inner-dead-centre again, where the cycle of operations recommences.

The D valve of figs. **11.2** and **11.3**, which only just covers the ports when in its mid-position, has two important disadvantages:

(i) It admits steam to the cylinder during the whole stroke of the piston, and thus uses steam non-expansively.
(ii) It opens the ports to boiler steam and also to exhaust just *after* instead of *before* the piston begins a stroke.

These disadvantages can be overcome:

(i) By extending the width of the valve face.
(ii) By *lead*—that is, causing the valve to open the ports before the piston arrives at the dead-centres.

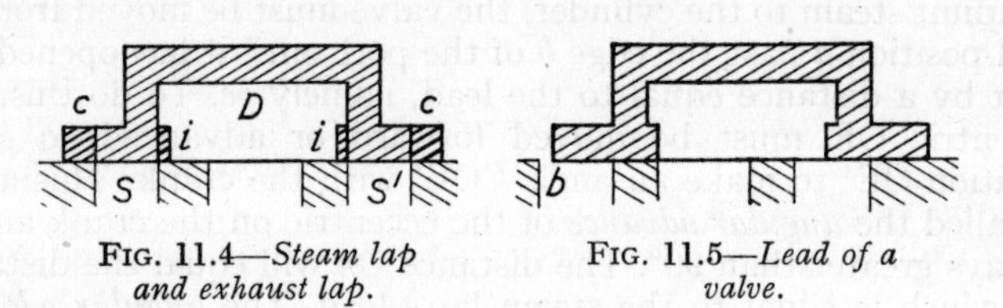

FIG. 11.4—*Steam lap and exhaust lap.* FIG. 11.5—*Lead of a valve.*

Definitions of Lap and Lead.—The distance by which the valve, *when at the middle of its stroke,* overlaps the steam port is called the *lap* of the valve. The distance overlapping on the outside is called the *outside lap* or *steam lap*, and the distance overlapping on the inside is called the *inside lap* or *exhaust lap*.

A valve with no lap is shown in fig. **11.3**. The darkly shaded pieces on fig. 11.4 indicate outside or steam lap *c c* and inside or exhaust lap *i i*.

The lead of a valve is the amount of port opening to steam when the piston is at the beginning of its stroke. Thus, in fig. **11.5** the opening *b* is the lead of the valve if the piston at that moment is at the beginning of its stroke. It will be seen from this figure that because the exhaust lap is less than the steam lap, the lead to exhaust is greater than the lead to steam, thus permitting of an early escape to exhaust.

If a valve, having steam lap, is to uncover the whole of the steam port, the radius of the eccentric OE, fig. **11.6**, must be equal to steam lap + width of port, and this equals half the valve travel.

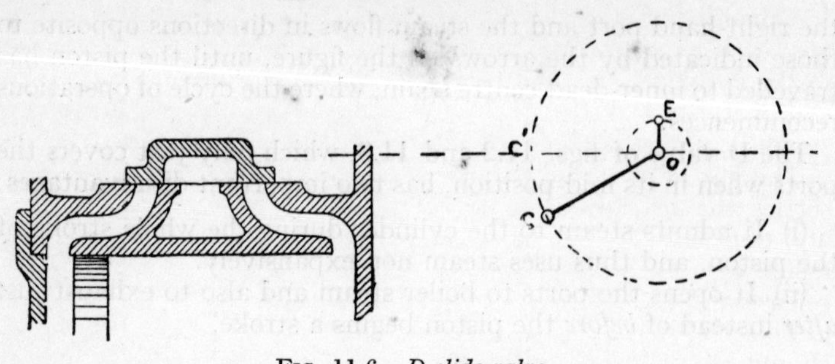

FIG. 11.6—*D slide valve.*

In order to set a valve so that there shall be lead, let the piston be placed at inner-dead-centre—the beginning of the outstroke as in fig. 11.7, where the crank is in position OC; then, in order to admit steam to the cylinder, the valve must be moved from its mid-position *a* past the edge *b* of the port until it has opened the port by a distance equal to the lead, namely *bc*. To do this, the eccentric OE must be moved forward or advanced to some position OE′ to make an angle COE′ with the crank. This angle is called the *angular advance* of the eccentric on the crank and is always greater than 90°. The distance O*n* will equal the distance *ac*, which is equal to the steam lap+lead. The *angular advance* COE′, showing the relative positions of crank and eccentric, is a fixed angle once the eccentric is set. The angle EOE′, being the angle in excess of 90° by which the eccentric is in advance of the crank, is called the *angle of advance.*

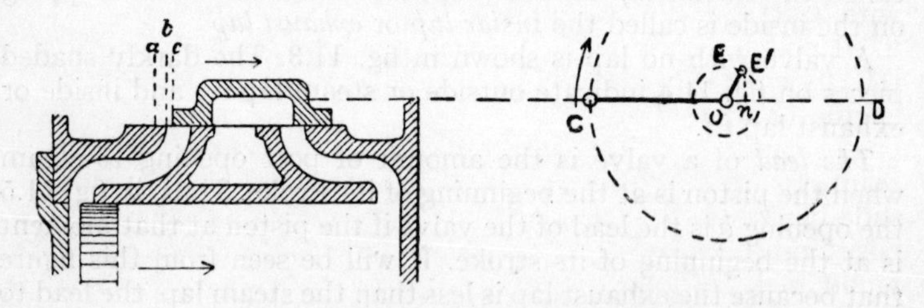

FIG. 11.7—*Lead and angle of advance.*

The addition of outside lap or steam lap: (i) makes cut-off occur earlier in the stroke; and (ii) necessitates advancing the eccentric relative to the crank, which in turn allows of the early opening of the exhaust port.

The addition of inside lap or exhaust lap: (i) closes the exhaust port earlier in the stroke, and so entraps a certain volume of steam in the cylinder for compression as the piston moves towards the end of its stroke (this entrapped steam is usually called "cushion steam"); and (ii) delays the opening of the exhaust port.

The steam lap or outside lap settles the points of admission and cut-off. The exhaust lap or inside lap settles the points of release and compression.

To set a slide valve, the crank should be put alternately on its two dead-centres and the port opening to steam (*i.e.* the lead) measured. The leads allowed for instroke and outstroke will not be the same owing to the obliquity of connecting rod and diameter of the piston rod.

In order to find the dead-centre points of an engine, place the crank at A, an angle of about 45° to the line which passes through the dead-centre points (fig. 11.8). Make a centre point on the slide and then with trammel, T, scribe an arc on the chalked slide block and put a centre point on the arc. Then, with trammel K resting on a fixed point, make a mark G on the flywheel. Next, turn the engine back so that the crank passes through the dead-centre point to the position B the slide-block being in its previous position as found by means of trammel T. When this position is found, make a mark H on the flywheel with the trammel K resting on the same point as before. Then bisect GH at J. When J is placed opposite the end of the long trammel (K), the engine is in the dead-centre position. The opposite dead-centre can be found in a similar manner.

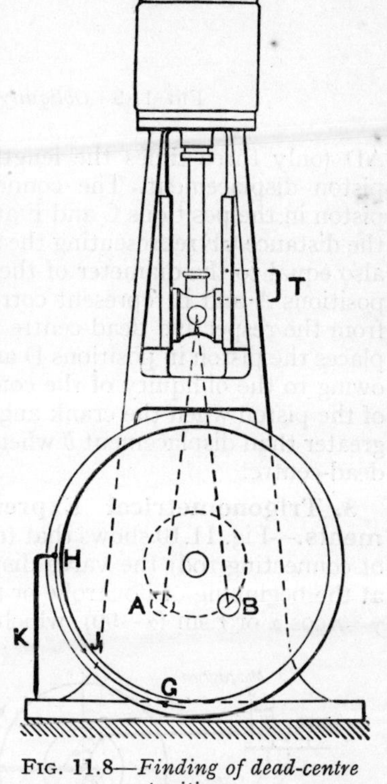

FIG. 11.8—*Finding of dead-centre positions.*

The effect of the obliquity of the connecting rod can be seen with reference to fig. 11.9, which shows how the short connecting rod

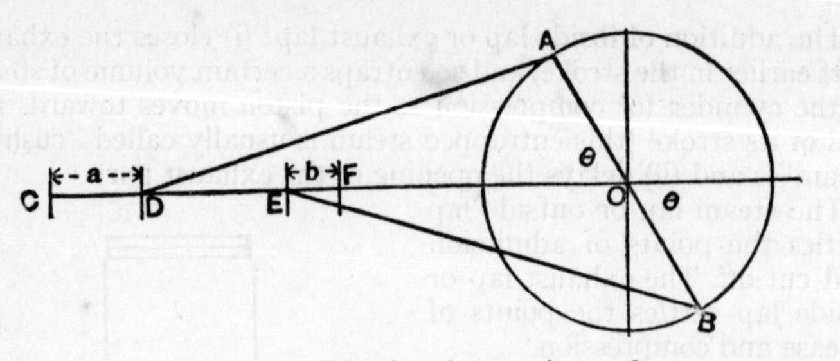

Fig. 11.9—*Obliquity of connecting reod.*

AD (only three times the length of the crank OA) affects the piston displacement. The connecting rod (AD=BE) puts the piston in the positions C and F at inner and outer-dead-centres—the distance CF representing the stroke of the piston and which is also equal to the diameter of the crank pin circle AB. The crank positions A and B represent corresponding angular movements θ from the respective dead-centre points. The connecting rod then places the piston in positions D and E, respectively. We find that, owing to the obliquity of the connecting rod, the displacement a of the piston when the crank angle is θ from inner-dead-centre, is greater than displacement b when the crank angle is θ from outer-dead-centre.

3. Trigonometrical Expressions for Valve Displacements.—Fig. 11.10 shows that (neglecting the effects of obliquity of connecting rod) the valve displacement y, when the piston is at the beginning of its stroke or at outer-dead-centre, is given by $y=r.\cos\alpha$ or $r.\sin(\alpha-90)$, which also equals the steam lap+the

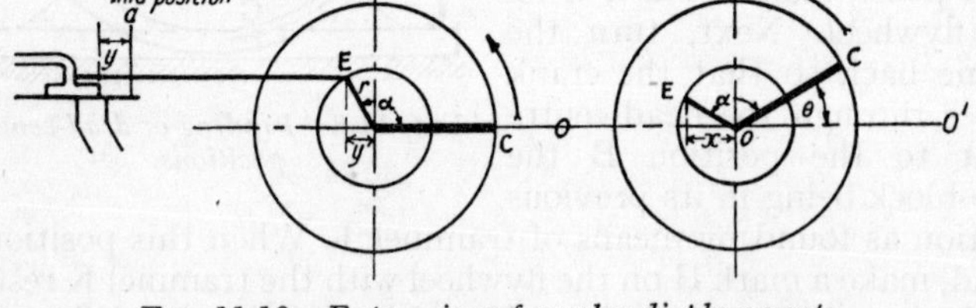

Fig. 11.10—*Expressions for valve displacements.*

lead, r being the eccentric radius and α the angular advance. When the crank is displaced an angle θ from the outer-dead-centre position OO′ in the direction of the arrow, the displacement of the valve is $x=r\cos(\alpha+\theta)=r\sin(\theta+\alpha-90)$. This equation is the general one for any angular displacement of crank θ.

The Reuleaux and Bilgram diagrams are geometrical constructions for obtaining the quantity x representing the valve displacement at any crank angle. That is, they are merely translations into geometry of the above trigonometrical equations.

4. The Reuleaux and Bilgram Diagrams.—*The Reuleaux diagram* is based on the valve displacement equation:

$$x=r \sin [\theta+(\alpha-90)].$$

To construct a diagram giving x in the above equation, first draw the straight line M_1OM_2 at angle $(\alpha-90)$ to the horizontal through O, fig. 11.11. This angle remains constant whatever the crank angle θ.

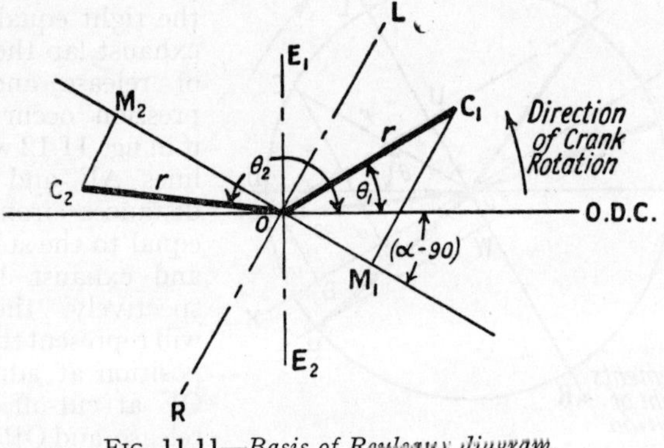

FIG. 11.11—*Basis of Reuleaux diagram.*

Next, for any position of crank C_1 at angle θ_1 from the outer-dead-centre position draw length OC_1 equal to the eccentric radius r; the angle M_1OC_1 is then $[\theta_1+(\alpha-90)]$, and the perpendicular, $M_1C_1=r.\sin[\theta_1+(\alpha-90)]=x_1$.

Thus the length of the perpendicular M_1C_1 represents the displacement of the valve when the crank is at angle θ_1 from outer-dead-centre. Similarly, M_2C_2 represents the valve displacement when the crank is in position θ_2. It will be noticed that when the crank is in position OM_1 or OM_2 the eccentric is in position OE_1 or OE_2 respectively—that is, at an angular advance α ahead of the crank position in each case. Hence, lengths measured perpendicular to M_1OM_2 in direction OL represent displacements of the valve to the left of its mid-position, and perpendicular measurements in direction OR represent valve displacements to the right of its mid-position.

If now a circle of radius r be drawn (fig. 11.12), every crank position is somewhere on its circumference. The line XX′ set back from the horizontal at angle $(\alpha-90)$ is the datum line from which perpendiculars are measured. All lines drawn from the perpendicular to XX′ represent a valve displacement. The perpendicular MC represents the valve displacement for any crank position OC, and, as drawn in the Figure, is seen to be a displacement to the left of the mid-position.

Referring back to fig. 11.10 we see that when the right-hand end of the valve is displaced a distance to the left equal to the steam lap the points of admission and cut-off occur, and when displaced a distance to the right equal to the exhaust lap the points of release and compression occur. Thus, if in fig. 11.12 we draw lines AF and PT at distances from XX′ equal to the steam lap and exhaust lap, respectively, then OA will represent the crank position at admission, OF at cut-off, OT at release, and OP at compression—these being settled by the right-hand end of the valve. It will be noticed that BD represents the displacement of the valve when the crank is at outer-dead-centre—that is, when the piston is at the beginning of its instroke. Therefore, the distance BD = steam lap + lead, and hence, distance GD = the lead for the instroke. The distance UL will represent the maximum port opening to admission steam, and distance WR will represent the maximum port opening to exhaust steam.

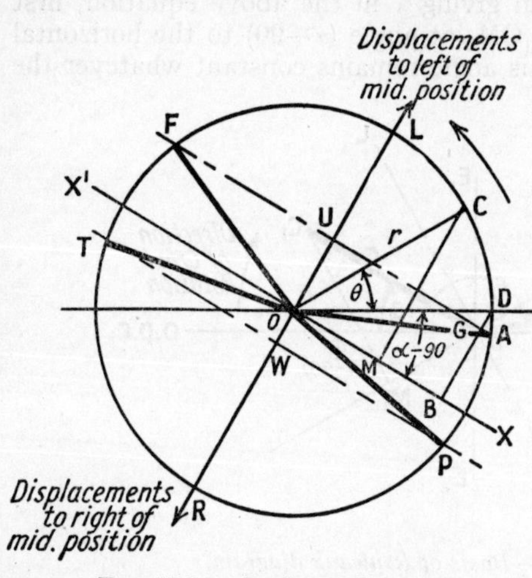

Fig. 11.12—*Reuleaux diagram.*

The Bilgram Diagram is also based on the equation

$$x=r \sin [\theta+(\alpha-90)]$$

which gives the displacement of the valve from its mid-position for any crank angle θ measured from the outer-dead-centre position as shown on fig. 11.10.

The diagram can be constructed to give any valve displacement x by first setting back line XOX′ (fig. 11.13) at an angle $(\alpha-90)$ from the outer-dead-centre line OD; then draw OC_1 equal

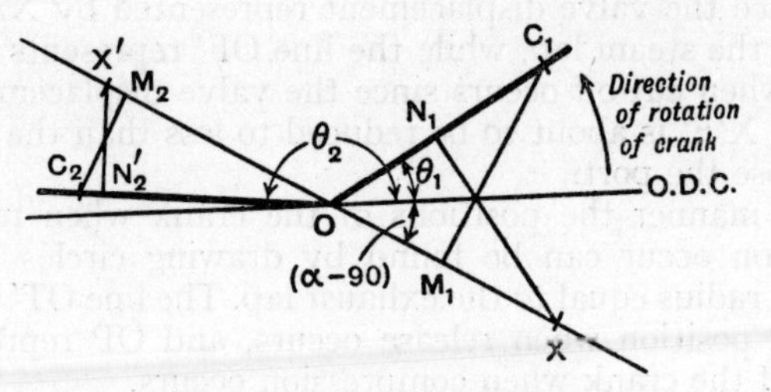

FIG. 11.13—*Basis of Bilgram diagram.*

to the eccentric radius r for any crank position corresponding to a crank angle θ_1. The perpendicular C_1M_1 is equal to

$$r \sin[\theta_1 + (\alpha-90)] = x_1,$$

the displacement of the valve from its mid-position when the crank is in position θ_1. Similarly, $C_2M_2 = x_2$ for a crank position θ_2. If, however, instead of drawing perpendiculars from points C_1 and C_2 on to the line XOX′, the fixed points X and X′ are chosen such that the lengths OX and OX′ are equal to the eccentric radius r, the perpendiculars XN_1, $X'N'_2$ represent the valve displacements for the two crank positions θ_1 and θ_2, since $XN_1 = C_1M_1$ and $X'N'_2 = C_2M_2$. Thus, perpendiculars XN and X′N′ drawn from the fixed points X and X_1 to any crank position OC (fig. 11.14) represents x, the displacement of the valve from its mid-position. The positions of the crank when the critical events of admission and cut-off occur can thus be found by drawing

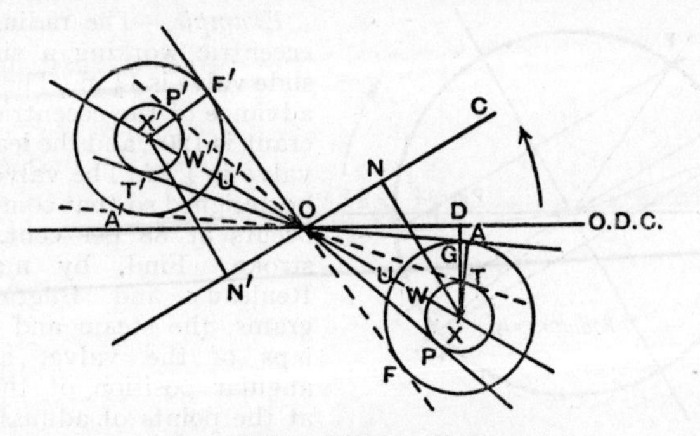

FIG. 11.14—*Bilgram diagram.*

circles AUF and A′U′F′ of radius equal to the steam lap and then drawing OA and OF′ tangents to these circles.

The line OA represents the crank position when admission occurs since the valve displacement represented by XA is about to exceed the steam lap, while the line OF′ represents the crank position when cut-off occurs since the valve displacement represented by X′F′ is about to be reduced to less than the steam lap and so close the port.

In like manner the positions of the crank when release and compression occur can be found by drawing circles PWT and P′W′T′ of radius equal to the exhaust lap. The line OT′ represents the crank position when release occurs, and OP represents the position of the crank when compression occurs.

It will be obvious that since XD is the perpendicular when the crank is at outer-dead-centre, the length XD represents the displacement of the valve from its mid-position when the piston is at the beginning of its stroke and hence is equal to the steam lap plus the lead. Thus the length GD represents the lead of the valve for the instroke or the crank end of the engine.

It will also be obvious that since OX represents the maximum displacement of the valve from its mid-position, OU represents the maximum port opening to steam, and OW the maximum port opening to exhaust.

After a certain amount of practice in using this diagram, students will realise that the four critical events, as determined by the right-hand end of the valve of fig. 11.10 (*i.e.* for the crank end of the engine), can be obtained with steam and exhaust lap circle about X as centre, thus leaving X′ as the centre for circles and critical events connected with the left-hand end of the valve which operates the head end of the engine.

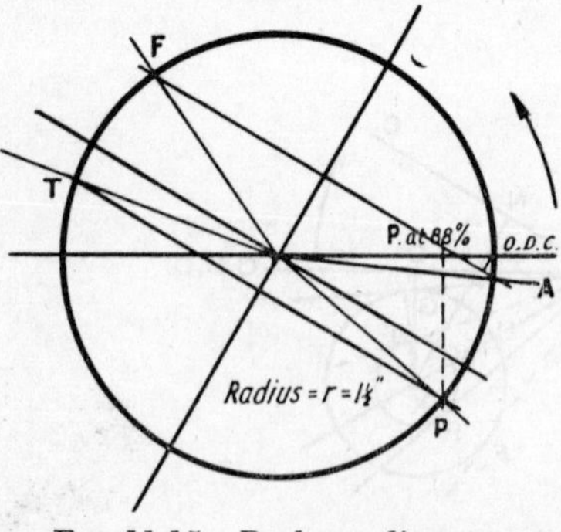

FIG. 11.15—*Reuleaux diagram.*

Example.—The radius of the eccentric working a simple D slide valve is $1\frac{1}{2}$ in. The angular advance of the eccentric on the crank is 120°, and the lead of the valve is $\frac{1}{8}$ in. The valve has to be designed so that compression occurs at 88 per cent. of the stroke. Find, by means of Reuleaux and Bilgram diagrams, the steam and exhaust laps of the valve, and the angular position of the crank at the points of admission, cut off, and release (reckoned from dead-centre) as settled by one end of the valve. The obliquity of the connecting and eccentric rods may be neglected.

Measurements from the Reuleaux diagram of fig. 11.15 and Bilgram diagram of fig. 11.14, which is also a solution to this problem, give steam lap $\frac{5}{8}$ in., exhaust lap $\frac{1}{4}$ in., and the points of admission, cut-off, and release as measured from outer dead-centre—6°, 126°, and 160°, respectively.

5. Effect of Valve Setting on Indicator Diagrams.—Fig. 3.13 shows the type of indicator diagram given by a single-cylinder non-condensing engine running with a good setting of the valve. The admission of steam from A to C shows, during the first part, AB, how the pressure of the steam in the cylinder rises after the admission point A, and BC shows how the pressure of the admission steam is maintained until the point of cut-off C is approached, when there is a rounding of the diagram owing to the

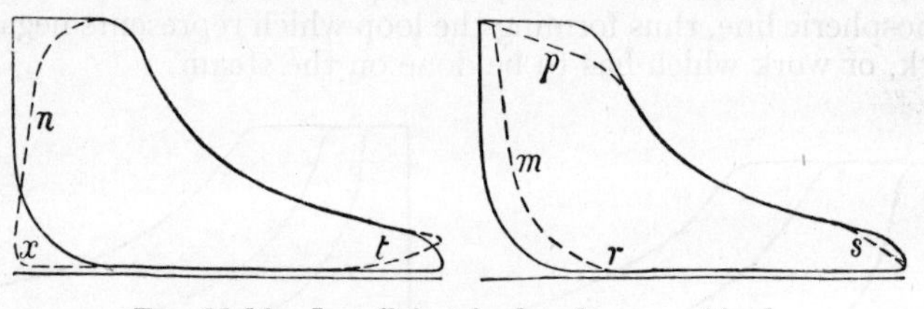

Fig. 11.16—*Insufficient lead and excess of lead.*

fall in pressure caused by steam flowing through the restricted passage immediately before the point of cut-off, known as "wire-drawing."

Release occurs at D—*i.e.* before the end of the stroke.

The exhaust takes place during motion of the piston from D to F. The first part of this (DE) represents the fall in pressure which occurs in the cylinder when the exhaust port opens. The back-pressure line EF represents the pressure acting against the piston during the return stroke and is seen to be slightly above the atmospheric line XY.

The point of compression is at F, and compression of steam takes place during motion of the piston from E to A, at which point admission occurs again.

Fig. 11.16 shows how the full-line diagram may be distorted by alterations in valve design and setting. Insufficient lead is shown by *n*, late exhaust by *t*, late compression by *x*; while, in the second diagram, *m* shows the effect of excess of lead, *r* early compression, *s* early release, and *p* wiredrawing.

Fig. 11.17 shows the effect of governing a steam engine by means of a throttle valve. The diagram was obtained by reducing the load on the engine in stages, the speed being kept constant by throttling the steam supply. The pressure line A for a heavy load was dropped to B for a medium load and to C for a light load. It will be noticed in all three diagrams that the points of admission, cut-off, release, and compression remain the same, because the valve has the same setting for the three diagrams—the pressure of the admission steam, only, being altered.

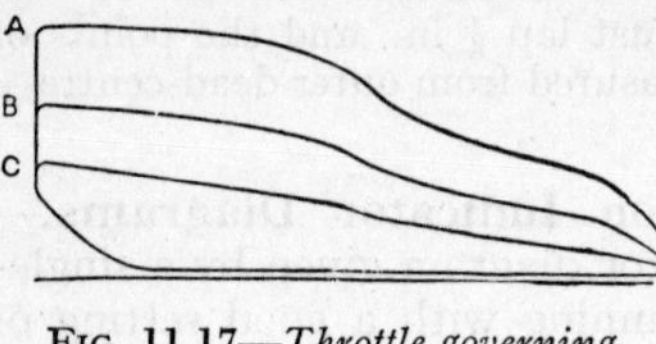

Fig. 11.17—*Throttle governing.*

Fig. 11.18 shows, on an indicator diagram, the effect of varying the point of cut-off in a non-condensing engine. It will be seen that, with the earliest cut-off, the expansion line falls below the atmospheric line, thus forming the loop which represents negative work, or work which has to be done on the steam.

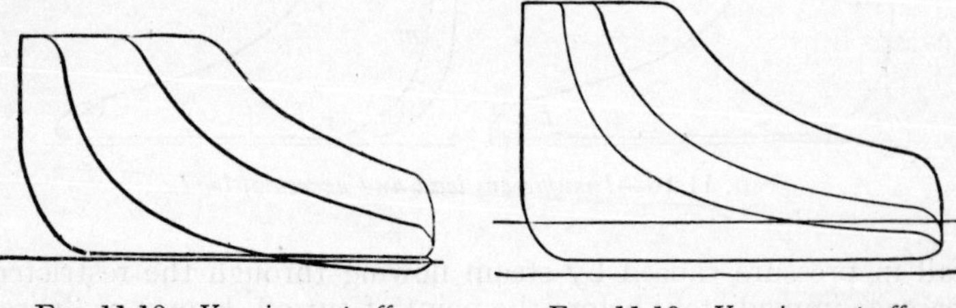
Fig. 11.18—*Varying cut-off.* Fig. 11.19—*Varying cut-off.*

Fig. 11.19 shows the effect of varying the point of cut-off in a condensing engine fitted with a trip gear to give a sharp point of cut-off.

Fig. 11.20 shows the effect of regulating the power by varying the cut-off in a slide-valve high-speed engine.

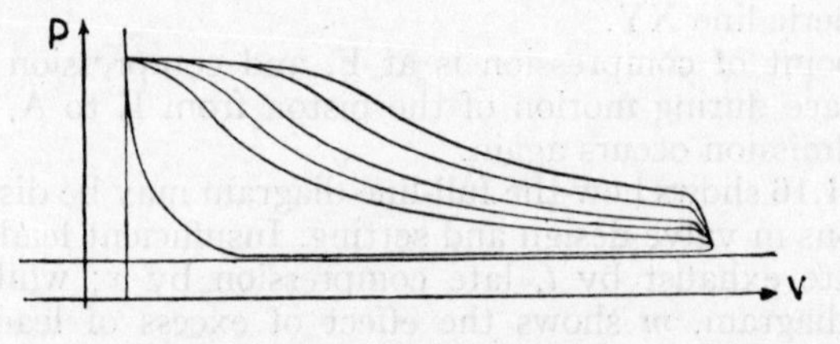

Fig. 11.20—*Varying cut-off.*

6. Meyer's Expansion Valve.—Fig. 11.21 illustrates Meyer's expansion valve, which consists of the simple slide valve previously considered with two blocks which slide on top. By movement of the two blocks the point of cut-off can be made earlier, as shown in fig. 11.20, without altering the other three critical points of admission, release, and compression. Two eccentrics on the crank-shaft give reciprocating motion to the main valve and to the expansion blocks, respectively, the main valve eccentric having the usual angular advance on the crank; and the eccentric giving motion to the expansion blocks is given 180° advance on the crank. By doing this an early cut-off is obtained, resulting in economy of steam due to more effective expansive working.

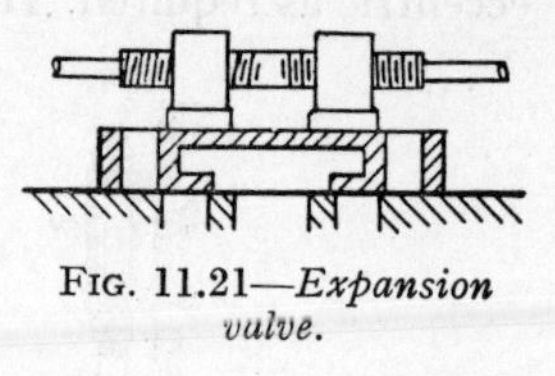

FIG. 11.21—*Expansion valve.*

A Meyer expansion valve can be seen fitted to the high-pressure cylinder of the compound engine shown in fig. 2.3.

7. Reversing Gear.—The underlying principle of reversing gears is illustrated in the simple diagrams of figs. 11.22 and 11.23.

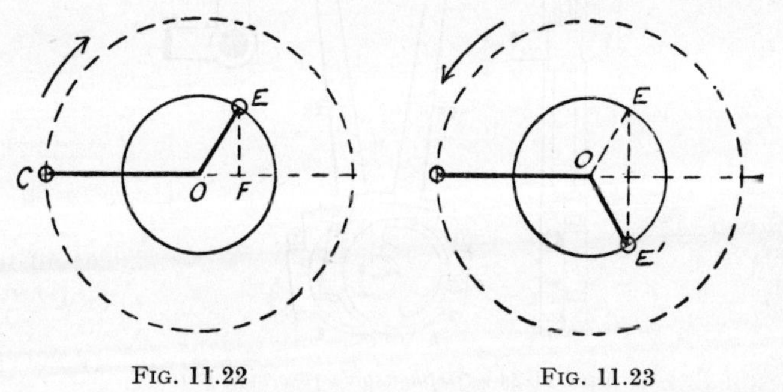

FIG. 11.22 FIG. 11.23

Principle of reversing gears.

It has previously been shown that when the crank is in a position OC the eccentric will be in advance of the crank by, say, an angular advance COE. Suppose we now wish to reverse the engine by changing the direction of rotation to that in fig. 11.23, then unless we have some means of shifting the eccentric from E to E′, the engine will not reverse.

In Stephenson's gear two eccentrics are used, one having its centre at E and the other at E′, fig. 11.23, and, by means of the link L, fig. 11.24, we can use which eccentric we please by throwing the other out of action. By this means the engine can be made to rotate in either direction. Each eccentric is attached by a rod to one end of the slotted bar or link which is moved transversely by the levers to bring the slide valve under the influence of either eccentric as required. The slide valve is attached by a rod to the

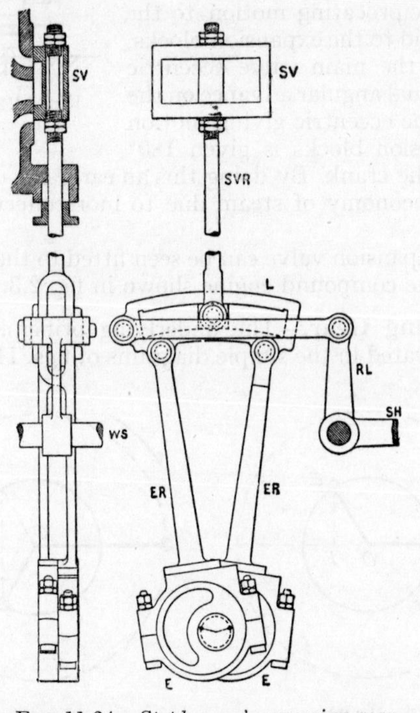

FIG. 11.24—*Stephenson's reversing gear.*

sliding block, which fits in the slot of the link, so that any movement of the link in the direction of the axis of the valve rod affects the position of the valve. When the block is in the middle of the link the valve is influenced equally by both eccentrics, with the result that the engine will not run in either direction. It is possible to vary the point of cut-off with this gear according to the position of the sliding block, although Walscheart's gear is now almost always used on high-speed steam engines of the locomotive type.

EXERCISES ON CHAPTER 11

(i)

1. Sketch and describe the action of a piston valve.
2. Define outside lap or steam lap, inside lap or exhaust lap, and lead, with reference to a simple D slide valve. What effect do they have on the action of the valve?
3. What is angle of advance and angular advance?
4. State whether steam lap or exhaust lap settle the points of compression, cut-off, admission, and release.
5. Make a sketch and describe with reference to it how you would place an engine on the dead-centre points.
6. What effect has the obliquity of the connecting rod on the piston displacement of an engine?
7. Make a sketch of a typical indicator diagram for a non-condensing steam engine showing clearly where the critical events of admission, cut-off, release, and compression occur.
8. Sketch and explain the function of Meyer's expansion valve.
9. Make sketches to show the principle underlying Stephenson's link motion for the reversing of steam engines.

(ii)

10. In a vertical steam engine the valve travel is $2\frac{1}{4}$ in. The critical events as determined from the indicator cards are: cut-off 60 per cent. and release 90 per cent. of the outstroke, compression 85 per cent. of the instroke. Neglecting the obliquity of the connecting rod find, by means of the Reuleaux diagram, the angle of advance, the lead, and the laps.
11. Repeat Question 10, taking into account the obliquity of the connecting rod, if the ratio of the length of connecting rod to crank is $4\frac{1}{2}$.
12. By means of a Bilgram diagram determine the eccentric radius, angle of advance, and steam lap for a simple slide valve from the following information: ratio of connecting rod to crank 4, lead $\frac{1}{8}$ inch, maximum port opening to steam $\frac{7}{8}$ inch, cut-off 70 per cent. of stroke.
13. The total travel of a simple D slide valve is $4\frac{1}{2}$ in. Cut-off occurs at half stroke, and admission commences 5° before the dead-centre point. The ratio of the lengths of connecting-rod and crank is 5. Find the steam lap required at the crank end of the valve, the angle by which the eccentric leads the crank, and the angular position of the crank measured from the dead-centre point when cut-off takes place.

CHAPTER 12

INTRODUCTORY WORK ON STEAM TURBINES

1. The Principle of Turbines.—Steam turbines are energy transformers in which part of the heat and pressure energy of steam are changed into mechanical energy by imparting rotary motion to turbine blade wheels. In ordinary steam engines the reciprocating motion of the piston is changed into rotary motion by means of a crank and connecting rod, but in turbines the rotary motion is obtained by direct action of the fluid on the rotating blade wheels or rotors.

In all types of steam turbines the steam is allowed to expand from a higher to a lower pressure either in nozzles or in the blading, and, consequently, increases its velocity at the expense of its heat and pressure. The velocity of the steam is then reduced by doing work on the moving blades.

2. Impulse and Reaction Turbines.—Turbines are usually classified as "impulse" and "reaction," although all steam turbines make use of the impulse principle in that they reduce the kinetic energy of the steam as it flows from inlet to outlet over turbine blades. Turbines in which the steam expands before entering the moving blades, but not while passing over them, are called *impulse turbines*. In impulse wheels the *direction* of flow of steam is changed while its speed remains the same except for the reduction due to friction. Thus, there is a change of momentum per second which, by Newton's second law of motion, is proportional to the impressed force. The Laval turbine, figs. 2.4 and 2.6, is one example of an impulse turbine.

In reaction turbines the moving blades are "in action" all the time, since steam flows along an annular space round the entire circumference, whereas fig. 2.6 shows that the blades of impulse turbines are only "in action" when in front of the nozzles.

Turbines in which steam expands while it is passing over the moving blades as well as while passing over the fixed blades are called *reaction turbines*. Fig. 12.12 illustrates a reaction turbine. Such a turbine thus transforms the energy of steam into mechanical energy partly by reducing the kinetic energy of the steam issuing from the fixed blades and partly by reducing the pressure energy and total heat or enthalpy of the steam flowing over the moving blades. The fall in pressure and total heat of the steam while passing over the moving blades result in an increase in the velocity of the steam relative to the blades (see fig. 12.11), and the force produced by the change of momentum (in magnitude and direction) of the flowing steam reacts on the blade-wheel, tending to make the wheel revolve.

Another way of distinguishing between impulse and reaction turbines is to say that turbines having the same pressure on the two sides of the moving blades are impulse turbines, and those which have different pressures on the two sides of the moving blades are reaction turbines.

3. Velocity of Steam.—The velocity of steam flowing in a pipe or through a nozzle increases as the pressure falls. If the velocities and total heats per unit mass of steam flowing past sections ① and ② of fig. 12.1 are V_1, H_1 and V_2, H_2 respectively, then, by the law of conservation of energy, which states that the total energy in the steam at section ① is equal to the total energy at section ② plus loss of energy (l) between the two sections, we may write, for unit *mass* of fluid flowing,

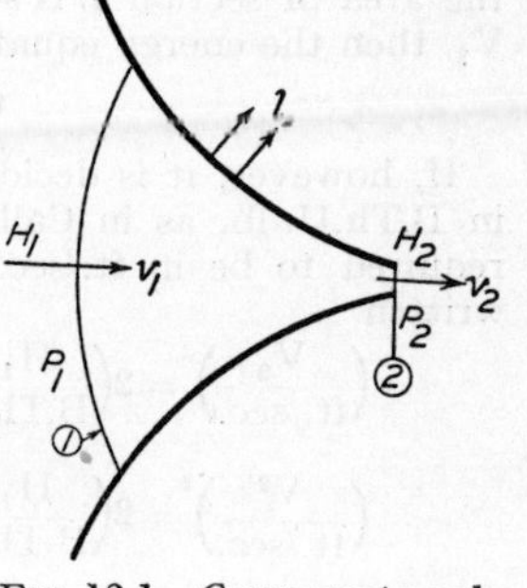

FIG. 12.1—*Convergent nozzle.*

$$\frac{V_1^2}{2}+H_1=\frac{V_2^2}{2}+H_2+l$$

which applies to all nozzles and ducts. If the fluid is steam the nozzle will need to be convergent when P_2 is greater than $0 \cdot 58\ P_1$ but when P_2 is less than $0 \cdot 58\ P_1$ the nozzle will need to be convergent-divergent, the pressure at the throat then being $0 \cdot 58\ P_1$.

The kinetic energy of a mass M moving with a velocity V is given by the physical formula $\frac{1}{2}MV^2$ in which symbols represent physical quantities, namely, numbers × units (see page xix).

If, however, it is decided to measure mass in lb. and velocity in ft./sec. then we may write $M=m$ lb. and $V=v$ ft./sec., where M and V are quantities (numbers × units) and m and v are numbers only.

$$\text{Hence, the kinetic energy}=\tfrac{1}{2}MV^2=\tfrac{1}{2}(m\text{ lb.})\left(\frac{v^2\text{ft.}^2}{\text{sec.}^2}\right)\left[\frac{\text{Lb. sec.}^2}{\text{lb.}\times 32\cdot 2\text{ ft.}}\right]$$

$$=\frac{1}{2}\frac{mv^2}{32\cdot 2}\text{ ft.-Lb.}$$

Thus, the *physical* formula $\frac{1}{2}MV^2$ has a corresponding *numerical* formula $\frac{1}{2}\frac{mv^2}{32\cdot 2}$ ft.-Lb. where m is the *number* of lb. of mass and v is the *number* of ft./sec. of speed.

Example 1.—The kinetic energy per lb. of steam flowing with a velocity of 2,000 ft./sec. is, using the physical formula,

$$\tfrac{1}{2}MV^2=\tfrac{1}{2}\,(1\text{ lb.})\,(4\times10^6)\,\frac{\text{ft.}^2}{\text{sec.}^2}\left[\frac{\text{Lb. sec.}^2}{\text{lb.}\times32\cdot2\text{ ft.}}\right]=62{,}200\text{ ft.-Lb.}$$

or using the numerical formula,

$$\frac{1}{2}\frac{mv^2}{32\cdot2}\text{ ft.-Lb.}=\frac{1}{2}\times\frac{1\times4\times10^6}{32\cdot2}\text{ft.-Lb.}=62{,}200\text{ ft.-Lb.}$$

If loss of heat (l) through the walls of the nozzle is negligible, and the area of section ① is so large as to make V_1 negligible relative to V_2, then the energy equation yields the physical formula:—

$$V_2=\sqrt{2(H_1-H_2)}$$

If, however, it is decided to measure total heat or enthalpy (H) in B.Th.U./lb. as in Callendar's steam tables, and the velocity is required to be in ft./sec., then this physical formula may be re-written

$$\left(\frac{V_2}{\text{ft./sec.}}\right)^2=2\left(\frac{H_1-H_2}{\text{B.Th.U./lb.}}\right)\left\{\frac{\text{B.Th.U.}}{\text{lb.}}\times\frac{\text{sec.}^2}{\text{ft.}^2}\right\}$$

$$\left(\frac{V^2}{\text{ft./sec.}}\right)^2=2\left(\frac{H_1-H_2}{\text{B.Th.U./lb.}}\right)\left\{\frac{\cancel{\text{B.Th.U.}}}{\cancel{\text{lb.}}}\times\frac{\cancel{\text{sec.}^2}}{\cancel{\text{ft.}^2}}\right\}\times$$

$$\left[\frac{\cancel{\text{lb.}}\times32\cdot2\cancel{\text{ft.}}}{\cancel{\text{Lb.-sec.}^2}}\right]\left[\frac{778\cancel{\text{ft.-Lb.}}}{\cancel{\text{B.Th.U.}}}\right]$$

$$=2\times32\cdot2\times778\left(\frac{H_1-H_2}{\text{B.Th.U./sec.}}\right)$$

and the corresponding numerical formula is

$$\boldsymbol{v_2=\sqrt{2\times32\cdot2\times778\,(h_1-h_2)}=223\cdot8\sqrt{(h_1-h_2)}},$$

where (h_1-h_2) is the numerical value of the " heat drop " when measured in B.Th.U. per lb.

$$\text{i.e.}\quad (H_1-H_2)=(h_1-h_2)\,\frac{\text{B.Th.U.}}{\text{lb.}}$$

and v_2 is the numerical value of the velocity in ft./sec.;

$$\text{i.e.}\quad \boldsymbol{V_2=v_2\text{ ft./sec.}=223\cdot8\sqrt{(h_1-h_2)}\text{ ft./sec.}}$$

Example.—Dry saturated steam at 50 Lb. per sq. in. abs. having negligible velocity at entry, expands in a convergent-divergent nozzle to 14·7 Lb. per sq. in. abs. and dryness fraction 0·94. Calculate the velocity of the steam leaving the nozzle assuming the latter to be impervious to heat.

From steam tables, $H_{s1}=1174\cdot8$ B.Th.U./lb. and H_2 is estimated as

$$h_{w2}+q_2L_2=180\cdot1+0\cdot94\times970\cdot6=1903\cdot1\text{ B.Th.U./lb.}$$

Hence, the " heat drop," $H_{s1}-H_2=81\cdot7$ B.Th.U./lb. and

$$v_2=223\cdot8\sqrt{81\cdot7}=2020$$

i.e. the velocity of the steam leaving the nozzle is 2,020 ft./sec. Alternatively, using the physical formula, $V_2 = \sqrt{2(H_1 - H_2)}$ we get, using two appropriate unity brackets,

$$V_2{}^2 = 2 \times 81 \cdot 7 \frac{\text{B.Th.U.}}{\text{lb.}} \left[\frac{778 \text{ ft. Lb.}}{\text{B.Th.U.}}\right]\left[\frac{\text{lb. } 32 \cdot 2 \text{ ft.}}{\text{Lb. sec.}^2}\right]$$

i.e. $$V_2{}^2 = 2 \times 32 \cdot 2 \times 778 \times 81 \cdot 7 \frac{\text{ft.}^2}{\text{sec.}^2}$$

or $$V_2 = 2020 \text{ ft./sec.}$$

4. The De Laval Impulse Turbine.—Fig. 2.6 shows a view of a De Laval wheel with four nozzles, and Fig. 2.5 shows the section of a Laval nozzle and shutting-off valve. The steam expands from the pressure in the nozzle box to that in the wheel chamber before entering the blade wheel. The velocity thus

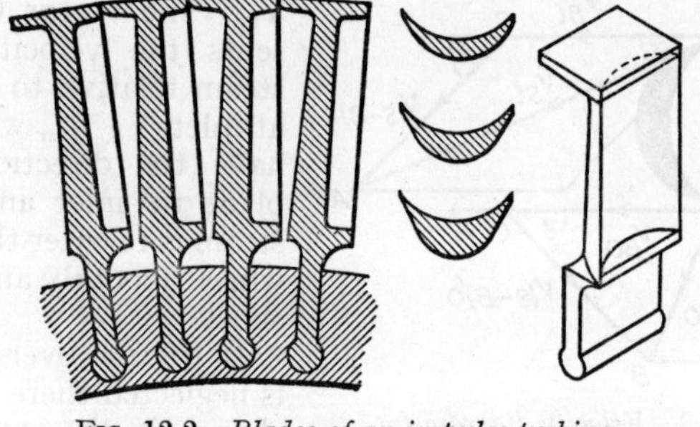

Fig. 12.2—*Blades of an impulse turbine.*

attained by the steam in expanding through the nozzles is very high, being of the order of 4,000 ft. per sec. for a pressure drop through the nozzle from 160 Lb. per sq. in. abs. to 1 Lb. per sq. in. abs.

A section through a De Laval turbine is shown in fig. 2.4. The speed of the blade wheel of this turbine is about 25,000 r.p.m. This high rate of revolution is a disadvantage, for speeds of this magnitude are never required in ordinary machinery. The diameter of the blade wheel in a 10 horse-power De Laval turbine is about 5 in. and the diameter of the shaft running at 25,000 r.p.m. is only about $\frac{3}{8}$ in. In the Curtis and Rateau impulse turbines (see pp. 258 and 257) a high speed of rotation is avoided by expanding the steam in a series of stages. By so doing, smaller velocities of steam are produced and hence the moving wheels revolve more slowly.

The blades of impulse turbine wheels (and also of reaction wheels, fig. 12.10), are specially shaped, fig. 12.2, to allow steam issuing from the nozzles to enter without shock or too sudden change of velocity. By Newton's second law of motion, the force produced by the steam on the blades=rate of change of momentum which is found from velocity diagrams.

5. Velocity Diagrams for Impulse Turbines.—Fig. 12.3 shows the parallelograms of velocities at inlet and outlet for one blade of an impulse turbine.

Steam leaves the nozzle with a velocity represented by vector OA, this being the velocity of steam at inlet to the blade, and therefore labelled V_{si}. It is usually known completely, i.e. in magnitude, direction, and sense.

Vector OC represents the velocity of the blade at the inlet tip, V_{Bi}, which is also equal to the vector OC′ representing the blade velocity at the outlet tip, V_{BO}. The vector CA represents the velocity of the steam relative to the blade at inlet, $V_{(S-B)i}$, which must have the direction of the blade tip inlet angle if the steam is to enter the moving wheel smoothly and without shock.

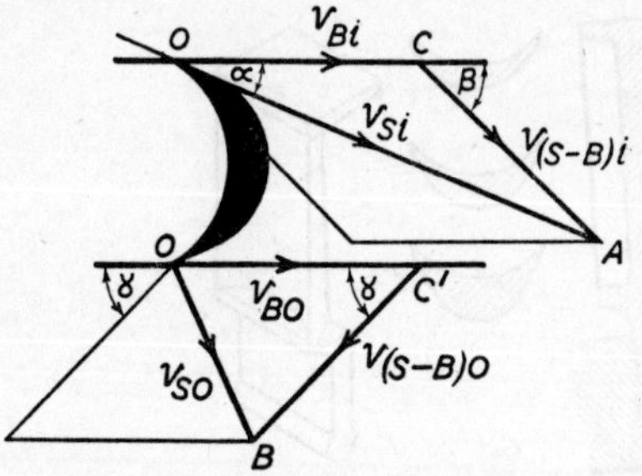

FIG. 12.3—*Velocity diagram for impulse turbine blades.*

If friction over the blade is neglected there will be no change in the *magnitude* of the velocity of steam relative to the blade as the steam passes over the blade. The velocity of the steam relative to the blade at outlet $V_{(S-B)o}$, represented by vector C′B tangential to blade tip at outlet will be equal in magnitude to the velocity of the steam relative to the blade at inlet $V_{(S-B)i}$, represented by vector CA. The actual velocity of the steam at outlet, V_{SO}, is the *vectorial sum* of the velocity of the steam relative to the blade at outlet, $V_{(S-B)o}$ and the blade velocity at outlet, V_{BO}—that is, vector OB=vector C′B+vector OC′.

Since the blade velocity is the same at inlet as at outlet, *i.e.* $V_{Bi}=V_{BO}$, the two diagrams can be superimposed with the blade velocity, V_B, as a common vector. Such a combined diagram is shown in fig. 12.4, from which it will be seen that triangle OCA is the triangle of velocities for the inlet tip of the blade, and triangle OCB is the triangle of velocities for the outlet tip of the blade.

In words, we may state the velocity (vector) equation at inlet as:

Velocity of steam at inlet = velocity of steam relative to blade at inlet + velocity of blade at inlet;

or, in symbols, $V_{Si} = V_{(S-B)i} + V_{Bi}$

and similarly at outlet, $V_{SO} = V_{(S-B)O} + V_{BO}$

It will be noticed that in these vector equations *the suffixes and signs add up to balance on each side of the equations.* Also, on referring to the inlet and outlet diagrams OCA and OC′B of fig. 12.3, it will be noticed that the sum of the suffixes of the vectors whose arrowheads follow round one way (OCA), add up to the suffix of the vector the arrowhead of which follows round the other way (OA). If this suffix notation is used, both the velocity equations and the velocity diagrams can be checked merely by adding suffixes.

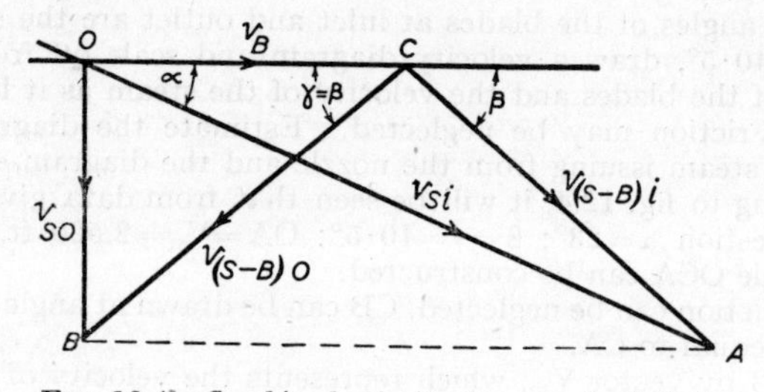

FIG. 12.4—*Combined velocity diagram for impulse turbine blades.*

In fig. 12.4 it will be seen that the steam enters the blade with velocity OA and leaves with the velocity OB. Therefore, since final velocity = initial velocity + change in velocity, the change in velocity of the steam while flowing over the blade must be represented by the vector AB which will be parallel to OC if the blade tip angles β and γ at inlet and outlet are equal and there is no reduction in relative velocity due to friction. Thus, if the rate of mass flow of steam over the blade is m, the rate of change of momentum of the steam is $m \times AB$. Hence, by Newton's second law of motion, the force on the steam producing this change $= m.AB$ and this must be the force exerted by the *blade on the steam.* Thus, by Newton's third law of motion, which states that action and reaction are equal and opposite, the force exerted by the *steam on the blade* must be $m.BA$ acting in the direction BA parallel to the direction of motion OC in this particular case. (If BA is not parallel to OC, the component of BA parallel to OC must be taken, namely DA as in fig. 12.8.)

Therefore, **the rate at which work is done is m.BA.OC** and the work done per unit mass of steam is BA.OC—called the "*diagram work,*" since it is estimated from the velocity diagram.

The rate at which energy is supplied to the wheel is $\frac{1}{2}m(OA)^2$, and the kinetic energy supplied in unit mass of the steam jet is $\frac{1}{2}(OA)^2$. Hence, the **"diagram efficiency,"** as represented by the ratio of work done to energy supplied in the jet **is** $\mathbf{\frac{2.BA.OC}{(OA)^2}}$.

In this wheel there will be no end thrust, since there is no component of the change in velocity of the steam (AB) at right-angles to OC. This is because the inlet and outlet blade tip angles β and γ are made the same, and friction has been neglected.

Example.—Steam issues from a nozzle with a velocity 2,520 ft. per sec. at an angle of 23° on to the blade wheel of an impulse turbine. If the tip angles of the blades at inlet and outlet are the same and equal to 40·5°, draw a velocity diagram and scale off from it the velocity of the blades and the velocity of the steam as it leaves the blades. Friction may be neglected. Estimate the diagram work per lb. of steam issuing from the nozzle and the diagram efficiency.

Referring to fig. 12.4, it will be seen that from data given in the above question $\alpha=23°$; $\beta=\gamma=40\cdot5°$; $OA=V_{si}=2{,}520$ ft. per sec. the triangle OCA can be constructed.

Since friction can be neglected, CB can be drawn at angle $\gamma=40\cdot5°$ of length equal to CA.

Join OB by vector V_{so}, which represents the velocity of steam at outlet from the wheel.

The lengths scaled off the diagram give: blade speed$=OC=V_B$ $=1{,}160$ ft. per sec., and velocity of steam at outlet$=OB=V_{so}=985$ ft. per sec.

Diagram work$=BA\times OC$.

$$=2{,}320\ \frac{\text{ft.}}{\text{sec.}}\times 1{,}160\ \frac{\text{ft.}}{\text{sec.}}\left[\frac{\text{Lb. sec.}^2}{\text{lb.}\times 32\cdot 2\ \text{ft.}}\right]$$

$$=83{,}600\ \text{ft. Lb./lb.}$$

Kinetic energy supplied$=\frac{1}{2}(OA)^2$

$$=\tfrac{1}{2}(2{,}520)^2\ \frac{\text{ft.}^2}{\text{sec.}^2}\left[\frac{\text{Lb. sec.}^2}{\text{lb.}\times 32\cdot 2\ \text{ft.}}\right]$$

$$=98{,}600\ \text{ft. Lb./lb.}$$

Hence, diagram efficiency$=\frac{836}{986}$ or 84·8 per cent.

6. Losses in a De Laval Turbine.—If the available energy obtained by expanding steam between two given pressures is represented by 100 when no loss takes place, the following approximate losses can be taken as occurring in a Laval turbine: a loss of about 15 per cent. in the nozzle owing to friction between the steam and the sides of the nozzle and the formation of eddies in the steam; 10 per cent. loss due to friction between steam and blades; and since the wheel revolves at very high speed there will be a loss of about 5 per cent. due to disc friction; the kinetic energy of the steam leaving the turbine will be about 10 per cent.; and radiation and mechanical friction about 5 per cent. Since *friction always produces heat* the "loss" in the nozzles, blades, and

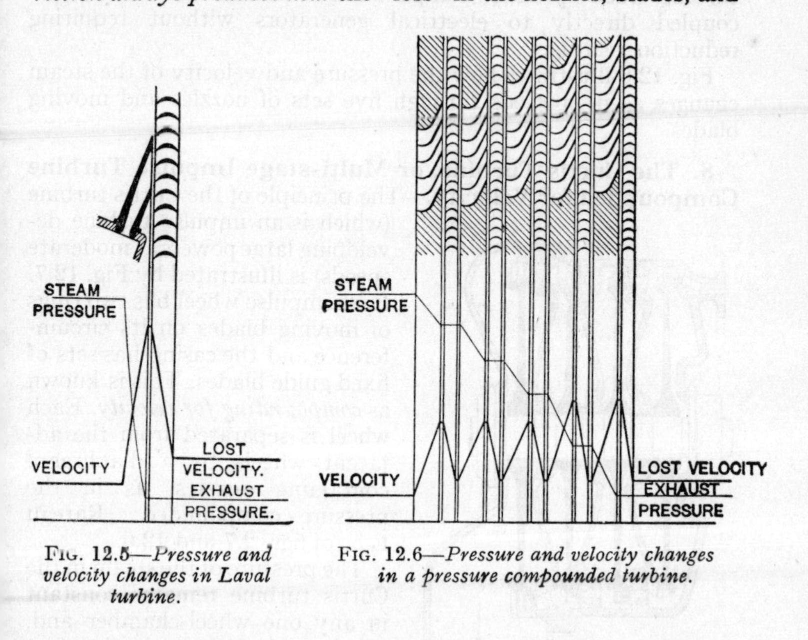

FIG. 12.5—*Pressure and velocity changes in Laval turbine.*

FIG. 12.6—*Pressure and velocity changes in a pressure compounded turbine.*

disc friction produces heat which appears in the exhaust steam, i.e. the exhaust steam is therefore drier than it would be if there were no friction. In all steam engine and turbine plant the greater part of the heat supplied is inevitably rejected in the exhaust steam.

Fig. 12.5 shows diagrammatically the fall of pressure in the nozzle of a Laval turbine, and the corresponding increase in velocity of the steam before entering the wheel. Also, it shows how the velocity of the steam falls as it passes through the blades due to work done by it on the blades of the moving wheel; and the final pressure and velocity of the steam as it leaves the turbine for the condenser.

7. The Rateau Turbine, or Multi-stage Impulse Turbine Compounded for Pressure.—A multi-stage impulse turbine is shown in fig. 2.7. This type is sometimes referred to as a "pressure-compounded turbine" or Rateau turbine. The comparatively low velocity of the steam which results from dividing the total fall of pressure into stages enables the turbine to run at a low rate of revolution compared with the single-wheel Laval turbine. Such "pressure-compounded" turbines can therefore be coupled directly to electrical generators without requiring reduction gearing.

Fig. 12.6 illustrates how the pressure and velocity of the steam changes as it proceeds through five sets of nozzles and moving blades.

8. The Curtis Turbine, or Multi-stage Impulse Turbine Compounded for Velocity.—The principle of the Curtis turbine (which is an impulse turbine developing large powers at moderate speeds) is illustrated by Fig. 12.7. Each impulse wheel has two rings of moving blades on its circumference and the casing has sets of fixed guide blades. This is known as *compounding for velocity*. Each wheel is separated from the adjacent wheels by a diaphragm containing nozzles, as in the pressure-compounded Rateau type of figs. 2.7 and 12.6.

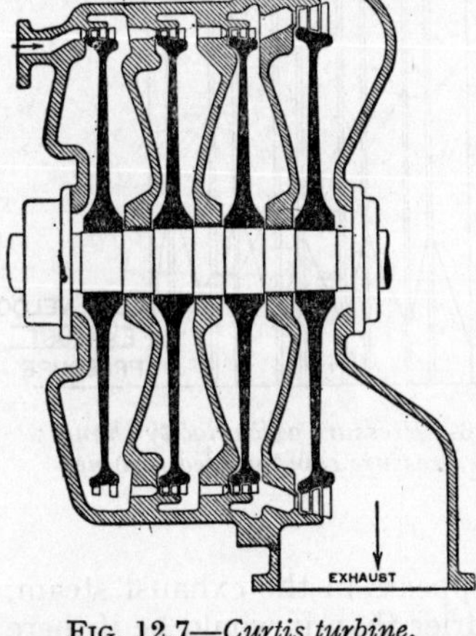

FIG. 12.7—*Curtis turbine.*

The pressure of the steam in the Curtis turbine remains constant in any one wheel-chamber and, after passing through the first ring of moving blades and reducing its speed as a result, the steam is received by the fixed guide blades and redirected on to the second ring of moving blades, where its speed is further reduced. A Curtis wheel is usually fitted at the high-pressure end of large turbine sets as in figs. 12.12 and 12.13.

The velocity diagram for two rings of moving blades compounded for velocity is shown in Fig. 12.8, in which

$$_1V_{si} = {}_1V_{(S-B)i} + {}_1V_{Bi}$$

$$_1V_{so} = {}_1V_{(S-B)o} + {}_1V_{BO}$$

are the velocity equations for the first wheel, giving the velocity triangles OCA_1 and OCB_1. The velocity equations for the second wheel are:

$${}_2V_{si} = {}_2V_{(S-B)i} + {}_2V_{Bi} \text{ for the inlet tip,}$$

and $${}_2V_{so} = {}_2V_{(S-B)o} + {}_2V_{Bo} \text{ for the outlet tip.}$$

These give the triangles of velocity OCA_2 and OCB_2.

It will be noticed in fig. 12.8 that friction has been taken into account, CB_1 being less than CA_1, OA_2 is less than OB_1 and CB_2 less than CA_2.

The total **power developed** by the two sets of moving blades in the stage is $\boldsymbol{m}.\mathbf{OC(D_1A_1+D_2A_2)}$, and the **end thrust** is given by $\boldsymbol{m}\mathbf{(B_1D_1+B_2D_2)}$, where m is the rate of mass flow of steam.

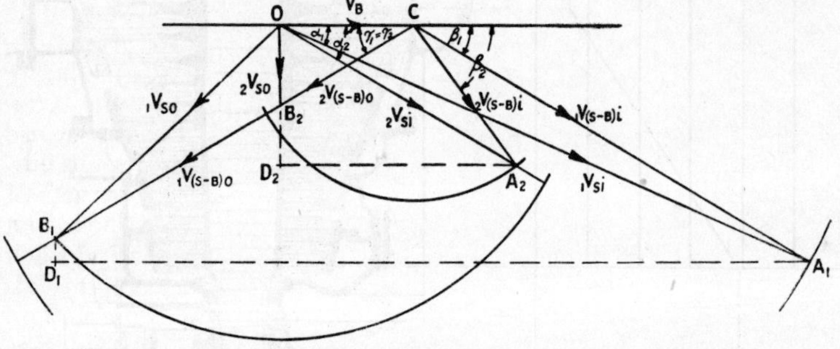

FIG. 12.8—*Velocity diagram for blades compounded for velocity.*

9. The Impulse-reaction Turbine.—Fig. 12.9 shows a section through a two-cylinder turbine having the high-pressure stage shown on the left and the low-pressure stage on the right. This type of turbine is part impulse and part reaction—as are most other large turbines, namely about 95 per cent. impulse and 5 per cent. reaction at the commencement of the high-pressure stage and about 50 per cent. impulse and 50 per cent. reaction at the end of the low-pressure stage. The upper graph of fig. 12.9 shows how the steam decreases in degree of superheat as it passes through the h.p. stage and how in the l.p. stage the steam gradually begins to condense and finally leaves the turbine containing 12 per cent. of moisture, i.e. the steam enters the condenser with a dryness fraction of 0·88.

It will be noticed that in the h.p. stage the high-pressure superheated steam (350 Lb. per sq. in. gauge and 260° F. of superheat) entering remains superheated while flowing through

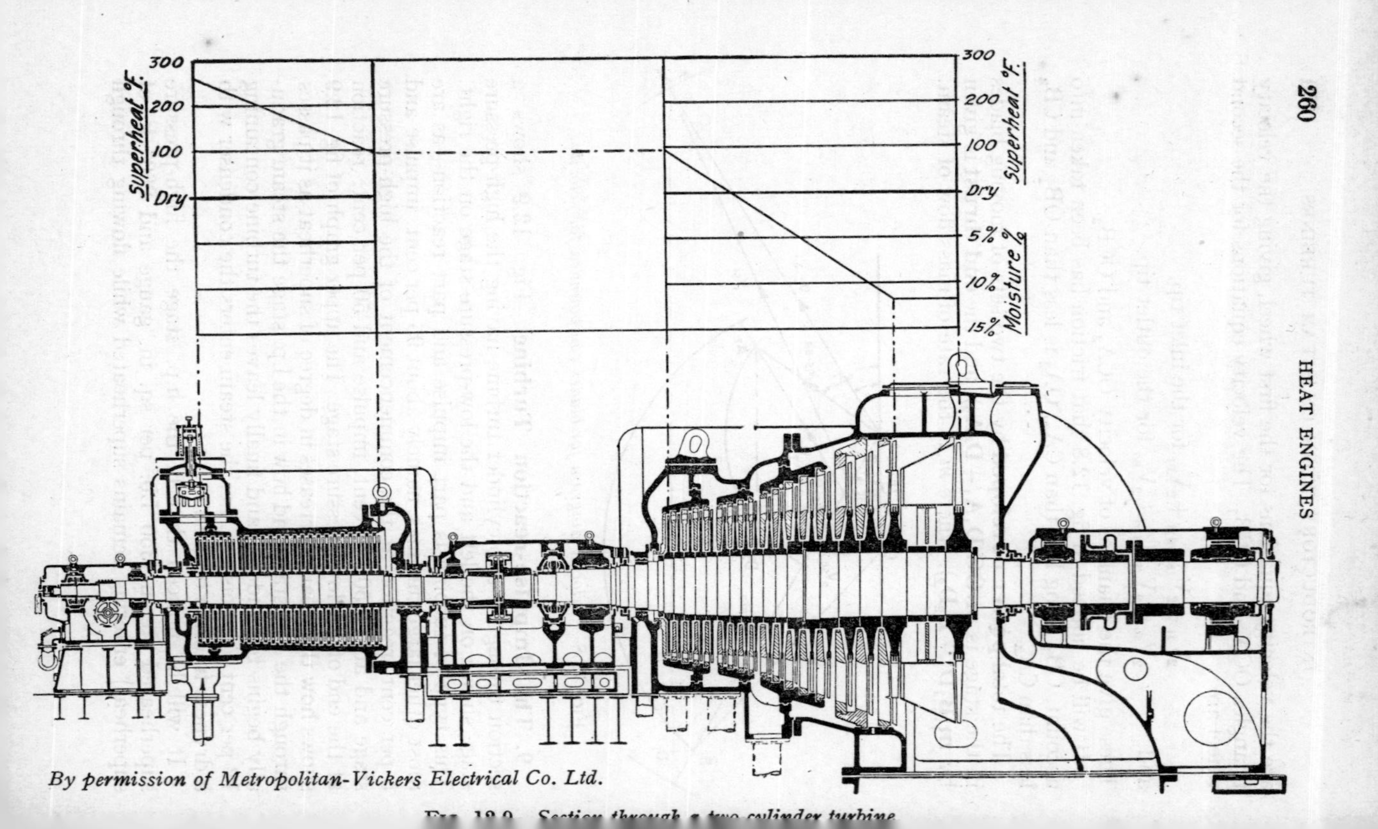

FIG. 12.9. Section through a two-cylinder turbine

the blades and that the blade heights are slightly increased to accommodate the comparatively small increase in volume due to the gradual pressure drop which occurs in the h.p. stage. In the l.p. stage it will be seen that the steam enters in a superheated state and begins to condense during the latter three-quarters of the stage. The blade-wheel diameters and the blade heights are increased to accommodate the increasing volume of steam which accrues as the steam flows through the blades owing to the continuous reduction of pressure. It will be noticed that the increase

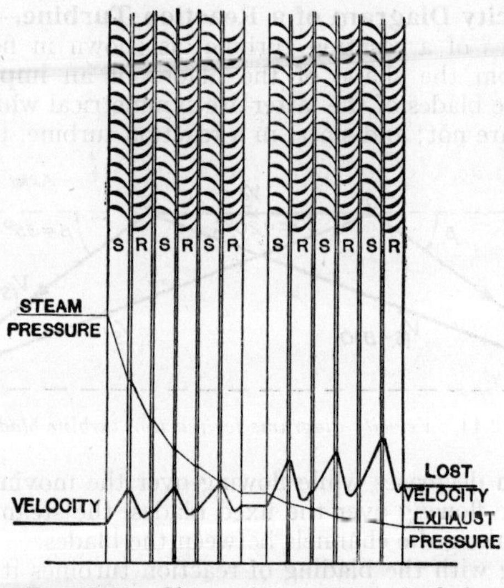

Fig. 12.10—*Changes in pressure and velocity through a reaction turbine.*

in blade heights at the back end of the l.p. stage are very much more than the increase in blade heights at the exit end of the h.p. turbine. This is because the volume of steam increases enormously at low-pressures as compared with the increase in volume at high-pressures. (See steam tables and fig. 6.1.)

The small fall in pressure over each of the fixed and moving blades of a reaction turbine is shown in fig. 12.10. The velocities resulting from the expansion of steam during the reductions in pressure are never very high, and thus the blade speeds are such that the rotor can be coupled direct to an electric generator.

Great care is required in the axial adjustment of the rotating blades to prevent them from coming into contact with the stationary blades, and the radial clearances between the blade tips and the casing are very small in order to prevent leakage of steam past the blades.

Small turbines are relatively inefficient and uneconomical in steam consumption, one reason for this being that blade clearances cannot be reduced when blade lengths are reduced. Reaction turbines are usually made in large units from 500 to over 20,000 horse-power in one casing, and multi-cylinder turbines of over 100,000 kw. are now constructed.

10. Velocity Diagram of a Reaction Turbine.—The shape of the blades of a reaction turbine, as shown in fig. 12.10, is different from the shape of the blades of an impulse wheel, fig. **12.5**. The blades of the latter are symmetrical whilst those of the former are not; and since, in a reaction turbine, the pressure

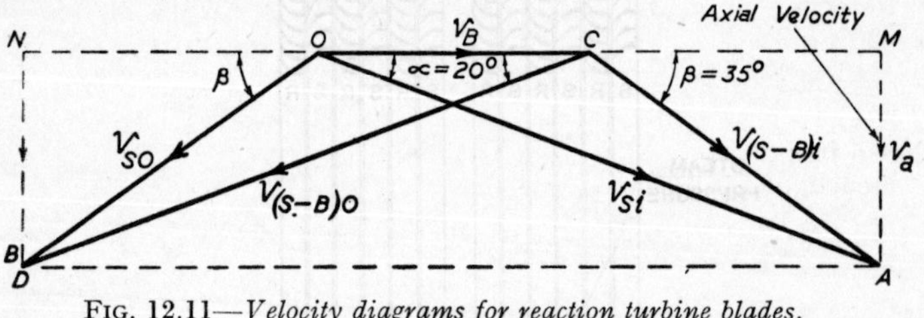

FIG. 12.11—*Velocity diagrams for reaction turbine blades.*

of the steam decreases while flowing over the moving blades as well as while flowing over the fixed blades, the steam must flow "full bore" along the channels between the blades.

In dealing with the blading of reaction turbines it is usual to consider a "turbine-pair," *i.e.* one ring of stationary blades, which act as convergent nozzles, and one ring of rotating blades, as illustrated in fig. 12.10. If the stationary and rotating blades of the turbine-pair have the same inlet and outlet angles, the velocity diagram will be as shown in fig. 12.11, from which one deduces that the "diagram work" (say, ft. Lb. per lb. of steam if measured in British units) is BA.OC.

It should be noted that although the diagram work for both impulse and reaction wheels is represented by the same expression, namely, BA.OC the shapes of the respective velocity diagrams are not the same. For, in the velocity diagram of an impulse wheel (figs. 12.4 and 12.8) CB is never greater than CA, whereas in the diagram of a reaction turbine (fig. 12.11) CB is greater than CA because of the increase in the velocity of steam relative to the blades consequent upon the fall in pressure (and total heat) which occurs while the steam is flowing over the moving blades.

Example.—The mean blade-circle diameter of a reaction turbine pair is 5 ft. and the blade height is 6 in. The steam passes through the pair at the rate of 31 lb. per sec. dry and saturated at 25 Lb. per sq. in. abs. The blade tip angles of fixed and moving blades at inlet and exit are 35° and 20° respectively. Find the axial velocity of the steam and the blade speed so that the steam shall pass on to the moving blades smoothly and without shock, and find the horse-power developed at this speed.

$$\text{Axial velocity} = \frac{\text{Volume of steam flowing in unit time}}{\text{Annular area of blade ring}}$$

$$\text{i.e.}\quad v_a = \frac{31\ \dfrac{\text{lb.}}{\text{sec.}} \times 16\cdot 3\ \dfrac{\text{ft.}^3}{\text{lb.}}}{\pi \times 5\ \text{ft.} \times 0\cdot 5\ \text{ft.}} = 64\cdot 3\ \text{ft./sec.}$$

Referring now to fig. 12.11, which is drawn for this Example, $\alpha = 20°$, $\beta = 35°$, hence the blade velocity, v_B,

$$= OC = 64\cdot 3(\cot 20 - \cot 35) = 64\cdot 3 \times 1\cdot 3194 = 84\cdot 9\ \text{ft. per sec.}$$

Also, $BA = OM + CM = 64\cdot 3\ (\cot 20 + \cot 35) = 64\cdot 3 \times 4\cdot 1756 =$ $268\cdot 5$ ft. per sec.

Hence, diagram power $= m \times BA \times OC$

$$= 31\ \frac{\text{lb.}}{\text{sec.}} \times 268\cdot 5\ \frac{\text{ft.}}{\text{sec.}} \times 84\cdot 9\ \frac{\text{ft.}}{\text{sec.}}$$

$$= 31 \times 268\cdot 5 \times 84\cdot 9\ \frac{\text{lb.-ft.}^2}{\text{sec.}^3}\left[\frac{\text{Lb.-sec.}^2}{\text{lb.} \times 32\cdot 2\ \text{ft.}}\right]\left[\frac{\text{h-p sec.}}{550\ \text{ft.-Lb.}}\right]$$

$$= 39\cdot 9\ \text{h-p.}$$

11. Impulse-reaction Turbine with Velocity-wheel.—Reaction turbines are more efficient at the low-pressure end than at the high-pressure end, because the blades are comparatively small at the high-pressure end and, therefore, a greater percentage of steam leaks over the blades than at the low-pressure end.

Impulse turbines are more efficient than reaction turbines at the high-pressure end, for there is little or no leakage of steam over the blades of an impulse turbine, since the pressure remains the same on two sides of an impulse wheel. A Curtis or velocity-wheel fitted at the high-pressure end of a turbine (see figs. 12.12 and 12.13) which afterwards continues as an impulse-reaction turbine, reduces the overall length of the turbine and gives a good efficiency at the high-pressure end. Fig. 12.12 shows a section through a single-cylinder turbine which develops 20,000 k.w. at 3,000 r.p.m. with a thermal efficiency of 34 per cent. when using steam, at 525 Lb. per sq. in. gauge and superheated to 800° F., and at a rate of less than 9 lb. per kilowatt-hour.

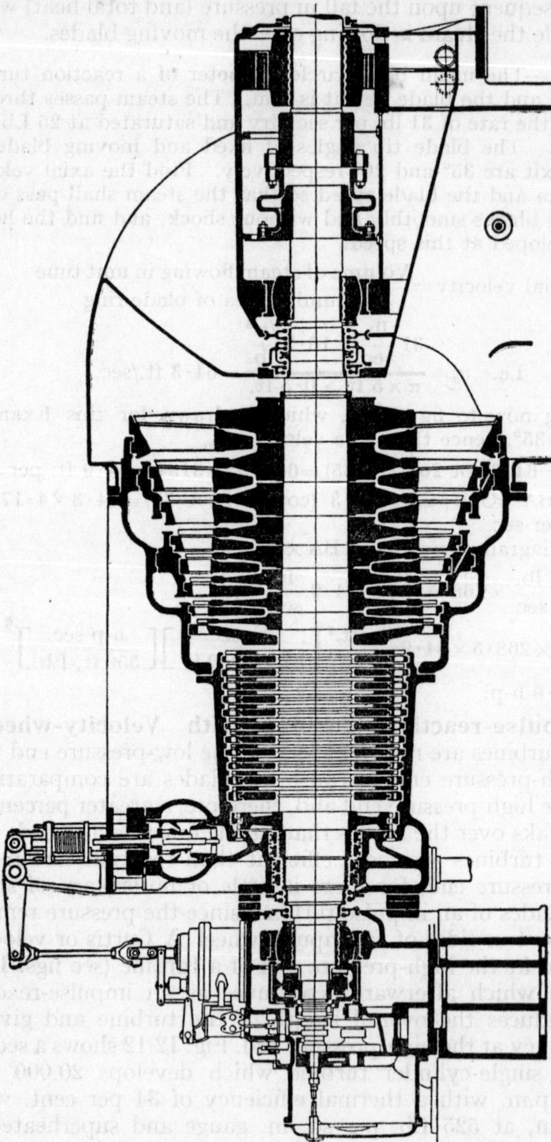

FIG. 12.12—*Single-cylinder turbine.*

12. Back-pressure Turbines.—The back-pressure turbine owes its name to the fact that in such turbines the exhaust pressure is generally higher than atmospheric, for the reason that expansion takes place only down to the pressure which is the lowest value suitable for the process work or heating purposes for which the exhaust steam is used in mills and factories. Many thermal processes are used in particular factories, such as laundries, dye-works, pulp and paper mills, dairies, breweries, gasworks, heating of buildings, etc. Back-pressure turbines are often used to generate power and also to supply the process-steam and heat required in the factory where the turbine is installed.

Fig. 12.13 shows a single-cylinder back-pressure turbine and also the fluid-governor arrangement which is fitted to many back-pressure turbines. It will be noticed that the steam first flows through an impulse wheel having two rings of moving blades compounded for velocity before it is passed on to the reaction drum, which has seven rings of moving blades. From the reaction end of the turbine the steam is led away as process steam at a pressure which may be considerably greater than that of the atmosphere.

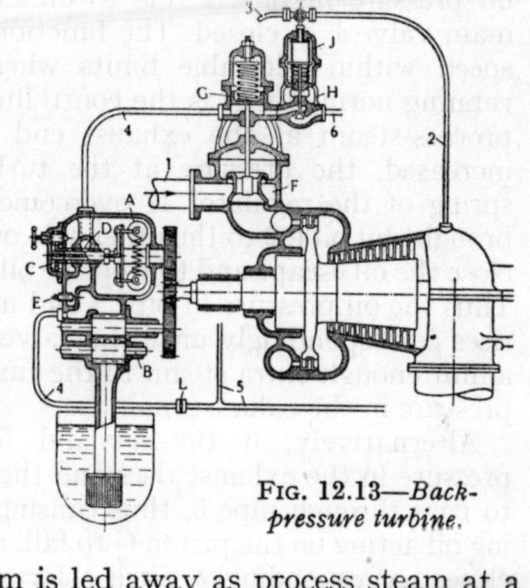

FIG. 12.13—*Back-pressure turbine.*

13. Oil-pressure Governing of Turbines.—This governing system is free from rods and complicated link motions. All valves are operated by oil under pressure. In back-pressure turbines the governing system does not control the steam flow according to the power demand but regulates it according to the low-pressure steam requirements so as to maintain, automatically, a constant pressure in the low-pressure steam main. Fig. 12.13 shows a governing system for the maintenance of constant back-pressure. A is the main governor which, owing to centrifugal force, actuates the control sleeve, in which there is an oil escape port D. The position of the control sleeve can be adjusted by C. Oil under pressure is delivered by the gear pump B through the adjustable valve E along the supply pipe 4 to the servo-motor G. This controls the amount of opening of the main inlet valve F, which admits steam to the turbine from the main steam supply pipe 1. The valve F is spring-loaded, and thus the amount of opening depends on the pressure which the oil exerts on the underside of the piston in the servo-motor. Besides supplying oil to the servo-motor the gear pump B supplies oil along pipe 4 through the baffle plate L to pipes 5, which feed the bearings.

Under normal conditions the machine is controlled solely by the pressure regulator H, for the oil port D is set so that it is uncovered only when the turbine speed rises above the normal no-load value. When this occurs there is a consequent drop in oil pressure in pipe 4 due to oil escaping through D, and the main valve F is closed. The function of D is merely to keep the speed within allowable limits when load is taken off. When running normally, H is the controlling device. If the demand for process-steam at the exhaust end of the turbine is suddenly increased, the pressure at the turbine exhaust falls, and the spring of the regulator H overcomes the pressure of the steam brought by pipe 2 to the other side of diaphragm J. This tends to close the oil escape and to stop the oil from flowing through pipe 6. Thus the oil pressure in pipe 4 and under the servo-motor piston, rises correspondingly until the valve F has opened sufficiently to admit enough extra steam to the turbine to maintain the desired pressure in the exhaust main.

Alternatively, if the demand for process-steam falls, the pressure in the exhaust rises and the oil escape opens to allow oil to pass through pipe 6, thus causing the pressure of the governing oil acting on the piston G to fall, and the steam supply valve F closes correspondingly. Such a form of governing is suitable for back-pressure turbines driving electrical generators. The above is just one example of oil-pressure governing of turbines as applied to one particular type of turbine. Variations of this idea of oil-pressure governing are made when the method is applied to other types of turbines.

14. Advantages and Disadvantages of Steam Turbines. —The chief merit of steam turbines as heat engines lies in their ability to make available for useful work the energy in the large volumes of low-pressure steam which would otherwise be rejected via the exhaust pipes of reciprocating engines into condensers before the steam has been expanded down to the pressures in the condensers. It is uneconomical and impracticable for reciprocating engines to be built of the size and bulk which would be necessary for l.p. cylinders to deal with the large volumes of steam at low pressures, whereas turbines can expand steam down to about 0·5 Lb. per sq. in. abs., which is the economical limit for condensers.

In fig. 12.14, *d* represents the pressure in a reciprocating engine where expansion stops. It is possible to obtain the additional area *edfga* by further expansion in a turbine, thus obtaining a greater amount of work per lb. of steam supplied.

The relative lengths of *ae* for the engine and *ag* for the turbine show that a reduction of vacuum, i.e. an increase in back-pressure would diminish the work done in a turbine by more than it would that done in a reciprocating engine. The economy of steam consumption and increased efficiency due to expanding steam down to low pressures (more important than high initial steam pressures) in turbines has led to the use of exhaust-steam turbines which receive steam from reciprocating engines. In certain plant an exhaust-steam turbine is substituted for the low-pressure

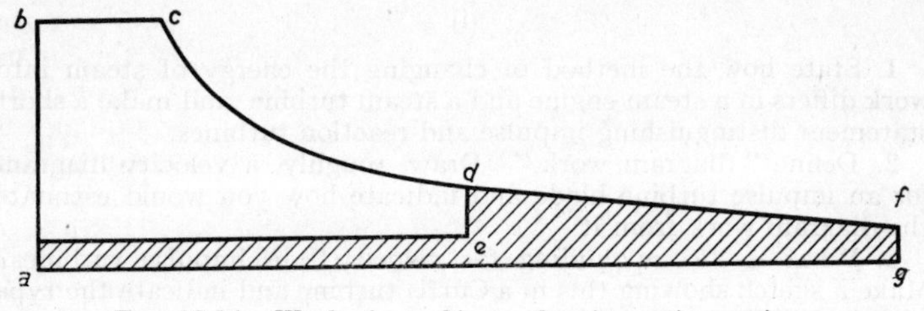

FIG. 12.14—*Work of a turbine and reciprocating engine.*

cylinder of a compound engine. Clearances in these turbines do not require to be as fine as when high pressures are used, and the relatively low temperatures produce little tendency for creep and distortion of the casing, which can therefore be of fairly light construction. In low-pressure turbines, however, the increasing wetness of the steam often results in corrosion of the casing and in erosion of the last few rings of blades.

Turbine plant is the right plant to use when very high powers are needed in a comparatively small space, but its use involves high pressures, high superheat, water-tube boilers requiring treated feed water, and well-trained specialist engineers to attend the plant. All modern power stations have turbines as their prime movers, and in ships, requiring over 5,000 horse-power, two, three, or four turbines, each driving a separate pinion on the main propeller gear-wheel, are often installed.

Steam turbines are built in units which develop up to 150,000 horse-power with perfectly balanced mechanisms of high mechanical efficiency. They will continue developing full load for months on end without trouble, whereas large-size internal-combustion engines have problems of vibration, balancing, and lubrication. Steam turbines are not, however, fitted to mobile vehicles, and are unsuited to frequent starting and stopping throughout the day.

Although internal-combustion engine sets can be built with overall thermal efficiencies approaching 40 per cent., they cannot be built to give such concentrations of power as large-scale steam turbine plant which will operate with overall thermal efficiencies approaching 30 per cent. Small turbine sets are, however, relatively inefficient for the reason that blade clearances cannot be reduced when length of blade is reduced.

EXERCISES ON CHAPTER 12

(i)

1. State how the method of changing the energy of steam into work differs in a steam engine and a steam turbine, and make a short statement distinguishing impulse and reaction turbines.

2. Define " diagram work." Draw, roughly, a velocity diagram for an impulse turbine blade and indicate how you would estimate the diagram work from it.

3. What is " compounding for velocity " in impulse turbines? Make a sketch showing this in a Curtis turbine and indicate the type of velocity diagram to be expected from a wheel consisting of two rings of moving blades compounded for velocity.

4. What is the chief merit of steam turbines as transformers of heat and pressure energy into mechanical energy, and make a list of the mechanical advantages and disadvantages of steam turbines.

5. Steam issues from a nozzle with a speed of 3,000 ft. per sec. at an angle of 25° on to the moving blades of an impulse turbine. If the blade tip angles at inlet and outlet are the same and equal to 35°, draw a velocity diagram allowing for a 10 per cent. reduction in relative velocity while the steam flows over the blades. Find, from the diagram the velocity of the blades, the exit velocity of the steam, the diagram work per lb. of steam, and the diagram efficiency.

6. In a Curtis turbine there are two wheels in one pressure stage compounded for velocity. Steam issues from a nozzle with a velocity of 2,500 ft. per sec. and is directed on to the first wheel at an angle of 20°. The mean blade velocity for both wheels is 500 ft. per sec. If the blades in the two wheels are of identical shape, having the same tip angles at inlet and outlet, find this tip angle and also the tip angles which the fixed guide vane must have if steam is to pass through the blade rings without shock. Friction may be neglected.

7. Find the diagram work in ft.-Lb. per lb. for each wheel in Question 6, and calculate the diagram efficiency.

(ii)

8. Distinguish between an impulse and a reaction turbine-pair, and sketch the shapes of the moving blades of both types.

Steam discharges from the directing blades of an impulse turbine at 1,200 ft. per sec. and inclined 20° to the direction of motion of the moving blades. The moving blades have a speed of 450 ft. per sec. and a discharging angle of 30°. Neglecting friction, find the horse-power developed and the axial thrust per lb. of steam flowing per sec.

9. The stage of an impulse turbine is compounded for velocity in two rings of moving blades separated by fixed blades. The steam issues from a nozzle at 1,500 ft. per sec. at an angle of 20°, and the fixed blades also discharge at 20°. The moving blades discharge at 30° and have a velocity of 250 ft. per sec. Assume a reduction in relative velocity of 15 per cent. owing to friction and draw the velocity diagram for the stage. Determine the efficiency of the stage.

10. A single-wheel impulse turbine uses 120 lb. per hour of dry saturated steam at 50 Lb. per sq. in. abs. which expands in nozzles to 14·7 Lb. per sq. in. abs. and dryness fraction 0·94. The nozzles direct the steam at 15° on to moving blades, the inlet and outlet angles of which are both 30°. Estimate the velocity of the moving blades so that the steam will enter the blades smoothly, and calculate the diagram horse-power assuming no loss of relative velocity due to blade friction. What is the diagram efficiency?

11. The shapes of fixed and moving blades of a reaction turbine-pair are the same, having entry angles of 45° and exit angles of 20°. The mean blade speed is 240 ft. per sec. Calculate, or measure from a velocity diagram, the velocities of the steam as it enters and leaves the moving blades, and the diagram work per lb. of steam used.

12. A reaction turbine-pair has fixed and moving blades of the same shape, the tip angles at entry and exit being 35° and 20°, respectively. If 840 lb. of steam per minute flow through the pair and the mean velocity of the blades is 170 m.p.h., estimate the diagram horse-power of the turbine-pair.

13. What is the fundamental difference between impulse and reaction turbines?

Steam is directed with a velocity of 2,000 ft. per sec. at an angle of 15° to the plane of rotation of an impulse-turbine wheel. The ratio of the blade speed to the tangential component of the steam speed at inlet is 0·4. Friction reduces the relative speed of steam over the blades by 15 per cent. Calculate (i) the angles of the blades so that steam may enter without shock and leave the wheel axially, and (ii) the diagram work per lb. of steam and the efficiency. If the steam enters the nozzle-blades of this stage of the turbine with a velocity of 200 ft. per sec., a pressure of 35 Lb. per sq. in. abs. and dryness fraction 0·96, and leaves the wheel at 10 Lb. per sq. in. abs. and dryness fraction 0·91, draw up an energy balance for the stage.

PART III

COMPRESSORS AND INTERNAL COMBUSTION ENGINES

CHAPTER 13

LAWS OF GASES

1. A Perfect Gas.—*A perfect gas* is an imaginary and ideal gas of which one of the properties is that of satisfying Boyle's and Charles' laws exactly. Hence **a perfect gas obeys the law $PV=RmT$,** which is a combination of Boyle's and Charles' laws as shown on p. 276. *This law refers to a gas in equilibrium states,* i.e. *states in which the gas can continue indefinitely without change.*

Suppose a gas to be contained in the cylinder of an engine, then there are four things which may be varied, namely: absolute pressure, P; volume, V; mass, m; and absolute temperature, T.

In order to find out the effect of the variation of one of these quantities it is necessary to keep two of the four variables constant and to experiment with the remaining two.

2. Boyle's Law.—If m and T are kept constant we can experiment with P and V and find out the law connecting them. This is known as Boyle's law, which states that the product of the pressure and volume of a given mass of gas remains constant if the temperature is kept constant.

That is, **$PV=c$ if m and T are kept constant.**

All "permanent" gases obey this law very nearly, and a perfect gas, by definition, obeys it exactly.

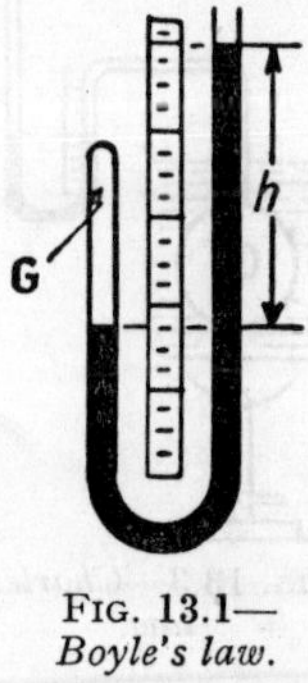

A laboratory experiment to verify Boyle's law can be performed with the simple apparatus of fig. 13.1 in which a definite mass of gas G at the constant temperature T_a of the atmosphere is put under a series of pressures by means of different heads of mercury h, and the corresponding volumes of the gas estimated. The experimental results when plotted give the rectangular hyperbola, $PV=$constant, shown in fig. 13.2. If the experiment is repeated with the gas kept at a higher constant temperature, T_b, the law $PV=c$ will still be found to

G
h

FIG. 13.1—*Boyle's law.*

apply, but the curve will be in a different position on the P, V diagram, fig. 13.2, than when the temperature was kept lower at T_a. It will be found for a permanent gas that whenever m and T are kept constant the product PV=constant. This is Boyle's law.

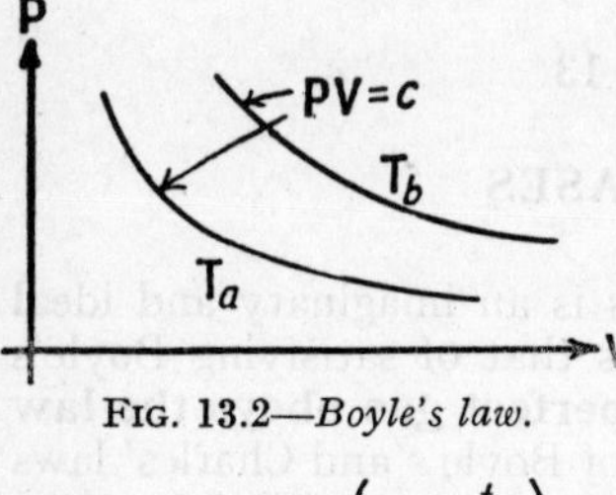

FIG. 13.2—*Boyle's law.*

3. Charles' Law.—If m and P are kept constant we can experiment with T and V and find the law connecting them, namely, $V=V_o\left(1+\frac{t}{273}\right)$ where V is the volume at $t°$ C. and V_o is the volume at 0° C. or 32° F., and t is the *number* on the ordinary centigrade scale.

All the "permanent" gases obey this law very nearly, and a perfect gas, by definition, obeys it exactly.

An experiment to verify the above formula can be performed with apparatus similar in principle to that of fig. 13.3, in which a definite mass of gas G kept at atmospheric pressure by the mercury levels at L, is subjected to a series of temperatures, and the corresponding volumes at each temperature estimated by means of the graduated scale. The experimental results when

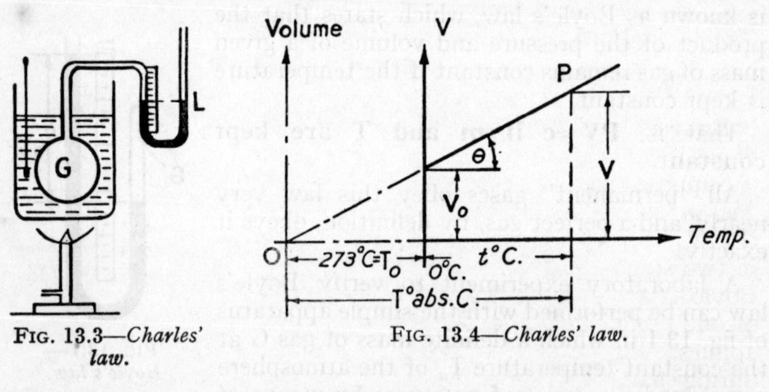

FIG. 13.3—*Charles' law.*

FIG. 13.4—*Charles' law.*

plotted give the straight line of fig. 13.4: $V=st+V_o=V_o\,(1+\alpha t)$, where $\alpha=\frac{s}{V}$ is found to be $\frac{1}{273}$ if t is measured in °C. That is,

$$V=V_o\left(1+\frac{t}{273}\right)=V_o\left(\frac{273+t}{273}\right)$$

or $\frac{V}{273+t}=\frac{V_o}{273}$ and similarly, $\frac{V}{460+t}=\frac{V_o}{492}$, where t is the number on the ordinary centigrade or Fahrenheit scales, respectively.

If the straight line is projected back until it cuts the horizontal axis, it will be found to be at a distance 273° C. or 460° F. from the 0° C. or 0° F. vertical, respectively, and the point of intersection is very close to the point representing absolute zero. Thus, if temperatures T are measured from absolute zero, the law of the straight line will be

$$\frac{V}{T}=\frac{V_o}{T_o}=\text{constant } (s, \text{ the slope of the line}).$$

The experiment shows that $\frac{V}{T}$**=constant for any gas when *m* and P are kept constant. This is known as Charles' law.**

It will be noticed in fig. 13.4 that if the law continued to hold right down to absolute zero of temperature the volume of a gas at −273° C. or −460° F. would be nothing at all; but in practice there would be a change of state before any near approach was made to absolute zero of temperature.

4. Combination of Boyle's and Charles' Laws to give the Characteristic Equation of a Perfect Gas, PV=R*m*T.—So far we have the two gas laws:

$$PV=\text{constant when } m \text{ and T are kept constant.}$$

$$\frac{V}{T}=\text{constant when } m \text{ and P are kept constant.}$$

But we require to know what law is obeyed when a definite mass of gas is subjected to changes in pressure, volume or temperature.

Suppose a definite mass of gas, m, is changed from a state (P_1, V_1, T_1) to a state (P_2, V_2, T_2) in two stages—the first such that Boyle's law will apply, and the second such that Charles' law applies. Fig. 13.5 shows that during change ①, in which m and T_1 are kept constant while P_1 is altered to P_2 with the consequent change in volume V_1 to V, Boyle's law will apply, giving $P_1V_1=P_2V$,

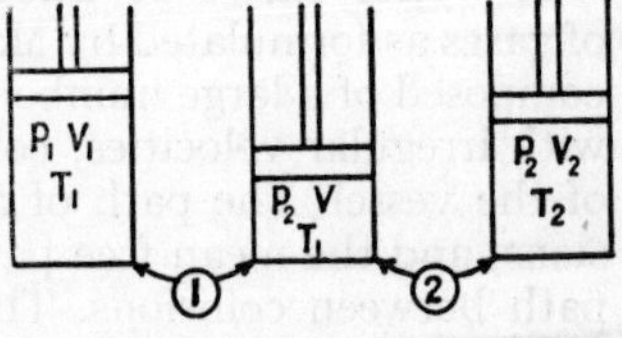

FIG. 13.5—*Combining of Boyle's and Charles' laws.*

or
$$V=\frac{P_1V_1}{P_2} \quad \ldots \ldots \quad \text{(i)}$$

During change ②, in which m and P_2 are kept constant while T_1 is altered to T_2 with the consequent change in volume from V to the final volume V_2, Charles' law will apply, giving

$$\frac{V}{T_1}=\frac{V_2}{T_2} \quad . \quad . \quad . \quad . \quad . \quad . \quad \text{(ii)}$$

Hence, eliminating V from equations (i) and (ii), we get

$$\frac{P_1V_1}{T_1}=\frac{P_2V_2}{T_2}=\frac{PV}{T} \text{ for any particular state,}$$

i.e. $\frac{PV}{T}=$ constant for a given mass of any gas.

If unit mass of gas be taken, the constant is written R.

Therefore, for a mass m of gas the constant will be Rm, giving the equation **PV=R*m*T for mass *m* of gas. This last equation is known as the characteristic equation of a *perfect* gas.** It is a point equation in that it refers to an equilibrium state of a gas. Permanent gases obey it more nearly as pressure is reduced.

The gas constant R can be found by substituting the appropriate figures in the equation $R=\frac{PV}{mT}$. For example: air at 32° F. and 14·7 Lb. per sq. in. abs. weighs 0·08071 Lb. per cu. ft., i.e. has a density $\frac{m}{V}$ of 0·08071 lb./ft.³; therefore,

$$R=\frac{PV}{Tm}=\frac{(14\cdot7\times144)}{492^\circ \text{ F.}}\frac{\text{Lb.}}{\text{ft.}^2}\times\frac{1}{0\cdot08071}\frac{\text{ft.}^3}{\text{lb.}}=53\cdot3\ \frac{\text{ft.-Lb.}}{\text{lb.}^\circ \text{ F.}}$$

Similarly, for hydrogen $R=768\ \frac{\text{ft.-Lb.}}{\text{lb.}^\circ \text{ F.}}$

5. Other Laws of Gases.—According to the kinetic theory of gases as formulated by Maxwell in 1875, a gas may be imagined composed of a large number of molecules moving in all directions with irregular velocities, colliding with each other and the walls of the vessel. The path of a molecule is zig-zag in three dimensions, and the mean free path is defined as the average length of path between collisions. The denser the gas the shorter will be the mean free path.

Direct observations cannot be made on the motions of molecules, but aggregate effects are indicated by pressure and temperature. On the assumption that molecules of gas are small elastic spheres, it can be shown that the pressure and absolute temperature of a gas are proportional to the mean kinetic energy of translation of the molecules bombarding the walls of the vessel enclosing the gas. Thus, at the same temperature, the average kinetic energy of translation of the molecules of any gas is the same whatever its mass—a molecule of large mass having a low velocity and a molecule of small mass having a high velocity.

Of the quantities or thermodynamic co-ordinates P, V, and T, only two are independent for a definite mass m *of gas since the equation of state or characteristic equation $PV = RmT$ fixes the third.*

The following experimental laws of gases are accounted for by the kinetic theory of gases:

(i) *Boyle's law:* $PV = \text{constant}$ when m and T are kept constant.

(ii) *Charles' law:* $\frac{V}{T} = \text{constant}$ when m and P are kept constant.

(iii) *Avogadro's law:* equal volumes of different gases at the same temperature and pressure contain the same number of molecules.

(iv) *Gay-Lussac's law:* the density of any gas at s.t.p. is proportional to its molecular weight.

(v) *Dalton's law of Partial Pressures:* the pressure of a mixture of gases is the sum of the pressures which each would exert if it alone were present in the containing vessel.

Because of the volume of molecules and forces of attraction between molecules, real gases deviate slightly from the above laws and from the characteristic law, $PV = RmT$, of a perfect gas. Many equations have been proposed in attempts to allow for the deviations in behaviour of real gases from that predicted by the perfect gas equation.

6. The Mol.—A mol of gas may be defined as that quantity of gas the weight of which is equal to the "molecular weight" in pounds. Molecular weight was originally defined as the *ratio* of the weight of a molecule of gas to the weight of an atom of hydrogen, but the present-day method is that of taking 16 as the number representing the atomic weight of oxygen and using this as the reference measure. Thus "molecular weight," as used in chemistry and physics, is the *ratio of two weights* and is, therefore, a pure number or non-dimensional quantity. Since mass is proportional to weight (i.e. the force created by the gravitational pull of the earth) the number known as "molecular weight" also represents the ratio of two masses, namely, the mass of a molecule of gas to that of an atom of oxygen. Thus, the relative masses of molecules are given by their "molecular weights," and although the term "molecular weight ratio" would be a more correct label for the number usually called molecular weight, we shall continue to use the latter term for the ratio, as is customary in physics and chemistry.

Thus, a mol (or lb.-mol) of substance is a physical quantity, i.e. is composed of a number and a unit. It is a mass which varies according to substance, e.g. $M_{O_2}=32$ lb. in the case of oxygen; $M_{H_2}=2$ lb. in the case of hydrogen; $M_{N_2}=28$ lb. in the case of nitrogen, and $M_{H_2O}=18$ lb. in the case of water and steam, and so on.

The mass of a lb.-mol of any other gas is

$$M=32 \text{ lb.}\left(\frac{\text{density of gas } \rho \text{ at s.t.p.}}{\text{density of oxygen } \rho_{O_2} \text{ at s.t.p.}}\right) \text{ or } 2\cdot016 \text{ lb.}\left(\frac{\rho}{\rho_{H_2}}\right).$$

The *numerical* value of the mass of a mol of substance in lb. is the same as that of the *weight* in London of a mol in Lb., *e.g.* in the case of CO_2 the mass of a lb.-mol is $M=44$ lb. and its weight is

$$W=Mg=44 \text{ lb.}\times g=44 \text{ lb.}\times g\left[\frac{\text{Lb.}}{\text{lb.}g_o}\right]$$

$$=44 \text{ Lb. in London where } g=g_o=32\cdot2 \text{ ft./sec.}^2$$

Similarly, in the case of a grm-mol or kg-mol; but in what follows we shall use the word "mol" to imply lb.-mol unless otherwise stated.

The number of molecules (f) in a mol of any gas is a constant known as Avogadro's number which has been estimated to be $f=27\cdot3\times10^{25}$ per lb.-mol. *A mol may, therefore, be thought of as a group of* (f) *molecules whose weight is equal to the molecular weight of the particular substance considered, or a group of* (f) *molecules whose mass* (M) *has a numerical value equal to the "molecular weight."*

In the case of gas-mixtures such as air or products of combustion, it is often convenient to regard the mixture as if it were a simple gas with a definite molecular weight, as in the following example.

Example 1.—Find the weight of one mol of air containing $0\cdot21$ mol of oxygen, $0\cdot7805$ mol of nitrogen, and $0\cdot0095$ mol of argon.

Constituent	Number of Mols N	Molecular Weight or Mass per Mol of Constituent M	Mass of Constituent N.M=*m*
O_2	21·00	32	672·0
N_2	78·05	28	2185·4
Ar	0·95	39·9	37·9
Totals	100·00	—	2895·3

Hence, the molecular weight or mass per mol of the gas-mixture known as air may be taken as

$$M_x=\frac{\Sigma NM}{\Sigma N}=\frac{m_1+m_2+m_3}{N_1+N_2+N_3}=\frac{2895\cdot 3 \text{ lb.}}{100 \text{ mol}}=28\cdot 95 \text{ lb. per mol.}$$

Using Avogadro's law we deduce that *the volume of a mol of different gases at the same temperature and pressure is the same* (359 ft.³. See Example 2), i.e. $V=R_1M_1\frac{T}{P}=R_2M_2\frac{T}{P}$=constant for all gases. Hence, **$R_1M_1=R_2M_2= \ . \ . \ .=\mathcal{R}$, the universal gas constant,** and since M_1, M_2, . . . are the masses of one mol of the different gases, we may write

$PV=\mathcal{R}T$ for one mol of any gas, and

$PV=\mathcal{R}NT$ for a number of N mols of any gas of volume V.

The characteristic equation, $PV=RmT$, on the "pound system" in which m is the mass of gas and R is the characteristic gas constant, becomes $PV=\mathcal{R}NT$ on the "mol system," where N is the mols of gas and $\mathcal{R}$ is the universal gas constant—so called because its numerical value is the same for all gases or mixtures of gases.

Thus, we may write **$PV=RmT=\mathcal{R}NT$,** from which it follows that **$Rm=\mathcal{R}N=\mathcal{R}\frac{m}{M}$** and, therefore, that **$R=\frac{\mathcal{R}}{M}$**—a useful fact to remember. **The value of the universal gas constant, $\mathcal{R}$, is 1545·5 ft.-Lb. per mol °F., or 1·986 B.Th.U. per mol °F. or 1·986 C.H.U. per mol °C as estimated from observations made on "permanent" gases.**

Example 2.—(i) Using the universal gas constant and "molecular weights" of gases, estimate their characteristic gas constants. (ii) Calculate the volume of one mol of any gas at s.t.p.

(i)

Gas	H_2	O_2	N_2	CO_2	H_2O	Air
M (lb.)	2	32	28	44	18	28·95
$R=\frac{\mathcal{R}}{M}$ (ft. Lb. per lb. °F.)	772·5	48·3	55·2	35·1	85·8	53·3

(ii) $PV=\mathcal{R}NT$; therefore $V=\frac{\mathcal{R}NT}{P}$.

Thus, the volume of one mol of any gas at 14·7 Lb. per sq. in. abs. and 492° abs. F. is

$$V=1545\cdot5\ \frac{\text{ft.Lb.}}{\text{mol}^\circ\ \text{F.}}\times\frac{1\ \text{mol}\times492^\circ\ \text{F.}}{14\cdot7\times144\ \text{Lb./ft.}^2}$$
$$=359\ \text{ft.}^3$$

The last calculation reveals the important fact that the volume of one mol of any gas or mixture of gases is constant when under the same conditions of temperature and pressure. *Thus 32 lb. of oxygen, 2 lb. of hydrogen, 44 lb. of carbon dioxide, etc., each occupy a volume of 359 cu. ft. (i.e. approximately a 7-ft. cube) when kept at s.t.p.*

A further important fact that follows from the characteristic equation on the "mol system," $PV=\mathcal{R}NT$, namely, since $N=\left(\frac{P}{\mathcal{R}T}\right)V$, *the number of mols of different gases at the same temperature and pressure, is proportional to their volumes.* Thus, in analysis of exhaust gases by means of Orsat's apparatus, in which each absorption takes place at atmospheric temperature and pressure, N_1 is proportional to V_1, the volume absorbed, $N_2 \propto V_2$, $N_3 \propto V_3$, etc. Thus, *a volumetric analysis carried out at constant temperature and pressure is also a "mol analysis"* since it shows, without further calculation, the number of mols of each gas contained in the mixture.

Example 3.—Using (*a*) the "mol system," and (*b*) the "pound system," find the characteristic gas constant R, of the dry products of combustion composed of the following constituent gases:

Constituent	Percentage Analysis by Volume; or number of Mols N	Molecular Weight or mass per mol M	Mass of constituent $NM=m$	Characteristic Gas Constant of each constituent R	Product Rm
CO_2	4·9	44	215·5	35·2	7,580
O_2	12·9	32	413·0	48·3	19,950
N_2	82·2	28	2300·0	55·2	127,000
Totals	100·0	—	2928·5	—	154,530

(*a*) Using columns 2 and 4, the mass of a mol of the gas mixture is

$$M_x = \frac{\Sigma NM}{\Sigma N} = \frac{2928\cdot 5 \text{ lb.}}{100 \text{ mol}} = 29\cdot 285 \text{ lb. per mol.}$$

Hence, the characteristic gas constant of the mixture is:

$$R = \frac{\mathcal{R}}{M_x} = 1545\cdot 5 \ \frac{\text{ft.-Lb.}}{\text{mol °F.}} \times \frac{1}{29\cdot 285} \ \frac{\text{mol}}{\text{lb.}} = 52\cdot 8 \ \frac{\text{ft.-Lb.}}{\text{lb. °F.}}$$

(*b*) Alternatively, using columns 4 and 6, the characteristic gas constant of the mixture is

$$R = \frac{\Sigma Rm}{\Sigma m} = \frac{154{,}530}{2928\cdot 5} = 52\cdot 8 \text{ ft.-Lb. per lb. ° F}$$

Thus, it is seen that the calculation of the characteristic gas constant, using the "pound system" ($PV = RmT$), involves the use of the two extra columns 5 and 6 which are not required in the more straightforward calculation when the "mol system" ($PV = \mathcal{R}NT$) is used. In many problems, however, there is little to choose between the two systems—the exceptions being those involving combustion, gas analysis, partial pressures, and problems allied to these, in which it will be found that the mol system has a slight advantage because the universal gas constant, $\mathcal{R}$, can be used instead of the numerous characteristic gas constants, R, of individual gases, which are necessary on the pound system. *It is, however, desirable for an engineer to have both systems, and the essential transformation relationships, at his disposal.*

Example 4.—Using the idea of the mol or the mol system, calculate the partial pressures of the constituent gases forming the flue gas shown on page 215 of the boiler trial if their total pressure is 15 Lb. per sq. in. abs.

$P = \left(\frac{\mathcal{R}T}{V}\right) N$, therefore $\frac{P_1}{P_t} = \frac{N_1}{N_t}$ since $\frac{\mathcal{R}T}{V}$ is the same for all the constituent gases in the sample contained in volume V at temperature T.

Constituent	H_2O	CO_2	O_2	N_2	Totals
Percentage flue gas analysis, by volume, or number of mols, N	10·3	11·1	3·9	74·7	$100\cdot 0 = N_t$
Partial pressure, $P = \frac{N}{N_t} P_t$ Lb. per sq. in. abs.	1·55	1·66	0·58	11·21	$15\cdot 0 = P_t$

EXERCISES ON CHAPTER 13

(i)

1. Define a " perfect gas." What does the term " permanent gas " signify?

2. State Boyle's law for a perfect gas, and describe a simple experiment to verify the law for a permanent gas.

3. State Charles' law for a perfect gas, and describe a simple experiment to prove the law for a permanent gas.

4. From Boyle's and Charles' laws prove that the characteristic equation $PV=RmT$ holds when a definite mass of gas m is subjected to changes in pressure, volume, and temperature.

5. Look up in Physical Tables data required for calculating the constants R in the characteristic equations for air, hydrogen, nitrogen, and carbon dioxide.

6. An unknown permanent gas occupies 5·5 cu. ft. at 32° F. It is heated at constant pressure until its temperature is 212° F. Calculate its final volume.

7. If the pressure of the gas in Question 6 is 100 Lb. per sq. in. abs. find the mass of the gas if it is (*a*) air, (*b*) hydrogen, (*c*) nitrogen, (*d*) carbon dioxide. Use the constants calculated in Question 5.

8. A volume of air at 350° F. exerts a pressure of 60 Lb. per sq. in. abs. in a vessel of fixed volume. What pressure will it exert when the temperature is reduced to 32° F.?

9. Air, occupying 15·5 cu. ft. at 100° C. and 60 Lb. per sq. in. abs. pressure, is expanded until its pressure is 15 Lb. per sq. in. abs. Calculate the mass of air expanded and temperature after expansion if the final volume is three times the initial volume.

(ii)

10. The molecular analysis of the gas contained in a gasometer of 1,000,000 cu. ft. capacity is as follows: CH_4 0·3; H_2 0·5; CO 0·1; N_2 0·1. Find the weight of gas in the gasometer at 60° F. and at a pressure equal to 4 in. of water above the standard atmospheric pressure of 14·7 Lb. per sq. in. abs. The universal gas constant is 1,545 ft.-Lb. per mol. °F.

11. The percentage volumetric analysis of the dry exhaust gases issuing from an oil engine was CO_2, 10·6; O_2, 5·8; N_2, 83·6. Calculate (i) the mass of 1 mol of the exhaust gas mixture; (ii) the density in lb. per cu. ft. at s.t.p.; (iii) the characteristic gas constant, R, of the dry exhaust gas in ft.-Lb. per lb. ° F.

12. A mixture of air and water vapour has a temperature of 193·2° F. and a pressure 14·7 Lb. per sq. in. abs. The vapour is in its dry and saturated state. Find:—

(*a*) The mass of vapour present in one cu. ft. of mixture;

(*b*) The partial pressures of the vapour and air;

(*c*) The values of the gas constant R, the specific heat at constant pressure, C_P, and the ratio of specific heats, γ, of the mixture.

Show by reference to the steam tables that the value of R for the dry saturated water vapour at the given temperature will be 84·6 ft.Lb. per lb. ° F., and that C_P, will be 0·48 B.Th.U./lb. °F.

(I.Mech.E., Sec. A.]

13. A closed vessel contains dry saturated steam at 14·7 Lb. per sq. in. abs. and 180° F. If the temperature is reduced by 36° F. estimate the final pressure and what proportion by weight of steam will be condensed.

14. (i) Find the volume of a closed vessel which contains 1 mol of hydrogen and 4 mols of air at 15 Lb. per sq. in. abs. and 60° F.

(ii) If air contains, by volume, 21 per cent. of oxygen and 79 per cent. of nitrogen, show that the products of combustion total 4·5 mols, and find the pressure of the products at 200° F.

(iii) The water vapour in the products will condense at 147° F. Assuming the resulting liquid to have negligible volume, calculate the pressure of the remaining 3·5 mols of gas at 60° F.

15. State and prove the relation between the specific heats of a gas at constant pressure and constant volume (C_P and C_V), and the characteristic constant (R) of the gas. A gaseous mixture consists of 35 per cent. of oxygen and 65 per cent. of nitrogen by volume. Find the appropriate value of R for the mixture and hence find the mass of 1 cu. ft. of mixture at 200 Lb. per sq. in. abs. and 240° F. For oxygen, $C_P=0·218$; $C_V=0·156$. For nitrogen, $C_P=0·249$; $C_V=0·178$ B.Th.U. per lb. ° F. [Part I, B.Sc. Lond.]

16. Define the quantity known as the "mol." Calculate the volume of a closed vessel containing 2 lb. of hydrogen and 115·2 lb. of air at 150 Lb. per sq. in. abs. and 60° F. Using the mol system or otherwise estimate the percentage volumetric composition of the products after combustion of the mixture, and the pressure of the products in the vessel at 3,540° F. The universal gas constant may be taken as 1,545·5 ft.-Lb. per mol Fahrenheit degree, or, alternatively the characteristic gas constants of oxygen, nitrogen, and steam may be taken as 48·3, 55·2, and 86 ft.-Lb. per lb. Fahrenheit degree. Air contains 21 per cent. of oxygen by volume, and the molecular weights of oxygen and nitrogen are 32 and 28, respectively.

17. The percentage volumetric analysis of dry exhaust gas from an oil engine using a hydrocarbon fuel-oil was CO_2 5·2, O_2 13·4, and N_2 81·4. Using molecular weights and the facts that one lb.-mol of gas at s.t.p. occupies a volume of 359 ft.^{3} and the ratio of oxygen to nitrogen (by weight) in air is 23 to 77, calculate for 100 ft.^{3} of dry flue gas at s.t.p.: (*a*) The mass of oxygen (i) in the air supplied, (ii) in excess of that required, (iii) actually used, (iv) the percentage excess air.; (*b*) The mass of oxygen (i) in the CO_2, (ii) in the H_2O being the difference between *a*(iii) and *b*(i); (*c*) Hence, find the mass ratio of carbon and hydrogen in the fuel and percentage of carbon and hydrogen in the fuel by weight.

18. A quantity of oxygen occupies 30 cu. ft. at 40° F. and 20 Lb. per sq. in. abs. It is compressed according to the law $PV^{1 \cdot 25} =$ constant, until the pressure is 300 Lb. per sq. in. abs. If the universal gas constant is 1,543 ft.-Lb. per lb.-mol per Fahrenheit degree, determine:—

(*a*) the final volume and temperatures of the oxygen;
(*b*) the change of entropy, stating whether this is a gain or a loss;
(*c*) the heat interchange between the gas and its surroundings, stating whether this is a reception or a rejection.

Assume C_v for oxygen is 0·170 B.Th.U. per lb. °F.

[Part I, B.Sc. Lond.]

19. A fuel whose analysis by weight can be taken as 84 per cent. carbon and 16 per cent. hydrogen, is burnt with 10 per cent. excess air. What weight and volume of gas at 20 Lb. per sq. in. abs. and 700° F. will pass through the exhaust per lb. of fuel burnt? The volume of *m* lb. of gas at 32° F. and 14·7 Lb. per sq. in. abs. is 359 cu. ft., where *m* is the molecular weight of the gas.

Air contains 23 per cent. oxygen by weight.

[Sec. A. I.Mech.E.,]

CHAPTER 14

ELEMENTARY THERMODYNAMICS

1. Expansion According to the General Law, $PV^n = c$.—Whenever expansion or compression curves on P,V indicator diagrams are analysed it is found that they can almost all be represented by the general law PV^n=constant—the index n being different according to the kind of gas and to conditions associated with the expansion or compression. An expansion or compression in which the gas obeys Boyle's law, $PV = c$, is a particular case of the general law $PV^n = c$ which specifies the relationship between pressure and volume of a gas for a continuous series of hypothetical equilibrium states so that $PV = RmT$ also applies.

Suppose a mass of gas, m, enclosed in a cylinder behind a piston of area A and at a state ① (that is, at absolute pressure P_1, volume V_1, abs. temperature T_1) is expanded to a state ② through a series of equilibrium states according to the law $PV^n = c$, then the work done by the gas on the piston against an equal opposing force balancing the force of the gas, will be equal to the area under the expansion curve shown in fig. 14.1, for the work done by the gas in moving the piston δx = force × displacement = $(PA) \times \delta x = P\delta V = \delta W$, the area of the shaded strip. Therefore the total work done by the gas during balanced (reversible) expansion from state ① to state ②

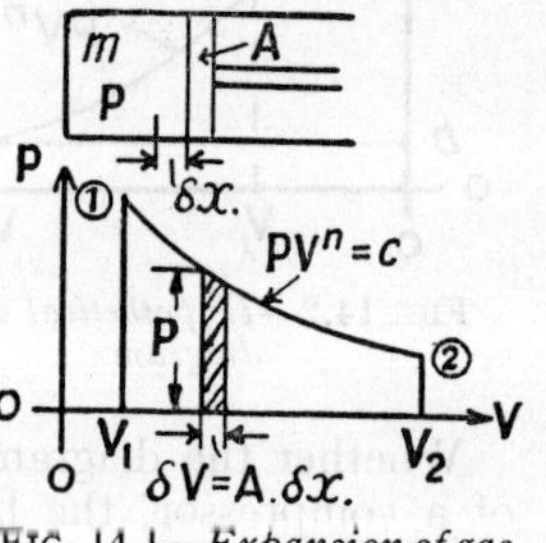

FIG. 14.1—*Expansion of gas.*

$$= \int_{V_1}^{V_2} P dV = c \int_{V_1}^{V_2} V^{-n} dV$$

$$= c \left[\frac{V^{-n+1}}{-n+1} \right]_{V_1}^{V_2} = c \left[\frac{V_1^{-n+1} - V_2^{-n+1}}{n-1} \right]$$

$$= \frac{P_1V_1 - P_2V_2}{n-1} = \frac{Rm(T_1 - T_2)}{n-1} \text{ (substituting } PV = RmT)$$

These two expressions represent the area ($V_1$①②V_2V_1). Whether the process be an expansion from ① to ② or a compression from ② to ① according to the law $PV^n = c$, the area under the curve is the same—the difference between them being that in the case of expansion from ① to ② the work is done *by* the gas and is therefore positive, whereas in the case of the compression from ② to ① the work is done *on* the gas and is therefore negative. P, V and T are co-ordinates, parameters or functions of *equilibrium states*; hence, lines on P,V diagrams are therefore hypothetical, and lines traced by spring and piston indicators only approximate to them.

Consider the cycle *a*①②*ba* of fig. 14.2, which can be imagined to represent that of a simple steam engine admitting steam from *a* to①, expanding it from ① to ②, and exhausting from ② to *b*. It could also be imagined to be the hypothetical cycle of an air motor working in the same way, or of a simple air compressor taking in a cylinder full of air from the atmosphere during stroke *b*②, compressing it during ②① until the delivery valve opens for delivery of the air into a receiver at constant pressure during ①*a*.

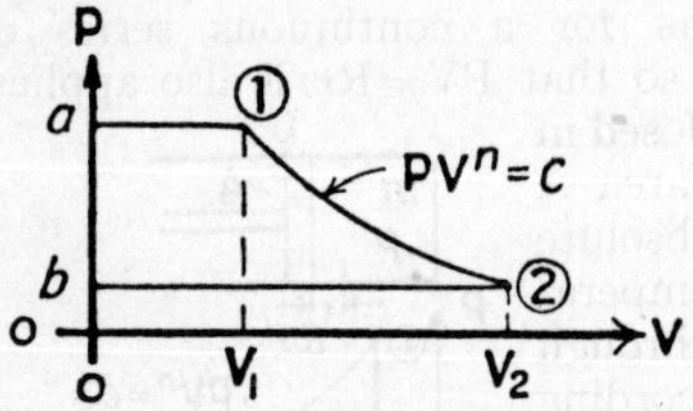

FIG. 14.2—*Hypothetical indicator diagram.*

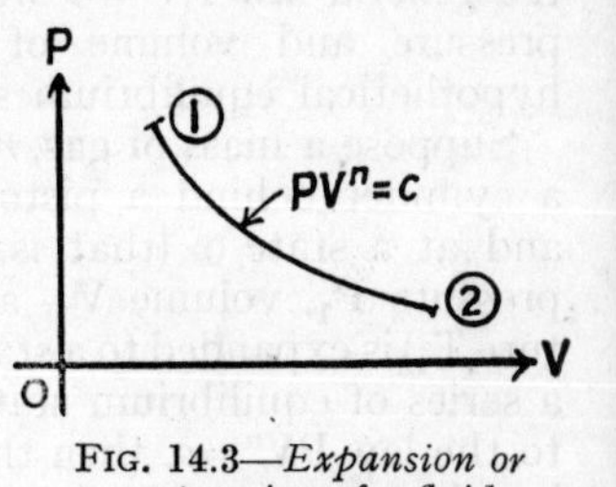

FIG. 14.3—*Expansion or compression of a fluid.*

Whether the diagram represents the working of an engine or of a compressor, the hypothetical work done in either case is represented by the enclosed area *a*①②*ba* on the P,V diagram, and which

$$=\left(a①V_1oa\right)+\left(V_1①②V_2V_1\right)-\left(V_2②boV_2\right)$$

$$=P_1V_1+\left[\frac{P_1V_1-P_2V_2}{n-1}\right]-P_2V_2$$

$$=(P_1V_1-P_2V_2)\left[1+\frac{1}{n-1}\right]$$

$$=\frac{n}{n-1}\left(P_1V_1-P_2V_2\right)=\frac{nRm}{n-1}(T_1-T_2)$$

$$=\text{enclosed area of P,V diagram.}$$

The enclosed area (*a*①②*ba*) is taken positive in the case of the steam engine and air motor because it then represents work done *by* the fluid on the piston. It should be noted that this cycle is traced out in a clockwise direction on the P,V diagram.

The enclosed area ($b②①ab$) is taken negative in the case of the compressor, because in that case it represents work done *on* the fluid by the piston. It should be noted that this cycle is traced out in an anticlockwise direction. In both cases it is assumed that while the piston is in motion the forces on each side of the piston are equal, in which case the work $\delta W = P\delta V$, otherwise part of the work would be needed to accelerate the piston.

2. Relation between Temperatures, Pressures, and Volumes of a Gas obeying the General Law, $PV^n = c$.—Referring to fig. 14.3, since the points ① and ② are on the curve,

$$P_1V_1^n = c = P_2V_2^n \quad . \quad . \quad . \quad . \quad . \quad (i)$$

Also, since the mass of gas in the cylinder is the same at ① and ②, and these are equilibrium states in the hypothetical case, we may write:

$$\frac{P_1V_1}{T_1} = Rm = \frac{P_2V_2}{T_2} \quad . \quad . \quad . \quad . \quad . \quad (ii)$$

From equation (ii)

$$\frac{T_1}{T_2} = \frac{P_1V_1}{P_2V_2} \quad . \quad . \quad . \quad . \quad . \quad . \quad . \quad (iii)$$

From equation (i)

$$\frac{P_1}{P_2} = \left(\frac{V_2}{V_1}\right)^n \text{ or } \frac{V_1}{V_2} = \left(\frac{P_2}{P_1}\right)^{\frac{1}{n}}$$

and substituting these in equation (iii) results in the relationship

$$\frac{T_1}{T_2} = \left(\frac{V_2}{V_1}\right)^{n-1} = \left(\frac{P_1}{P_2}\right)^{\frac{n-1}{n}}$$

Example 1.—(i) 5·16 cu. ft. of air at 60 Lb. per sq. in. abs. are expanded according to the law $PV^{1\cdot3}$ = constant until the pressure is 15 Lb. per sq. in. abs. Calculate the volume of the air after expansion.

Referring to fig. 14.3, from the data given we get

$$V_2 = V_1\left(\frac{P_1}{P_2}\right)^{\frac{1}{1\cdot3}} = 5\cdot16 \text{ ft.}^3\left(\frac{60}{15}\right)^{\frac{1}{1\cdot3}} = 5\cdot16 \text{ ft.}^3 \times 2\cdot905 = 14\cdot96 \text{ cu. ft.}$$

(ii) Calculate the work done by the air during expansion in the above case.

Work done during expansion is given by $\dfrac{P_1V_1 - P_2V_2}{n-1}$

$$= \frac{(60 \times 5\cdot16 - 15 \times 14\cdot96)}{0\cdot3} \frac{\text{Lb.-ft.}^3}{\text{in.}^2}\left[\frac{144 \text{ in.}^2}{\text{ft.}^2}\right] = 40{,}690 \text{ ft.-Lb.}$$

(iii) If the temperature of the air before expansion is 257° F., calculate the mass of air expanded, and the temperature at the end of expansion. Use these figures to check the work done as calculated in (ii).

$$\text{The mass of air } m=\frac{P_1V_1}{RT_1}=\frac{(144\times 60)\frac{\text{Lb.}}{\text{ft.}^2}\times 5\cdot 16\text{ft.}^3}{53\cdot 3\frac{\text{ft.-Lb.}}{\text{lb. }^\circ\text{F.}}\times 717^\circ\text{ abs. F.}}=1\cdot 167 \text{ lb.}$$

$$\text{Since } \frac{T_1}{T_2}=\left(\frac{V_2}{V_1}\right)^{n-1}=\left(\frac{P_1}{P_2}\right)^{\frac{n-1}{n}}=\left(\frac{60}{15}\right)^{\frac{0\cdot 3}{1\cdot 3}}=1\cdot 377, \text{ we get}$$

$$T_2=\frac{717}{1\cdot 377}=520^\circ \text{ abs. F.} \quad \text{Hence, } t_2=60^\circ \text{ F.}$$

$$\text{Work done during expansion}=\frac{Rm}{n-1}(T_1-T_2)$$

$$=53\cdot 3\frac{\text{ft.-Lb.}}{\text{lb. }^\circ\text{F.}}\times\frac{1\cdot 167 \text{ lb.}}{0\cdot 3}(717-520)^\circ \text{ F.}=40{,}690 \text{ ft.-Lb.}$$

Example 2.—If 5·16 cu. ft. of air are admitted to an air motor at 60 Lb. per sq. in. abs. and 257° F. and expanded according to the law $PV^{1\cdot 3}$=constant until the final pressure is 15 Lb. per sq. in. abs. and then exhausted at this pressure, calculate the work done per cycle.

Referring to fig. 14.2, we have proved that the area of the diagram *a*①②*ba* is given by the expression

$$\frac{n}{n-1}(P_1V_1-P_2V_2) \text{ or } \frac{n}{n-1}Rm(T_1-T_2).$$

We have calculated in the previous example that $V_2=14\cdot 96$ cu. ft., $m=1\cdot 167$ lb., and $T_2=520°$ abs. F.

Hence, the work done per cycle

$$=\frac{1\cdot 3}{0\cdot 3}\times 144(60\times 5\cdot 16-15\times 14\cdot 96) \text{ ft.-Lb.}$$

$$=53{,}000 \text{ ft.-Lb.}$$

This could have been found alternatively from the expression

$$\frac{n}{n-1}Rm(T_1-T_2)=\frac{1\cdot 3}{0\cdot 3}\times 53\cdot 3\times 1\cdot 167\times(717-520) \text{ ft.-Lb.}$$

$$=53{,}000 \text{ ft.-Lb.}$$

3. Reversibility and Reversible Processes.—In the thermodynamic sense *reversibility is an ideal which cannot be attained in practice*. It is important to distinguish between the theoretical, ideal, frictionless processes which are reversible, and actual processes which are irreversible. For instance, if there were no friction or air resistance, a simple pendulum would behave in accordance with a reversible operation—the potential energy at one end of the swing would become kinetic energy of equivalent amount at the bottom of the swing, which, in turn, would become the equivalent potential energy again at the other end of the swing.

If such a pendulum were possible it would, of itself, go on swinging for ever without requiring energy from any outside source. Actually, of course, there are frictional and air resistances which cause a dissipation of mechanical energy. This has to be made up from an external source if the pendulum is to swing continuously over a long period.

An expansion or compression would be reversible in the thermodynamic sense if it could be carried out in such a manner that the substance would pass back through all the stages through which it passed during the expansion or compression, and be in the same condition in all respects at each corresponding stage in both direct and reversed processes.

Thus, a reversible process in the thermodynamic sense would, when undone, leave no trace of itself; and a perfectly executed process would be reversible.

A reversible expansion and a reversible compression carried out by means of a piston and cylinder would have to be infinitely slow processes during which the forces on each side of the piston would only be infinitesimally different. In such cases **the work done is $W = \int PdV$ = area under a trace on a P,V diagram representing a continuous series of equilibrium states of the working fluid as specified by the characteristic equation $PV = RmT$ in the case of a perfect gas.**

A trace, in which P and V represent thermodynamic co-ordinates of equilibrium states, could only be traced out by an infinitely slow process. Irreversible processes (i.e. *in which eddies, turbulence and friction occur*) *cannot be shown on such diagrams.*

The areas of *actual* indicator diagrams taken from working engines or compressors do, however, represent the actual work done on or by the face of the piston. In the case of actual expansion the area under the line traced would be less than could be obtained by reversible expansion, and in case of actual compression the numerical value of the work done on the gas would be greater than that required for reversible compression since in real (*i.e.* irreversible) compression some of the mechanical energy supplied is dissipated into heat. *Thus, reversible expansion implies that the substance must expand smoothly without setting up the whirls and eddies which always occur when a fluid enters and expands in the cylinder of a real engine. Such whirls and eddies cannot be reversed. A reversible process, therefore, is one in which the fluid passes through a continuous series of equilibrium states which, incidentally, are independent of time.* Often we consider what has happened when the working agent or a system has passed from an initial to a final equilibrium state, *i.e.* a state in which a substance or a system can continue indefinitely without further change. The intervening states are not, in general, states of equilibrium although, in exceptional cases, they may approximate to equilibrium states, in which case the process approaches the ideal, namely, a reversible process.

Only equilibrium states can be represented on diagrams whose co-ordinates are properties of equilibrium states, e.g. P, V, T, E, H, φ. For states other than equilibrium states the pressure and temperature and other variables specifying properties of a fluid, will vary from point to point within the fluid. *In a real or irreversible process or transformation, it is possible to represent initial and final equilibrium states on state diagrams but not the intermediate states. If, however, a fluid passes through a succession of equilibrium states* (i.e. *a reversible process*) *the process can be represented by a continuous line or curve on a state diagram such as a* P,V *diagram and the work done during the reversible process will be represented by the area under the curve, namely,* $W = \int PdV$. Any equation which specifies a reversible change is a condition of the equilibrium of the system. Thus, **although there is no restriction on the general equation $\delta Q = \delta E + \delta W$ expressing the first law of thermodynamics, it is restricted to reversible processes when written as $\delta Q = \delta E + PdV$,** which applies only to balanced fully-resisted or quasi-static changes during which there is no turbulence or dissipation of mechanical energy into heat by friction. It follows that flow of fluids through valves and throttles are irreversible processes since the heat generated by friction, eddies and turbulence cannot be reconverted completely into its previous form of pressure energy and kinetic energy of flow.

Transfer of heat to or from any substance would be reversible only if the substance were at the same temperature as the body from which heat was being taken or to which heat was being given, since thermal contact between bodies at different temperatures involves an irreversible transfer of heat.

It may be taken as a broad rule that discontinuity in any operation means irreversibility, and that a truly reversible operation would be composed of a succession or continuous series of equilibrium states.

All natural changes are irreversible in the sense that they proceed in directions which never reverse of their own accord. **Reversible changes are ideal or limiting cases of real (*i.e.* irreversible) changes.** The initial condition of a system cannot be restored by its own efforts from the final condition resulting from a real process. To do this, energy from an external source must be supplied. There is a dissipation of energy in natural processes—the energy available for doing work being reduced.

We may take as an illustration Joule's determination of the heat equivalent of work by means of apparatus similar to that of fig. 1.8. Suppose the falling weight does work W, then the water will receive heat energy equivalent to mechanical energy W. To restore the system to its initial condition the heat would have to be removed from the water, and work W, done on the weight to lift it back to its initial position. If T_1 is the temperature of the water and T_2 the lowest temperature available, then the maximum mechanical energy obtainable from an amount of heat equivalent to W removed from the water would be

$$W\frac{(T_1-T_2)}{T_1}=W-W\frac{T_2}{T_1} \text{ (see page 351).}$$

This is not sufficient to raise the weight back to its initial position, for that would require mechanical energy equal to W. It will be seen that there is a deficiency equal to $W\frac{T_2}{T_1}$ which cannot be recovered.

All natural processes are similarly irreversible. Kelvin, in 1852, was the first to perceive the tendency in Nature of energy becoming less and less available for the production of mechanical energy or work—that such available energy is always lost and never gained. He enunciated the principle of dissipation of energy.

Thus, the idea of reversibility in the thermodynamic sense can be used as a test of the imperfection of a process or misuse of work and available energy. Irreversible processes dissipate energy which would be transformed into work if the processes could be carried out reversibly. Although there is no *destruction* of energy during an irreversible process, since the first law of thermodynamics is always obeyed, there is, however, a *degradation* or dissipation of energy from an energy potential or grade of energy which could yield useful work, into a form or grade which is incapable of further conversion into work, i.e. the quality of the energy goes on dropping, and there is a progressive degradation of energy.

Thus, *irreversibility is an imperfection.* It is easy to transform work into heat but impossible to convert all the heat back into work—the latter being the more precious form of energy. Hence, processes which allow work or a potentiality for doing work to be dissipated in, say, eddies and friction, must be avoided if possible. An approximation to a reversible process can be achieved by changing the condition so slowly that the system has time to adjust itself gradually through a series of near-equilibrium states. *Thus, reversible processes are hypothetical or imaginary processes for use in theoretical analysis. They are limits towards which irreversible processes can approach but never reach, i.e. reversibility can be approached as a limiting condition.*

4. Isothermal and Adiabatic Processes.—Two particular cases of ideal and reversible processes are:—

(i) **A reversible isothermal process is an imaginary, ideal, and frictionless process during which the temperature of the medium is assumed to remain constant while passing through a continuous series of equilibrium states.**

If a definite mass of gas be imagined to expand isothermally and reversibly in the cylinder of an engine, then, since m and T remain the same $PV=RmT=$constant for a gas passing through a series of equilibrium states, which is a condition of a reversible process. That is, Boyle's law, $PV=c$, represents the reversible isothermal expansion, and it will be seen that the index n of the general law is, in this particular expansion, equal to unity.

Since, in this case, $P_1V_1=P_2V_2$ and $n=1$, the previous formula for area $V_1①②V_2V_1$ of fig. 14.4 becomes indeterminate $\left(=\frac{0}{0}\right)$ and we have to go to first principles again to find that the area

$$=\int_{V_1}^{V_2} PdV=c\int_{V_1}^{V_2}\frac{dV}{V}=PV\log_\varepsilon\frac{V_2}{V_1}=RmT\log_\varepsilon r,$$

where T is the absolute temperature of the isothermal and r is the ratio of expansion $\frac{V_2}{V_1}$.

It may be noted that since the internal energy of a gas is a function of its temperature (see p. 296), *an isothermal expansion of a gas or an isothermal compression is one in which the internal energy does not change*; hence, the work done during isothermal expansion or compression is equal to the heat added to or abstracted from the gas, respectively.

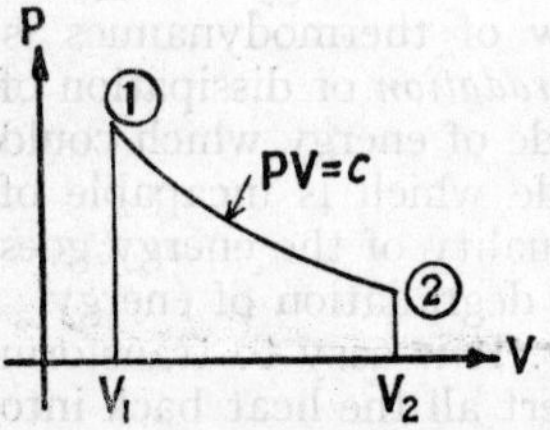

FIG. 14.4—*Isothermal expansion.*

(ii) **A reversible adiabatic process is an imaginary, ideal, and frictionless process during which the medium is assumed to be thermally insulated while passing through a continuous series of equilibrium states.**

We shall see presently (p. 301) that the law for reversible adiabatic expansion or compression of a gas is $PV^\gamma=c$, where γ represents the ratio of the specific heat of the gas at constant pressure to that at constant volume. γ is always greater than unity, so that the formula for area $V_1①②V_2V_1$ (fig. 14.1) is the same as that proved for the general law $PV^n=c$, where n becomes equal to γ in this particular case.

Thus, the work done during a reversible adiabatic expansion or compression

$$=\frac{P_1V_1-P_1V_2}{\gamma-1}=\frac{Rm(T_1-T_2)}{\gamma-1},$$

being the area under the trace on the P,V diagram representing a series of equilibrium states.

We may note in passing that, according to the first law of thermodynamics, namely, that the heat added to a substance =increase in internal energy of the substance+external work done by the substance, or $\delta Q=\delta E+\delta W$, since in an adiabatic expansion $\delta Q=0$ then $\delta W=-\delta E$. That is, *all the external work done by the substance on the piston during adiabatic expansion would be done at the expense of the stock of internal energy*. The work done by the expanding fluid is, therefore, equal to the decrease in internal energy of the fluid.

Example 1.—1·5 lb. of a certain gas occupies 35·3 cu. ft. at 15 Lb. per sq. in. abs. and 15° C. It is then compressed to half its volume according to the law PV^n=constant.

(*a*) If the final pressure is observed to be 31·2 Lb. per sq. in. abs., calculate the value of n for the compression.

(*b*) It is calculated that if the compression of this particular gas had been adiabatic and reversible, the final pressure would be 36·1 Lb. per sq. in. abs. Using this figure, calculate the index γ for reversible adiabatic compression of the gas.

(*a*) If the gas is compressed from a state (1) to a state (2) according to the law $PV^n=c$, then $\left(\frac{V_1}{V_2}\right)^n=\frac{P_2}{P_1}$ and therefore, $(2)^n=\frac{31\cdot2}{15}$

$$\therefore\ n\log 2=\log 31\cdot2-\log 15.$$

$$\therefore\ n=\frac{1\cdot4942-1\cdot1761}{0\cdot3010}=\frac{0\cdot3181}{0\cdot3010}=1\cdot058.$$

(*b*) For reversible adiabatic compression

$$\left(\frac{V_1}{V_2}\right)^\gamma=\frac{P_2}{P_1}$$

$$\therefore\ (2)^\gamma=\frac{36\cdot1}{15}$$

$$\therefore\ \gamma\log 2=\log 36\cdot1-\log 15$$

$$\therefore\ \gamma=\frac{1\cdot5575-1\cdot1761}{0\cdot301}=\frac{0\cdot3814}{0\cdot3010}=1\cdot266.$$

Example 2.—Find the final temperature in the previous example, and the work done on the gas in each case after calculating the characteristic gas constant, R.

(*a*) The final temperature could be calculated either from formula $\frac{T_2}{T_1}=\left(\frac{V_1}{V_2}\right)^{n-1}=\left(\frac{P_2}{P_1}\right)^{\frac{n-1}{n}}$ or from the characteristic equation

$$\frac{P_1V_1}{T_1}=Rm=\frac{P_2V_2}{T_2}$$

Using the latter, $T_2=T_1\,\frac{P_2V_2}{P_1V_1}=288°\text{ abs. C.}\times\left(\frac{31\cdot2}{15}\right)\times\left(\frac{1}{2}\right)$

$$=300°\text{ abs. C.}\quad\therefore\ t_2=27°\text{ C.}$$

$$\text{Gas constant } R=\frac{P_1V_1}{mT_1}=(144\times15)\,\frac{\text{Lb.}}{\text{ft.}^2}\times\frac{35\cdot3\text{ ft.}^3}{1\cdot5\text{ lb.}\times288°\text{ abs.C.}}$$

$$=176\cdot5\,\frac{\text{ft.-Lb.}}{\text{lb.° C.}}$$

$\therefore$ Work done during compression

$$=\frac{Rm}{n-1}(T_2-T_1)=176\cdot5\,\frac{\text{ft.-Lb.}}{\text{lb. °C.}}\times\frac{1\cdot5\text{ lb. }(300-288)°\text{ C.}}{0\cdot058}$$

$$=54{,}900\text{ ft.-Lb.}$$

(*b*) $T_2=\frac{T_1P_2V_2}{P_1V_1}=288\times\left(\frac{36\cdot1}{15}\right)\left(\frac{1}{2}\right)=347°\text{ abs. C.}\quad\therefore\ t_2=74°\text{ C.}$

$\therefore$ Work done during reversible adiabatic compression

$$=\frac{176\cdot5\,\frac{\text{ft.-Lb.}}{\text{lb. °C.}}\times1\cdot5\text{ lb.}\times(347-288)\text{ °C.}}{0\cdot266}$$

$$=58{,}750\text{ ft.-Lb.}$$

5. Internal Energy of a Gas, and Joule's Law.—A gas in a given state has internal energy associated with the translational, rotational, and vibrational motion of its molecules.

Although, in the broadest sense, the internal or intrinsic energy of a substance includes the energy due to the translational, rotational and vibrational motions of its molecules, together with that due to intra-molecular and intra-atomic forces, in processes or changes which do not involve combustion the changes in internal energy (δE) only involve changes in the translational, rotational and vibrational energy of the atoms and molecules. Thus, in these cases a change in internal energy means a change in molecular kinetic energy.

Internal energy is a function of the state and is independent of the way in which that state has been reached, *i.e. although the absolute value of the internal energy of a substance is unknown, the difference of internal energy, δE, between initial and final equilibrium states as a result of any process, is quite definite.*

For example, referring to fig. 14.5, since for a reversible adiabatic expansion $\delta Q=\delta E+\delta W=\delta E+P\delta V=0$, the work done by a fluid during reversible adiabatic expansion from state A to zero pressure or infinite volume (C) is

$$\int_A^\infty dW = -\int_A^\infty dE = \int_A^\infty PdV$$

i.e. $E_A - E_\infty =$ area aACa.
Similarly, $E_B - E_\infty =$ area bBDb.

Hence, the change in internal energy $(E_B - E_A)$ due to a change along either of the paths AmB or AnB is represented by the difference between the areas bBDb and aACa which is obviously independent of the path of the change between A and B. Although $(E_B - E_A)$ is independent of the path between A and B, the work done during the change between A and B say, along path AmB is represented by area aAmBba which is different from the work done for any other path between A and B. Also, the quantity of heat added to a substance in order to achieve the change of state from A to B along a reversible path AmB is $\int_A^B dQ = (E_B - E_A) +$ area aAmBba which, because of the last term, depends on the shape of path between A and B.

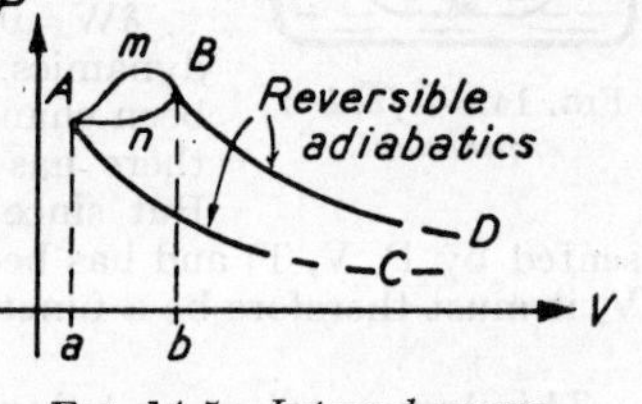

FIG. 14.5—*Internal energy.*

Thus, although E, Q and W have the same dimension, namely, energy, only E is a function (or parameter) of the state of a substance. The state of a substance cannot be specified by W or Q since these only exist when a change of state is being caused by a process, after the completion of which W and Q no longer exist, but E remains as the internal energy of the substance in the final equilibrium state.

Joule's Law states that when a perfect gas expands without doing external work ($\delta W=0$), and without taking in or giving out heat ($\delta Q=0$) and, therefore, without changing its stock of internal energy (i.e. $\delta E=0$), its temperature does not change—thus showing that the internal energy of a gas depends upon temperature only and not upon changes in pressure and volume.

Joule formulated the above law as the result of an experiment, the principle of which can be stated with reference to the simple apparatus shown in fig. 14.6.

At the start of the experiment, vessel A contains gas at high pressure and is kept from flowing into the evacuated vessel B by the closed cock C. The whole is submerged in a tank of water and, when steady, the common temperature of the apparatus is noted. Then the cock C is opened and the gas in A expands into B until a uniform pressure of gas obtains in both vessels. The temperature of the water is found to be the same as before. Thus, although the pressure and volume of the gas change, there is no change in temperature.

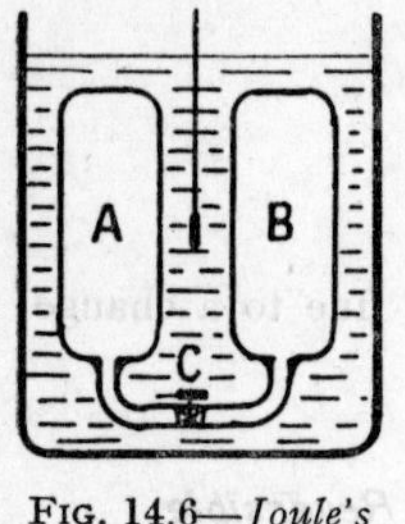

FIG. 14.6—*Joule's experiment.*

In this experiment no heat has been added, $\therefore\ \delta Q=0$. No external work has been done, $\therefore\ \delta W=0$. Hence, by the first law of thermodynamics, $\delta E=0$—that is, although there have been changes in pressure and volume of the gas there has been no change in internal energy. But since E is a function of the state (represented by P, V, T) and has been shown to be independent of P and V, it must therefore be a function of T only.

This law is taken as being exactly true in the case of an imaginary "perfect gas." With an actual gas there is always a slight departure from it, as was shown by Joule and Kelvin by experiments performed between 1852 and 1862 on flow of gases through a porous plug in which a small change in temperature was observed in air, CO_2, H_2, and in all other gases used. *A perfect gas obeys Joule's law exactly—that is, the internal energy of a perfect gas is a function of the temperature only.* All gases may be regarded as perfect if their pressures are sufficiently low, *i.e.* they obey the law $PV=RmT=\mathcal{R}NT$ very nearly.

An important consequence of Joule's law is that if the temperature of a mass of gas changes from T_1 to T_2, the change in internal energy (E_2-E_1) will be the same no matter how the pressure (P) and volume (V) have changed, since, by Joule's law, E is independent of P and V, and depends only on T.

The expansion in Joule's experiment does not, of course, constitute a continuous sequence of equilibrium states and is, therefore, irreversible, and although it is possible to represent the initial and final *equilibrium states* on diagrams whose co-ordinates are properties of equilibrium states (*e.g.* P, V, T, H. E, φ), *the intermediate states cannot be shown.*

6. Specific Heat at Constant Pressure and at Constant Volume.—The specific heat of a substance was defined on p. 8 as the amount of heat required to raise the temperature of 1 lb. of the substance by 1°.

Specific heat of a substance may alternatively be defined as the ratio of the heat necessary to raise the temperature of mass M of the substance by an amount of δT to the heat required to raise the temperature of the same mass of water by the same number of degrees. Thus, according to this latter definition, specific heat, being the ratio of two quantities of heat, is a pure number $|S|$—the vertical lines being used to emphasize that S is a number only.

Since, however, the heat required to raise the temperature of 1 lb. of water by 1° F. is called a B.Th.U. the heat required to raise the temperature of 1 lb. of substance by 1° F. is $|S|$B.Th.U. Therefore, the heat required to raise the temperature of m lb. of substance by δt °F. is $\delta Q = m \times |S| \times \delta t$ B.Th.U., i.e. the heat required to raise the temperature of mass $M = m$ lb. by an amount $\delta T = \delta t$ °F. is

$$\delta Q = \left(\frac{M}{\text{lb.}}\right) \times |S| \times \left(\frac{\delta T}{°\text{F.}}\right) \text{B.Th.U.}$$

$$= M \times |S| \frac{\text{B.Th.U.}}{\text{lb. °F.}} \times \delta T = M \times C \times \delta T,$$

where M, C and δT are quantities composed of numbers × units, whereas m, $|S|$ and δt represent numbers only. Thus, $C = |S| \frac{\text{B.Th.U.}}{\text{lb. °F.}}$ *i.e.* $|S|$ is the numerical value of specific heat and C is a number × a unit.

Hence, since $\frac{dQ}{dT} = C$ when unit mass is considered, and the heat added (δQ) depends on the path between two equilibrium states, there are an infinite number of specific heats possible at any given temperature in the case of gases, depending upon what external work is allowed to be done during the raising of the temperature by 1°. There are, however, two important cases when dealing with a gas, namely, the specific heat of the gas at constant pressure and its specific heat at constant volume.

The specific heat of a gas at constant pressure, C_P, is the amount of heat required to raise the temperature of unit mass of the gas by 1° when the pressure is kept constant.

The specific heat of a gas at constant volume, C_V, is the amount of heat required to raise the temperature of unit mass of gas by 1° when the volume is kept constant.

The specific heats, C_P and C_V, of a perfect gas are assumed to remain constant at all temperatures, but for real gases they increase considerably at high temperatures.

A perfect gas conforms to the following laws exactly:—

(i) The characteristic equation $PV = RmT$ (from Boyle's and Charles' laws).

(ii) The internal energy is a function of temperature only—that is, $E = f(T)$ (Joule's law).

(iii) The specified heats C_P and C_V remain constant at all temperatures.

These laws are those of an imaginary, ideal, or perfect gas. No real gas obeys them with strict accuracy, but the so-called permanent gases very nearly do at ordinary temperatures and low pressures.

7. The Relationship $C_P - C_V = R$.

Heating at Constant Volume.—If heat is added at constant volume (fig. 14.7) to a definite mass of gas, *m*, and its state changes

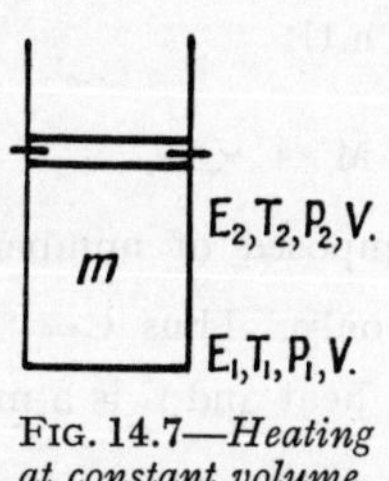

FIG. 14.7—*Heating at constant volume.*

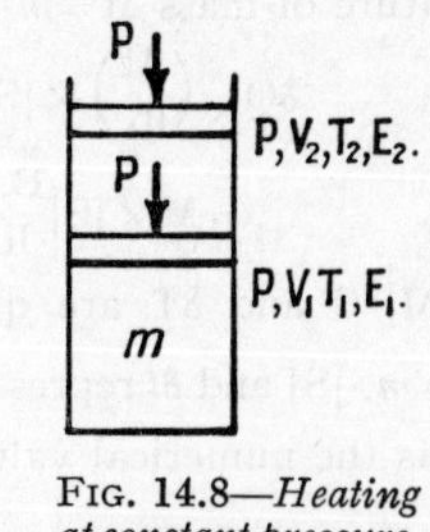

FIG. 14.8—*Heating at constant pressure.*

from initial conditions P_1, V, T_1, E_1, to final conditions P_2, V, T_2, E_2, then by the first law of thermodynamics, which states that heat added (δQ) = increase in internal energy (δE) + external work done (δW), we have,

$$mC_V(T_2 - T_1) = (E_2 - E_1) + 0$$

(Note that this equation can be deduced from $\delta E = mC_V \delta T$.) That is, a rise in temperature $(T_2 - T_1)$ of the gas when heated at constant volume produces an increase in internal energy

$$(E_2 - E_1) = mC_V(T_2 - T_1) \quad . \quad . \quad . \quad \text{(i)}$$

Heating at Constant Pressure.—If heat is added gradually to a mass *m* of gas maintained at constant pressure P to change its state from initial conditions P, V_1, T_1, E_1, to final conditions, P, V_2, T_2, E_2 (fig. 14.8), then, by the first law of thermodynamics we have:

$$mC_P(T_2 - T_1) = (E_2 - E_1) + P(V_2 - V_1)$$

That is, a rise in temperature (T_2-T_1) of the gas when heated at constant pressure, produces an increase in internal energy

$$(E_2-E_1)=mC_P(T_2-T_1)-P(V_2-V_1) \quad . \quad . \quad . \quad \text{(ii)}$$

Since the temperature rise during the heating processes at constant volume and at constant pressure is the same (T_2-T_1), we can say, by Joule's law, that the increase in internal energy in the two cases must be the same because E is independent of how P and V have changed and depends only on the change in T. Hence, the expressions for (E_2-E_1) in equations (i) and (ii) are equal, and result in the equation:

$$(E_2-E_1)=mC_V(T_2-T_1)=mC_P(T_2-T_1)-Rm(T_2-T_1)$$

$$\therefore\ C_V=C_P-R \qquad \therefore\ C_P-C_V=R.$$

If the mol (see p. 277) be used as a unit, it can be shown that

$${}_MC_P-{}_MC_V=\mathcal{R}=1\cdot986\ \frac{\text{B.Th.U.}}{\text{mol }^\circ\text{F.}}$$

where ${}_MC_P$ and ${}_MC_V$ represent the molecular heats or molal specific heats in B.Th.U. per mol degree F. at constant pressure and constant volume, respectively, and $\mathcal{R}$ is the universal gas constant, namely, 1545·5 ft.-Lb. per mol °F. It will also be obvious that

$$M\times C_P={}_MC_P \text{ and } C_V=\frac{{}_MC_V}{M}$$

where M is the "molecular weight" or the mass per mol of gas.

Example 1.—Calculate the change of internal energy of air, initially occupying a volume of 15 cu. ft. at 100° F. and 100 Lb. per sq. in. abs. and finally occupying 150 cu. ft. at 20 Lb. per sq. in. abs. For air, take $C_V=0\cdot17$ B.Th.U. per lb. ° F. and $R=53\cdot3$ ft.-Lb. per lb. ° F.

Since $\quad \dfrac{P_1V_1}{T_1}=Rm=\dfrac{P_2V_2}{T_2}$

the mass of air, $m=\dfrac{P_1V_1}{RT_1}=\dfrac{\dfrac{100\text{Lb.}}{\text{in.}^2}\times15\text{ft.}^3\left[\dfrac{144\text{ in.}^2}{\text{ft.}^2}\right]}{53\cdot3\dfrac{\text{ft.-Lb.}}{\text{lb. }^\circ\text{F.}}\times560^\circ\text{ abs. F.}}=7\cdot24\text{ lb.}$

and the final temperature, $T_2=\dfrac{P_2}{P_1}\dfrac{V_2}{V_1}T_1=\dfrac{20}{100}\times\dfrac{150}{15}\times560^\circ$ abs. F.

$$=1{,}120^\circ \text{ abs. F. or } 660^\circ \text{ F.}$$

Hence, since $\delta E=mC_V\delta T$, the gain in internal energy,

$$E_2-E_1=mC_V(T_2-T_1)=7\cdot24\text{ lb.}\times0\cdot17\frac{\text{B.Th.U.}}{\text{lb. }^\circ\text{F.}}\times(1{,}120-560)^\circ\text{ F.}$$

$$=690\text{ B.Th.U.}$$

Example 2.—The molecular heat at constant volume of a gas is 4·98 B.Th.U. per mol °F. Ten cu. ft. of the gas at 15 Lb. per sq. in. abs. and 64° F. are compressed to a volume of 1 cu. ft., and the law of compression is $PV^{1\cdot15}$=constant. Find the work done, the change in internal energy, and the heat leakage from the gas during compression.

Referring to fig. 14.3,

$$P_1=P_2\left(\frac{V_2}{V_1}\right)^{1\cdot15}=15\times144(10)^{1\cdot15}=212\times144 \text{ Lb./ft.}^2$$

$$\text{Work done on gas}=\frac{P_1V_1-P_2V_2}{n-1}=\frac{144(212\times1-15\times10)}{0\cdot15}$$

$$=59{,}500 \text{ ft.-Lb. or } 76\cdot5 \text{ B.Th.U.}$$

$$\text{Also, } N=\frac{P_2V_2}{\mathcal{R}T_2}=144\times15\,\frac{\text{Lb.}}{\text{ft.}^2}\times\frac{\text{mol }^\circ\text{F.}}{1{,}545 \text{ ft.-Lb.}}\times\frac{10 \text{ ft.}^3}{524^\circ\text{ F.}}$$

$$=0\cdot0267 \text{ mol},$$

$$\text{and}\quad T_1=T_2\left(\frac{V_2}{V_1}\right)^{n-1}=524(10)^{0\cdot15}=742^\circ \text{ abs. F.}$$

The increase in internal energy of the gas during compression is

$$(E_1-E_2)=mC_V(T_1-T_2)=N\times{}_MC_V(T_1-T_2)$$

$$=0\cdot0267 \text{ mol}\times4\cdot98\,\frac{\text{B.Th.U.}}{\text{mol }^\circ\text{ F.}}\times(742-524)^\circ\text{ F.}$$

$$=29 \text{ B.Th.U.}$$

Hence, by the first law of thermodynamics, namely, $\delta Q=\delta E+\delta W$, the heat added to the gas during compression=29−76·5=−47·5 B.Th.U., or the heat leakage=47·5 B.Th.U.

8. The Law of Reversible Adiabatic Expansion and Compression, PV^γ=c.—It is stated on p. 292 that the law of a reversible adiabatic expansion or compression is PV^γ=constant. One way of proving this law is as follows:

(i) Assume that $PV^n=c$ can represent a reversible adiabatic expansion, and then proceed to prove that $n=\gamma$.

Work done during reversible adiabatic expansion (fig. 14.9) from a to b

$$=\frac{P_aV_a-P_bV_b}{n-1}=\frac{Rm}{n-1}(T_a-T_b)$$

By the first law of thermodynamics:—heat added (which, by definition of an adiabatic, is 0)=increase in internal energy+external work done by the gas.

∴ Increase in internal energy= − external work done by the gas,

$$\text{or}\quad mC_V(T_b-T_a)=\frac{-Rm}{(n-1)}(T_a-T_b)$$

for a reversible adiabatic expansion of a perfect gas.

$$\therefore\ m\frac{R}{(\gamma-1)}(T_b-T_a)=\frac{Rm}{(n-1)}(T_b-T_a)$$

$$\left[\text{since, from } C_p-C_v=R \text{ follows } C_v=\frac{R}{(\gamma-1)}\right]$$

$$\therefore\ (n-1)=(\gamma-1)$$

$$\therefore\ n=\gamma$$

(ii) Alternatively, since, for reversible expansion, $\delta W=P\delta V$, then for reversible adiabatic expansion or compression of a mass m of gas

$$\delta Q=\delta E+\delta W=mC_v\delta T+P\delta V=0$$

then
$$m\left(\frac{R}{(\gamma-1)}\right)\left(\frac{P\delta V+V\delta P}{Rm}\right)+P\delta V=0$$

$$\therefore\ \gamma P\delta V+V\delta P=0$$

$$\therefore\ \gamma\int\frac{dV}{V}+\int\frac{dP}{P}=\text{constant } k=\log_\varepsilon PV^\gamma$$

$$\therefore\ PV^\gamma=\varepsilon^k=\text{constant, c.}$$

Hence, $PV^\gamma=c$ is the law for a reversible adiabatic expansion or compression of a gas, or alternatively, since $PV=RmT$, the law can be written

$$TV^{\gamma-1}=\text{constant, or } \frac{T}{P^{1-1/\gamma}}=\text{constant.}$$

The law PV^γ =constant would define all the states of equilibrium through which a perfect gas would pass if it could be expanded or compressed adiabatically and reversibly. We may note, in particular, that *although a free expansion* (as in Joule's experiment) *or throttling process may take place adiabatically* (i.e. $\delta Q=0$), *such a process is irreversible and, therefore, the law PV^γ=constant does not apply.* The general law joining the terminal equilibrium states of an irreversible expansion or compression is PV^n=constant, where the index n may vary from unity to a value greater than γ according as the heat abstracted varies from a maximum value, as in an isothermal compression,

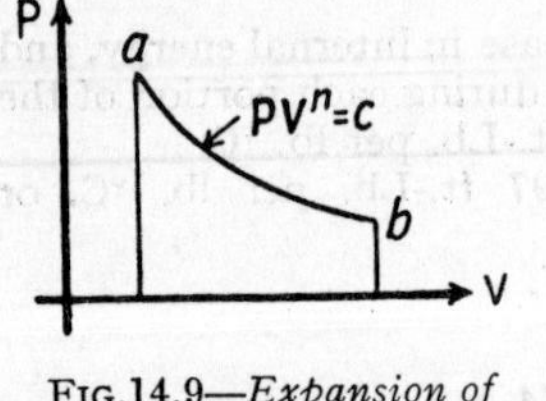

FIG. 14.9—*Expansion of fluid.*

FIG. 14.10—*Expansion through a throttle or orifice.*

to zero as in a real adiabatic, i.e. in a heat-insulated or uncooled process.

Example 1.—Prove that when a fluid expands through a throttle valve or constricted orifice the total (i.e. enthalpy) heat of the fluid remains constant.

Expansion through a throttle valve or constricted orifice is not a *reversible* adiabatic process, though it may be done, and generally is done, without heat entering or leaving the substance. Expansion through a throttle valve or constricted orifice is irreversible. The terminal equilibrium states of such an expansion have the same total heats or enthalpies, as can be proved with reference to the accompanying diagram (fig. **14.10**) in which the orifice plate is contained between two pistons which, together with the cylinder, are impervious to heat. The orifice is assumed small relative to the area of the pistons, and changes in kinetic energy negligible. Suppose gas contained on the left of the orifice, having a state represented by P_1, V_1, T_1, E_1, is forced through the orifice by the left-hand piston exerting a constant pressure P_1, and suppose the constant pressure on the right-hand piston is P_2 so that, when all the gas is through the orifice, the gas is in a state P_2, V_2, T_2, E_2. No heat can get in or out of the gas through the impervious walls and pistons during expansion through the orifice; hence by the first law of thermodynamics: heat added = 0 = increase in internal energy + external work done by the gas.

$$\therefore\ 0=(E_2-E_1)+(P_2V_2-P_1V_1)$$

$$\therefore\ E_1+P_1V_1=E_2+P_2V_2$$

or

$$H_1=H_2$$

That is, the total heat or enthalpy of a fluid remains constant during expansion through a throttle valve or constricted orifice. This fact was used on page 120 when dealing with the throttling calorimeter for the estimation of the dryness fraction of steam.

Example 2.—If 0·1 lb. of gas occupying ½ cu. ft. is expanded in the cylinder of an engine at the constant pressure 150 Lb. per sq. in. abs. until its volume is 1 cu. ft. It is then assumed to expand adiabatically and reversibly to 5 cu. ft. Find the temperature of the gas, (*a*) at the end of the constant pressure stage, (*b*) at the end of the reversible adiabatic expansion.

Also, calculate the work done, the increase in internal energy, and the heat added to or rejected from the gas during each portion of the expansion. Given $C_p=356$ and $C_v=259$ ft.-Lb. per lb. °C.

For this gas $R=C_p-C_v=356-259=97$ ft.-Lb. per lb. °C. or

$$97\,\frac{\text{ft.-Lb.}}{\text{lb. °C.}}\left[\frac{5\text{ °C.}}{9\text{ °F.}}\right]=53\cdot 9 \text{ ft.-Lb. per lb. °F.}$$

$$\text{and } \gamma=\frac{C_p}{C_v}=\frac{356}{259}=1\cdot 374.$$

$$\text{Temperature } T_1 = \frac{P_1 V_1}{Rm} = \frac{(144 \times 150)\frac{\text{Lb.}}{\text{ft.}^2} \times 0\cdot 5 \text{ ft.}^3}{97 \frac{\text{ft.-Lb.}}{\text{lb. °C.}} \times 0\cdot 1 \text{ lb.}}$$

$$= 1{,}113° \text{ abs. C. or } 2{,}004° \text{ abs. F.}$$

(*a*) Temperature of the gas at the end of the constant pressure stage (fig. 14.11)—that is at state ②—is given by

$$T_2 = \frac{P_2 V_2}{Rm} = \frac{144 \times 150 \times 1}{97 \times 0\cdot 1} = 2{,}226° \text{ abs. C. or } 4{,}007° \text{ abs. F.}$$

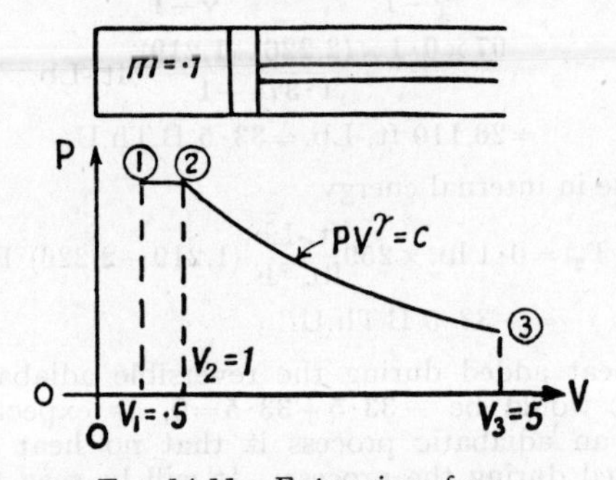

FIG. 14.11—*Expansion of gas.*

(*b*) Temperature at the end of the reversible adiabatic expansion—that is at state ③—is given by $\frac{T_3}{T_2} = \left(\frac{V_2}{V_3}\right)^{\gamma-1} = \left(\frac{1}{5}\right)^{0\cdot 374} = \frac{1}{1\cdot 826}$

$$\therefore\ T_3 = \frac{2{,}226° \text{ abs. C.}}{1\cdot 826} = 1{,}219° \text{ abs. C. or } 2{,}194° \text{ abs. F.}$$

The work done is given by the area under the PV curve, the increase in internal energy is $mC_V dT$, and the heat added or rejected is given by $\delta Q = \delta E + \delta W$.

(*a*) During the constant pressure stage from ① to ② the work done by the gas = area under ①②

$$= P_1(V_2 - V_1) = (144 \times 150)\frac{\text{Lb.}}{\text{ft.}^2} \times (1 - 0\cdot 5)\text{ft.}^3$$

$$= 10{,}800 \text{ ft.-Lb.} = 13\cdot 9 \text{ B.Th.U.}$$

$$C_V = 259 \frac{\text{ft.-Lb.}}{\text{lb. °C.}} \left[\frac{5° \text{ C.}}{9° \text{ F.}}\right] \left[\frac{\text{B.Th.U.}}{778 \text{ ft.-Lb.}}\right]$$

$$= 0\cdot 185 \text{ B.Th.U. per lb. °F.}$$

The increase in internal energy

is $mC_v\,(T_2-T_1)=0\cdot1\text{ lb.}\times0\cdot185\dfrac{\text{B.Th.U.}}{\text{lb. °F.}}(4{,}007-2{,}004)\text{ °F.}$

$$=37\cdot1\text{ B.Th.U.}$$

Hence, the heat added during the constant pressure process

$$=37\cdot1+13\cdot9=51\text{ B.Th.U.}$$

(*b*) During the reversible adiabatic expansion ② to ③, the work done by the gas = area under curve ②③

$$=\frac{P_2V_2-P_3V_3}{\gamma-1}\text{ or }\frac{Rm(T_2-T_3)}{\gamma-1}$$

$$=\frac{97\times0\cdot1\times(2{,}226-1{,}219)}{1\cdot374-1}\text{ ft.-Lb.}$$

$$=26{,}110\text{ ft.-Lb.}=33\cdot5\text{ B.Th.U.}$$

The increase in internal energy

$$=mC_v(T_3-T_2)=0\cdot1\text{ lb.}\times259\frac{\text{ft.-Lb.}}{\text{lb. °F.}}(1{,}219-2{,}226)\text{°F.}\left[\frac{\text{B.Th.U.}}{778\text{ ft.-Lb.}}\right]$$

$$=-33\cdot5\text{ B.Th.U.}$$

Hence, the heat added during the reversible adiabatic expansion from ② to ③ would be $-33\cdot5+33\cdot5=0$, as expected, since the definition of an adiabatic process is that no heat is added and none is rejected during the process. It will be seen that the work done would be at the expense of the internal energy, the decrease in internal energy being equal to the work done by the gas.

Example 3.—Find a formula relating change of area of a convergent-divergent nozzle with change in pressure and velocity of a gas flowing through the nozzle, and deduce results regarding *subsonic, sonic and supersonic* flow of the gas.

(I) *Hypothesis or Assumptions.*

The flow is assumed to be horizontal and unidirectional, frictionless and adiabatic (i.e. reversible adiabatic flow), and the gas is assumed perfect.

(II) *Science.*

Relevant laws are:—(i) conservation of matter, (ii) conservation of energy, (iii) Newton's second law of motion, (iv) laws of gases, (v) definitions of enthalpy and Mach number.

(III) *Mathematics.*

Statements of these laws in symbols are:

(i) Rate of mass flow $\dot{m}=\rho Av=\text{constant}$, where ρ is the density of gas at a section where the area is A and the velocity is v. Hence, taking logarithms and differentiating we get $\dfrac{d\rho}{\rho}+\dfrac{dA}{A}+\dfrac{dv}{v}=0.$

(ii) $\frac{P}{w}+\frac{v^2}{2g}+Z+\frac{C_V T}{g}$ = constant for adiabatic (i.e. heat-insulated) flow, being the energy per unit *weight* of fluid flowing (where $w=\rho g$, the specific weight of fluid). Alternatively, $\frac{P}{\rho}+\frac{v^2}{2}+C_V T$ = constant for horizontal adiabatic flow, being equal to the energy per unit *mass* of fluid flowing, which also equals $C_P T+\frac{v^2}{2}=H+\frac{v^2}{2}$ = constant, using $dH=C_P dT$ from (v).

(iii) Using Newton's second law: Force = rate of mass flow × change in velocity of fluid, or $F=\dot{m}dv$, we deduce from fig. 14.12 that $-\delta P\times\delta a=(\rho v\delta a)\delta v$ for frictionless unidirectional flow.

Hence, $-dP=\rho v dv$ and $\frac{dv}{v}=-\frac{dP}{\rho v^2}$.

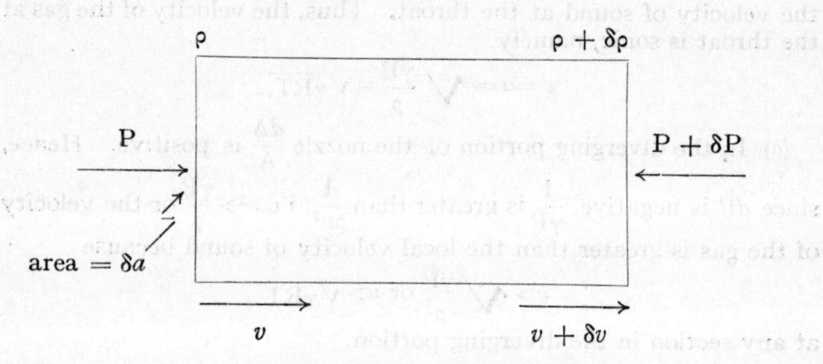

FIG. 14.12—*Gasflow through a nozzle.*

(iv) The characteristic law of a perfect gas may be written $PV=RmT$ or $P=\rho RT$. Also, $C_P-C_V=R$ or $\frac{\gamma-1}{\gamma}=\frac{R}{C_P}$.

(v) By definition, total heat or enthalpy of unit mass of perfect gas may be expressed as $H=E+PV=E+RT$.

Hence, $dH=(C_V+R)dT=C_P dT$.

Also, by definition, Mach number $=\frac{\text{velocity of gas}}{\text{local velocity of sound}}$

$$\text{i.e.}\quad \mathcal{M}=\frac{v}{a}=\frac{v}{\sqrt{\gamma RT}}.$$

From (ii), (iii) and (iv) we deduce that $\frac{P}{\rho^\gamma}$ = constant or PV^γ = constant, as expected for reversible adiabatic flow.

From (i), (iii), (iv) and (v) we deduce, since

$$\mathcal{M}^2=\left(\frac{v}{a}\right)^2=\frac{\rho v^2}{\gamma P},$$

that $$\frac{dA}{A}=\left(\frac{1}{\rho v^2}-\frac{1}{\gamma P}\right)dP=(\mathcal{M}^2-1)\frac{dv}{v}$$

Deductions regarding subsonic and supersonic flow in a convergent divergent nozzle can be made from the last expression, e.g.:

(*a*) In the converging portion of the nozzle $\frac{dA}{A}$ is negative hence, since $\frac{dv}{v}$ is positive, $\mathcal{M}$ is less than 1, i.e. the velocity of the gas is less than the local velocity of sound at any section in the converging portion in which the flow is, therefore, subsonic.

(*b*) At the throat of the nozzle $\frac{dA}{A}=0$, hence

$$\mathcal{M}^2=1 \text{ or } \left(\frac{1}{\rho v^2}-\frac{1}{\gamma P}\right)=0, \textit{ i.e. } v^2=\frac{\gamma P}{\rho} \text{ or } v=a,$$

the velocity of sound at the throat. Thus, the velocity of the gas at the throat is sonic, namely,

$$v=a=\sqrt{\frac{\gamma P}{\rho}}=\sqrt{\gamma RT}.$$

(*c*) In the diverging portion of the nozzle $\frac{dA}{A}$ is positive. Hence, since dP is negative, $\frac{1}{\gamma P}$ is greater than $\frac{1}{\rho v^2}$, i.e. $v^2>\frac{\gamma P}{\rho}$ or the velocity of the gas is greater than the local velocity of sound because

$$v>\sqrt{\frac{\gamma P}{\rho}} \text{ or } v>\sqrt{\gamma RT}$$

at any section in the diverging portion.

Example 4.—Calculate the velocity of sound in air at 60° F.

The expression for velocity of sound, namely,

$$a=\sqrt{\frac{\gamma P}{\rho}}=\sqrt{\gamma RT}$$

is often seen written as $a=\sqrt{g\gamma RT}$. This seems confusing in that it would appear that both formulae cannot be correct. They are, however, correct if it is realised that the first is a *physical formula*, i.e. one in which symbols represent numbers × units, whereas the second is a *numerical formula* in which symbols represent numbers only.

E.g. If the gas is air at 60° F. then the physical formula gives

$$a^2=\gamma RT=1\cdot 4\times 53\cdot 3\,\frac{\text{ft.-Lb.}}{\text{lb. °F.}}\times 520\text{ °F.}\left[\frac{\text{lb.}\times 32\cdot 2\text{ ft.}}{\text{Lb. sec.}^2}\right]$$

$$=1\cdot 25\times 10^6\,\frac{\text{ft.}^2}{\text{sec.}^2} \text{ or } a=1{,}120 \text{ ft./sec.}$$

and the numerical formula in f.p.s. units gives

$$a^2=g\gamma RT=32\cdot 2\times 1\cdot 4\times 53\cdot 3\times 520$$

or $a=1{,}120$ which is the *number* of ft./sec. constituting the velocity of sound.

EXERCISES ON CHAPTER 14

(i)

1. 1 lb. of air is expanded in the cylinder of an air motor from 75 Lb. per sq. in. abs. and temperature 57° C., according to the law $PV^{1\cdot3}$=constant, until its pressure is 15 Lb. per sq. in. abs. Calculate the volume and temperature at the end of expansion and the work done by the air during the expansion.

2. (*a*) 1 cu. ft. of air at 15 Lb. per sq. in. abs. and 68° F. is compressed in the cylinder of a compressor according to the law $PV^{1\cdot13}$ =constant until the pressure is 75 Lb. per sq. in. abs. Calculate the volume after compression, and the work done on the air during compression.

(*b*) Calculate the mass of air compressed, and the temperature after compression. Use these figures to check the work done calculated in (*a*).

3. One pound of air at a pressure 15 Lb. per sq. in. abs. and temperature 15° C. is assumed to be compressed reversibly and adiabatically until its pressure is 200 Lb. per sq. in. abs. Find the volume and temperature after compression, taking $\gamma=1\cdot4$, and calculate the work done on the air during compression.

4. (*a*) Write down the characteristic equation for a perfect gas, and prove the relationship $\frac{T_1}{T_2}=\left(\frac{V_2}{V_1}\right)^{n-1}=\left(\frac{P_1}{P_2}\right)^{\frac{n-1}{n}}$ for a gas expanding according to the law PV^n=constant.

(*b*) 1 cu. ft. of air at 14 Lb. per sq. in. abs. and 59° F. is compressed to a pressure of 700 Lb. per sq. in. abs. Calculate the final volume and temperature assuming: (i) the compression is reversible and adiabatic according to the law $PV^{1\cdot4}=c$, (ii) the compression is reversible and isothermal according to the law $PV=c$.

(*c*) Calculate the work done during compression in each case.

5. 20 cu. ft. of air at 100 Lb. per sq. in. abs. are raised in temperature from 15° C. to 50° C. at constant volume. Calculate the amount of heat added to the air in order to do this, taking C_v for air=0·169 B.Th.U. per lb. ° F.

6. Make statements distinguishing between reversible and irreversible processes.

7. (*a*) Show that in an isothermal compression, the work done on a fluid would be equal to the heat which would have to be abstracted in order to maintain the isothermal.

(*b*) Show that during an adiabatic expansion, the work done by a working fluid would be equal to the decrease in internal energy of the fluid, or that the work would be done at the expense of the internal energy.

8. Show that alternative ways of writing down the reversible adiabatic law for a perfect gas are PV^γ=constant, $TV^{\gamma-1}$=constant, and $P^{\gamma-1/\gamma}=T\times$constant.

9. (*a*) The numerical values of the specific heats at constant pressure and constant volume of oxygen are 0·2175 and 0·155, respectively. Calculate the gas constant R, in ft.-Lb. per lb. ° C., and the mass of 4 cu. ft. of this gas at 20 Lb. per sq. in. abs. and 25° C.

(*b*) Deduce γ for oxygen. If oxygen is assumed compressed reversibly and adiabatically from the above state until its volume is 1 cu. ft., calculate its final pressure and temperature. Also calculate the work done on the gas during the compression, and show that this is equal to the increase in the internal energy of the oxygen due to compression.

10. 10 cu. ft. of air at 90 Lb. per sq. in. abs. and temperature 65 °F. are expanded according to the law $PV^{1\cdot 25}$=constant to four times the original volume in the cylinder of an engine. Calculate: (i) the temperature of the air at the end of expansion and hence, the decrease in internal energy of the air taking C_v for air=0·169 B.Th.U. per lb. ° F.; (ii) the work done by the air during expansion; (iii) the amount of heat absorbed from or rejected to the cylinder walls during the expansion.

11. 5 cu. ft. of air at 15 Lb. per sq. in. abs. are compressed to a final volume of 1 cu. ft. Calculate the final pressure when the compression is assumed (i) reversible isothermal, and (ii) reversible adiabatic (γ=1·4). Estimate the excess of work which would be done during reversible adiabatic compression over that done during reversible isothermal compression.

(ii)

12. (*a*) Prove that the law for the reversible adiabatic expansion of a perfect gas can be represented as PV^{γ}=constant.

(*b*) A gas occupies 4 cu. ft. at 15 Lb. per sq. in. abs. and 68° F. It is assumed to be compressed adiabatically to 100 Lb. per sq. in. abs. Find the final temperature, the final volume, and the change in internal energy of the gas, given that the density is 0·0868 lb. per cu. ft. at s.t.p. and the specific heat at constant volume is 0·175 B.Th.U. per lb. ° F. [Part I, B.Sc. Lond.]

13. Two pounds of a certain gas at 59° F., assumed compression reversibly and adiabatically to one quarter of the original volume, would increase in temperature to 217° F. owing to the expenditure of 56,800 ft.-Lb. of work. Calculate the specific heat of the gas for constant volume and constant pressure heating, the gas constant R. [I.Mech.E., Sec. A.]

14. The numerical values of the specific heats of a gas at constant pressure and at constant volume are 0·201 and 0·155, respectively. If a quantity of this gas, occupying 1 cu. ft. at 14·7 Lb. per sq. in. abs. and 50° F., is assumed compressed reversibly and adiabatically to 70 Lb. per sq. in. abs. and then cooled at constant volume to 100° F., calculate the work done in the compression, the final pressure, and the amount of heat given out in the cooling. [Part I, B.Sc. Lond.]

15. A rigid vessel containing air is divided into two compartments of equal volume, each 5 cu. ft. The pressure on one side of the division is 20 Lb. per sq. in. abs. and on the other side 40 Lb. per sq. in. abs., the temperatures being the same. 100 B.Th.U. of heat are then added and the division plate is punctured. What is the final pressure in the vessel when equilibrium is attained?

[I.Mech.E., Sec. A.]

16. What is meant by the *internal energy* of a gas?

Under what condition of expansion does the internal energy of a gas remain constant?

Find the change in internal energy per lb. of air when a given mass of it expands from a pressure of 80 Lb. per sq. in. abs., volume 15 cu. ft., and temperature 40° C. to a pressure of 20 Lb. per sq. in. abs. and volume 120 cu. ft. $C_v = 0 \cdot 17$ B.Th.U. per lb. ° F. $R = 96$ ft.-Lb. per lb. ° C. [I.Mech.E., Sec. A.]

17. In a jet engine nozzles are required to expand gases from 60 Lb./in.^{2} abs. and 1000° F. to a pressure of $25 \cdot 4$ Lb./in.^{2} abs., the adiabatic efficiency of expansion being 82 per cent. Calculate the temperature and velocity of the gases leaving the nozzles and the exit area if 2,400 lb./min. flows through. Adiabatic efficiency of expansion is the ratio of the drop in enthalpy of the gas during actual (irreversible) adiabatic flow to that of reversible adiabatic flow.

18. Define precisely the term " specific heat " and explain its relation to the capacity of a substance for taking up heat. What would be the specific heat of a gas during (*a*) an isothermal process, (*b*) an adiabatic process.

During the constant pressure heating of 10 lb. of hydrogen from 100° F. to 300° F., 6,820 B.Th.U. were supplied as heat and 1,548,000 ft.-Lb. of work were done by the gas. Deduce the specific heats at constant pressure and at constant volume for the gas, and also its gas constant. [I.Mech.E., Sec. A.]

19. Given that one lb. of air expands according to the law $PV^{1 \cdot 2} =$ constant from the initial conditions $P_1 = 100$ Lb. per sq. in. abs., $t_1 = 500$° F. to a final pressure $P_2 = 10$ Lb. per sq. in. abs., find the difference between the work done and the work when the air expands adiabatically from the same initial conditions to the same final pressure.

If the two processes are assumed to be performed in an ideal manner, explain how the difference comes about and calculate the amount of heat transferred in either process. [I.Mech.E., Sec. A.]

CHAPTER 15

AIR COMPRESSORS AND AIR MOTORS

THE object of all compressors is to raise the pressure of a gas with the minimum expenditure of energy. Compressors fall into two main categories:

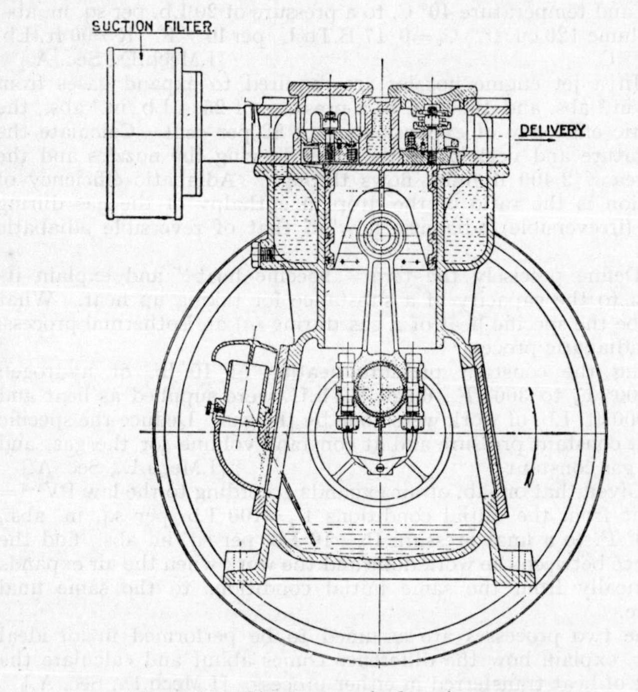

FIG. 15.1—*Single-stage single-acting compressor.*

(i) reciprocating-piston or positive-displacement compressors, from which there is intermittent delivery; and

(ii) rotary compressors, in which there is a transference of energy from a rotor or impeller to air or gas which is being forced through continuously.

1. Single-stage Reciprocating-piston Air Compressors. —Compressed air is used nowadays for many purposes, e.g. in gas-turbine plant and jet engines, air motors, pneumatic drills and riveters, starting of engines, brakes and servo-mechanisms, and in many light tools such as hand grinding wheels and hammers. The leads to the various air-driven parts are usually tapped off a main which conveys the air from a reservoir. The supply and the pressure of the air in the reservoir are maintained by fresh supplies of atmospheric air being raised in pressure by means of compressors and blowers which deliver into the reservoir.

A measure of the performance is the number of cu. ft. of free atmospheric air pumped per horse-power hour. Shaft horse-power required per cu. ft. of air pumped per minute is also a useful ratio to consider.

Fig. 15.1 shows a single-stage single-acting vertical compressor suitable for pressures up to 100 Lb. per sq. in. and speeds up to 1,000 r.p.m.

Fig. 15.2 shows the theoretical or hypothetical indicator diagram of a single-stage, single-acting reciprocating-piston air compressor when clearance volume is neglected. Air is taken in from the atmosphere during the suction stroke a①; then, during the first part of the return stroke ①②, it is compressed according to the law $PV^n = c$ until the pressure (P_2) in the cylinder is sufficient to force open the delivery valve (at ②), after which point no more compression takes place. Delivery occurs during the remainder (②b) of the return stroke. Thus, one complete cycle per revolution is traced out in this single-acting compressor, the lines or traces being assumed to represent a continuous series of equilibrium states so that the equation of state for a gas, namely, $PV = RmT$, applies throughout.

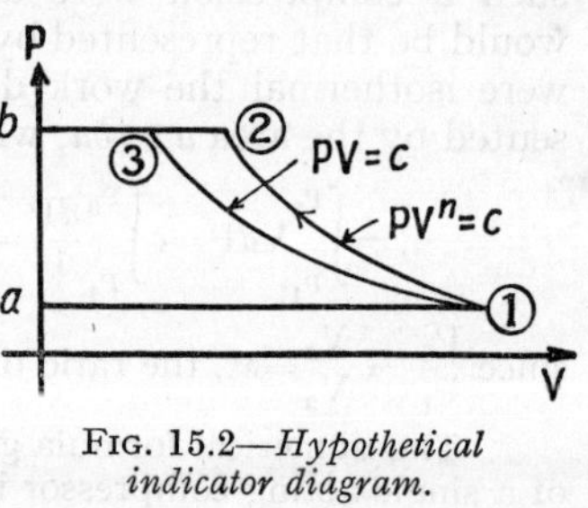

FIG. 15.2—*Hypothetical indicator diagram.*

The hypothetical work done on the air per cycle = area a①②ba, which, as proved on page 286, is equal to

$$\frac{n}{n-1}(P_2V_2 - P_1V_1).$$

Hence, if C is the rate at which the cycles are traced (i.e. the cyclic frequency), the rate at which energy is imparted to the air as estimated from the hypothetical indicator diagram is

$$\frac{n}{n-1}(P_2V_2-P_1V_1)C,$$

which represents the power (i.e. energy per unit of time) delivered to the air. The numerical formula corresponding to this is:—

$$\text{air horse-power}=\frac{n}{n-1}\left(\frac{P_2V_2-P_1V_1}{33{,}000}\right)N, \quad \text{or} \quad \frac{n}{n-1}\,Rm\left(\frac{T_2-T_1}{33{,}000}\right)$$

where m is lb. of air pumped per minute, P is in Lb. per sq. ft. abs. V is in cu. ft. and N is the number of cycles per minute, i.e. the number of r.p.m. in the case of a single-acting compressor.

The actual air horse-power is, of course, greater than that calculated from the hypothetical diagram (see fig. 15.4) and the b.h.p. or shaft horse-power of the engine required to drive the compressor

$$=\frac{\text{actual air horse-power}}{\text{mechanical efficiency } (\eta_m) \text{ of compressor}}.$$

Since power has to be supplied to do work on the air in compressing it we desire the power to be as small as possible. *The ideal compression would be a perfect, reversible, isothermal—that is, would obey Boyle's law $PV=c$.* It will be seen from fig. 15.2 that if such a compression were achieved the work saved per cycle would be that represented by the area ①②③①. If the compression were isothermal the work done per cycle would be that represented by the area *a*①③*ba*, which

$$=\int_{P_1}^{P_3} V\,dP = c\int_{P_1}^{P_3}\frac{dP}{P} = P_1V_1\log_\varepsilon\left(\frac{P_3}{P_1}\right) = P_1V_1\log_\varepsilon M,$$

since $\frac{P_3}{P_1}=\frac{V_1}{V_3}=M$, the ratio of isothermal compression.

∴ The numerical formula giving the ideal isothermal horse-power of a single-acting compressor is

$$\frac{P_1V_1(\log_\varepsilon M)N}{33{,}000},$$

where P is in Lb./ft.^{2} abs., V is in ft.^{3}, and N is the number of r.p.m.

This is taken as a standard of comparison with which to compare the performance of actual reciprocating compressors. The isothermal efficiency is a measure of the departure from the ideal of isothermal compression, and is defined as:

$$\eta_{iso}=\frac{\textbf{calculated isothermal h.p.}}{\textbf{air h.p. of compressor}}$$

When based on the air horse-power calculated from the hypothetical indicator diagram of fig. 15.2, the overall isothermal efficiency is:—

$$ {}_o\eta_{iso} = \frac{\textbf{calculated isothermal h.p.}}{\textbf{shaft h.p. to drive compressor}} $$

$$ = \frac{P_1V_1 \log_\varepsilon \frac{P_2}{P_1}}{\frac{n}{n-1}[P_2V_2 - P_1V_1]\frac{1}{\eta_m}} \quad \text{or} \quad \frac{\eta_m T_1 \log_\varepsilon\left(\frac{P_2}{P_1}\right)}{\frac{n}{n-1}(T_2 - T_1)} $$

the mechanical efficiency of the compressor being defined as:

$$ \frac{\textbf{air h.p. of compressor}}{\textbf{shaft h.p. to drive compressor}} = \eta_m $$

Thus, ${}_o\eta_{iso} = \eta_{iso} \times \eta_m$

Example 1.—(*a*) 1,500 cu. ft. of air per min. are drawn into a cylinder at 15 Lb. per sq. in. abs. and compressed according to the law $PV^{1\cdot 3}$=constant to a pressure of 60 Lb. per sq. in. abs. before being delivered at this pressure into a receiver. Calculate the air horse-power of the compressor from the hypothetical indicator diagram.

(*b*) If the temperature of the air at the beginning of compression is 60° F., calculate the mass of air compressed per minute and the temperature of the air after compression. From this check the horse-power calculation of part (*a*).

(*c*) Calculate the isothermal horse-power and the overall isothermal efficiency of the compressor assuming a mechanical efficiency of 80 per cent.

The cycle traced out will be that represented by fig. **14.2**, *b*② being the suction stroke and ②①*a* the return stroke during which the air is compressed from ② to ① and delivered into the receiver during ①*a*.

(*a*) If the rate at which cycles are traced is C, then the air drawn into the cylinder per cycle will be $\frac{1500}{C}\frac{\text{ft.}^3}{\text{min.}} = V_2$

Since $P_2V_2^{1\cdot 3} = P_1V_1^{1\cdot 3}$, the volume after compression will be

$$ V_1 = V_2\left(\frac{P_2}{P_1}\right)^{\frac{1}{1\cdot 3}} = \frac{1500}{C}\left(\frac{1}{4}\right)^{\frac{1}{1\cdot 3}} = \frac{516}{C}\frac{\text{ft.}^3}{\text{min.}} $$

Work done on the air per cycle

$$ = \frac{n}{n-1}(P_1V_1 - P_2V_2) $$

$$ = \frac{1\cdot 3}{0\cdot 3} \times \frac{144}{C} \times (60 \times 516 - 15 \times 1500)\ \frac{\text{Lb.}}{\text{ft.}^2} \times \frac{\text{ft.}^3}{\text{min.}} $$

$$ = \frac{5{,}278{,}400}{C}\frac{\text{ft.-Lb.}}{\text{min.}} $$

Since the rate at which cycles are traced is C, the rate at which work is done on the air is 5,278,400 ft.-Lb./min.

$\therefore$ Hypothetical air horse-power of the compressor

$$=5{,}278{,}400\ \frac{\text{ft.-Lb.}}{\text{min.}}\left[\frac{\text{h-p.-min.}}{33{,}000\ \text{ft.-Lb.}}\right]=160\ \text{h-p.}$$

(*b*) Temperature before compression $=60°$ F.

$$\therefore\ T_2=520°\ \text{abs. F.}$$

Hence, the mass of air compressed per minute is

$$m=\frac{PV}{RT}=(144\times15)\frac{\text{Lb.}}{\text{ft.}^2}\times1500\frac{\text{ft.}^3}{\text{min.}}\times\frac{\text{lb. °F.}}{53\cdot3\ \text{ft.-Lb.}}\times\frac{1}{520\ \text{°F.}}=116\cdot7\ \frac{\text{lb.}}{\text{min.}}$$

The temperature after compression can be calculated from the formula (referring to fig. 14.2):

$$\frac{T_1}{T_2}=\left(\frac{P_1}{P_2}\right)^{\frac{n-1}{n}}=\left(\frac{60}{15}\right)^{\frac{0\cdot3}{1\cdot3}}=1\cdot374$$

$$\therefore\ T_1=520°\ \text{abs. F.}\times1\cdot377=716°\ \text{abs. F.}\qquad\therefore\ t_1=256°\ \text{F.}$$

An alternative expression to that used in part (*a*) for the rate at which work is done is $\dfrac{n}{n-1}Rm(T_1-T_2)$.

$$=\frac{1\cdot3}{0\cdot3}\times53\cdot3\ \frac{\text{ft.-Lb.}}{\text{lb.° F.}}\times116\cdot7\ \frac{\text{lb.}}{\text{min.}}\times(716-520)°\ \text{F.}\left[\frac{\text{h-p. min.}}{33{,}000\ \text{ft.-Lb.}}\right]$$

$=160$ h.p. $=$ hypothetical air horse-power (as before).

Hence, shaft power driving the compressor $=\dfrac{160}{0\cdot8}$ h.p. $=200$ h.p.

(*c*) Isothermal power $=$ isothermal work per cycle $\times$ rate at which the cycles are traced.

$$=P_2(V_2\,C)\log_\varepsilon\left(\frac{P_1}{P_2}\right),\ \text{referring to fig. 14.2.}$$

$$=(144\times15)\ \frac{\text{Lb.}}{\text{ft.}^2}\times1500\ \frac{\text{ft.}^3}{\text{min.}}\times\log_\varepsilon4\times\left[\frac{\text{h-p. min.}}{33{,}000\ \text{ft.-Lb.}}\right]$$

$=136$ h.p.

$\therefore$ Overall isothermal efficiency

$$=\frac{\text{Isothermal h-p.}}{\text{Shaft h.p.}}=\frac{136}{200}=0\cdot68\ \text{or 68 per cent.}$$

Taking Clearance Volume into Account.—A single-stage, single-acting compressor in which the clearance volume is represented by V_c will have a hypothetical indicator diagram as illustrated by fig. 15.3 in which the clearance volume V_4 at pressure

P_4 expands to the state ⑤ before any fresh air is drawn into the cylinder. That is, although the stroke of the piston is from ① to ② having a swept volume (V_2-V_1), the suction is only from ⑤ to ②, giving a volume (V_2-V_5) taken into the cylinder per cycle. The volumetric efficiency, as deduced from the hypothetical indicator diagram, is thus

$$\eta_v=\frac{(V_2-V_5)}{(V_2-V_1)}=\frac{\textbf{volume of air pumped per cycle}}{\textbf{stroke volume of cylinder}}$$

$$=\frac{\textbf{mass of air delivered per cycle}}{\textbf{mass of air to fill the stroke volume'}}$$

both being reckoned from free atmospheric air conditions.

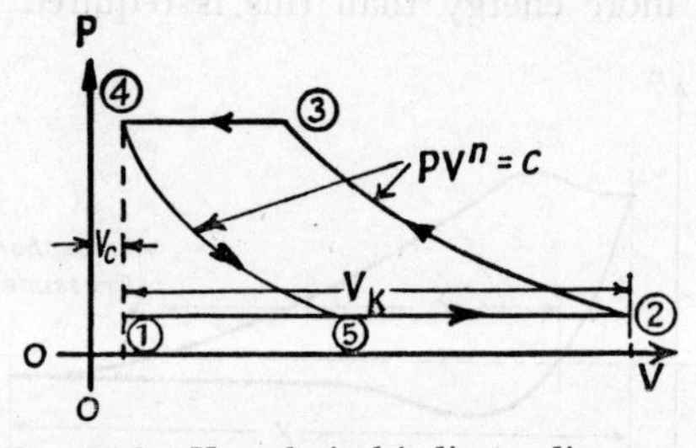

FIG. 15.3—*Hypothetical indicator diagram.*

If we assume that the compression curve ②③ and the expansion curve ④⑤ follow the same law $PV^n=c$, then

$$\left(\frac{V_2}{V_3}\right)^{n-1}=\left(\frac{P_3}{P_2}\right)^{\frac{n-1}{n}}=\left(\frac{P_4}{P_5}\right)^{\frac{n-1}{n}}=\left(\frac{V_5}{V_4}\right)^{n-1}$$

Hence, the ratio of compression $\frac{V_2}{V_3}=r=\frac{V_5}{V_4}$, the ratio of expansion.

Therefore, the volumetric efficiency $=\frac{V_2-V_5}{V_2-V_1}=\frac{(V_C+V_K)-rV_C}{V_K}$

$$\textbf{\textit{i.e.}}\ \eta_v=1-(r-1)\frac{V_C}{V_K}=1-\left\{\left(\frac{P_3}{P_2}\right)^{\frac{1}{n}}-1\right\}\frac{V_C}{V_K}$$

From this it will be seen that the smaller V_c is the higher will be the volumetric efficiency; hence the necessity for making clearance as small as is practically possible, say, 3 to 5 per cent. of the stroke volume.

When clearance is taken into account, the hypothetical work done on the air per cycle = area (5, 2, 3, 4, 5)

$$=\frac{n}{n-1}(P_3V_3-P_2V_2)-\frac{n}{n-1}(P_4V_4-P_5V_5)$$

Hence, the hypothetical air horse-power of the above single-acting, single-stage compressor as estimated from the indicator diagram of fig. 15.3 is given by the numerical formula

$$\frac{n}{n-1}\,N\left\{\frac{(P_3V_3-P_2V_2)-(P_4V_4-P_5V_5)}{33{,}000}\right\},$$

where N is the number of r.p.m., P is in Lb. per sq. ft. abs. and V is cu.ft.

Diagrams from actual compressors differ from the above hypothetical diagrams because of delay in operation of valves and inertia of automatic spring-loaded suction and delivery valves. The areas of actual indicator diagrams are proportional to the work done by the face of the piston on the fluid being compressed, but more energy than this is required to be supplied

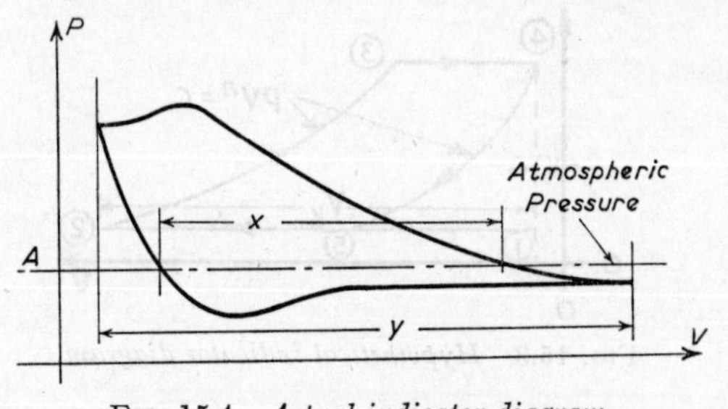

FIG. 15.4—*Actual indicator diagram.*

along the shaft driving the compressor because of the energy in the inevitable eddies, turbulence and friction occurring in real compressors.

Fig. **15.4** shows an actual indicator diagram from which a good approximation to volumetric efficiency can be made, namely, as the ratio of the lengths x to y measured on the atmospheric line.

The performance of a reciprocating compressor regarded as an air pump is thus measured by the ratio:

$$\frac{\textbf{equivalent vol. of free atmospheric air delivered per cycle}}{\textbf{vol. swept by the piston.}}$$

This is the actual volumetric efficiency of the compressor

Example 2.—A single-stage air compressor takes in air at a pressure **15** Lb. per sq. in. abs. and delivers it at **115** Lb. per sq. in. abs. The clearance volume is 5 per cent. of the stroke volume. Assuming the law $PV^{1 \cdot 25}$=constant to hold during compression and expansion, calculate the volume of free air delivered per horse-power-hour. Neglect mechanical friction and assume the hypothetical diagram.

Referring to fig. 15.3, $\frac{V_2}{V_3}=\left(\frac{P_3}{P_2}\right)^{\frac{1}{n}}=\left(\frac{115}{15}\right)^{\frac{1}{1\cdot 25}}=5\cdot 102$

$$V_2=V_K+V_C=\left\{\left(\frac{100}{5}\right)+1\right\}V_C=21V_C \qquad \therefore\ V_3=\frac{21V_C}{5\cdot 102}=4\cdot 12V_C$$

$$\frac{V_5}{V_4}=\left(\frac{P_4}{P_5}\right)^{\frac{1}{n}}=5\cdot 102 \qquad \therefore\ V_5=5\cdot 102V_C$$

Volume of free air drawn in per cycle $=(V_2-V_5)=21V_C-5\cdot 102V_C$
$=15\cdot 898V_C$

Work done per cycle

=area of indicator diagram (2, 3, 4, 5, 2)

$$=\frac{n}{n-1}\left\{(P_3V_3-P_2V_2)-(P_4V_4-P_5V_5)\right\}$$

$$=\frac{1\cdot 25}{0\cdot 25}\times 144\left\{\begin{matrix}(115\times 4\cdot 12V_C-15\times 21V_C)\\ -(115\times V_C-15\times 5\cdot 102V_C)\end{matrix}\right\}\text{Lb./ft.}^2$$

$$=5\times 144\times\left\{159-38\cdot 4\right\}\frac{\text{Lb.}}{\text{ft.}^2}\times V_C=86{,}800V_C\,\frac{\text{Lb.}}{\text{ft.}^2}$$

That is, work per cycle equal to $86{,}800V_C\,\frac{\text{Lb.}}{\text{ft.}^2}$ is required to deliver a volume of free air equal to $15\cdot 898V_C$.

$\therefore$ 1 horse-power-hour, which is 1,980,000 ft.-Lb. of work, will deliver

$$\frac{15\cdot 898V_C}{86{,}800V_C\,\frac{\text{Lb.}}{\text{ft.}^2}}\times 1{,}980{,}000\text{ ft.-Lb.}=356\cdot 2\text{ ft.}^3$$

Hence, the calculated capacity of the compressor is 356·2 cu. ft. of free air per horse-power-hour.

2. Multi-stage Compression.—If air at high pressure is required, compression in stages is more efficient than in a one-stage compressor. The reason for this can be seen in fig. 15.5. Suppose it is required to compress air from a pressure P_1 to a pressure P_4, then, if the compression be done in one stage, the hypothetical work required per cycle (neglecting clearance

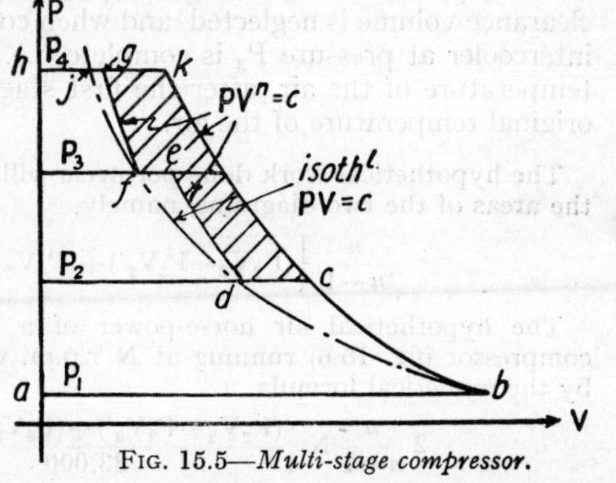

FIG. 15.5—*Multi-stage compressor.*

volumes) would be that represented by area *abckha* and the isothermal work would be represented by the area *abdfjha*. If, now, instead of compressing in one stage only, the compression *bc* is stopped at pressure P_2 and the air at *c* delivered into a receiver through which cooling water circulates sufficiently to cool the air down to its original temperature (i.e. the temperature of the isothermal curve), and then the air is drawn from the receiver into a second cylinder and compressed along *de* to a pressure P_3 and passed into a second receiver for cooling down to the isothermal temperature again before being drawn into a third cylinder for compression along *fg* to the final pressure P_4, it will be seen that, by compressing in the three stages from P_1 to P_4 along the curves *bc*, *de*, *fg*, rather than in one stage along the curve *bk*, a saving in work done per cycle is achieved and is represented by the shaded area *cdefgkc*. Thus, by compressing in stages, it is possible to keep the actual compression curve nearer to the isothermal than would be the case with only one-stage compression, and the required final air pressure is obtained with expenditure of work approaching that of the ideal isothermal compression.

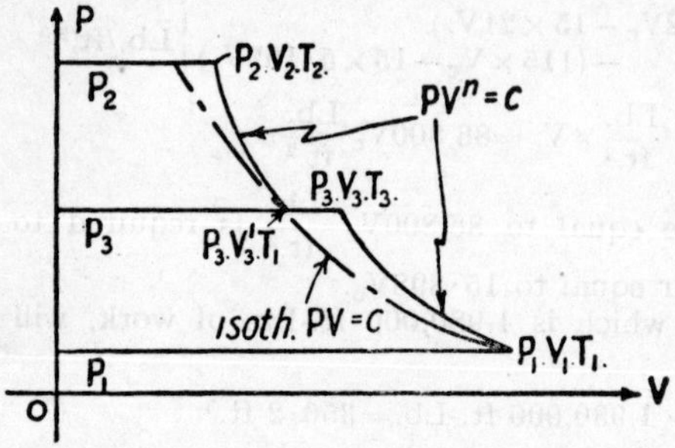

FIG. 15.6—*Hypothetical indicator diagram.*

Fig. 15.6 shows the hypothetical indicator diagrams on the same P,V axes for a two-stage single-acting air compressor when clearance volume is neglected, and when cooling in the receiver or intercooler at pressure P_3 is complete, i.e. such as to reduce the temperature of the air, after the first stage, from T_3 to T_1, the original temperature of the air.

The hypothetical work done per cycle will be equal to the sum of the areas of the two diagrams, namely,

$$\frac{n}{n-1}\left\{(P_2V_2-P_3V_3')+(P_3V_3-P_1V_1)\right\}$$

The hypothetical air horse-power of a *double-acting* two-stage compressor (fig. 15.6) running at N r.p.m. will, therefore, be given by the numerical formula

$$2\,\frac{n}{n-1}\,N\left\{\frac{(P_2V_2-P_3V_3')+(P_3V_3-P_1V_1)}{33,000}\right\},$$

and the ideal isothermal horse-power of the *single-acting* single-stage compressor will be given by the numerical formula

$$=\frac{NP_1V_1}{33{,}000}\log_\varepsilon\left(\frac{P_2}{P_1}\right),$$

where P is the number of Lb./ft.² abs., V is the number of cu. ft. and N the number of r.p.m.

Condition for Minimum Work.—In a two-stage air compressor the pressures P_1 and P_2 are usually fixed, being the pressure of atmospheric air and that to which it is desired to compress. The pressure P_3 in the intercooler depends upon the design of the compressor, and can be arranged so that the work done is the minimum possible for compressing air from P_1 to P_2.

To find P_3 such that the work done in a compressor (based on the hypothetical indicator diagrams of fig. 15.6 in which the temperature of the air at the beginning of compression in both stages is on the same isothermal) is a minimum, take the expression representing hypothetical work done per cycle, namely,

$$\frac{n}{n-1}\left\{(P_2V_2-P_3V_3')+(P_3V_3-P_1V_1)\right\},$$

and express it as a function of P_3; then differentiate with respect to P_3, and equate to zero to find the condition for a minimum.

Thus, the hypothetical work done per cycle

$$=\frac{n}{n-1}P_1V_1\left\{\frac{P_2V_2}{P_3V_3'}+\frac{P_3V_3}{P_1V_1}-2\right\}$$

since $P_1V_1=P_3V_3'$. Therefore, since

$$\frac{V_2}{V_3'}=\left(\frac{P_3}{P_2}\right)^{\frac{1}{n}} \text{ and } \left(\frac{V_3}{V_1}\right)=\left(\frac{P_1}{P_3}\right)^{\frac{1}{n}},$$

the hypothetical work done per cycle is

$$W=\frac{n}{n-1}P_1V_1\left\{\left(\frac{P_3}{P_2}\right)^{\frac{1}{n}-1}+\left(\frac{P_3}{P_1}\right)^{1-\frac{1}{n}}-2\right\}$$

$$\therefore \frac{dW}{dP_3}=\frac{n}{n-1}P_1V_1\left\{\left(\frac{1-n}{n}\right)\left(\frac{1}{P_2}\right)^{\frac{1-n}{n}}(P_3)^{\frac{1-2n}{n}}+\left(\frac{n-1}{n}\right)\left(\frac{1}{P_1}\right)^{\frac{n-1}{n}}(P_3)^{-\frac{1}{n}}\right\}$$

$$=0 \text{ when } \frac{P_3^{\,1-2n}}{P_2^{\,1-n}}=\frac{P_3^{\,-1}}{P_1^{\,n-1}}, \text{ or when } (P_3)^{2(1-n)}=(P_1P_2)^{1-n}$$

that is, when $\mathbf{P_3=\sqrt{P_1P_2}}$ **or when** $\mathbf{\frac{P_2}{P_3}=\frac{P_3}{P_1}}$. From this we deduce that

$$\frac{T_2}{T_3'}=\frac{T_3}{T_1} \quad\text{or}\quad T_2-T_1=T_3-T_1 \text{ if } T_3'=T_1,$$

i.e. the rise in temperature due to compression is the same in each cylinder.

This would be the condition for minimum work if the two-stage compressor could trace the P,V diagram of fig. 15.6 in which there is complete intercooling, and the work done in each cylinder would be the same namely

$$Rm \frac{n}{n-1}(T_3-T_1) \text{ per cycle.}$$

Similarly, if a three-stage reciprocating-piston compressor could work according to fig. 15·5, the condition for minimum work would be

$$\frac{P_4}{P_3}=\frac{P_3}{P_2}=\frac{P_2}{P_1}$$

and this relationship can be extended to any number of stages in which the commencement of compression in each stage is on the same isothermal and clearance volumes are neglected.

Example 1.—A two-stage air compressor takes in 50 cu. ft. of air per minute at 14·7 Lb. per sq. in. abs. and delivers it into a reservoir at 2,000 Lb. per sq. in. abs. after the second compression.

The air is cooled between the two stages in an intercooler to its original temperature. Find the pressure in the intercooler if the work done is to be a minimum, and the horse-power required to drive the compressor if the law of compression is $PV^{1\cdot 3}$=constant in the two stages. Clearance volumes may be neglected. Assume a mechanical efficiency of 80 per cent.

Referring to fig. 15.6, in which the air is cooled in the intercooler to its original temperature, the intermediate pressure $P_3=\sqrt{P_1P_2}$ for minimum work.

$$\therefore\ P_3=\sqrt{14\cdot 7\times 2000}$$

$$=171\cdot 3 \text{ Lb. per sq. in. abs.}$$

$$\frac{V_3}{V_1}=\left(\frac{P_1}{P_3}\right)^{\frac{1}{n}}=\left(\frac{14\cdot 7}{171\cdot 3}\right)^{\frac{1}{1\cdot 3}}$$

$$\therefore\ V_3=50\ \frac{\text{ft.}^3}{\text{min.}}\times\left(\frac{14\cdot 7}{171\cdot 3}\right)^{\frac{1}{1\cdot 3}}=7\cdot 574 \text{ cu. ft. per min.}$$

The hypothetical work done in the low pressure cylinder

$$=\frac{n}{n-1}(P_3V_3-P_1V_1)$$

$$=\frac{1\cdot 3}{0\cdot 3}\,144(171\cdot 3\times 7\cdot 574-14\cdot 7\times 50)\ \frac{\text{Lb.}}{\text{ft.}^2}\times\frac{\text{ft.}^3}{\text{min.}}$$

$$=352{,}000 \text{ ft.-Lb. per min.}$$

The hypothetical work done in the high pressure cylinder will be found to be the same as that done in the low-pressure cylinder.

∴ Total work done in the two stages=704,000 ft.-Lb./min. Hence, the brake horse-power of the motor required to drive the compressor when assumed working on the hypothetical cycle shown in fig. 15·6 is

$$\frac{704{,}000}{0\cdot 8}\ \frac{\text{ft.-Lb.}}{\text{min.}}\left[\frac{\text{h-p.-min.}}{33{,}000 \text{ ft.-Lb.}}\right]=26\cdot 6 \text{ h-p.}$$

In reciprocating air compressors isothermal conditions can be approached by means of water jackets round the cylinders and especially on the cylinder covers, since the highest temperatures occur at the ends of the stroke. The cooling effect of the jackets is small, however, compared with that obtained by compression stages with an intercooler between each stage.

As will be seen from the theory of the two-stage air compressor, mechanical and thermodynamical considerations require that the work done shall be divided equally between the two stages in order to obtain greatest efficiency. It is not usually practicable, however, to make the intercooler big enough to cool the air to the original inlet temperature before entering the high-pressure cylinder, and therefore, in order to avoid a high final temperature in the h.p. cylinder, it is usual to design for only about 40 per cent. of the total work to be done in that cylinder in a two-stage compressor.

Clearance volume is, of course, kept down to a minimum, because the air in this space expands and reduces the volumetric efficiency (as seen on p. 315). For maximum volumetric efficiency the air in the clearance space should be made to expand reversibly and adiabatically, but little can be done towards ensuring this.

The valves fitted to compressors are automatic on both suction and delivery sides, and are placed in the cylinder covers whenever possible so as to minimise clearance space (see fig. 15.1). This, however, reduces the cooling surface on the cylinder covers where the highest temperature occurs at the end of the piston stroke.

Example 2.—The air in a compressor taking in 400 cu. ft. of air per minute at 60° F. and 14·7 Lb. per sq. in. abs. is cooled during compression by spraying water at 60° F. into the cylinder. The resulting law of compression for the air is $PV^{1\cdot 2}=c$, and the delivery pressure is 115 Lb. per sq. in. abs. It may be assumed that the only effect of the water is to cool the air, and that it remains as water droplets in the air. How much water (lb. per min.) will be required? Any formula for the heat taken in by the air must be proved. C_v for air is 0·171 B.Th.U./lb. ° F. [I.Mech.E., Sec. A.]

If ① and ② represent the states at the beginning and end of compression, respectively, as in fig. 15.2, then

$$\frac{T_2}{T_1}=\left(\frac{P_2}{P_1}\right)^{\frac{n-1}{n}}=(7\cdot 825)^{\frac{1}{6}}=1\cdot 409 \text{ and } T_2=1\cdot 409\times 520=733° \text{ abs. F.}$$

The mass of air compressed is

$$m=\frac{P_1V_1}{RT_1}=(144\times 14\cdot 7)\ \frac{\text{Lb.}}{\text{ft.}^2}\times 400\ \frac{\text{ft.}^3}{\text{min.}}\times\frac{1}{53\cdot 3}\ \frac{\text{lb. °F.}}{\text{ft.-Lb.}}\times\frac{1}{520°\text{ F.}}$$

$$=30\cdot 5 \text{ lb./min.}$$

Restating the first law of thermodynamics to apply to the air being compressed, we may write:

$$[-\delta Q]=[-\delta W]-[\delta E]$$

or, in words: Heat abstracted from air

$$=[\text{Work done on air}]-[\text{Increase in internal energy of air}]$$

$$=\left\{\frac{Rm}{(n-1)}(T_2-T_1)\right\}-\left\{mC_v(T_2-T_1)\right\}$$

$$=m(T_2-T_1)\left\{\frac{R}{(n-1)}-C_v\right\}$$

If this heat is abstracted by water flowing at a rate w the temperature of which rises by (T_2-T_1), then the mass of water required is given by

$$w\times s=m\left\{\frac{R}{(n-1)}-C_v\right\}$$

$$=30\cdot5\frac{\text{lb.}}{\text{min.}}\left\{\frac{1}{0\cdot2}53\cdot3\frac{\text{ft.-Lb.}}{\text{lb. °F.}}\left[\frac{\text{B.Th.U.}}{778\text{ ft.-Lb.}}\right]-0\cdot171\frac{\text{B.Th.U.}}{\text{lb. °F.}}\right\}$$

$$\text{i.e. } w\times\frac{1\text{ B.Th.U.}}{\text{lb. °F.}}=5\cdot25\frac{\text{B.Th.U.}}{\text{min. °F.}}$$

$$\text{or } w=5\cdot25\text{ lb./min.}$$

3. Report on Test of a Single-stage Single-acting Air Compressor

OBJECT OF TEST

To test the performance of the compressor as regards air delivery, volumetric efficiency and isothermal efficiency when the compressor is delivering against a constant pressure. Also, to draw up a heat account for the test.

THE PLANT

(a) *Diagrammatic Sketch or Line Diagram.*

The plant under test has been enclosed within a boundary in fig. 15.7. The mechanical energy entering the boundary from the

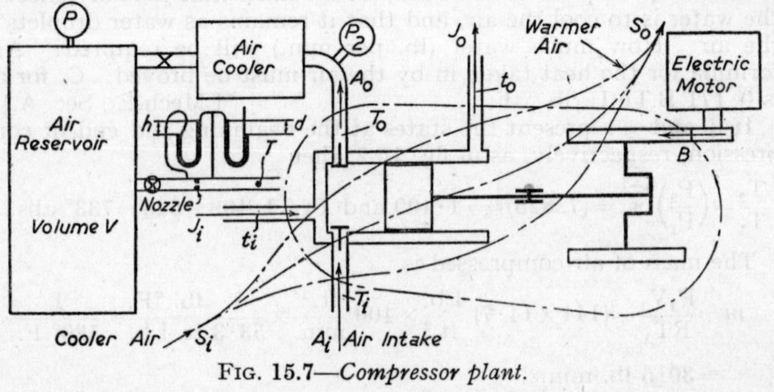

FIG. 15.7—*Compressor plant.*

motor is transformed into pressure energy and heat. The energy streams flowing into and out of the boundary are indicated by means of arrows attached to which are letters representing the rate at which energy is entering or leaving the boundary in each particular stream.

When the plant has been running for a time sufficient for conditions to have become steady, then, by the law of conservation energy, the rate at which energy flows along the streams into the boundary must be equal to the rate of flow of energy along the outgoing streams. Thus, we deduce the energy equation:

$$B+A_i+J_i+S_i=A_o+J_o+S_o$$

which, when re-arranged becomes:

$$B=(A_o-A_i)+(J_o-J_i)+(S_o-S_i)$$

This latter equation can be shown on an energy stream diagram as follows.

(*b*) *Energy Stream Diagram for the Plant in, say, B.Th.U. per minute.*

ENERGY SUPPLIED BY MOTOR

(Stream B)

[Heat equivalent of b.h.p. of motor]

ENERGY IMPARTED TO AIR	HEAT GAINED BY COOLING WATER	HEAT GAINED BY SURROUNDING AIR
(Stream (A_o-A_i))	(Stream (J_o-J_i))	(Stream (S_o-S_i))
[Mass of air per min. $\times C_p \times (T_o-T_i)$]	[Mass of water per min. $\times$ sp. ht $\times (t_o-t_i)$]	[Obtained by difference]

Also, we may note:

POWER SUPPLIED

[B.h.p. of electric motor]

POWER INDICATED IN COMPRESSOR CYLINDER	POWER ABSORBED IN FRICTION
[Air h.p. of compressor]	[F.h.p. of compressor]

(*c*) *Description of Plant and Method of Testing.*—The compressor tested was a single-stage single-acting reciprocating-piston type driven by an electric motor through reduction gearing.

A charge of air taken from the atmosphere each cycle was delivered at pressure P_2, which could be controlled by regulation of the needle valve opening the reservoir to the nozzle pipe through which the air flows back into the atmosphere.

The air delivered by the compressor at temperature T_o was passed through a cooler in order to reduce the temperature of the air before it entered the air reservoir. The temperatures of the air T_i and T_o at intake and delivery from the compressor, and the rate of flow of cooling water and its inlet and outlet temperatures t_i and t_o were noted. The amount of air delivered was estimated from observations of head of water h over a standard nozzle, temperature t of the air and head d below atmospheric pressure on the downstream side. When conditions had become steady for the particular setting of the needle valve, observations were made simultaneously on all instruments every two minutes over the period of the trial which, in this case, was of 16 minutes duration. The mean values of the observations and the resulting calculated figures were entered on the report sheet.

REPORT SHEET FOR TRIAL OF SINGLE-STAGE SINGLE-ACTING AIR COMPRESSOR

Plant data: Stroke of piston 4 in. Piston diameter 3 in.
Duration of test: 16 min.

Energy Supplied by Motor.		
Speed of compressor	r.p.m.	700
Power supplied	kilowatts	2·25
Horse power supplied	h.p.	3·01
Equivalent heat energy supplied	B.Th.U./min.	127·5
Jacket Water.		
Rate of flow of cooling water	lb./min.	1·25
Inlet temperature, t_i	°F.	53
Outlet temperature, t_o	°F.	105·6
Heat carried away by jacket cooling water	B.Th.U./min.	65·75
Air Measurements.		
Absolute temperature of air entering compressor, T_i,	°abs. F.	515·5
Absolute temperature air of leaving compressor, T_o,	°abs. F.	738·3
Height of barometer $B = m_i$	inches of mercury	30·19
Pressure of atmosphere, $P_a = 0 \cdot 49\, m_i$.	Lb./in.² abs.	14·8
Gauge pressure of air delivered	Lb./in.²	80·0
Absolute pressure of air delivered, P_2	Lb./in.₂ abs.	94·8
Pressure difference over nozzle, h	in. of water	5·0
Pressure below atmospheric on downstream side, d	in. of water	1·45

Absolute pressure of air on downstream side $\left(m_i - \frac{d}{13 \cdot 6}\right) = m_o$	in. of mercury	30·08
Absolute temperature on downstream side, T	°abs. F.	515·5
Volume of free atmospheric air delivered, $V = C\,\frac{T_i}{m_i}\sqrt{\left(\frac{hm_o}{T}\right)}$	ft.³ /min.	7·23
Mass of air delivered, m	lb./min.	0·561
Energy imparted to air, $mC_p(T_o - T_i)$	B.Th.U./min.	29·8

Heat Account.	B.Th.U./min	Per cent.
Energy supplied (Stream B)	127·5	100·0
Energy imparted to air $(A_o - A_i)$	29·8	23·4
Energy carried away by jacket water $(J_o - J_i)$	65·8	51·6
Energy to surrounding air (by difference) $(S_o - S_i)$	31·9	25·0
Totals	127·5	100·0

Efficiencies and Deductions.		
Volumetric efficiency	per cent.	63
Overall isothermal efficiency	per cent.	28·8
Volume of free atmospheric air delivered per h.p.-hour	ft.³	144
Kilowatts required per ft.³ /min. of free atmospheric air delivered	kilowatt	0·311
Mechanical energy required per ft.³ of free atmospheric delivered	ft.-Lb.	13,750

SPECIMEN SET OF CALCULATIONS

Energy Supplied.

Electrical power supplied

$$= 2 \cdot 25 \text{ kilowatts}\left[\frac{\text{h-p.}}{0 \cdot 746 \text{ k.-watt}}\right] = 3 \cdot 01 \text{ h.p.}$$

Hence, heat equivalent of rate of supply of energy is

$$3 \cdot 01 \text{ h.p.}\left[\frac{33{,}000 \text{ ft.-Lb.}}{\text{h-p. min.}}\right]\left[\frac{\text{B.Th.U.}}{778 \text{ ft.-Lb.}}\right] = 127 \cdot 5 \text{ B.Th.U./min.}$$

Jacket Water.

Rate of mass flow $= 0 \cdot 96$ lb./min.

Rise in temperature $(t_o - t_i) = 105 \cdot 6°\text{ F.} - 53°\text{ F.} = 52 \cdot 6°\text{ F.}$

Hence, heat carried away by cooling water

$$= 1 \cdot 25 \frac{\text{lb.}}{\text{min.}} \times \frac{1 \text{ B.Th.U.}}{\text{lb. °F.}} \times 52 \cdot 6°\text{ F.} = 65 \cdot 75 \text{ B.Th.U./min.}$$

Air Delivered.

The formula supplied as a result of calibration of the nozzle was a numerical formula giving volume of free atmospheric air per minute, namely:

$$V=0\cdot78\,\frac{T_i}{m_i}\sqrt{\frac{hm_o}{T}}=0\cdot78\times\frac{515\cdot5}{30\cdot19}\sqrt{\frac{5\cdot0\times30\cdot08}{515\cdot5}}=7\cdot23\text{ ft.}^3\text{/min.}$$

This volume has a mass

$$m=\frac{P_aV}{RT_a}=\frac{(144\times14\cdot8)\,\frac{\text{Lb.}}{\text{ft}^2}\times7\cdot23\,\frac{\text{ft.}^3}{\text{min.}}}{53\cdot3\,\frac{\text{ft.-Lb.}}{\text{lb.}^\circ\text{ F.}}\times515\cdot5^\circ\text{ abs. F.}}=0\cdot561\text{ lb./min.}$$

The energy imparted to the air by the compressor is equal to the difference in total heat (or enthalpy) of the air at outlet and inlet, *i.e.* (H_o-H_i). But since, by definition, $H=E+PV=E+RT$ for unit mass of air, then $\delta H=\delta E+R\delta T=(C_v+R)\delta T=C_p\delta T$.

Hence, $H_o-H_i=mC_p(T_o-T_i)$

$$=0\cdot561\,\frac{\text{lb.}}{\text{min.}}\times0\cdot238\,\frac{\text{B.Th.U.}}{\text{lb. }^\circ\text{F.}}\times(738\cdot3-515\cdot5)^\circ\text{ F.}$$

$$=29\cdot8\text{ B.Th.U./min.}$$

Efficiencies and Deductions.

Suction volume swept by piston

$$=\frac{\pi}{4}\times9\text{ in.}^2\times4\text{ in.}\times\frac{700}{\text{min.}}\left[\frac{\text{ft.}^3}{1728\text{ in.}^3}\right]=11\cdot45\text{ ft.}^3\text{/min.}$$

Hence, volumetric efficiency $=\frac{7\cdot23}{11\cdot45}=0\cdot63$ or 63 per cent.

Ideal isothermal power based on free atmospheric air delivered

$$=P_aV\log_\varepsilon\frac{P_2}{P_a}=(14\cdot8\times144)\,\frac{\text{Lb.}}{\text{ft.}^2}\times7\cdot23\,\frac{\text{ft.}^3}{\text{min.}}\times\log_\varepsilon\left(\frac{94\cdot8}{14\cdot8}\right)$$

$$=28{,}600\,\frac{\text{ft.-Lb.}}{\text{min.}}\left[\frac{\text{B.Th.U.}}{778\text{ ft.-Lb.}}\right]=36\cdot7\text{ B.Th.U./min.}$$

Hence, overall isothermal efficiency

$$=\frac{\text{ideal isothermal power}}{\text{power supplied to plant}}$$

$$=\frac{36\cdot7\text{ B.Th.U./min.}}{127\cdot5\text{ B.Th.U./min.}}=0\cdot288\text{ or }28\cdot8\text{ per cent.}$$

Volume of free atmospheric air delivered per horse-power-hour of energy supplied

$$=7\cdot23\,\frac{\text{ft.}^3}{\text{min.}}\times\frac{1}{3\cdot01\text{ h.p.}}\left[\frac{60\text{ min.}}{\text{hour}}\right]=144\,\frac{\text{ft.}^3}{\text{h.p.-hour}}$$

Kilowatts of electrical energy supplied per cu. ft. of free atmospheric air delivered per minute

$$=\frac{2\cdot 25 \text{ kilowatts}}{7\cdot 23 \text{ ft.}^3/\text{min.}}=0\cdot 311\ \frac{\text{kilowatt min.}}{\text{ft.}^3}$$

Mechanical energy required per cu. ft. of free atmospheric air delivered

$$=0\cdot 311\ \frac{\text{kilowatt min.}}{\text{ft.}^3}\left[\frac{\text{h-p.}}{0\cdot 746 \text{ k-watt}}\right]\left[\frac{33{,}000 \text{ ft.-Lb.}}{\text{h-p. min.}}\right]$$

$$=13{,}75 \text{ ft.-Lb./ft.}^3$$

GRAPHICAL REPRESENTATION OF RESULTS

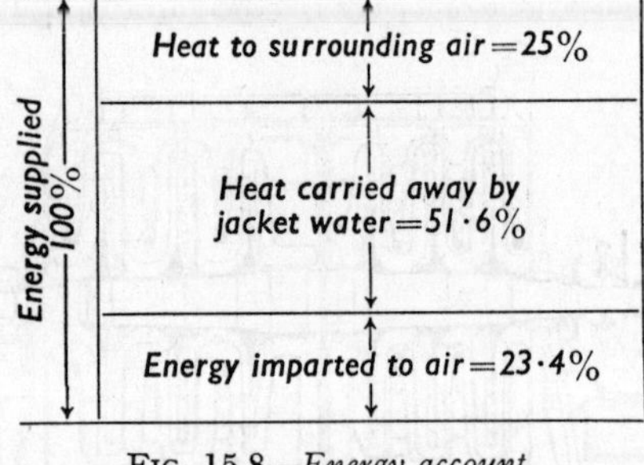

FIG. 15.8—*Energy account.*

CONCLUSIONS AND CRITICISMS

It will be noticed from the heat account on the report sheet and from fig. 15.8, which represents the heat account graphically, that the largest proportion of the energy supplied is carried away by the circulating water which cools the cylinder of the compressor of some of the heat of compression. Piston friction, or the friction between the cylinder walls and the sliding piston, generates heat, some of which appears in the cooling water. Piston friction is relatively large in small machines such as this, and is therefore more conspicuous than in large machines.

It should be noted that because an accurate figure for the efficiency of the electric motor and gearing is not known the energy supplied, as used in the calculations, is not that supplied to the crankshaft of the compressor but is the electrical energy supplied to the motor. This, however, is what has to be paid for in practice, and the figures resulting from the electrical energy input to the plant are those which matter commercially. The isothermal efficiency is low, and suggests that the plant should be tuned up. Also, the plant should be tested over a range of delivery pressures and performance curves obtained. The most important measuring device on the plant is that from which the amount of air delivered is calculated, namely, the nozzle and its manometer gauges. It is suggested that the constant in the formula used may not be quite correct. The nozzle and gauge might well be sent to the N.P.L. for recalibration against direct observations made on an air reservoir of the gasometer type.

4. Rotary compressors or Turbo-compressors.—Rotary or turbo-compressors deal with larger volumes of air per minute than is possible in reciprocating compressors but usually at lower delivery pressures. Rotary compressors or blowers are

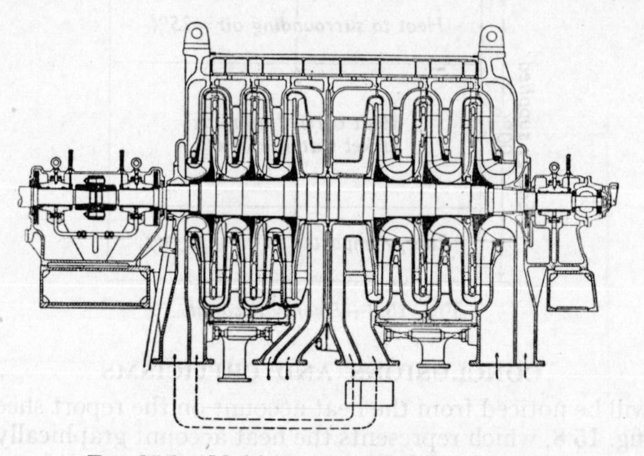

FIG. 15.9—*Multi-stage centrifugal compressor.*

capable of running at high speeds, and are suitable for direct coupling to steam turbines, electric motors, and high-speed internal-combustion engines. They are usually multi-stage machines of the centrifugal or axial-flow types as shown in figs. 2.21 and 2.20. In the centrifugal type a single impeller as in fig. 2.21, or a series of impellers as in fig. 15.9 are mounted on the same rotor which revolves at a high speed in an appropriate casing. Air from the atmosphere enters the eye of the first impeller and then, at successively higher pressures, the eyes of a series of impellers in turn. In each impeller the air acquires pressure and velocity before being flung off into stationary diffuser vanes which transform kinetic energy into pressure energy and, at the same time, direct the air delivered from one impeller into the channel leading to the eye of the next impeller in which the operation is repeated at a higher pressure. Finally, after passing through several stages and, maybe, one or more intercoolers, the air is delivered at a pressure depending upon the speed, size, and number of impellers. Fig. 15.9 shows a section through a six-stage centrifugal compressor requiring 10,000 horse-power to deliver 62,000 cu. ft. per min. at 55 Lb. per sq. in., there being one intercooler after three stages. The blades of the impellers are bent to the form required by the speed of rotation, as also are the blades of the diffusers which receive the air from the impellers.

Turbo-blowers have a low compression ratio—delivering several thousand cu. ft. of air per minute at 2 to 20 Lb. per sq. in. gauge pressure—and are suitable for such purposes as supplying air to furnaces, cupolas, mines, etc.

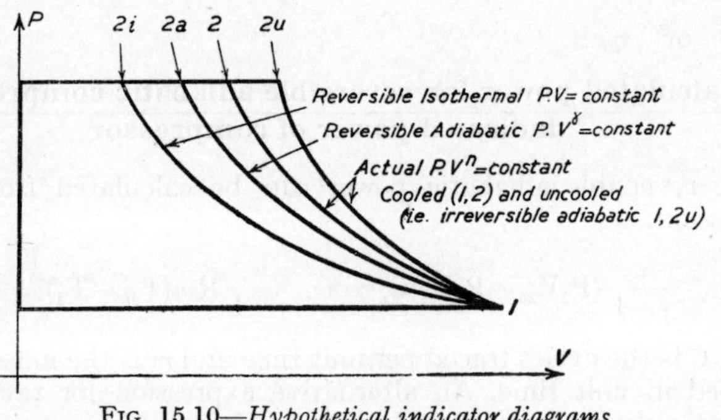

FIG. 15.10—*Hypothetical indicator diagrams.*

Rotary compressors of the axial flow and centrifugal types are capable of delivering at pressures from 60 to 100 Lb. per sq. in. after a relatively large number of stages unless the speeds are very high as in gas-turbine plant. Passages in the casing are usually water-cooled, and one or two intercoolers may also be provided according to size of compressor. Such compressors deliver air at a uniform rate without the large receiver which is needed between the compressor and the air main of a reciprocating-piston compressor. The volumetric efficiency of turbo-compressors may be defined as the ratio:

$$\frac{\text{equivalent volume of free atmospheric air finally delivered}}{\text{volume of free atmospheric air entering the suction tube}}.$$

Although minimum work and, therefore, ideal compression is achieved when compression follows the isothermal curve 1-2*i* of fig. 15.10, compression in rotary compressors is often more usefully compared with the reversible (*i.e.* ideal-frictionless) adiabatic compression curve 1-2*a* since, in rotary compressors, the actual compression 1-2 may be, and usually is, to the right of the curve 1-2*a*. If actual compression were uncooled (*i.e.* heat-insulated or irreversible adiabatic) the curve 1-2*u* would be traced. In these cases n would be greater than γ owing to the friction between fast-moving air and the surfaces of the passages, viscous resistance between air particles, eddy heat, and shock due to sudden changes of velocity, all of which help to increase the temperature and volume of the air to a value greater than would be produced by reversible adiabatic compression alone. Thus, in a way analogous to that in which "isothermal efficiency" was defined on p. 312, we may define the "adiabatic efficiency" of compression in a rotary or turbo-compressor as

$$\eta_{adiab} \text{ or } \eta_a = \frac{\textbf{calculated power for reversible adiabatic compression}}{\textbf{indicated power of compressor}}$$

The reversible adiabatic power can be calculated from the expression:

$$\frac{\gamma}{\gamma-1}(P_2V_{2a}-P_1V_1)C, \quad \text{or} \quad \frac{\gamma}{\gamma-1}Rm(T_{2a}-T_1),$$

where C is the cycles traced per unit time and m is the mass of air pumped in unit time. An alternative expression for reversible adiabatic power is $m(H_{2a}-H_1)$, where H_1 and H_{2a} are the total heats or enthalpies per unit mass of air before and after reversible adiabatic compression, respectively. The latter expression can be deduced from the former since

$$\frac{\gamma R}{\gamma-1}=C_p, \quad \text{and} \quad C_p(T_{2a}-T_1)=(H_{2a}-H_1)$$

as indicated on p. 326.

Thus, when based on the hypothetical indicated power calculated from the diagram of fig. 15.10, the adiabatic efficiency,

$$\eta_{adiab}=\frac{\frac{\gamma}{\gamma-1}(P_2V_{2a}-P_1V_1)}{\frac{n}{n-1}(P_2V_2-P_1V_1)}=\frac{\frac{\gamma}{\gamma-1}(T_{2a}-T_1)}{\frac{n}{n-1}(T_2-T_1)}$$

but when based on the power required to drive an uncooled rotary compressor, in which all the energy supplied goes to increase the total heat of the air during its passage from inlet to outlet, the adiabatic efficiency is given by the expression:

$$\eta_{adiab}=\frac{\text{energy required for reversible adiabatic compression}}{\text{energy required for actual (\textit{i.e.} irreversible) adiabatic compression}}$$

$$\text{or } \eta_a=\frac{H_{2a}-H_1}{H_{2u}-H_1}=\frac{T_{2a}-T_1}{T_{2u}-T_1},$$

where $(H_{2u}-H_1)$ and $(T_{2u}-T_1)$ represent the increase in total heat and temperature, respectively, of unit mass of air in passing from inlet to outlet through an uncooled blower or rotary com pressor, and $(H_{2a}-H_1)$ and $(T_{2a}-T_1)$ represent the increases which would have occurred had the compression been reversible and adiabatic (see also p. 477).

The overall performance of compressors—rotary and reciprocating—as regards the power required to drive them compared with the power needed to drive the ideal compressor may be measured by the ratio:

$$\frac{\textbf{calculated power for isothermal compression}}{\textbf{shaft power required}}={}_o\eta_{iso}$$

the "overall isothermal efficiency," as on p. 313.

If, however, it is more convenient to compare the shaft power required to drive a rotary compressor with the power required for reversible adiabatic compression, the "overall adiabatic efficiency" may be defined as:

$${}_o\eta_{adiab}=\frac{\textbf{calculated power for reversible adiabatic compression}}{\textbf{shaft power required}}$$

Thus, ${}_o\eta_{adiab}=\eta_{adiab}\times\eta_m$ in the same way as ${}_o\eta_{iso}=\eta_{iso}\times\eta_m$ (proved on p. 313).

Example 1.—An uncooled blower absorbs 100 horse-power when delivering air with a rise in temperature of 110° F. due to passing through the blower. If loss of heat to surrounding air and difference in kinetic energy of the air at inlet and outlet can be neglected, calculate the mass and the s.t.p. volume of air delivered per minute and per horse-power-hour. C_p for air is 0·24 B.Th.U. per lb. °F.

The energy streams of a compressor or blower, which is cooled are shown diagrammatically in fig. 15.11. Thus, assuming that the blower has been running long enough for steady conditions to have been achieved, the rate of flow of energy into the boundary enclosing

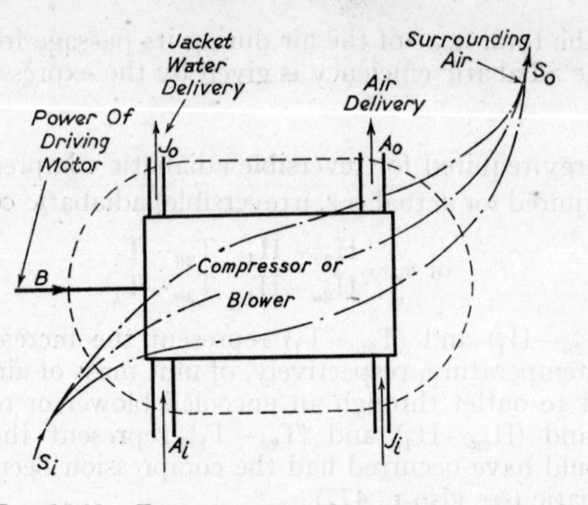

FIG. 15.11—*Energy streams of a compressor or blower.*

the blower must be equal to the rate of flow of energy leaving the boundary, as shown by the equation:

$$B + A_i + J_i + S_i = A_o + J_o + S_o$$

which, when rearranged, becomes:

$$B = (A_o - A_i) + (J_o - J_i) + (S_o - S_i) = (A_o - A_i) + Q_c$$

where Q_c is the cooling achieved by the jacket water and surrounding air. If, however, it is assumed that the blower is uncooled, then $Q_c = 0$, and the energy equation for the uncooled blower becomes $B = (A_o - A_i)$ which, when translated into words, states that the rate at which mechanical energy is supplied to drive the blower is the rate at which energy is received (total heat and kinetic energy) by the air during compression. That is, per unit mass of air:

$$B_u = (H_o - H_i) + \left(\frac{v_o^2 - v_i^2}{2}\right),$$

where H and v represent total heat per unit mass and velocity of air, respectively. If, however, the gain in kinetic energy of the air $\left(\frac{v_o^2 - v_i^2}{2}\right)$, can be neglected, the energy equation reduces to:

$$B_u = (H_o - H_i) = C_P(T_o - T_i),$$

as proved on page 326. In this example,

$$C_P(T_o - T_i) = 0 \cdot 24 \text{ B.Th.U./lb. °F.} \times 110° \text{ F.} = 26 \cdot 4 \text{ B.Th.U. per lb.}$$

and the mechanical energy input is equivalent to

$$100 \text{ h-p.} \left[\frac{33{,}000 \text{ ft.-Lb.}}{\text{h.p. min.}}\right]\left[\frac{\text{B.Th.U.}}{778 \text{ ft.-Lb.}}\right] = 4240 \text{ B.Th.U. per min.}$$

Hence, the mass of air delivered

$$=4240\,\frac{\text{B.Th.U.}}{\text{min.}}\;\frac{1}{26\cdot4}\,\frac{\text{lb.}}{\text{B.Th.U.}}=160\text{ lb. per min.}$$

Thus, the s.t.p. volume of air delivered

$$=V=\frac{RmT}{P}=53\cdot3\,\frac{\text{ft.-Lb.}}{\text{lb. °F.}}\times160\,\frac{\text{lb.}}{\text{min.}}\times\frac{492°\text{ F. ft.}^2}{144\times14\cdot7\text{ Lb.}}=1985\text{ ft.}^3\text{/min.}$$

Thus, 100 h-p. or 3,300,000 ft.-Lb./min. deliver the equivalent s.t.p. volume of air at the rate of 1,985 ft.³/min., hence, 1 h.p.-hour or 1,986,000 ft.-Lb. of work delivers

$$1985\,\frac{\text{ft.}^3}{\text{min}}\times\frac{1}{3{,}300{,}000}\,\frac{\text{min.}}{\text{ft. Lb.}}\times1{,}986{,}000\text{ ft.-Lb.}=1191\text{ ft}^3$$

Example 2.—A blower takes in air from the atmosphere at 519° abs. F. and 14·7 Lb. per sq. in. abs. and delivers 7,200 lb. per hour at 667° abs. F. and 29·4 Lb. per sq. in. abs. The blower is uncooled, and it may be assumed that no heat is lost to the surrounding air.

Calculate: (i) the temperature which the air would have achieved if the compression had been reversible and adiabatic, taking $\gamma=1\cdot4$,

(ii) the adiabatic efficiency,

(iii) the index n in the law of compression PV^n=constant;

(iv) the horse-power required to drive the blower, taking $C_P=0\cdot24$ B.Th.U./lb. ° F., and

(v) the equivalent volume of atmospheric air delivered per horse-power-hour.

(i) Referring to fig. 15.10, the temperature of the air if compression had been reversible and adiabatic, would have been

$$T_{2a}=T_1\left(\frac{P_2}{P_1}\right)^{\frac{\gamma-1}{\gamma}}=519\left(2\right)^{\frac{0\cdot4}{1\cdot4}}=632°\text{ abs. F. or }172°\text{ F.}$$

(ii) Thus, the adiabatic efficiency,

$$\eta_a=\frac{T_{2a}-T_1}{T_{2u}-T_1}=\frac{632-519}{667-519}=0\cdot764\text{ or }76\cdot4\text{ per cent.}$$

(iii) The curve 1-2u on fig. 15.10 represents the compression of the uncooled air according to the law PV^n=const.

Therefore, $\dfrac{T_{2u}}{T_1}=\left(\dfrac{P_2}{P_1}\right)^{\frac{n-1}{n}}$.

Hence, $$\frac{n-1}{n}=\frac{\log T_{2u}-\log T_1}{\log P_2-\log P_1}=\frac{\log 667-\log 519}{\log 29\cdot4-\log 14\cdot7}=0\cdot362$$

and $n=1\cdot566$.

(iv) From the previous example we take the fact that the rate at which mechanical energy is supplied to the uncooled blower is equal to the rate at which energy is received by the air being compressed, *i.e.* $B_u=(H_{2u}-H_1)=C_P(T_{2u}-T_1)$ per unit mass, neglecting the difference in kinetic energy of the air entering and leaving the blower, Thus, if m is the rate at which air is delivered, the power required to drive the uncooled blower is

$$mB_u = mC_P(T_{2u} - T_1)$$

$$= \frac{7200 \text{ lb.}}{60 \text{ min.}} \times 0{\cdot}24 \frac{\text{B.Th.U.}}{\text{lb. °F.}} \times (667-519)° \text{ F.}$$

$$= 120 \times 0{\cdot}24 \times 148 \frac{\text{B.Th.U.}}{\text{min.}} \left[\frac{778 \text{ ft.-Lb.}}{\text{B.Th.U.}}\right]\left[\frac{\text{h.p. min.}}{33{,}000 \text{ ft.-Lb.}}\right]$$

$$= 100 \text{ h.p.}$$

(v) The equivalent volume of atmospheric air delivered is

$$53{\cdot}3 \frac{\text{ft.-Lb.}}{\text{lb. °F.}} \times 7200 \frac{\text{lb.}}{\text{hour}} \times \frac{519° \text{ F. ft.}^2}{14{\cdot}7 \times 144 \text{ Lb.}}$$

$$= 93{,}800 \frac{\text{ft.}^3}{\text{hour}}, \textit{ i.e. } 938 \text{ft.}^3/\text{h-p.-hour.}$$

Example 3.—Show that eddies, turbulence and friction, which cause irreversible compression, increase the amount of energy required for compression of air in an uncooled compressor above that required for reversible adiabatic compression.

The energy required per unit mass during uncooled irreversible compression is

$$B_u = C_P(T_{2u} - T_1) = \frac{\gamma}{\gamma - 1}(P_2V_{2u} - P_1V_1),$$

and during reversible adiabatic compression is

$$B_a = C_P(T_{2a} - T_1) = \frac{\gamma}{\gamma - 1}(P_2V_{2a} - P_1V_1)$$

$$\textit{i.e. } B_u = B_a + \frac{\gamma}{\gamma - 1}P_2(V_{2u} - V_{2a}) = B_a + C_P(T_{2u} - T_{2a})$$

Thus, because of irreversibility, the work (B_u) required for actual adiabatic (i.e. uncooled, signified by suffix u) compression of unit mass of gas is greater than that (B_a) required for reversible adiabatic compression by an amount equivalent to the friction heat, namely, $C_P(T_{2u} - T_{2a})$. *In other words, irreversibility leads to a wastage of mechanical energy or work.*

5. Air Motors.—There are many types of air motors fitted to the tools and mechanisms which use compressed air, each being specially designed for its particular job. Some are of the rotary type using air non-expansively.

Motors fitted with the ordinary steam engine valve gear can be made to do work if compressed air is supplied to them. Those having hypothetical indicator diagrams similar to that of fig. 14.2 (which neglects clearance) do an amount of work equal to

$$\frac{n}{n-1}(P_1V_1-P_2V_2)$$

per cycle. Thus, if the number of cycles traced in unit time is C, the hypothetical power developed is

$$C\frac{n}{n-1}(P_1V_1-P_2V_2).$$

If full expansion is not achieved the hypothetical indicator diagram will be as shown in fig. 15.12.

Unlike steam, compressed air cannot be used expansively unless pre-heated (e.g. by means of hot water), because any moisture present in the air would become frozen owing to the low temperature at the end of expansion (see p. 340) and the passages in the machine would be blocked with ice and snow. The efficiencies of motors using air non-expansively are of the order of 20 per cent. Thus, with an efficiency of 60 per cent. in a compressor, the overall efficiency for air or pneumatic transmission is only about 12 per cent. Compared with other forms of power transmission this is a poor performance, but there are several important reasons justifying the use of compressed air:

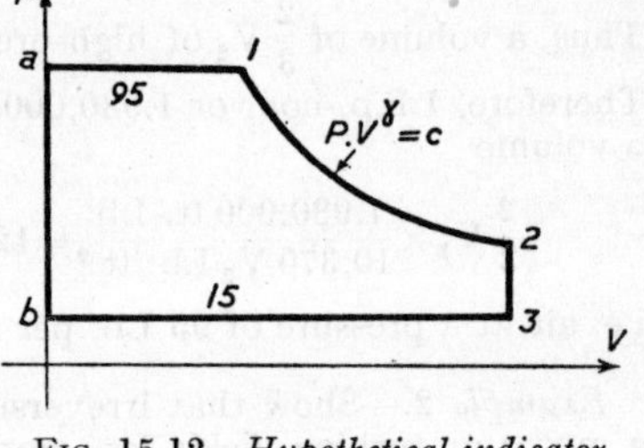

FIG. 15.12—*Hypothetical indicator diagram.*

(i) The undoubted convenience of compressed air for certain purposes, especially in tools of light construction. It has to be used in machinery down certain mines, in explosive factories, and in other places where risk of fire cannot be permitted.

(ii) Machinery using compressed air is comparatively light and capable of withstanding large overloads.

(iii) Such machinery costs little in maintenance and can be operated by semi-skilled labour.

Example 1.—Air at 95 Lb. per sq. in. abs. is supplied to the cylinder of a pneumatic tool. Cut-off occurs at two-thirds of the stroke and exhaust is at 15 Lb. per sq. in. abs. Assuming that the air expands reversibly and adiabatically, and neglecting clearance and throttling, calculate the mean effective pressure in the cylinder and the volume of air required per indicated horse-power-hour. The adiabatic index for air is $\gamma=1\cdot4$. [Part I, B.Sc. Lond.]

The indicator diagram of the motor of the tool will be *a*①②③*ba* of fig. 15.12, the m.e.p. of which $=\dfrac{\text{area}}{\text{stroke volume}}$.

Thus,

$$\text{m.e.p.}=\frac{P_1V_1+\left(\dfrac{P_1V_1-P_2V_2}{\gamma-1}\right)-P_3V_3}{V_3}=\frac{\gamma}{\gamma-1}\left(\frac{P_1}{r}\right)-\frac{P_2}{\gamma-1}-P_3,$$

$$\text{and } P_2=P_1\left(\frac{V_1}{V_2}\right)^{\gamma}=\frac{95}{1\cdot 764}=53\cdot 8 \text{ Lb. per sq. in. abs.}$$

$$\text{Hence, m.e.p.}=\frac{1\cdot 4}{0\cdot 4}\left(\frac{95}{1\cdot 5}\right)-\frac{53\cdot 8}{0\cdot 4}-15=72 \text{ lb. per sq. in.}$$

$$\text{Work done per cycle}=(\text{m.e.p.})\text{L.A.}=(144\times 72)\ \frac{\text{Lb.}}{\text{ft.}^2}\times V_2$$

Thus, a volume of $\frac{2}{3}\,V_2$ of high-pressure air does work $10{,}370\ V_2\ \frac{\text{Lb.}}{\text{ft.}^2}$

Therefore, 1 h.p.-hour or 1,980,000 ft.-Lb. of indicated work requires a volume

$$\frac{2}{3}\,V_2\times\frac{1{,}980{,}000 \text{ ft.-Lb.}}{10{,}370\ V_2 \text{ Lb./ft.}^2}=127 \text{ ft.}^3 \text{ of high-pressure air.}$$

i.e. air at a pressure of 95 Lb. per sq. in. abs.

Example 2.—Show that irreversible adiabatic expansion of gas in a motor or turbine yields less work than would be delivered if the expansion could be reversible and adiabatic.

If gas expands in a turbine from a state 1 to a state 2 the energy obtained from unit mass by irreversible adiabatic flow and expansion is

$$B_u=H_1-H_{2u}=C_P(T_1-T_{2u})=\frac{\gamma}{\gamma-1}\,(P_1V_1-P_2V_{2u})$$

whereas, if the expansion could be reversible and adiabatic the work obtained from unit mass would be

$$B_a=H_1-H_{2a}=C_P(T_1-T_{2a})=\frac{\gamma}{\gamma-1}\,(P_1V_1-P_2V_{2a})$$

$$\text{Hence, } B_u=B_a-\frac{\gamma}{\gamma-1}\,P_2(V_{2u}-V_{2a})=B_a-C_P(T_{2u}-T_{2a})$$

i.e., *due to irreversibility, the work or energy obtained from unit mass of gas during adiabatic expansion is reduced* by an amount $\frac{\gamma}{\gamma-1}\,P_2(V_{2u}-V_{2a})$ or $C_P(T_{2u}-T_{2a})$ which is equivalent to the " friction heat."

6. Joule's Air Engine.—In 1851 Joule invented the air engine shown diagrammatically in fig. 15.13. In effect it is a combination of an air motor and an air compressor.

Air at pressure P_1 is admitted from the hot chamber through the valve represented at A into the expansion cylinder. This admission is represented by *na* on the hypothetical P,V diagram of fig. 15.14. Cut-off occurs at *a*, and, for the remainder of the stroke, the air expands along *ab* until its pressure is P_2—its temperature then having dropped from T_a to T_b. At pressure P_2 the air is exhausted (*bm*) at temperature T_b into the cooler, and heat is abstracted from it by cooling water until its temperature has fallen from T_b to T_c. This results in the corresponding shrinkage in volume from *mb* to *mc*. Air, at pressure P_2 and temperature T_c, is then admitted to the compressor cylinder through valve C, as represented by the line *mc* on the hypothetical P,V diagram, fig. 15.14. In the compressor it is compressed (*cd*) to pressure P_1, when it is delivered (*dn*) into the hot chamber at temperature T_d. Heat is then supplied from an external source to raise temperature of the air from T_d to T_a. The same cycle of operations can then be repeated.

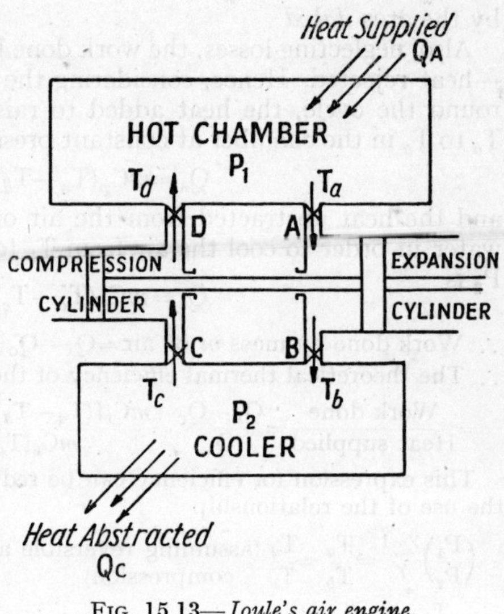

FIG. 15.13—*Joule's air engine.*

FIG. 15.14—*Hypothetical indicator diagram for Joule engine.*

It will be seen from fig. 15.14 that the work done *by* the air in the expansion cylinder is represented by the area *nabmn*, and the work done *on* the air in the compressor cylinder is represented by the area *mcdnm*. Thus, the net work done *by* the air is represented by the area *dabcd*.

Also, neglecting losses, the work done by the air = heat supplied —heat rejected. Hence, considering the passage of mass m of air round the cycle, the heat added to raise the temperature from T_d to T_a in the chamber at constant pressure P_1 is

$$Q_A = mC_p(T_a - T_d)$$

and the heat abstracted from the air or rejected to the cooling water in order to cool the air from T_b to T_c at constant pressure P_2 is

$$Q_C = mC_p(T_b - T_c)$$

$\therefore$ Work done by mass m of air $= Q_A - Q_C = mC_P[(T_a - T_d) - (T_b - T_c)]$

$\therefore$ The theoretical thermal efficiency of the engine

$$= \frac{\text{Work done}}{\text{Heat supplied}} = \frac{Q_A - Q_C}{Q_A} = \frac{mC_P[(T_a - T_d) - (T_b - T_c)]}{mC_P(T_a - T_d)} = 1 - \frac{(T_b - T_c)}{(T_a - T_d)}$$

This expression for efficiency can be reduced to a simpler form by the use of the relationship

$$\left(\frac{P_1}{P_2}\right)^{\frac{\gamma-1}{\gamma}} = \frac{T_a}{T_b} = \frac{T_d}{T_c}$$ (assuming reversible adiabatic expansion and compression)

$$\therefore \frac{T_b}{T_c} - 1 = \frac{T_a}{T_d} - 1$$

Subtracting unity from each side does not alter the equality of the equation but gives us the relationship we want, namely:

$$\frac{T_b - T_c}{T_a - T_d} = \frac{T_c}{T_d} = \frac{T_d}{T_a}$$

Hence, the theoretical efficiency of the engine

$$= 1 - \frac{T_b}{T_a} \quad \text{or} \quad 1 - \frac{T_c}{T_d}$$

$$= \frac{T_a - T_b}{T_a} \quad \text{or} \quad \frac{T_d - T_c}{T_d}$$

Air engines of the Joule type have been used for small powers, but for large powers such "externally fired" engines are inconvenient and bulky because of the large volumes of air with which they have to deal. Another drawback is that air is a bad conductor of heat, which means that the speed of such engines must necessarily be low.

It will be noticed that the working fluid (air) travels round a closed circuit in Joule's engine and that heat, Q_A, is supplied from an external source. Such "externally fired" engines are no longer used. The present-day method is to put the air and the source of heat inside the cylinder and so get an "internally fired" engine or internal-combustion engine.

The air and the source of heat in the internal-combustion engine are in direct contact, hence the best possible conductivity is obtained. Also, combustion takes place rapidly, and there is no great length of time to wait for heat transfer to the air, as in externally fired engines. There is also no question of cooling the air as in the Joule engine, for in internal-combustion engines the gases are exhausted into the atmosphere, and a fresh charge of air is taken in each cycle. Thus, the hot chamber, the cooler, and the compression cylinder, to be seen in Joule's engine, are done

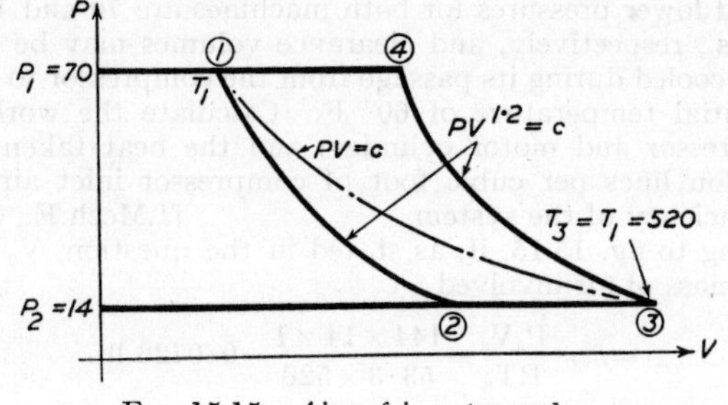

FIG. 15.15—*Air refrigerator cycle.*

away with, leaving only one cylinder as an internal-combustion engine. Because of quicker heat transfers, higher speeds can be obtained in internal combustion engines, and a great reduction in weight and size of engine is achieved for a given power.

The reason why an increase in speed usually results in a reduced weight can be seen from the physical formula for indicated power, namely, $\mathcal{P}_i$=PLAC. For, assuming the mean effective pressure, P, to remain approximately the same over a certain range of speed, then, for a definite power, if C be increased, the product LA can be reduced. Thus, increasing the speed of the engine means that the cylinder dimensions, L and A, can be reduced, and the weight per horse-power is consequently reduced.

The most important development from Joule's air engine was the internal-combustion engine. Another development from it was the Bell-Coleman air refrigerator, which works on Joule's cycle reversed.

Consider air at pressure P_1 and at atmospheric temperature T_1, as in fig. 15.15, expanded down to a pressure P_2 according to the law $PV^n=c$, then the temperature at the end of the expansion will be $T_2=\left(\frac{P_2}{P_1}\right)^{\frac{n-1}{n}} T_1$, which is less than the atmospheric temperature T_1 (see example below).

Thus, after expansion, the air is at a temperature less than that of atmospheric air and can, therefore, be used to cool things to a temperature below that of the atmosphere—that is, to produce a refrigerating effect. This principle is made use of in air refrigerators.

Example.—A system using compressed air for power transmission consists of a single-stage compressor and air motor both having mechanical efficiencies of 80 per cent., and in which compression and expansion take place according to the law $PV^{1\cdot 2}=c$. The higher and lower pressures for both machines are 70 and 14 Lb. per sq. in. abs., respectively, and clearance volumes may be neglected. The air is cooled during its passage from the compressor to the motor to the initial temperature of 60° F. Calculate the work done in the compressor and motor cylinders and the heat taken from the transmission lines per cubic foot of compressor inlet air, and the overall efficiency of the system. [I.Mech.E., Sec. A.]

Referring to fig. 15.15, if, as stated in the question, $V_3=1$ cu. ft. then the mass of air involved

$$=m=\frac{P_3V_3}{RT_3}=\frac{144\times 14\times 1}{53\cdot 3\times 520}=0\cdot 0726 \text{ lb.}$$

Also: $$\frac{T_4}{T_3}=\frac{T_1}{T_2}=\left(\frac{P_1}{P_2}\right)^{\frac{n-1}{n}}=\left(5\right)^{\frac{1}{6}}=1\cdot 3077.$$

Hence, $T_4=1\cdot 3077\times 520°$ abs. F. $=680°$ abs. F. or 220° F.

and $$T_2=\frac{520° \text{ abs. F.}}{1\cdot 3077}=398° \text{ abs. F. or } -52° \text{ F.}$$

Work done on air in compressor cylinder $=\frac{n}{n-1}(P_4V_4-P_3V_3)$

or $\frac{Rmn}{n-1}(T_4-T_3)=53\cdot 3\times 0\cdot 0726\times 6\times (680-520)=3{,}720$ ft.-Lb.

Work done by air in motor cylinder

$$=Rm\frac{n}{n-1}(T_1-T_2)=53\cdot 3\,\frac{\text{ft.-Lb.}}{\text{lb. °F.}}\times 0\cdot 0726 \text{ lb.}\times 6\times (520-398)° \text{ F.}$$

$$=2{,}830 \text{ ft.-Lb.}$$

Heat abstracted from transmission lines

$$=mC_p\times (T_4-T_1)=0\cdot 0726 \text{ lb.}\times 0\cdot 24 \text{ B.Th.U./lb. °F.}\times (680-520) \text{ °F.}$$

$$=2\cdot 79 \text{ B.Th.U.}$$

Shaft input to compressor $=\frac{3620}{0 \cdot 8}$ ft.-Lb., and shaft output of motor

$$=2830 \times 0 \cdot 8 \text{ ft.-Lb.}$$

Hence, overall efficiency $=\frac{2830 \times 0 \cdot 64}{3720}=0 \cdot 487$ or $48 \cdot 7$ per cent.

EXERCISES ON CHAPTER 15

(i)

1. A single-stage single-acting air compressor takes in 100 cu. ft. of air per min. at 15 Lb. per sq. in. abs. and 68° F. The law of compression is found to be $PV^{1 \cdot 13}$=constant, and the pressure after compression 75 Lb. per sq. in. abs. Find the volume of air delivered per minute at this pressure, and the air horse-power of the compressor. Calculate the mass of air compressed per minute, the temperature after compression, and, using these figures, check the horse-power previously calculated.

2. Air is drawn into an air compressor at a pressure 14·7 Lb. per sq. in. abs. and at 15° C. The volume drawn in per stroke is 12 cu. ft. and the final pressure is 90 Lb. per sq. in. abs.

Find the work done during compression assuming (i) compression is isothermal; (ii) compression is adiabatic and reversible; (iii) What is the saving in work due to isothermal rather than reversible adiabatic compression in a complete cycle?

3. Estimate the brake horse-power of an engine required to drive a single-stage air compressor which handles 260 cu. ft. of air per min. at 60° F. and 15 Lb. per sq. in. abs. if the final pressure is 150 Lb. per sq. in. abs.; compression assumed reversible adiabatic and mechanical efficiency of compressor 86 per cent. Neglect losses and effects of clearance volume.

4. (*a*) A two-stage reciprocating-piston air compressor takes in 0·1 lb. of air per cycle at 15 Lb. per sq. in. abs. and 17° C. It delivers, after the second stage, into a reservoir at 80 Lb. per sq. in. absolute pressure. Calculate the pressure in the intercooler if the work done is to be a minimum, and find the temperature at the end of compression in the low-pressure cylinder if the law of compression in both cylinders is $PV^{1 \cdot 2}$=constant.

(*b*) The temperature at the beginning of the second compression is the same as at the beginning of the first compression, hence show that the increase in temperature during both compressions is the same.

(*c*) Show that the total work done in the two cylinders per cycle is given by the expression $\frac{2n}{n-1} \times R \times m \times$ (temperature rise due to compression in either cylinder).

(*d*) Find the air horse-power of the compressor if it is double-acting and running at 100 r.p.m. Neglect clearance volumes.

5. An air motor is supplied with compressed air at a pressure 90 Lb. per sq. in. abs. and 65° F. The air is expanded according to the law $PV^{1\cdot3}$=constant down to 15 Lb. per sq. in. abs. at which pressure it is exhausted. Find the temperature at the end of expansion and the mass of air used per air horse-power-hour if clearance volume is neglected, given that 1 cu. ft. of air weighs 0·0807 Lb. at an absolute pressure of 2,116 Lb. per sq. ft. and 32° F.

6. Find the volumetric efficiency of the compressor fitted to a CO_2 refrigerator in which the pressure range is from 320 to 1,000 Lb. per sq. in abs. Assume reversible adiabatic compression and that, for CO_2, $\gamma=1\cdot262$. The ratio of clearance volume to stroke volume in the compressor is 1/10.

7. Find the air horse-power of a two-stage reciprocating-piston air compressor in which 5 cu. ft. of air are drawn into the low-pressure cylinder per stroke at 59° F. and 15 Lb. per sq. in. abs. The final pressure after the second stage is to be 60 Lb. per sq. in. abs. and the temperature before the second compression, 59° F. Find the inter-cooler pressure if the total work done is to be a minimum, and the air horse-power of the compressor when running at 100 r.p.m. The compressor is double-acting; neglect clearance volumes; the law of compression in both stages is $PV^{1\cdot3}$=constant.

(ii)

8. The following are the mean values of the observations made on a single-stage single-acting air compressor which delivers into a closed receiver; duration of trial, 14·57 min.; atmospheric temperature and pressure, 17° C. and 29·27 in. of mercury, respectively; gauge pressure in delivery main, 110 Lb. per sq. in.; temperature of air leaving compressor, 227° C.; volume of receiver, 22·62 cu. ft.; final gauge pressure in receiver, 110 Lb. per sq. in.; final temperature in receiver, 29° C.; r.p.m. 322·2; mean effective pressure, 39·1; cooling water per min., 7·76 lb.; rise in temperature of cooling water, 5·53° C.

Draw up a report sheet and calculate the quantities required to complete it. Also, show the heat account diagrammatically.

9. (*a*) Sketch the hypothetical indicator diagram for a reciprocating compressor taking clearance volume into account, and write down an expression for volumetric efficiency.

(*b*) A single-cylinder single-acting compressor delivers 1 lb. of air per minute at 60 Lb. per sq. in. abs. having compressed it from 15 Lb. per sq. in. abs. and 60° F. according to the law $PV^{1\cdot25}$=constant. Using the hypothetical indicator diagram without clearance, calculate the air horse-power, the horse-power required to compress the air isothermally, and the isothermal efficiency of compression. Assuming the mechanical efficiency of the compressor to be 75 per cent., what would be the shaft horse-power supplied to the compressor? The characteristic constant for air may be taken as 53·3 ft.-Lb. per lb. ° F.

10. Define " Volumetric Efficiency " of an air compressor. Neglecting the effect of clearance volume, show that the work done per lb. of air in a reciprocating-piston air compressor taking in air at temperature T_1 and pressure P_1, compressing it to pressure P_2 according to the law PV^n=constant, and then delivering at constant pressure, is given by the expression

$$\frac{n}{n-1}RT_1\left\{\left(\frac{P_2}{P_1}\right)^{\frac{n-1}{n}}-1\right\}, \text{ where } PV=RT \text{ for unit mass of air.}$$

Find the horse-power required to drive a single-acting single-cylinder compressor which delivers 40 lb. of air per minute at 55 Lb. per sq. in. abs., the air being drawn into the cylinder at 15 Lb. per sq. in. abs. and 70° F. Mechanical efficiency of compressor=90 per cent. $n=1\cdot35$. $R=53\cdot3$ ft.-Lb. per lb. ° F. [Part I, B.Sc. Lond.]

11. The air in the cylinder of a piston type air motor is assumed to expand adiabatically and reversibly. Derive an expression for the work done during admission and expansion, and show that it is equal to the loss of total heat (enthalpy) of the air during the expansion period.

If there is 1 cu. ft. of air at 125 Lb. per sq. in. abs. in the cylinder when expansion commences, how much work is done in an expansion to 15 Lb. per sq. in. abs.? [I.Mech.E., Sec. A.]

12. A single-acting air compressor has a cylinder 8 in. diameter, and 12 in. stroke. If the suction pressure and temperature are 14 Lb. per sq. in. abs. and 60° F., respectively, and the delivery pressure is 70 Lb. per sq. in. abs., calculate the horse-power required to drive the compressor at 150 r.p.m., assuming $PV^{1\cdot3}$=constant and the mechanical efficiency of the compressor to be 85 per cent. Neglect clearance volume.

An after-cooler cools the compressed air to 100° F. Calculate the quantity of cooling water required in lb. per minute for a rise in temperature of 10° F. $C_p=0\cdot238$; $C_v=0\cdot160$ B.Th.U. per lb. ° F. [Part I, B.Sc. Lond.]

13. A centrifugal supercharger draws in air at the rate of 45 lb./min. when running at 150 rev./sec. The temperature and pressure of the air at entry are 65° F. and 12·4 Lb./in.^{2} abs. and at exit 162° F. and 20·5 Lb./in.^{2} abs. If the shaft power required to drive this compressor is 27·5 horse-power, calculate the adiabatic efficiency and mechanical efficiency of the compressor, assuming compression to be uncooled or adiabatic.

14. (i) State the first law of thermodynamics and Joule's law. Also, define total heat or enthalpy of a gas and show that the ratio of the change in enthalpy to the change in internal energy of a gas is γ, the ratio of the specific heats at constant pressure and constant volume.

(ii) Five pounds of air per minute are drawn into a centrifugal compressor from the atmosphere whose temperature is 60° F. and pressure 14·7 Lb. per sq. in. abs. The change in enthalpy of the air, when compressed adiabatically, is 25 B.Th.U. per lb. Calculate the horse-power required to drive the compressor assuming a mechanical efficiency of 95 per cent. Also, calculate the volume of free atmospheric air compressed per shaft horse-power hour. The characteristic constant for air is 53·3 ft.-Lb. per lb. ° F.

15. A two-stage reciprocating-piston air-compressor is required to deliver 110 $ft.^3$ of free atmospheric air per minute. The pressure range is from 15 to 120 Lb. per $in.^2$ abs. Neglecting clearance volumes calculate the pressure in the intercooler if minimum work is to be done. Assume that intercooling is complete. Also, calculate the shaft horse-power required to drive the compressor taking 78 per cent. as the mechanical efficiency. The law of compression in both stages may be assumed to be $PV^{1\cdot25}$=constant.

16. In a test of a single-cylinder single-acting air compressor of 4 in. bore and 5 in. stroke air is taken from the atmosphere at 14·5 Lb. per sq. in. abs. and delivered through a valve, which maintains a delivery pressure of 120 Lb. per sq. in. abs., to a reservoir of 40 cu. ft. capacity. A motor giving 2·5 b.h.p. drives the compressor at 420 r.p.m. and the i.m.e.p. is 31·2 Lb. per sq. in. The reservoir is initially at atmospheric pressure and 64° F. and after 19 minutes running reaches 110 Lb. per sq. in. abs. and 145° F. Calculate the delivery in cu. ft. of free air per min. at 64° F., the volumetric efficiency at atmospheric conditions, the isothermal efficiency and the mechanical efficiency. [Part I., B.Sc. Lond.]

17. An air compressor receives air at 14·8 Lb. per sq. in. abs. and 58° F., and delivers it at 111 Lb. per sq. in. abs. and 298° F. Assuming that compression follows a law PV^n=constant, and ignoring temperature changes during admission and delivery, calculate the value of n.

(ii) The delivery rate is 51 cu. ft. of free air per minute. If it were possible to maintain constant temperature during compression, how much power could be saved? [Part I., B.Sc. Lond.]

18. A compressor works adiabatically during compression of air. Show that the net work done on 1 lb. of air during the whole cycle of operations in the compressor is given by: Work$=C_p\delta T$, where δT is the temperature rise of the air during compression. Show also that internal energy of 1 lb. of air will increase by an amount

$$\delta E=\frac{1}{\gamma-1}(P_2V_2-P_1V_1);$$ where P_1V_1 represent the conditions of the air at commencement and P_2V_2 at the end of compression, γ being the ratio C_P to C_V. Estimate the work done in a complete cycle when a compressor draws in 3 cu. ft. of air at 70° F. and 14 Lb. per sq. in. abs. and compresses it adiabatically to 390° F. before delivering it at constant pressure to the receiver. [I.Mech.E., Sec. A.]

19. Air flowing steadily through a compressor is raised from 14 Lb. per sq. in. abs. and 60° F. to 50 Lb. per sq. in. abs. and 237° F. It is found that 3·0 B.Th.U. are removed by the cooling medium per lb. of air, and that the air velocities at inlet and outlet are 1,800 and 3,000 ft. per minute, respectively. Calculate the power required to drive the compressor if the air flow at inlet is 200 cu. ft. per minute, and the mechanical efficiency of the compressor is 90 per cent. [I.Mech.E., Sec. A.]

CHAPTER 16

INTERNAL COMBUSTION ENGINE CYCLES

1. Fundamental Question of Efficiency.—In Chapter 2 several types of internal combustion engines were mentioned and their action described. They can be classified broadly according to characteristics as to whether they work on the four-stroke or two-stroke cycle; have electric-ignition or rely on compression-ignition; use gaseous or liquid fuel. Combinations of these sets of alternatives are possible in engines.

Now consider the thermodynamics of the cycles on which internal combustion engines work, with a view to finding out on what their efficiencies depend and what limitations there are preventing the maximum possible efficiency from being attained.

The fundamental question of heat engine efficiency is: *What greatest fraction of the heat taken from a source is it possible to convert into work—that is, what is the limiting efficiency of conversion?*

In 1824 Carnot gave a complete answer to this question. He showed that maximum work would be obtained from a given amount of heat if it could be made to pass from source to receiver through an engine working in a strictly reversible manner.

We shall prove that the maximum efficiency theoretically possible is that of the Carnot cycle which, being an ideal cycle of reversible operations, can only be conceived in imagination and is impossible of realisation in any working engine. It is, however, one of the aims of designers to get nearer and nearer to the maximum efficiency of conversion of heat into work or mechanical energy, and it is necessary to study the ideal, reversible cycle of Carnot as that of the perfect engine. In practical engines, high efficiency is only one of many desirable things. Cost of plant and fuel, also, are prime factors when the relative merits of power plant are being considered.

Unlike steam engines and turbines, the efficiency of reciprocating internal-combustion engines is nearly independent of size, and a compression-ignition engine can be made to approach a thermal efficiency of 40 per cent. as against an efficiency of 30 per cent. in spark-ignition petrol engines.

Economic efficiency based on running costs is as important (if not more) as thermal efficiency. For this reason the compression-ignition engine with a thermal efficiency approaching 40 per cent. has not displaced steam plant in power stations whose overall efficiency is only about 30 per cent.

2. The Carnot Cycle for a Perfect Gas.—*The Carnot cycle is an ideal and theoretical cycle consisting of four reversible operations, two of them being adiabatic and two isothermal.* It can best be described with reference to fig. 16.1 in which the hot source, the

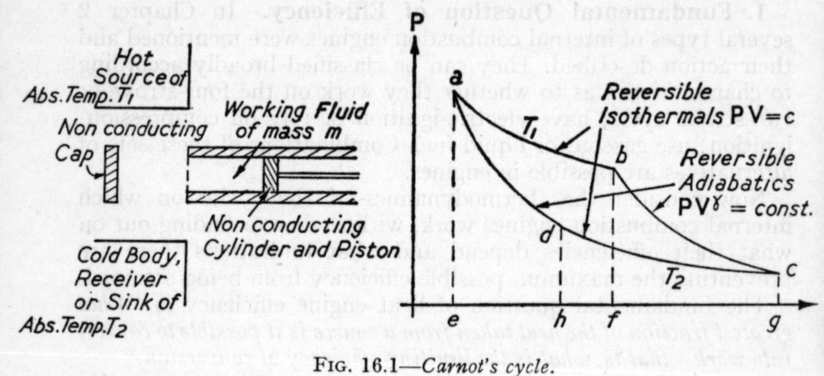

Fig. 16.1—*Carnot's cycle.*

non-conducting cap, and the receiver can be imagined applied to the end of the cylinder at will and instantaneously whenever they are required.

An imaginary working fluid is contained in, and never leaves, the cylinder—it being there merely as an agent for the perfect receiving and rejecting of heat, and for expanding and contracting during the four ideal, reversible, operations.

The hot source is imagined to have an infinite supply of heat at the constant upper temperature T_1, and the receiver is imagined to have an infinite capacity for heat at the lower temperature T_2.

The working fluid in the case illustrated by fig. 16.1 is imagined to be a perfect gas, and at the commencement of the cycle it is imagined to be at the state point *a* represented on the P,V diagram, the pressure being P_a, volume V_a, and temperature T_1. The hot source is applied to the cylinder, and heat is given to the working agent reversibly at the constant temperature T_1, the effect of this being to trace out the isothermal expansion *ab* at temperature T_1. Since the temperature does not change during this addition of heat, the internal energy (E) does not change. Hence, by the first law of thermodynamics, the heat supplied=work done by the

working agent=area $abfea = P_aV_a\log_e\frac{V_b}{V_a} = RmT_1\log_e\frac{V_b}{V_a}$

At the state represented by *b* on the P,V diagram the hot

source is replaced at the head of the cylinder by the non-conducting cap and the working agent is expanded reversibly in a cylinder impervious to heat, thus tracing out the reversible adiabatic expansion line *bc*. Since, in an adiabatic process, no heat is allowed to enter or leave the substance, the work done by it is done at the expense of its stock of internal energy, and hence, by the first law of thermodynamics, the loss in internal energy= work done by the working agent=area *bcgfb*. That is, the work done by the working agent

$$=E_b-E_c=\frac{P_bV_b-P_cV_c}{\gamma-1}=\frac{Rm(T_1-T_2)}{\gamma-1}$$

The temperature of the working fluid at *c* is T_2 and the receiver is now imagined to replace the non-conducting cap. The piston is moved back, and heat is rejected into the receiver reversibly at temperature T_2 while tracing out the isothermal compression *cd* on the P,V diagram. By the first law of thermodynamics the work done *on* the working fluid=heat *rejected* to the receiver

$$=\text{area } cdhgc=P_cV_c\log_\varepsilon\frac{V_c}{V_d}=RmT_2\log_\varepsilon\frac{V_c}{V_d}$$

The reversible isothermal compression is stopped at such a point, *d*, that a reversible adiabatic through this point will bring the working fluid back to its original state *a*, ready to repeat the four operations of the cycle. The fourth operation *da* is thus a reversible adiabatic compression—the non-conducting cap having replaced the receiver at the head of the cylinder, and the work done *on* the fluid during this compression=area *daehd*=increase in internal energy (since, by the first law, $-dW=dE$ for an adiabatic)

$$=E_a-E_d=\frac{P_aV_a-P_dV_d}{\gamma-1}=\frac{Rm(T_1-T_2)}{\gamma-1}$$

It will be seen that for the reversible adiabatic expansion *bc* and for the reversible adiabatic compression *da*

$$\frac{T_1}{T_2}=\left(\frac{V_c}{V_b}\right)^{\gamma-1}=\left(\frac{V_d}{V_a}\right)^{\gamma-1} \text{ and, therefore, } \frac{V_b}{V_a}=\frac{V_c}{V_d}=r,$$

being the ratio of isothermal expansion and isothermal compression.

The transferences of heat and work done during the four reversible operations of the Carnot cycle can be tabulated and clearly shown as follows:

Reversible Process	Heat Supplied to Working Fluid by Hot Source T_1	Heat Rejected from Fluid to Receiver T_2	Work done *by* Working Fluid	Increase in Internal Energy of Working Fluid
Isothermal expansion *ab.*	$RmT_1 \log_\varepsilon r$	0	$RmT_1 \log_\varepsilon r$	0
Adiabatic expansion *bc.*	0	0	$\frac{Rm(T_1-T_2)}{\gamma-1}$	$-\frac{Rm(T_1-T_2)}{\gamma-1}$
Isothermal compression *cd.*	0	$RmT_2 \log_\varepsilon r$	$-RmT_2 \log_\varepsilon r$	0
Adiabatic compression *de.*	0	0	$-\frac{Rm(T_1-T_2)}{\gamma-1}$	$+\frac{Rm(T_1-T_2)}{\gamma-1}$
TOTALS.	$RmT_1 \log_\varepsilon r$	$RmT_2 \log_\varepsilon r$	$Rm(T_1-T_2) \log_\varepsilon r$	0

Thus it is seen that in the Carnot cycle the total work done by the fluid is $Rm(T_1-T_2)\log_\varepsilon r$ from a supply of heat $RmT_1\log_\varepsilon r$. Hence, the efficiency of the Carnot cycle

$$=\frac{\text{work done}}{\text{heat supplied}}=\frac{T_1-T_2}{T_1}$$

Example 1.—An internal combustion engine takes in a mixture of fuel and air at 27° C., and the highest temperature after combustion is 377° C. Calculate the Carnot efficiency of an engine working between these two limits of temperature.

$$T_1=273+377=650° \text{ abs. C.}$$
$$T_2=273+27\ =300° \text{ abs. C.}$$

$$\therefore \text{ Carnot efficiency}=\frac{650-300}{650}=53 \cdot 8 \text{ per cent.}$$

Example 2.—An ideal engine is imagined working on the Carnot cycle, heat being received at 800° F. and rejected at 70° F. If the maximum and minimum pressures are 1,800 and 15 Lb. per sq. in. abs., respectively, what will be the work done per lb. of air?

[I.Mech.E., Sec. A.]

Referring to fig. 16.1 it has been proved that the work done is represented by $Rm(T_1-T_2) \log_\varepsilon r$, where $r=\frac{V_b}{V_a}=\frac{P_a}{P_b}$

Since $\frac{T_1}{T_2}=\left(\frac{P_b}{P_c}\right)^{\frac{\gamma-1}{\gamma}}$, then $P_b=P_c\left(\frac{T_1}{T_2}\right)^{\frac{\gamma}{\gamma-1}}=15\frac{\text{Lb.}}{\text{in.}^2}\left(\frac{1260}{530}\right)^{\frac{1\cdot4}{0\cdot4}}$

$$=312 \text{ Lb. per sq. in. abs.}$$

Hence, $r=\frac{P_a}{P_b}=\frac{1800}{312}=5\cdot77$, and the work done per lb. of air

$$=53\cdot3\frac{\text{ft.-Lb.}}{\text{lb. °F.}}\times 1\text{ lb.}\times(1260-530)°\text{ F.}\log_\varepsilon 5\cdot77=68{,}300\text{ ft.-Lb.}$$

Example 3.—Carnot's cycle consists of four *reversible* operations. If the whole cycle is worked in a reversed direction, heat would be abstracted from the "cold body" at T_2, and rejected to the "hot body" at T_1, and so produce a cooling or refrigerating effect in the "cold body." What would be the coefficient of performance in such a case?

Carnot's cycle is entirely reversible, and if reversed would become a heat pump in which external work $Rm(T_1-T_2)\log_\varepsilon r$ would have to be supplied to do work on the fluid in order to pump heat $RmT_2 \log_\varepsilon r$ from the cold body (T_2) and deliver the amount $RmT_1 \log_\varepsilon r$ into the hot source (T_1). (See Table on page 348).

The performance of such a heat pump or refrigerator

$$=\frac{\text{heat abstracted}}{\text{work done in order to abstract it}}=\frac{RmT_2\log_\varepsilon r}{Rm(T_1-T_2)\log_\varepsilon r}$$

i.e. the coefficient of performance $=\frac{T_2}{T_1-T_2}$

We have proved that the thermal efficiency of the reversible Carnot engine is $\frac{T_1-T_2}{T_1}$. It now remains to be proved that this is the maximum efficiency possible for any engine working between temperatures of source and receiver T_1 and T_2, respectively. Before this can be done it is necessary to mention the second law of thermodynamics again.

3. The Second Law of Thermodynamics.—It might be thought, since heat and work are mutually convertible (1 B.Th.U. being equivalent to 778 ft.-Lb.), that there is nothing to prevent all the heat which a source can supply, from being converted into work. *While it is true that a given quantity of mechanical energy can be changed into its equivalent amount of heat energy (by friction, for example), the converse of this is not true—that is, a quantity of heat energy cannot be changed into an equivalent quantity of mechanical energy. This is a consequence of a fundamental law known as the second law of thermodynamics.*

This law may be stated in a variety of ways, but the simplest way is probably that of Clausius, who said: **"It is impossible for a self-acting machine, unaided by any external agency,**

to convey heat from one body to another which is at a higher temperature." This is an axiom, being an abstraction from the whole field of physical experience, and although it is not possible to prove the law or deduce it from other laws, no exception to it has yet been found.

The second law of thermodynamics says, in effect, that heat will not pass automatically (i.e. of itself without assistance) from a colder to a hotter body. We can force (or pump) heat from a cold to a hot body, as in the case of a refrigerating machine, but only by applying an external agency to drive the machine.

The second law of thermodynamics may be thought of in another way as dealing with the question of the *availability* of the heat received by a system for the production of mechanical energy or work. It relates to the *quality* of energy as distinct from the *quantity* of energy. (It will be remembered that the first law of thermodynamics deals with quantity of energy, which is pronounced to be invariable in a closed system.)

In every kind of heat engine, heat is let down from a high level of temperature (T_1) *to a lower level* (T_2), *and it is by so letting heat down that the engine is able to do work.* This is somewhat analogous to the way in which a water-wheel does work by letting water down from a high level to a lower level, except that in the water-wheel all the water which is taken in is rejected at the lower level, whereas a heat engine rejects less heat than it takes in—some of the heat having been converted into mechanical energy or work. *A much larger quantity of heat has to be let down from the higher temperature* (T_1) *to the lower temperature* (T_2) *than is converted into work, and the heat becomes "degraded" as regards temperature when passed through an engine.* Thus, there is degradation of energy in the process of producing mechanical work from heat. The availability of heat for transformation into mechanical energy depends on the range of temperature ($T_1 - T_2$) through which the heat is let down. Thus, no work could be produced if all bodies were at the same level of temperature—i.e. if the source of heat and sink or receiver were not at different temperatures.

The second law of thermodynamics may be said to have its foundation in the fact that there is a continuous running down of the utility value of the energy in the Universe. The ultimate effect of the process in an isolated system would be such a distribution of energy in the system that none could be used for the production of work since it would all be at the same level of temperature. Because of diffusion of energy we are told that the whole Universe will ultimately arrive at a common level of temperature. Scientists sometimes speak of " the dying sun " and of the ultimate fate of the earth being that of the moon—lifeless and dead, but they add that the diffusion of solar heat will continue for a length of time of the order of a million million years before life will be extinguished from the earth. This may be the truth, but such a far-flung deduction seems premature in view of the enormous number of years predicted for human activity when set against the many discoveries of Nature's Laws and processes during the past mere three hundred years! There is no certainty that future discoveries will not reveal a reverse process as yet unknown but which even now may be continuously working in some way or other restoring diffused energy to a state of greater availability again.

A clock cannot run down unless it has been wound up, and there must have been a time when the reverse processes of those we now see were going on during the winding up period. No one has proved that those days are gone for ever.

Carnot, in 1824, discovered what is now known as the second law of thermodynamics when he investigated conditions for giving maximum efficiency of an ideal engine. He showed that in order to have maximum efficiency, there must not be any direct interchange of heat between bodies at different temperatures, for if that takes place a difference of temperature is wasted which might have been used to produce mechanical energy or work. In practice, where actual engines are dealt with, there is, of course, loss of efficiency due to heat passing from higher to lower temperatures, but theoretical cases can be *imagined* where there are no losses. *One can imagine, for instance, operations conducted so as to form a succession of reversible equilibrium positions although in practice such operations do not exist.* **Thus, Carnot formulated the principle that the maximum possible efficiency of an engine working in a given range of temperature is that of a reversible engine.** *Furthermore, this efficiency depends only on the limits of temperatures between which the engine works, and is independent of the working substance.*

From a practical point of view the second law of thermodynamics may be regarded as stating that the maximum quantity of mechanical energy available from a quantity of heat, Q, is equivalent to $Q\frac{(T_1-T_2)}{T_1}$, where T_1 is the absolute temperature of reception and T_2 that of rejection of heat.

In this connection **"available energy" is defined as that portion of a quantity of heat which could be transformed into work by means of a reversible engine.** Thus, in general the term "available energy" is used to signify the maximum amount of work (mechanical energy) which it is *theoretically* possible to obtain from a given quantity of heat. It denotes the latent capacity of a quantity of heat to do work, the temperature of the atmosphere or the sea usually imposing a lower limit to the temperature drop.

On p. 6 it is stated that the absolute scale of temperature in thermodynamics is independent of the properties of the working substance. This scale is such that any two temperatures T_1 and T_2 are to each other in the same ratio as the quantity of heat Q_1 taken in at higher temperature T_1 is to the quantity of heat Q_2 rejected at the lower temperature T_2 by a reversible engine working between these two temperatures of source and receiver. Thus, $\frac{Q_1}{T_1}=\frac{Q_2}{T_2}=\text{etc.}=\varphi$ (say), and a thermodynamic thermometer could be imagined to consist of a series of reversible engines each doing the same amount of work $W=Q_1-Q_2=Q_2-Q_3=\ldots$ Then, since

$$Q_1=\varphi T_1 \text{ and } Q_2=\varphi T_2 \ldots \text{etc.}, \frac{W}{\varphi}=T_1-T_2=T_2-T_3=\ldots \text{etc.},$$

i.e. **equal temperature differences on the absolute thermodynamical scale may be defined as the intervals between the temperatures of sources and receivers of heat in a series of reversible engines each doing the same amount of work.** The zero of the absolute scale is such that, if it could be reached, no heat would be rejected by a reversible engine, for all the heat received would be converted into work.

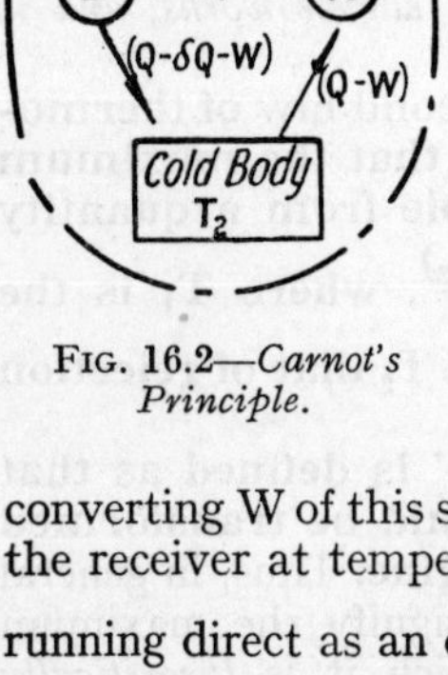

4. Proof that no Engine can be More Efficient than a Reversible One.—Carnot stated the principle that "no engine can be more efficient than a reversible one." This principle can be proved with reference to fig. 16.2, which represents an isolated system containing a hot body T_1, a cold body T_2, an engine E, and a *reversible* heat pump R (i.e. a reversed perfect engine) assumed working on the Carnot cycle reversed.

Hot Body T_1

Q

(Q-δQ)

E

W

R

(Q-δQ-W)

(Q-W)

Cold Body T_2

FIG. 16.2—*Carnot's Principle.*

First, consider R working as an engine on the Carnot cycle and taking in heat Q from the hot source at temperature T_1, and converting W of this supply into work, thus rejecting $(Q-W)$ into the receiver at temperature T_2. Therefore, the efficiency of R, if running direct as an engine, would be $\frac{W}{Q}=\frac{T_1-T_2}{T_1}$.

Now, consider engine E, *assumed* to be more efficient than the reversible Carnot engine R—that is, E is assumed to do the *same* work W for *a less* quantity of heat than Q supplied from the hot source, say $(Q-\delta Q)$. Thus, of the $(Q-\delta Q)$ units of heat which are supplied from T_1, E is assumed to convert W into work. Engine E therefore rejects $(Q-\delta Q-W)$ into the cold body at T_2.

The engine E, producing W units of work, can thus be made to drive the reversed Carnot engine R, which requires W units to drive it. Thus, if E is more efficient than the reversible engine R, the flow of heat will be as shown in fig. 16.2, where it will be seen that the result is such that δQ units of heat are transferred from the cold body T_2 to the hotter body T_1 without the aid of any agency from outside the system. Hence, *if the original assumption were true,* we should have a self-acting system conveying heat from a cold body to a hotter body *unaided* by any external agency. This would be contrary to the second law of thermodynamics and leads us to conclude that *the assumption from which this result came is wrong,* and that the driving engine (E) cannot have a higher efficiency than (R) the reversible one which is driven. Therefore, we are led to agree with Carnot's principle that no engine can be more efficient than a reversible one; and, since the imaginary Carnot engine is reversible, **no engine can be more efficient than Carnot's imaginary reversible engine.** Similarly, it can be proved that no reversible engine can be less efficient than Carnot's imaginary engine. Hence, reversible engines have the same efficiency when working between the same limits of temperature—all the heat added being transferred at the highest temperature T_1, and rejection of heat taking place at the lower constant temperature T_2. This efficiency, namely $(T_1-T_2)/T_1$, is the maximum attainable by any heat engine.

We have seen that all heat engines act by letting heat pass down through a working agent from a hotter to a colder body, and that, by operations of expansion and compression of the working agent, a part of the heat passing down is converted into work. We can now also state that whenever there is an available temperature drop, work can be obtained; also, the maximum efficiency of conversion of heat into work would be that obtained in the imaginary Carnot engine, and equal to the ratio of the temperature drop (T_1-T_2) to the temperature (T_1) of the hot source.

Although the Carnot cycle is impracticable both for steam and internal combustion engines, the importance of having a wide temperature range (T_1-T_2) *is fully confirmed in practice.* As regards T_1 it will be realised that the internal combustion engine achieves a higher upper temperature than the steam engine, for the upper limit for superheated steam used in steam turbines at the present time is about 1,000° F. (538° C.). This is some 3,600° F. (2,000° C.) less than temperatures reached in internal combustion engines in which fuel is burnt inside the engine cylinders, and the working agent is, therefore, heated directly and without loss of heat. In the case of steam engine and turbine plant there is a large irreversible temperature drop (say 1,500° F.) between the furnace temperature and that of the steam generated causing a loss of efficiency. The only restrictions on the maximum temperature to be reached in internal-combustion engines are connected with the combustion of all oxygen present in the cylinder, and the increase in the specific heat of the gases as their temperature rises. These factors impose a limit of about 5,000° F. or 2,800° C. on temperatures to be reached in the cylinders of internal-combustion engines using ordinary fuels.

As regards T_2, steam plant achieves a lower temperature of exhaust than is possible in internal-combustion engines, for, with the high vacua in modern condensers, the steam turbine succeeds in expanding its working agent down to less than 100° F., whereas the minimum temperature of the exhaust gases in single-cylinder internal-combustion engines is about 900° F., and this temperature is often much higher in large multi-cylinder plant.

It should be noted, however, that the lower the source temperature (T_1) for a given temperature drop the greater is the Carnot efficiency, e.g. if $T_1 - T_2 = 1{,}000°$ F. and T_1 is 2,000° abs. F. the efficiency is 50 per cent. whereas if T_1 is 1,500° abs. F. the efficiency is 67 per cent. Lowering the sink temperature T_2 causes a greater increase in efficiency than raising the source temperature T_1.

We have seen on p. 128 that the cycle with which the actual efficiencies of steam engines and turbines are compared is the Rankine cycle—not the impracticable Carnot cycle. Also we shall see on p. 366 that the efficiencies of internal-combustion engines are compared with the efficiency of the "air standard cycle" and not with the Carnot cycle. The greatest brake thermal efficiency at present for steam turbines is about 34 per cent., which, with a boiler efficiency of 90 per cent., gives an overall plant efficiency of about 30 per cent., whereas the greatest brake thermal efficiency of a modern compression-ignition internal-combustion engine is about 40 per cent.

5. Internal-combustion Engine Cycles.—Although an engine imagined working on the Carnot cycle is theoretically the most efficient engine possible, it has not proved practicable. It only works in imagination. No real engine can work in a strictly reversible manner, for the gases cannot escape eddying motions, nor can transferences of heat between working substances and bodies at lower temperatures be avoided.

Other defects of the Carnot cycle from a practical point of view are that the resultant work is small compared with the quantities of energy involved in the four reversible operations, and the small temperature differences necessary for close approximations to isothermal-compression and expansion make the rate of heat transfer too slow for acceptance in engineering practice.

Hypothetical cycles such as the Otto and Diesel cycles for internal combustion engines, and the Rankine cycle for steam engines and turbines, necessarily less efficient than the Carnot cycle, have been projected as practical ideals or standards of comparison for actual engines.

Type 1. Cycles in which heat is added at constant volume without previous compression.—The hypothetical indicator diagram of an engine working on this cycle would be that shown in fig. 16.3, in which *sa* represents the suction of a charge of combustible gas into the cylinder; *a1* represents addition of heat at constant volume; *12* represents reversible adiabatic expansion; *2s* represents the exhaust stroke.

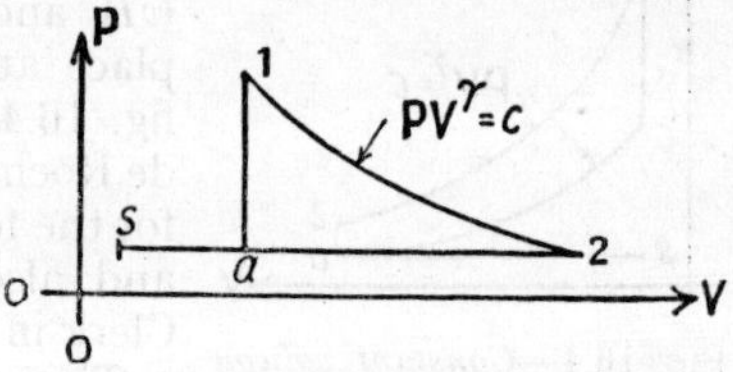

FIG. 16.3—*Cycle without previous compression.*

In this cycle the heat supplied at constant volume $(a1) = mC_v(T_1 - T_a)$ and raises the temperature of the charge from T_a to T_1. The heat rejected from the engine is that of the exhaust gases at temperature $(T_2 - T_a)$ above atmospheric, the amount being $= mC_p(T_2 - T_a)$. The thermal efficiency of this hypothetical cycle

$$= \frac{\text{work done}}{\text{heat supplied}} = \frac{\text{heat supplied} - \text{heat rejected}}{\text{heat supplied}}$$

$$= 1 - \frac{\text{heat rejected}}{\text{heat supplied}} = 1 - \frac{mC_p(T_2 - T_a)}{mC_v(T_1 - T_a)}$$

This expression for efficiency can be reduced by use of

$$\frac{T_1}{T_2} = \left(\frac{V_2}{V_1}\right)^{\gamma-1} = (r)^{\gamma-1} = \left(\frac{P_1}{P_2}\right)^{\frac{\gamma-1}{\gamma}}$$

and

$$\frac{T_1}{T_a} = \frac{P_1 V_1}{P_a V_a} = \frac{P_1}{P_a} = \frac{P_1}{P_2} = (r^{\gamma})$$

From these equations we get $T_1 = r^{\gamma} T_a$ and $T_2 = \frac{T_1}{r^{\gamma-1}} = r T_a$.

On substituting these we get an expression for the efficiency of the cycle $= 1 - \gamma\left(\frac{r-1}{r^{\gamma}-1}\right)$.

The original Lenoir engines of 1860 aimed at this theoretical cycle before the advantages of compressing the charge were realised. The above cycle is now never followed in any modern engine, but it is of historical interest and serves to illustrate the method of calculating the thermal efficiency of hypothetical cycles.

Type 2. Cycles in which heat is added at constant volume with previous compression.—(*a*) *In which heat is rejected at constant volume.*—The hypothetical indicator diagram of an engine working on this cycle, in which addition of heat (*c1*) and rejection of heat (*2a*) takes place at constant volume, is shown in fig. 16.4. This cycle, proposed by Beau de Rochas in 1862, was made practicable for the four-stroke cycle by Otto in 1876, and also for the two-stroke cycle by Clerk in 1880.

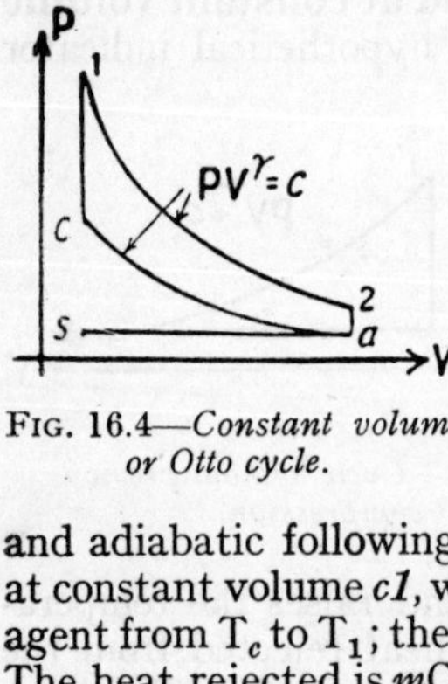

FIG. 16.4—*Constant volume or Otto cycle.*

The compression curve *ac* and the expansion curve *12* are assumed reversible and adiabatic following the law PV^{γ}=constant. Heat is supplied at constant volume *c1*, which raises the temperature of the working agent from T_c to T_1; the amount is therefore equal to $mC_v(T_1 - T_c)$. The heat rejected is $mC_v(T_2 - T_a)$. By definition, no heat is added to or rejected from the gas during the adiabatic compression *ac* or during the adiabatic expansion *12*. Hence the thermal efficiency of this hypothetical cycle

$$= 1 - \frac{\text{heat rejected}}{\text{heat supplied}}$$

$$= 1 - \frac{mC_v(T_2 - T_a)}{mC_v(T_1 - T_c)} = 1 - \left(\frac{T_2 - T_a}{T_1 - T_c}\right)$$

This expression can be reduced by means of the relationship

$$\frac{T_c}{T_a} = \left(\frac{V_a}{V_c}\right)^{\gamma-1} = (r)^{\gamma-1} = \frac{T_1}{T_2}$$

where r is the ratio of compression which, in this cycle, is also equal to the ratio of expansion.

$$\therefore \frac{T_2}{T_a}-1=\frac{T_1}{T_c}-1$$

$$\therefore \frac{T_2-T_a}{T_1-T_c}=\frac{T_a}{T_c}=\left(\frac{1}{r}\right)^{\gamma-1}$$

∴ The efficiency of this constant volume or Otto cycle is

$$\eta=1-\left(\frac{1}{r}\right)^{\gamma-1}$$

Also, since $1-\frac{T_a}{T_c}=1-\frac{T_2}{T_1}$, the efficiency of the Otto cycle is

$$\eta=\frac{T_c-T_a}{T_c}=\frac{T_1-T_2}{T_1}.$$

(*b*) *In which heat is rejected at constant pressure.*—Fig. 16.5 represents the hypothetical indicator diagram of an engine working on the cycle in which heat is added at constant volume during *c1* and rejected at constant pressure during *2a*. This cycle is usually known as the Atkinson cycle.

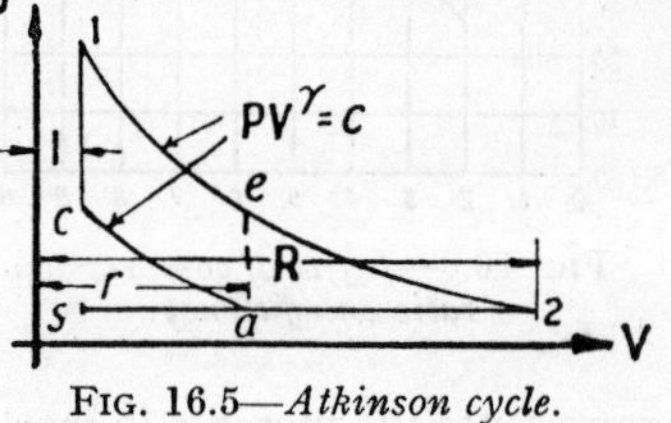

FIG. 16.5—*Atkinson cycle.*

It has not yet been successfully used in practice in ordinary engines owing to difficulties experienced in the mechanism for making the expansion stroke *12* longer than the compression stroke *ac*, but it is obvious that if these mechanical difficulties could be overcome an engine working on this cycle would have a greater efficiency than one working on the constant volume cycle, since, for the same amount of heat supplied during *c1*, we should get the work represented by area *e2ae* in addition to that of the constant volume cycle *ac1ea*.

Heat supplied during $c1=mC_v(T_1-T_c)$

Heat rejected during $2a=mC_p(T_2-T_a)$

$$\therefore \text{Efficiency of cycle}=1-\frac{\text{heat rejected}}{\text{heat supplied}}=1-\frac{mC_p(T_2-T_a)}{mC_v(T_1-T_c)}$$

$$=1-\gamma\frac{(T_2-T_a)}{(T_1-T_c)}$$

In actual spark-ignition engines explosion will only occur when the mixture is correct. In a petrol engine the ratio of air to petrol by weight must be within the region of about 10 to 20 (representing very rich and very weak mixtures, respectively) in order for ignition to take place by means of a spark. If the mixture is either too rich or too weak, burning will not take place.

From the efficiency expression, $1-\left(\frac{1}{r}\right)^{\gamma-1}$, it will be seen that the higher the compression ratio, r, the higher will be the efficiency (see fig. 16.6). The ratio of compression, however, is limited by the ignition temperature of the mixture. If r were too great, the temperature due to compression may be higher before the end of compression than the ignition temperature of the mixture, and pre-ignition would occur. This must be avoided and the compression ratio is therefore limited in these types of engines. A compression ratio of the order of 6 is about the limit in ordinary petrol engines.

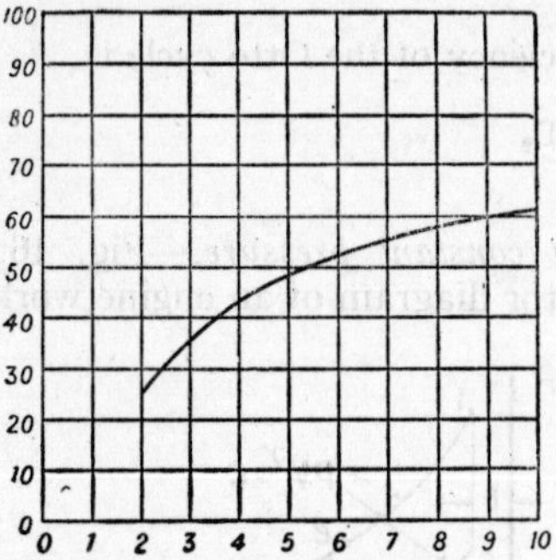

FIG. 16.6—*Effect of compression ratio on efficiency.*

The effect of compressing the mixture to a higher pressure before ignition is shown by the dotted area in fig. 16.7 which represents the increase in work obtained from higher compression —the clearance volume having been reduced from *a* to *b* and the stroke correspondingly increased.

Advantages of compressing the mixture before ignition are: (i) greater mean effective pressure acting on the piston, resulting in a smaller cylinder (and therefore less weight) for a given power developed; (ii) a weaker mixture may be used and ignited with greater certainty, and hence with greater economy of fuel.

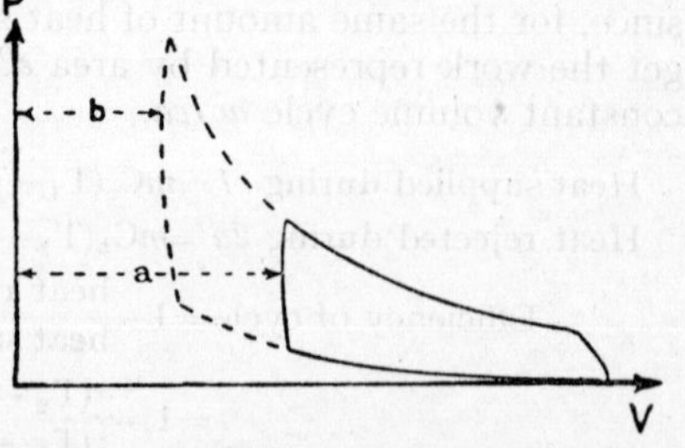

FIG. 16.7—*Effect of compression ratio.*

If a weak spring is put in the indicator and a diagram taken, it will be found that the suction and exhaust lines are quite distinct and similar to those shown in fig. 16.8. The loop is known as the pumping loop, and the horse-power expended on the gases in drawing the fresh

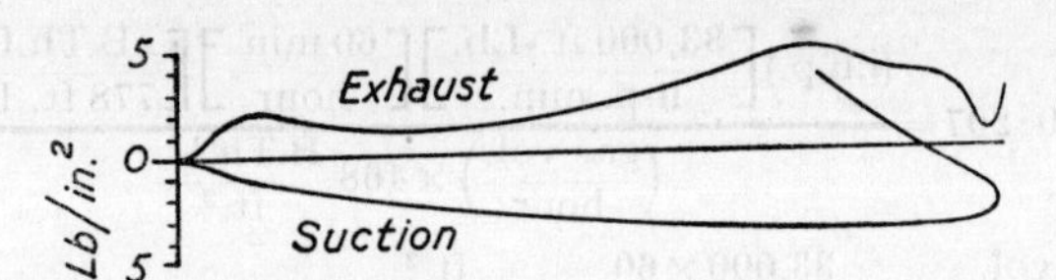

FIG. 16.8—*The pumping loop.*

mixture into the cylinder and in exhausting the burnt gases is known as the pumping horse-power which, if the pumping loop be assumed the same in firing and non-firing cycles,

$$=(\text{m.e.p. of pumping loop})\ LAC\left[\frac{\text{h.p. min.}}{33{,}000\ \text{ft. Lb.}}\right]$$

where L is the stroke, A the piston area and C the cycles traced out in unit time, i.e. the cyclic frequency.

The net indicated horse-power developed by the engine=gross indicated horse-power—pumping horse-power.

Example 1.—Calculate the efficiency of a four-stroke gas engine assumed working on the constant-volume cycle of stroke 16 in., piston diameter 12 in., and clearance volume 0·485 cu. ft.

$$\text{Swept volume}=\frac{\pi}{4}\times(12)^2\times16=1{,}810\ \text{cu. in.}=V_K$$

$$\text{Clearance volume}=1{,}728\times0\cdot485=838\ \text{cu. in.}=V_C$$

$$\therefore\ \text{Volume of cylinder to outer dead-centre}=2{,}648\ \text{cu. in.}=V_K+V_C$$

$$\therefore\ \text{Ratio of compression}=\frac{V_K+V_C}{V_C}=\frac{2648}{838}=3\cdot16=r$$

$$\therefore\ \text{Thermal efficiency}=1-\left(\frac{1}{r}\right)^{\gamma-1}$$

$$=1-\left(\frac{1}{3\cdot16}\right)^{1\cdot4-1}=37\ \text{per cent.}$$

Example 2.—If the relative efficiency of the above engine is 56 per cent. find the gas consumption in cu. ft. per i.h.p.-hour if the calorific value of the gas is 468 B.Th.U. per cu. ft.

$$\text{Relative efficiency or efficiency ratio}=\frac{\text{actual efficiency}}{\text{hypothetical efficiency}}$$

$$\therefore\ \text{Actual thermal efficiency}=0\cdot56\times37=20\cdot7\ \text{per cent.}$$

$$\text{Also, indicated thermal efficiency}=\frac{\text{heat equivalent of i.h.p.}}{\text{heat supplied to the engine}}$$

i.e. $$0 \cdot 207 = \frac{(\text{i.h.p.})\left[\frac{33{,}000 \text{ ft.-Lb.}}{\text{h-p. min.}}\right]\left[\frac{60 \text{ min.}}{\text{hour}}\right]\left[\frac{\text{B.Th.U.}}{778 \text{ ft.-Lb.}}\right]}{\left(\frac{\text{gas vol.}}{\text{hour}}\right) \times 468 \frac{\text{B.Th.U.}}{\text{ft.}^3}}$$

$$\therefore \frac{\text{gas vol.}}{\text{i.h.p.-hour}} = \frac{33{,}000 \times 60}{0 \cdot 207 \times 468 \times 778} \frac{\text{ft.}^3}{\text{h-p.-hour}}$$

$$= 26 \cdot 3 \text{ cu. ft. per i.h.p.-hour.}$$

Example 3.—(*a*) Self-ignition would occur in an engine using a certain brand of petrol if the temperature due to compression reached 350° C. Calculate the highest ratio of compression that may be used to avoid pre-ignition if the law of compression is $PV^{1 \cdot 35} =$ constant, and the initial temperature of the charge in the cylinder is 50° C. Take $\gamma = 1 \cdot 4$.

Referring to fig. 16.9, $r = \left(\frac{V_a}{V_c}\right) = \left(\frac{T_c}{T_a}\right)^{\frac{1}{n-1}} = \left(\frac{623}{323}\right)^{\frac{1}{0 \cdot 35}} = 6 \cdot 4.$

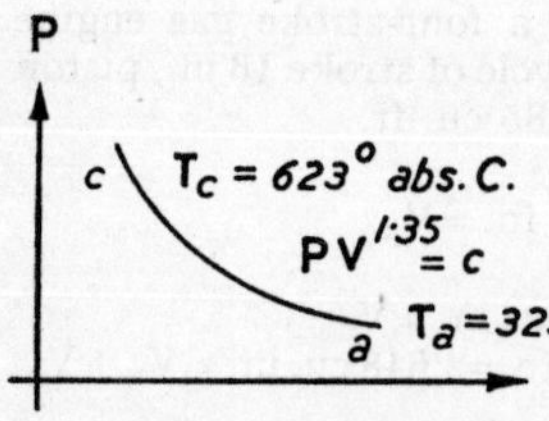

Fig. 16.9—*Compression of fuel-air mixture.*

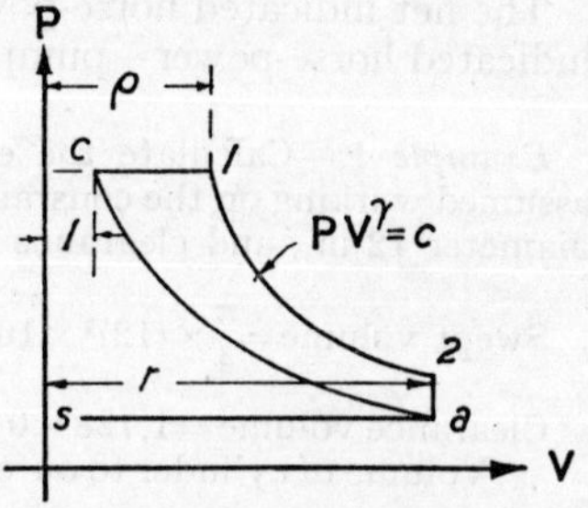

Fig. 16.10—*Diesel cycle.*

(*b*) If compression had been reversible and adiabatic the law of compression would have been $PV^{1 \cdot 4} =$ constant. If, also, the initial temperature of the charge = 100° C. the highest ratio of compression, which could be used avoiding pre-ignition at 350° C., would be

$$r = \left(\frac{623}{373}\right)^{\frac{1}{0 \cdot 4}} = 3 \cdot 6.$$

These last two examples indicate how r is influenced by the initial temperature of the charge before compression, and by the cooling of the cylinder which reduces the index from γ to n.

Type 3 Cycles in which heat is added at constant pressure with previous compression.—(*a*) *In which heat is rejected at constant volume.*—Diesel proposed the hypothetical cycle in which heat is added at constant pressure as shown in fig. 16.10. Heat is assumed added at constant pressure represented by *c1*. Reversible adiabatic expansion takes place from *1* to *2*. Heat is abstracted at a constant volume (*2a*) and compression of the working agent is assumed to be reversible and adiabatic (*ac*). Fig. 16.10 also represents the hypothetical indicator diagram of a two-stroke compression-ignition engine.

Heat supplied during $c1 = mC_p(T_1 - T_c)$

Heat rejected during $2a = mC_v(T_2 - T_a)$

$$\therefore \text{ Thermal efficiency of cycle} = 1 - \frac{C_v(T_2 - T_a)}{C_p(T_1 - T_c)}$$

$$= 1 - \frac{1}{\gamma}\left(\frac{T_2 - T_a}{T_1 - T_c}\right)$$

This expression can be reduced by the use of the relationships:—

$$\frac{T_c}{T_a} = \left(\frac{V_a}{V_c}\right)^{\gamma-1} = (r)^{\gamma-1} \qquad \therefore T_c = (r)^{\gamma-1}T_a$$

$$\frac{T_1}{T_c} = \frac{P_1V_1}{P_cV_c} = \frac{V_1}{V_c} = \rho \qquad \therefore T_1 = \rho T_c = \rho(r)^{\gamma-1}T_a$$

$$\frac{T_2}{T_1} = \left(\frac{V_1}{V_2}\right)^{\gamma-1} = \left(\frac{\rho}{r}\right)^{\gamma-1} \qquad \therefore T_2 = \left(\frac{\rho}{r}\right)^{\gamma-1}T_1 = \rho^{\gamma}T_a$$

Hence the efficiency of the above hypothetical Diesel cycle is

$$\eta = 1 - \frac{1}{\gamma}\left(\frac{\rho^{\gamma} - 1}{\rho - 1}\right)\left(\frac{1}{r}\right)^{\gamma-1}$$

(*b*) *In which heat is rejected at constant pressure.*—In this cycle (known as the Brayton cycle) heat would be added and rejected at constant pressure. This means that the expansion *12* would be carried on until P_2 is equal to the original pressure P_a (fig. 16.10). A mechanism similar to that mentioned for engine (*b*) of Type 2 would be required for making the expansion ratio greater than the compression ratio (r). It will be found that this cycle gives a theoretical efficiency the same as the Otto or constant volume cycle of Type 2, namely $1 - \left(\frac{1}{r}\right)^{\gamma-1}$. Thus, since, in the Diesel cycle, heat is rejected at constant volume (*i.e.* the toe of the diagram in which heat is rejected at constant pressure, is cut off) it follows that the factor $\frac{1}{\gamma}\left(\frac{\rho^{\gamma}-1}{\rho-1}\right)$ is always greater than unity and that, for the *same* compression ratio, the efficiency of the Otto cycle is greater than that of the Diesel cycle.

But since, in an engine working on the Diesel cycle, there is no combustible gas in the cylinder during compression, r, the compression ratio, is made higher than in an engine working on the Otto cycle; for the danger of pre-ignition does not arise. By increasing the ratio of compression r to, say, 16 or 18, a higher efficiency is obtainable in the Diesel than is possible in the Otto cycle which has a limiting r of about 6. The temperature due to compression in a compression-ignition engine is sufficient to ignite the fuel-oil which is injected into the cylinder near the end of compression; thus electric ignition or sparking apparatus is eliminated altogether from the engine. A high compression ratio sets up high pressures and stresses, which necessitate the use of much stronger and weightier parts in compression-ignition engines than in spark-ignition engines. Explosion pressures of over 800 Lb. per sq. in. are attained in compression-ignition engines.

Example 4.—In a compression-ignition engine the ratio of compression is 14. Find the temperature at the end of the compression stroke if: (*a*) the initial temperature of the air is 212° F. and compression is assumed reversible and adiabatic, $\gamma=1\cdot4$; (*b*) the initial temperature of the air is 122° F. and the law of compression $PV^{1\cdot35}=$ constant.

$$(a) \qquad \frac{T_c}{T_a}=\left(\frac{V_a}{V_c}\right)^{\gamma-1}=(r)^{\gamma-1}$$

$$\therefore\ T_c=T_a r^{\gamma-1}=672° \text{ abs. F.}\times(14)^{0\cdot4}=1934° \text{ abs. F.}$$

$\therefore$ Temperature after reversible adiabatic compression

$$=1{,}474° \text{ F. or } 800° \text{ C.}$$

$$(b) \qquad \frac{T_c}{T_a}=(r)^{n-1}. \quad \therefore\ T_{c1}=582° \text{ abs. F.}\times(14)^{0\cdot35}=1{,}466° \text{ abs. F.}$$

$$\therefore\ t_c=1{,}006° \text{ F. or } 540° \text{ C.}$$

Both these temperatures are above the ignition point of fuel oil, which is sprayed into the compressed air at the end of the compression stroke.

Example 5.—A compression-ignition engine has a stroke of 10·6 in. and a cylinder diameter of 6·5 in. The clearance volume is 26·5 cu. in., and the fuel injection takes place at constant pressure for 4·5 per cent. of the stroke. Find the efficiency of the engine assuming its works on the Diesel cycle.

$$\text{Stroke volume } V_k=\frac{\pi}{4}\times(6\cdot5)^2\times10\cdot6=352 \text{ cu. in.}$$

$$\text{Clearance volume } V_c=26\cdot5 \text{ cu. in.}$$

$$\therefore \text{ Total cylinder volume } V_k+V_c=378\cdot5 \text{ cu. in.}$$

$$\therefore \text{ Compression ratio } r=\frac{378\cdot5}{26\cdot5}=14\cdot26.$$

$$\rho=\frac{V_c+\frac{4\cdot5}{100}V_k}{V_c}=1+\frac{4\cdot5}{100}\times\frac{352}{26\cdot5}=1\cdot597.$$

$$\therefore \text{ Efficiency of Diesel cycle}=1-\left(\frac{1}{r}\right)^{\gamma-1}\left\{\frac{\rho^\gamma-1}{\gamma(\rho-1)}\right\}$$

$$=1-\left(\frac{1}{14\cdot26}\right)^{1\cdot4-1}\left\{\frac{(1\cdot597)^{1\cdot4}-1}{1\cdot4(1\cdot597-1)}\right\}$$

$$=1-0\cdot385$$

$$=61\cdot5 \text{ per cent.}$$

Example 6.—If the mean effective pressure of a working engine of dimensions given in Example 5 is 65 Lb. per sq. in. when the mass of oil consumed per cycle is 0·0003 lb., find, on the i.h.p. basis, the actual thermal efficiency of the engine and the relative thermal efficiency if the calorific value of the oil is 18,000 B.Th.U. per lb.

$$\text{Work done per cycle}=(\text{m.e.p.})\times A\times L$$

$$=65\,\frac{\text{Lb.}}{\text{in.}^2}\times\left\{\frac{\pi}{4}\times(6\cdot5)^2\right\}\text{in.}^2\times\left(\frac{10\cdot6}{12}\right)\text{ ft.}$$

$$=1{,}910 \text{ ft.-Lb.}=2\cdot46 \text{ B.Th.U.}$$

$$\text{Heat supplied per cycle}=0\cdot0003 \text{ lb./cycle}\times18{,}000 \text{ B.Th.U./lb.}$$

$$=5\cdot4 \text{ B.Th.U./cycle.}$$

$$\therefore \text{ Actual thermal efficiency on i.h.p. basis}=\frac{2\cdot46}{5\cdot4}=0\cdot45.$$

$\therefore$ Relative efficiency, or efficiency ratio (i.h.p. basis)

$$=\frac{0\cdot45}{0\cdot615}=0\cdot732 \text{ or } 73\cdot2 \text{ per cent.}$$

Type 4. Cycles in which heat is added part at constant volume and part at constant pressure with previous compression.—Fig. 16.11 represents the hypothetical indicator diagram for this cycle, in which heat is assumed to be added part at constant volume (*c1*) and part at constant pressure (*12*). Heat is rejected at constant volume (*3a*); compression (*ac*), and expansion (*23*), being reversible and adiabatic.

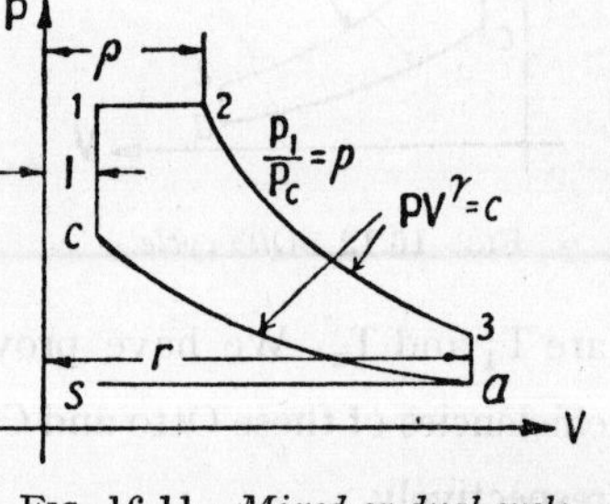

Fig. 16.11—*Mixed or dual cycle.*

Heat supplied $= mC_v(T_1 - T_c) + mC_p(T_2 - T_1)$

Heat rejected $= mC_v(T_3 - T_a)$

Hence the thermal efficiency of this hypothetical cycle

$$= 1 - \frac{\text{heat rejected}}{\text{heat supplied}} = 1 - \frac{C_v(T_3 - T_a)}{C_v(T_1 - T_c) + C_p(T_2 - T_1)}$$

This expression can be reduced by substitutions:

$$T_c = r^{\gamma-1}T_a;\ T_1 = pr^{\gamma-1}T_a;\ T_2 = \rho p r^{\gamma-1}T_a;\ T_3 = p\rho^{\gamma}T_a;$$

which give a thermal efficiency

$$\eta = 1 - \left(\frac{1}{r}\right)^{\gamma-1}\left\{\frac{p\rho^{\gamma} - 1}{(p-1) + \gamma p(\rho - 1)}\right\}$$

From this latter expression we can deduce both the Otto and the Diesel expressions for efficiency. For, suppose we make $\rho = 1$ (i.e. $V_2 = V_1$) or V_2 is decreased to equal V_1, so that the diagram becomes that of the Otto cycle of fig. 16.4, then, on substituting $\rho = 1$ in the above expression, we get $\eta = 1 - \left(\frac{1}{r}\right)^{\gamma-1}$. Similarly, if we make $p = 1$ (i.e. $P_c = P_1$) or P_c is increased to equal P_1, so that the diagram becomes that of the Diesel cycle of fig. 16.10, then, on substituting $p = 1$, we get $\eta = 1 - \left(\frac{1}{r}\right)^{\gamma-1}\left\{\frac{\rho^{\gamma} - 1}{\gamma(\rho - 1)}\right\}$. This is the expression previously proved for efficiency of the Diesel cycle.

6. Comparison of Efficiencies of Otto and Carnot Cycles operating between the Same Extreme Limits of Temperature.—It will be seen that the extreme limits of temperature in the Otto and Carnot cycles of figs. 16.12 and 16.13, respectively,

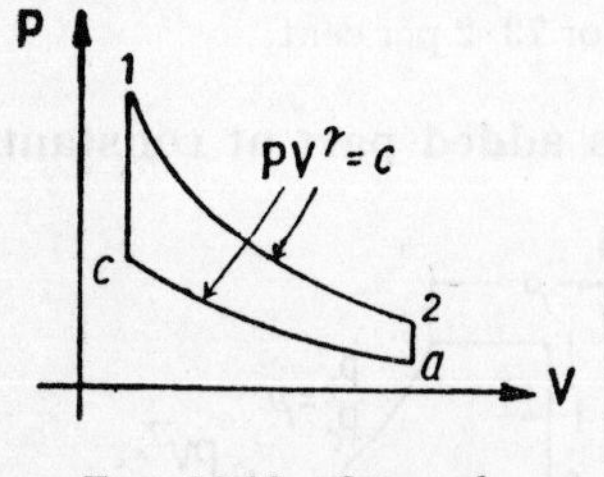

Fig. 16.12—*Otto cycle.*

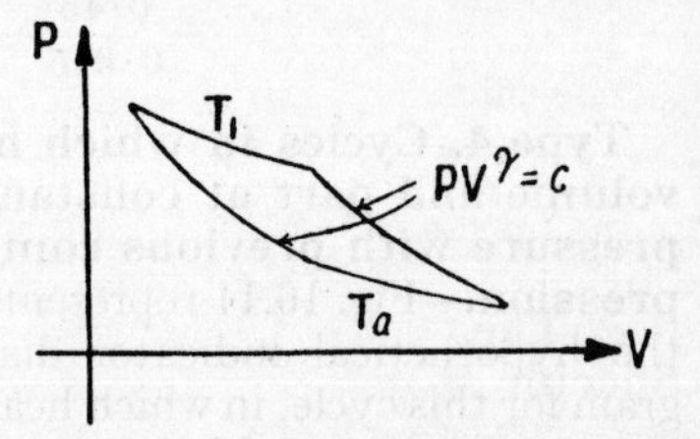

Fig. 16.13—*Carnot cycle.*

are T_1 and T_a. We have proved on pp. 357 and 348 that the efficiencies of these Otto and Carnot cycles are $\frac{T_c - T_a}{T_c}$ and $\frac{T_1 - T_a}{T_1}$ respectively.

In the Otto cycle of fig. 16.12, it is obvious that

$$T_a < T_c < T_1$$

$$\therefore \frac{T_a}{T_c} > \frac{T_a}{T_1}$$

$$\therefore 1 - \frac{T_a}{T_c} < 1 - \frac{T_a}{T_1}$$

$$\therefore \frac{T_c - T_a}{T_c} < \frac{T_1 - T_a}{T_1}$$

That is, the efficiency of an engine working on the Otto cycle is less than that of an engine working on the Carnot cycle (fig. **16.13**) between the same extreme limits of temperature.

Example.—Sketch the P,V diagram for the Otto and Carnot cycles superimposed, and find the efficiency of an Otto cycle engine relative to the Carnot cycle using the same maximum pressure 300 Lb. per sq. in. abs. and temperature 3,000° F., and the same minimum pressure 15 Lb. per sq. in. abs. and temperature 100° F. Assume the working fluid to be air. [I.Mech.E., Sec. A.]

Referring to fig. 16.12 we know that:

$$\frac{T_c}{T_a} = \left(\frac{P_c}{P_a}\right)^{\frac{\gamma-1}{\gamma}} \text{ and } \frac{T_1}{T_c} = \frac{P_1}{P_c}$$

Hence, $\left(\frac{T_c}{T_a}\right)^{\frac{\gamma}{\gamma-1}} \times \frac{T_1}{T_c} = \frac{P_c}{P_a} \times \frac{P_1}{P_c} = \frac{P_1}{P_a}$

Therefore, $T_c = T_a{}^{\gamma}\left(\frac{P_1}{P_a T_1}\right)^{\gamma-1} = (560)^{1\cdot4}\left(\frac{300}{15 \times 3460}\right)^{0\cdot4} = 896°$ abs. F.

The efficiency of the Otto cycle $= \frac{T_c - T_a}{T_c} = \frac{336}{896} = 0\cdot375$.

The efficiency of the Carnot cycle $= \frac{T_1 - T_a}{T_1} = \frac{2900}{3460} = 0\cdot838$

Thus, the efficiency of the Otto cycle relative to the Carnot cycle is 44·7 per cent.

7. The "Air Standard Efficiency," and Variation of Specific Heats of Gases.—In paragraph 5 four types of cycles were considered, and an expression for the thermal efficiency of each was developed from their hypothetical indicator diagrams. No real engine can, of course, follow exactly those theoretical cycles, because heat, being supplied by the process of combustion, cannot be added strictly at constant volume or at constant pressure, nor can any actual expansion or compression be carried out in a strictly reversible adiabatic manner or without friction.

Further, the working agent was assumed to be air or gas which never left the cylinder, and to have constant values for specific heats, which is not the case in practice. Also, in actual reciprocating-piston internal-combustion engines, although the mechanism undergoes a cycle of operations, the working agent does not undergo a cyclic process, for it is not brought back to its original condition but is replaced by a new charge of mixture or air.

The expression $\eta=1-\left(\frac{1}{r}\right)^{\gamma-1}$ has become known as the "air standard efficiency" because it is usually taken as a standard of comparison for the performance of actual internal-combustion engines. What is true of imaginary engines as regards thermal efficiency increasing with r is true of actual engines. The limiting r in petrol engines as set by pre-ignition considerations is about 6, whereas in compression-ignition engines r is taken up to about 18. It will be remembered that the expression was proved as the efficiency of the Otto or constant-volume cycle on the assumption that the specific heat C_v remained constant over the range of temperature involved. In actual engines the working agent, after combustion, is neither a perfect gas, nor even air, but a mixture containing nitrogen, oxygen, water vapour, carbon dioxide and carbon monoxide; and the specific heats of these gases vary with temperature. At high temperatures the specific heats increase considerably; hence, during combustion, a lower maximum temperature is produced in the cylinder of an engine (due to an increase in specific heat) than would be produced if the specific heat remained constant. The expression for air standard efficiency thus always gives a higher value than can be attained in an actual engine.

In high-speed compression-ignition engines the rate of rise of pressure is so high that the assumption made in the Diesel cycle, namely, that heat is added at constant pressure, is far from what really happens, for in many injection engines the increase of pressure is as rapid as in petrol engines. Because of this it is thought that the expression $\eta=1-\left(\frac{1}{r}\right)^{\gamma-1}$ may quite reasonably be taken as the standard of comparison for compression-ignition engines as well as for engines working with electric ignition. Thus, the efficiencies of all internal-combustion engines are usually compared with the "air standard efficiency" as calculated from the above expression. It will be remembered, when dealing with steam, that all steam engine plant is compared with one standard cycle, namely, the Rankine cycle. The "air standard efficiency" for internal combustion engines is therefore analogous to the Rankine efficiency for steam engines.

8. Combustion Turbines or Gas Turbines.—Fig. 16.14 is a simple diagrammatic sketch of a continuous-combustion or

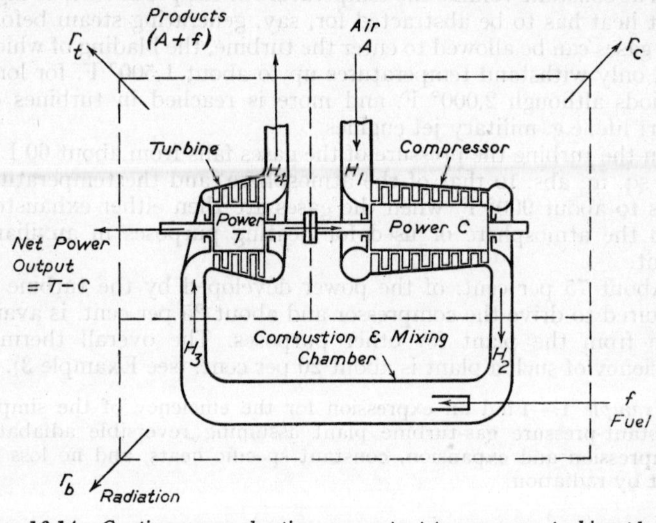

FIG. 16.14—*Continuous combustion or constant-pressure gas-turbine plant.*

constant-pressure gas-turbine plant. Such engines are internal-combustion engines of the rotary type as distinct from the reciprocating-piston type.

Air from the atmosphere is compressed in an axial-flow compressor and delivered at about 60 Lb. per sq. in. abs. to the combustion chamber into which fuel, say kerosene ($C_{12}H_{24}$), is injected through burners or nozzles. Combustion is continuous in the constant pressure type of gas-turbine plant, and takes place in the primary air stream which flows through apertures into an inner flame-tube or high-temperature chamber which is necessary in order to achieve rapid and efficient combustion. The flame tube is situated within the main casing of the combustion chamber, and the secondary air flows between this tube and the outer casing of the combustion chamber and mixes with the products of combustion to reduce the resultant gas temperature to, say, 1,500° F., this being about the limit of endurance of the material of which the turbine blades are made.

The hypothetical P,V diagram for the constant-pressure combustion turbine is that of Joule's air engine shown in fig. 15.14, and for the constant volume type that of the Atkinson cycle shown in fig. 16.5, the products of combustion being expanded in the turbine until atmospheric pressure is reached. After combustion at constant volume the temperature of the products is so high that heat has to be abstracted for, say, generating steam before the gases can be allowed to enter the turbine, the blading of which will only withstand temperatures up to about 1,500° F. for long periods although 2,000° F. and more is reached in turbines of short life, e.g. military jet engines.

In the turbine the pressure of the gases falls from about 60 Lb. per sq. in. abs. to that of the atmosphere, and the temperature falls to about 900° F. when the gases are then either exhausted into the atmosphere or used for heating purposes in auxiliary plant.

About 75 per cent. of the power developed by the turbine is required to drive the compressor and about 25 per cent. is available from the plant for other purposes. The overall thermal efficiency of such a plant is about 20 per cent. (see Example 3).

Example 1.—Find an expression for the efficiency of the simple constant-pressure gas-turbine plant assuming reversible adiabatic compression and expansion, constant specific heats, and no loss of heat by radiation.

The hypothetical cycle would be 1, 2*a*, 3, 4*a*, 1 of fig. 20.8, and the efficiency is $\dfrac{\text{work done}}{\text{heat supplied}}$

i.e.
$$\eta = 1 - \frac{\text{heat rejected}}{\text{heat supplied}} = 1 - \frac{(H_{4a} - H_1)}{(H_3 - H_{2a})}$$
$$= 1 - \frac{C_P(T_{4a} - T_1)}{C_P(T_3 - T_{2a})}$$

or, since
$$\frac{T_{4a}}{T_3} = \frac{T_1}{T_{2a}} = \left(\frac{P_1}{P_2}\right)^{\frac{\gamma-1}{\gamma}} = \left(\frac{1}{r_P}\right)^{\frac{\gamma-1}{\gamma}} = \frac{1}{Z}$$

and
$$\frac{T_{4a} - T_1}{T_3 - T_{2a}} = \frac{T_1}{T_{2a}} = \frac{1}{Z}$$

the expression for the efficiency of the ideal hypothetical cycle is
$$\eta = 1 - \left(\frac{1}{r_P}\right)^{\frac{\gamma-1}{\gamma}} = 1 - \frac{1}{Z}$$

where r_P is the pressure ratio and Z is the ratio of the temperatures at the extremes of reversible adiabatic compression or expansion.

Example 2.—If the constant pressure in a simple gas-turbine plant are 14·7 and 60 Lb. per sq. in. abs. and $\gamma=1\cdot4$, calculate the efficiency of the ideal hypothetical cycle.

$$Z=(r_P)^{\frac{\gamma-1}{\gamma}}=\left(\frac{60}{14\cdot7}\right)^{\frac{0\cdot4}{1\cdot4}}=1\cdot494.$$

Hence, the efficiency of the ideal hypothetical cycle is

$$\eta=1-\frac{1}{Z}=1-0\cdot67=0\cdot33 \text{ or } 33 \text{ per cent.}$$

In actual plant, however, neither the compression nor expansion would be reversible adiabatic processes, since in actual processes there are always eddies, turbulence and friction. Also, C_P would increase slightly with temperature. Thus, the temperatures after actual (i.e. irreversible) adiabatic compression (T_2) and expansion (T_4) would be higher than those (T_{2a} and T_{4a}) which would result if reversible adiabatic compression and expansion could take place. This can be seen on fig. 20.8 and the effect of it is seen numerically in Example 3.

The energy equations for the separate units composing the simple open-circuit plant of fig. 16.14, where H represents the enthalpy or total heat per unit mass of working agent, A and f represent rate of mass flow of air and fuel, respectively, r represents the rate of energy flow to the surroundings by radiation, and T and C are the rates at which energy is delivered and required by the turbine and compressor, respectively, can be drawn up as follows:

Compressor unit: $AH_1+C=AH_2+r_c$

Combustion and mixing chamber:

$$AH_2+f(h+Q_P)=(A+f)H_3+r_b$$

where h is the enthalpy per unit mass of fuel and Q_P the calorific value per unit mass of fuel.

Turbine unit: $(A+f)H_3=(T-C)+C+(A+f)H_4+r_t$

Rearranging these equations for addition, we get

$$0=-C+A(H_2-H_1)+r_c$$
$$f(h+Q_P)=(A+f)H_3-AH_2+r_b$$
$$0=T+(A+f)(H_4-H_3)+r_t$$

which, when added, give the equation

$$f(h+Q_P)=(T-C)+\{(A+f)H_4-AH_1\}+\Sigma r$$

This last equation is seen on referring to fig. 16.14 to be the energy equation for the plant as a whole, the overall efficiency of which is

$$\eta_o = \frac{T - C}{f(h+Q_P)} = 1 - \frac{\{(A+f)H_4 - AH_1\} + \Sigma r}{f(h+Q_P)}$$

Example 3.—The gas-turbine plant of fig. 16.14 uses 3 lb. of air per second. The adiabatic efficiencies of the compressor and turbine are 0·85 and 0·87, respectively. Air enters the compressor at 14·7 Lb./in.² abs. and 60° F. and leaves at 60 Lb./in.² abs. It is then raised at constant pressure to a temperature of 1900° abs. F. by the combustion of 3 lb. of fuel per minute, the efficiency of the combustion process being 98 per cent. Calculate the horse-power required to drive the compressor, the net output and the overall efficiency of the plant. The mean specific heats at constant pressure for the air and products of combustion may be taken as 0·24 and 0·27 B.Th.U. per lb. ° F., and the mechanical efficiencies of the turbine and compressor 99 per cent. Estimate the temperature of the gases leaving the turbine.

During compression $\gamma_c = \frac{1}{1 - R/C_P}$, since $C_P - C_V = R$ and $\gamma = C_P/C_V$.

Hence, since $\frac{R}{C_P} = 53\cdot3 \frac{\text{ft.-Lb.}}{\text{lb. °F.}} \times \frac{\text{lb. °F.}}{0\cdot24 \text{ B.Th.U.}}\left[\frac{\text{B.Th.U.}}{778 \text{ ft.-Lb.}}\right] = 0\cdot2855$

$$\gamma_c = \frac{1}{0\cdot7145} = 1\cdot4$$

and the ratio of the absolute temperatures of the terminal points of reversible adiabatic compression would be

$$\frac{T_{2a}}{T_1} = \left(\frac{P_2}{P_1}\right)^{\frac{\gamma_c - 1}{\gamma_c}} = \left(\frac{60}{14\cdot7}\right)^{\frac{0\cdot4}{1\cdot4}} = 1\cdot494 = Z_c$$

Thus, $T_{2a} = 1\cdot494 \times 520°$ abs. F. $= 777°$ abs. F., and the power required to drive the compressor is, referring to fig. 16.14,

$$C = \frac{A(H_2 - H_1)}{{}_c\eta_m}, \text{ where } {}_c\eta_m \text{ is its mechanical efficiency,}$$

i.e. $$C = \frac{A \times {}_c\bar{C}_P(T_2 - T_1)}{{}_c\eta_m} = \frac{A \times {}_c\bar{C}_P(T_{2a} - T_1)}{{}_c\eta_m \cdot {}_c\eta_a}$$

$$= \frac{180\frac{\text{lb.}}{\text{min.}} \times 0\cdot24 \frac{\text{B.Th.U.}}{\text{lb.° F.}}(777 - 520)° \text{ F.}}{0\cdot99 \times 0\cdot85}\left[\frac{778 \text{ ft.-Lb.}}{\text{B.Th.U.}}\right]\left[\frac{33{,}000 \text{ ft.-Lb.}}{\text{h.p. min.}}\right]$$

$$= 311 \text{ h-p.}$$

During expansion in the turbine $\gamma_t = \frac{1}{1 - R/C_P}$, i.e. assuming R for gases in the turbine is the same as for air which, of course, constitutes the bulk of the expanding gas mixture,

$$\frac{R}{C_p}=53\cdot3\,\frac{\text{ft.-Lb.}}{\text{lb. °F.}}\times\frac{\text{lb. °F.}}{0\cdot27\text{ B.Th.U.}}\left[\frac{\text{B.Th.U.}}{778\text{ ft.-Lb.}}\right]=0\cdot2535$$

and $\gamma_t=\dfrac{1}{0\cdot7465}=1\cdot34.$

Hence, the ratio of the absolute temperatures of the terminal points of reversible adiabatic expansion would be

$$\frac{T_3}{T_{4a}}=\left(\frac{P_3}{P_4}\right)^{\frac{\gamma_t-1}{\gamma_t}}=\left(\frac{60}{14\cdot7}\right)^{\frac{0\cdot34}{1\cdot34}}=1\cdot429=Z_t$$

Thus, $T_{4a}=\dfrac{1900°\text{ abs. F.}}{1\cdot429}=1330°$ abs. F., and the power delivered along the turbine shaft is

$$T=(A+f)(H_3-H_4)_t\eta_m=(A+f)_t\bar{C}_p(T_3-T_{4a})_t\eta_a\cdot{}_t\eta_m$$
$$=183\,\frac{\text{lb.}}{\text{min.}}\times0\cdot27\,\frac{\text{B.Th.U.}}{\text{lb. °F.}}\times(1900-1330)°\text{ F.}\times0\cdot87\times0\cdot99$$
$$=24{,}250\,\frac{\text{B.Th.U.}}{\text{min.}}\left[\frac{778\text{ ft.-Lb.}}{\text{B.Th.U.}}\right]\left[\frac{\text{h-p. min.}}{33{,}000\text{ ft.-Lb.}}\right]$$
$$=572\text{ h.p.}$$

The rate at which energy is supplied in the fuel

$$=\frac{\text{rate at which heat is produced in combustion chamber}}{\text{efficiency of combustion}}$$

$$=\frac{(A+f)(H_3-H_2)}{\eta_b}=\frac{(A+f)_b\bar{C}_p}{\eta_b}\left\{(T_3-T_1)-\frac{(T_{2a}-T_1)}{{}_c\eta_a}\right\}$$

since $\quad {}_c\eta_a=\dfrac{T_{2a}-T_1}{T_2-T_1}$, i.e. $T_2=T_1+\dfrac{(T_{2a}-T_1)}{{}_c\eta_a}$

Thus, the rate of supply of energy in the fuel is

$$183\,\frac{\text{lb.}}{\text{min.}}\times0\cdot27\,\frac{\text{B.Th.U.}}{\text{lb. °F.}}\times\frac{1}{0\cdot98}\left\{(1900-520)-\left(\frac{777-520}{0\cdot85}\right)\right\}\text{°F.}$$
$$=54{,}300\text{ B.Th.U. per min.}$$

The net output of the plant is $572-311=261$ h.p. and the overall efficiency is

$$\frac{261\text{ h.p.}\left[\dfrac{33{,}000\text{ ft.-Lb.}}{\text{h.p. min.}}\right]\left[\dfrac{\text{B.Th.U.}}{778\text{ ft.-Lb.}}\right]}{54{,}300\,\dfrac{\text{B.Th.U.}}{\text{min.}}}=0\cdot204\text{ or }20\cdot4\text{ per cent.}$$

and the temperature of the gases leaving the turbine is

$$T_4=T_3-{}_t\eta_a(T_3-T_{4a})=1900°\text{ abs. F.}-0\cdot87(1900-1330)°\text{ abs. F.}$$
$$=1404°\text{ abs. F. or }944°\text{ F.}$$

The above Example shows that the gases leave the turbine at a relatively high temperature T_4. If this is considerably higher than the temperature T_2 of the air leaving the compressor, some of the heat of the exhaust gases can be transferred to the air leaving the compressor before the air enters the combustion chamber or heater of a closed-circuit plant as in fig. 2.22. Thus, the amount of fuel required to raise the temperature of the working agent to its maximum value (T_4 in fig. 2.22) will be reduced. This will increase the overall efficiency of the plant, since slightly less fuel will be required to raise the temperature of the working agent to the permissible temperature of, say, 1,500° F. Also, intercooling in the compressor would reduce the power required to drive the compressor and thus increase the output of the plant. With these additions together with reheating, overall efficiencies of over 30 per cent. can be achieved.

In the case of the closed-circuit gas-turbine plant with a heat exchanger as shown diagrammatically in fig. 2.22 the working agent follows the cycle 1, 2, 3, 4, 5, 6, 1 of fig. 20.9, and from which it is seen (trace 2, 3) that the working agent is preheated before it enters the heater by heat recovered (trace 5, 6) from the exhaust of the turbine. The temperature difference available for heat recovery in the heat exchanger is T_5-T_2, but in practice only about 75 per cent. of the possible heat is transferred to the air flowing from the compressor towards the heater or combustion chamber.

The introduction of a heat exchanger will obviously improve the efficiency of the plant for, although the power output is not increased, the amount of fuel is reduced, since heat is needed only to raise the temperature of the working agent from T_3 to T_4 instead of from T_2 to T_4 which would be the case if there were no heat exchanger.

The efficiency of the hypothetical cycle of figs. 2.22 and 20.9 is

$$\eta=\frac{\text{Work done W}}{\text{Heat supplied}}=\frac{\text{T}-\text{C}}{\text{Heat supplied}}=\frac{(H_4-H_5)-(H_2-H_1)}{(H_4-H_3)},$$

where H is the enthalpy or total heat per unit mass of working agent. Thus, if the specific heat C_P be assumed to remain constant, the efficiency of the hypothetical cycle may be written

$$\eta=\frac{(T_4-T_5)-(T_2-T_1)}{(T_4-T_3)}.$$

EXERCISES ON CHAPTER 16

(i)

1. Calculate the piston diameter and stroke of a four-stroke gas engine which develops 25 b.h.p. at 300 r.p.m. with a mechanical efficiency of 80 per cent. The mean effective pressure is 85 Lb. per sq. in. and the stroke of the engine $1\frac{1}{2}$ times the piston diameter.

2. If the clearance volume of the engine of Question 1 is 25 per cent. of the swept volume, calculate the efficiency of the constant-volume cycle. If the relative thermal efficiency, on the i.h.p. basis, is 55 per cent., calculate the consumption of gas in cu. ft. per b.h.p.-hour if the calorific value of the gas is 496 B.Th.U. per cu. ft.

3. Show by means of a curve how the efficiency of the Otto cycle increases as the compression ratio increases. Take compression ratios $r=2, 3, 4, 5, 7, 10, 20, 60, 100$.

4. The piston diameter and stroke of a compression-ignition engine are 16 in. and 21 in., respectively. Air is supplied at 20 Lb. per sq. in. abs. and 64° F. The pressure at the end of adiabatic compression is 480 Lb. per sq. in. abs. Find the temperature at the end of compression, the clearance volume, and the compression ratio of the engine.

5. If injection of fuel in the engine of Question 4 takes place at constant pressure for $\frac{1}{6}$ of the stroke, calculate the value of ρ and the efficiency of the Diesel cycle.

6. Calculate the stroke and diameter of a four-stroke gas engine to develop 20 i.h.p. when running at 300 r.p.m. The stroke is to be $1\frac{1}{2}\times$piston diameter, the clearance volume $\frac{1}{4}$ of the swept volume, maximum pressure 320 Lb. per sq. in. abs., pressure before compression 14·7 Lb. per sq. in. abs. The law of the compression is $PV^{1\cdot2}=$constant, and the law of expansion curve is $PV^{1\cdot4}=$constant.

7. In an ideal air engine receiving heat at constant pressure ($C_p=0\cdot238$) and rejecting heat at constant volume ($C_v=0\cdot169$) the expansion and compression are assumed to be reversible and adiabatic. The ratio of compression is 15 and of expansion is 7. The temperature at the beginning of compression is 104° F., and the pressure is 15 Lb. per sq. in. abs. The pressure at release is 45 Lb. per sq. in. abs. Find the work done per lb. of air and the efficiency of the cycle.

(ii)

8. Prove that the coefficient of performance of an ideal refrigerator assumed working on the reversed Carnot cycle is $\frac{T_2}{T_1-T_2}$, where T_2 is the temperature of the cold body from which heat is abstracted and T_1 the temperature of the hot body into which heat is rejected.

9. (*a*) Sketch a typical indicator diagram for a four-stroke gas or petrol engine and show the manner in which the diagram is modified when the power of the engine is reduced by throttling.

(*b*) In a brake test of a petrol engine running at 2,200 r.p.m. the weight on the brake was 32 Lb. at a radius of 1·5 ft. from the centre of the shaft. The engine used 12·6 lb. of petrol per hour, of calorific value 18,200 B.Th.U. per lb. The compression ratio was 5·5. Calculate the thermal efficiency of the engine and find the ratio of this efficiency to that of an air-standard cycle of the same compression ratio. [Part I, B.Sc. Lond.]

10. Explain briefly, with the aid of a P,V diagram, the operation of the Otto or constant volume four-stroke cycle for a gas engine. An engine working with a constant volume cycle and having a compression ratio 12/1 takes in the mixture of gas and air at 14·5 Lb. per sq. in. abs. The maximum pressure reached is 800 Lb. per sq. in. abs. Assuming that compression and expansion both take place according to the relation $PV^{1\cdot 3}$=constant, what is the mean effective pressure and the brake horse-power for a 4-inch diameter cylinder, four-stroke, four-cylinder engine with a mean piston speed of 2,000 ft. per min. and mechanical efficiency 75 per cent.?

If the charge is drawn in with a temperature 120° F. what will be the temperature after compression and the maximum temperature in the cycle? [I.Mech.E., Sec. A.]

11. A quantity of gas at atmospheric pressure in a cylinder has a volume of 5 cu. ft. at a temperature of 150° F. It is taken through the following cycle of operations:—

(*a*) Isothermal compression until the pressure is 15 atmospheres.

(*b*) Heat addition at constant volume, the temperature being raised by 2,000° F.

(*c*) Heat addition at constant pressure, the volume being increased by 50 per cent.

(*d*) Reversible adiabatic expansion to its original volume.

(*e*) Cooling at constant volume, so that the gas is brought to its initial state.

Find the pressure, volume and the temperature at the end of each stage of the cycle and tabulate the values. Sketch a P,V diagram to show the stages. $C_p=0\cdot 237$; $C_v=0\cdot 169$ B.Th.U./lb.° F. [Part I, B.Sc. Lond.]

12. Find the efficiency of the dual or mixed cycle in which air is compressed reversibly and adiabatically from 14 Lb. per sq. in. abs. and 240° F. to 550 Lb. per sq. in. abs., after which 60 per cent. of the heat supplied is supplied at constant volume raising the pressure to 850 Lb. per sq. in. abs. The remainder of the heat supplied is supplied at constant pressure, after which expansion is adiabatic and reversible to the end of the stroke. $C_p=0\cdot 238$ and $C_v=0\cdot 170$ B.Th.U./lb. °F.

13. An ideal engine is assumed to work with air on the Carnot cycle, heat being received at 800° F. and rejected at 70° F. If the maximum and minimum pressures are 1,800 Lb. per sq. in. abs. and 15 Lb. per sq. in. abs., respectively, what will be the work done per pound of air? [I.Mech.E., Sec. A.]

14. Explain the term *reversible process*, with special reference to Carnot's cycle, and prove that all engines working on a reversible cycle have the same efficiency between the same temperature limits.

Calculate the heat required per horse-power per minute for a steam engine with an efficiency of 62 per cent. of the Carnot efficiency operating between the temperatures 150° F. and 350° F. [I.Mech.E., Sec. A.]

15. Air enters the first of two compressors of a gas-turbine plant at 15 Lb. per sq. in. abs. and 55° F. Assuming that compression is reversible and adiabatic and that the pressure ratio in each compressor is 3 to 1, calculate the efficiency of the plant and the output as shaft horse-power per lb. of air/sec. if the air is delivered from the second compressor to a heater and raised to a temperature of 1,300° F. at constant pressure and then passed to a turbine in which it is assumed to expand reversibly and adiabatically to a pressure of 15 Lb. per sq. in. abs. State briefly how and why the actual cycle would differ from the above hypothetical cycle.

16. If the mechanical efficiencies of the turbine and of the compressors of the plant in Question 15 are 98 per cent. and the adiabatic efficiency of both is 85 per cent., calculate the efficiency of tho plant and the shaft horse-power per lb. of air/sec. Take $\gamma=1\cdot4$ and $C_p=0\cdot238$ B.Th.U./lb. °F.

17. A gas-turbine plant is assumed to work on the Joule (or Brayton) cycle using air as working agent. Compression and expansion take place reversibly and adiabatically according to the law PV^γ constant and heat is added and rejected at constant pressure. Prove that the efficiency of the cycle is $1-\left(\frac{1}{r}\right)^{\frac{\gamma-1}{\gamma}}$, where r is the ratio of the pressure limits. Also, show that the work done is a maximum when the temperatures after completion of compression and expansion are equal, the temperatures of the air entering the compressor and turbine being fixed.

Calculate the maximum output per lb. of air, the efficiency and pressure ratio when maximum output occurs if the air enters the compressor at 60° F. and the turbine at 1,620° F. Why cannot this performance be realised in practice? Take $\gamma=1\cdot4$ and C_p for air $=0\cdot24$ B.Th.U./lb. °F.

18. The pressure ratio in a continuous-combustion gas-turbine plant is $4\cdot5$. Air at $57\cdot2$° F. enters the compressor whose adiabatic efficiency is 85 per cent. A heat exchanger transfers 60 per cent. of the heat which is available because of the difference in temperature in the gases rejected from the turbine and the air leaving the compressor. The maximum temperature of the gases entering the turbine unit is 1,470° F., and the gases expand down to the initial pressure, the adiabatic efficiency of expansion in the turbine being 82 per cent. Estimate the air to fuel ratio by weight and the overall efficiency of the plant if the heating value of the fuel is 18,000 B.Th.U. per lb. and C_p and C_v are assumed constant at $0\cdot238$ and $0\cdot17$ B.Th.U. per lb. °F. throughout.

19. Air at $14\cdot7$ Lb./in.^{2} abs. and 50° F. is drawn from the atmosphere into the uncooled compressor of an open-circuit gas turbine installation. The pressure ratio is 3 and the rise in temperature due to adiabatic compression is 15 per cent. greater than that which would occur if reversible adiabatic compression could be achieved. Combustion at constant pressure raises the temperature of the gas to 900° F., the fuel being kerosene of calorific value, 18,500 B.Th.U.

per lb. The adiabatic efficiency of expansion of gases in the turbine down to atmospheric pressure may be taken as 85 per cent. and C_p the same throughout the cycle. Calculate :

(i) the horse-power required to drive the compressor if air is used at the rate of 4·825 tons per hour;
(ii) the horse-power developed by the turbine;
(iii) the net horse-power available from the plant;
(iv) the overall efficiency of the plant;
(v) the specific output in B.Th.U. per lb. of air; and
(vi) the air to fuel ratio by weight.

20. Describe carefully the processes of a Carnot cycle. Discuss the practicability of each process where the working substance is (*a*) a gas, (*b*) a vapour, illustrating your remarks by pressure volume diagrams.

An engine working with air in an Otto cycle has a thermal efficiency relative to a corresponding Carnot cycle of 70 per cent. If the temperature limits of the cycles are 1,740° F. and 60° F., estimate the compression ratio of the Otto cycle engine.

[I.Mec.E., Sec. A.]

CHAPTER 17

CARBURATION; FUEL-INJECTION; AIR SUPPLY; AND COMBUSTION

1. Fuel-air Mixtures and Mixture Strength.—In gas engines the fuel is supplied in the gaseous state, and the oxygen of the air, with which the fuel-gas mixes, has a better chance of contacting more individual fuel molecules than when liquid or pulverised solid fuels are used, and, in consequence, a more complete combustion process is to be expected.

In engines using liquid fuels the fuel is either vaporised in air, as in spark-ignition engines, or split up into very small droplets, as when injected into compression-ignition engines—the droplets still containing, however, a very large number of molecules. It is more difficult to achieve complete combustion of the heavier fuel-oils used in compression-ignition engines than of the highly volatile liquid fuels used, say, with a carburettor in spark-ignition engines.

The efficiency of the process of combustion depends upon how well the fuel has been split up and mixed with the oxygen molecules of the air before and during combustion. In spark-ignition engines a more or less gaseous and homogeneous fuel-air mixture is compressed, and there is little difficulty in the whole of the fuel particles finding the oxygen necessary for complete combustion if an excess of air is present, or of consuming the whole of the oxygen in a "rich" fuel-air mixture. For the average petrol used in spark-ignition engines, the chemically-correct mixture is about 15 to 1 of air to petrol by weight. Experiment shows, however, that maximum power is developed with a mixture-strength about 10 to 15 per cent. richer than the chemically correct one because of the possibility of the complete consumption of the oxygen in the charge and also because of the dissociation which occurs at high temperatures. The power falls off as the mixture strength is weakened and, if the air to fuel ratio increases above, say, 20 to 1, combustion may be so slow as to continue during the whole of the expansion stroke as indicated in fig. 17.1 and, if the gases are still burning when the inlet valve opens, the incoming charge may be ignited and cause a back-fire along the induction manifold. Weak mixtures may be caused by air leaks in the induction system or by partially choked or incorrect setting of carburettor jets.

For starting up, and for slow running of spark-ignition engines, a rich mixture is desirable and, also, in order that, when the throttle of the carburettor is opened resulting in an increased flow of air, the mixture will not be suddenly weakened below the strength on which the engine will not run.

One way of specifying mixture strength is in relation to the air used. Thus, if a mass of air A is used per unit mass of fuel which

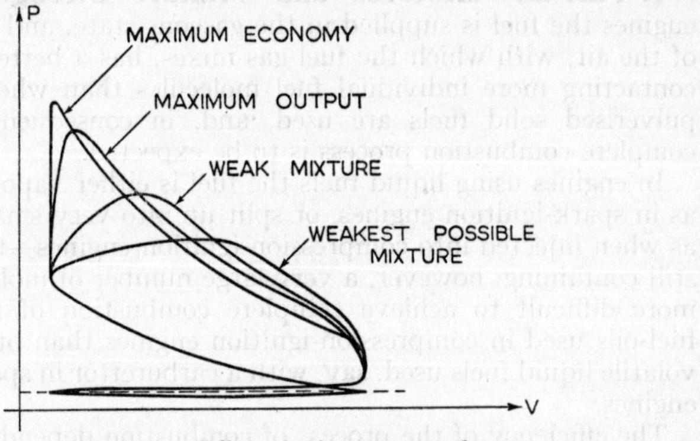

FIG. 17.1—*Effect of mixture strength.*

requires a mass of air T for (theoretically) perfect combustion, the percentage of air excess used is $\left(\frac{A-T}{T}\right)\times 100=x$ per cent.; and the actual air used per unit mass of fuel is $A=T\left(1+\frac{x}{100}\right)$, which also represents the mixture strength by weight. Hence, the fuel-air mixture may be said to be x per cent. weak or x per cent. rich according as x is positive or negative, respectively.

A second way of specifying mixture strength is in relation to the fuel used. Thus, f, the percentage richness or weakness can be specified as the percentage of fuel which is present in excess of or below that required to "load" the theoretical air correctly. Thus, if 1 lb. of fuel is required to load a mass $T=t$ lb. of air for perfect combustion, and f per cent. more fuel is supplied, the mixture strength is $\frac{T}{F}=\frac{t}{\left(1+\frac{f}{100}\right)}$ where t and f are numbers and T and F are quantities, *i.e.* numbers × units. The mass of fuel mixed with the theoretical air is $F=\left(1+\frac{f}{100}\right)$ lb. and the mixture may be said to be f per cent. rich or weak according as f is positive or negative, respectively.

Example 1.—If 15 lb. of air are required theoretically for the perfect combustion of 1 lb. of petrol, estimate the mixture strength when (*a*) 20 per cent. rich, and (*b*) 10 per cent. weak; taking these percentages to refer to:

(i) a deficiency or excess of air.
(ii) an excess or deficiency of petrol.

(i) Mixture strength $=A=T\left(1+\frac{x}{100}\right)$

In case (*a*) $x=-20$, $\therefore$ mixture strength $=15\left(1-\frac{20}{100}\right)$

$=12$ lb. of air per lb. of petrol.

In case (*b*) $x=+10$, $\therefore$ mixture strength $=15\left(1+\frac{10}{100}\right)$

$=16\cdot5$ lb. of air per lb. of petrol.

(ii) Mixture strength $=\frac{T}{F}=\frac{t}{\left(1+\frac{f}{100}\right)}$

In case (*a*) $f=20$, $\therefore$ mixture strength $=\frac{15}{1+\frac{20}{100}}$

$=12\cdot5$ lb. of air per lb. of petrol.

In case (*b*) $f=-10$, $\therefore$ mixture strength $=\frac{15}{1-\frac{10}{100}}$

$=16\cdot7$ lb. of air per lb. of petrol.

Example 2.—If 15 lb. of air are required theoretically for the perfect combustion of 1 lb. of fuel, and a mixture strength of 20 is actually used in an engine, find the percentage weakness of the mixture used basing the calculation (*a*) on an excess of air; (*b*) on a deficiency of fuel.

(*a*) Mixture strength $=A=T\left(1+\frac{x}{100}\right)$

Hence, $x=\left(\frac{A}{T}-1\right)100=\left(\frac{20}{15}-1\right)\times 100=33$ per cent.

Thus, based on an excess of air, calculation shows the mixture to be 33 per cent. weak.

(*b*) Mixture strength $=\frac{T}{F}=\frac{t}{1+\frac{f}{100}}=s$

Hence, $f=\left(\frac{t}{s}-1\right)100=\left(\frac{15}{20}-1\right)\times 100=-25$ per cent.

Thus, based on a deficiency of fuel, the mixture is 25 per cent. weak.

2. Carburettors and Carburation.—Petrol alone is not an explosive, but when petrol vapour is mixed with a certain quantity of air the mixture can be exploded. Mixing petrol vapour with air is called carburation, and the instrument for achieving this is called a carburettor. The object of a carburettor is to supply an explosive mixture of petrol vapour in the correct proportion of air, to the cylinder of an engine. There is usually no difficulty in supplying a working mixture, but difficulties arise when an economical mixture is required at all speeds and in all states of the atmosphere.

Petrol is easily evaporated, as will be noticed by the quick disappearance of a small quantity exposed to the atmosphere. By drawing air over petrol, evaporation occurs much more rapidly. A carburettor consists fundamentally of a float-chamber which regulates the supply of petrol to a jet past which air is flowing at a speed sufficiently high to enable a fine spray of petrol to be drawn into the air-stream. Thus, the basic principle employed in the working of a carburettor is that of creating a pressure-difference between the float chamber and an open-ended pipe in the choke or Venturi tube. The increased velocity of the air-stream at the throat results (by Bernoulli's theorem $\frac{P}{w}+\frac{v^2}{2g}+Z=\text{constant}$) in a reduced pressure there. The tube delivering petrol into the air is situated in the throat where the velocity of the air-stream is greatest and, therefore, where the pressure is lowest. Changes in the rate of air flow automatically produce changes in the rate at which fuel flows into the choke tube.

It is easy to supply a good mixture when the air flow is steady. But the rate of flow of air very often changes, and the speed of an engine is regulated by making the air flow past the jet greater or less by opening or closing the throttle. When an increase in speed is desired the accelerator pedal is pressed so as to open the throttle.

More air flows past the jet, but since petrol is heavier than air the petrol tends to be left behind. Thus the engine will be in danger of stopping because of the mixture strength being too weak, unless there is some arrangement whereby the supply of petrol can be suddenly increased when the throttle is quickly opened. But, as soon as the flow of air has steadied again, the extra supply of petrol must be reduced or the mixture will be too rich, for it is known that if the rate of air flow past a jet is, say, doubled, the air picks up more than double the previous amount of petrol vapour after the flow of petrol has adjusted itself to the new rate of flow of air. Thus, as the rate of air flow increases through the choke tube there is a richening of the mixture strength unless a compensating device is fitted in order to maintain a more or less constant air to fuel ratio. The device is a compensating jet in some carburettors, and in others a diffuser tube is used as shown in figs. 17.2 and 17.5 respectively.

Ingenious methods are adopted to achieve the required mixture strength when the throttle is suddenly opened, e.g. an extra reservoir of petrol may come into action automatically: temporarily bringing into action extra jets; increasing the size of jet for a moment; and other ways, all of which make the carburettor a delicate and sensitive instrument.

Fig. 17.2 shows a diagram illustrating the principle on which many carburettors work. The main jet *a* and compensating jet *b* are in communication with the float chamber. The height is such that petrol will not flow except under the influence of a depression in the choke tube. The amount of petrol issuing from the main jet *a* depends on the speed at which air travels through the choke tube. The compensating jet *b*, which surrounds the main jet, can only deliver as much petrol as flows through the small orifice *d*. This is limited to the quantity that can pass through the restricted orifice *d* in a given time irrespective of engine speed or throttle position, for since tube *c* is open to atmosphere the flow through orifice *d* depends only on the head of petrol behind it and which is more or less constant. Thus, the flow through the compensating jet *b* remains practically constant when once the tube *c* has been emptied, whereas the flow of petrol through the main jet *a* will have increased with increase of engine speed. Hence, as the air speed through the choke tube increases, the proportion of petrol to air from the main jet *a* increases, and from the compensating jet *b* decreases. Thus, as the air speed increases, the action of the main jet is to make the mixture strength richer and that of the compensating jet to make it weaker. If carefully designed, a carburettor will give fairly correct strengths at all speeds. Care is

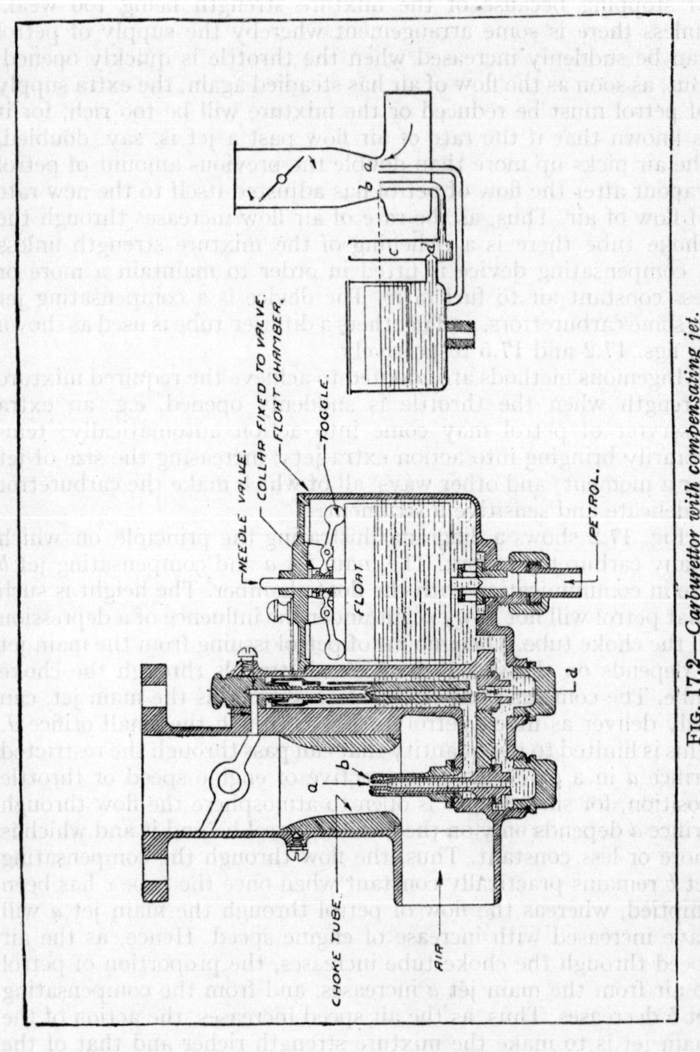

FIG. 17.2—*Carburettor with compensating jet.*

needed in designing the choke tube in order that it may have the effect of speeding up the air past the jets so as to increase the velocity of issue of petrol and not have the effect of merely throttling the air and inducing eddy currents.

3. Compensating-jet Carburettor.—Fig. 17.3 illustrates a type of vertical carburettor fitted to car engines. Liquid petrol enters the carburettor at the union 1, and passes through a gauze filter mounted on the end of the fixing plug 2. It then flows through the needle seating 3 into the float chamber 4. The flow through the needle valve is regulated by the float 5, which rises

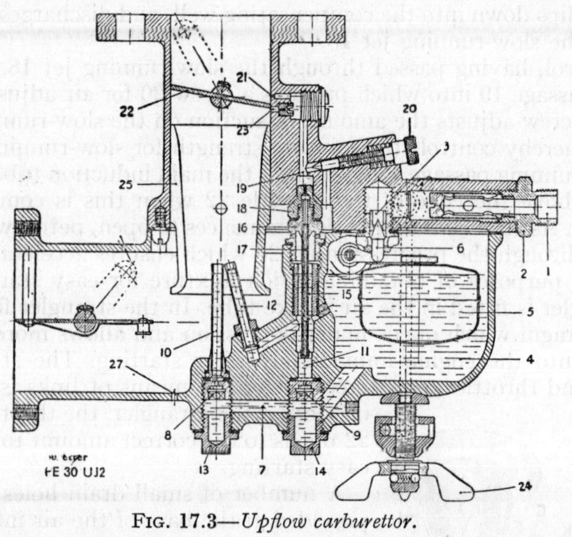

FIG. 17.3—*Upflow carburettor.*

as the chamber fills, and at a certain height pushes the needle 6 on to its seating. This cuts off the flow of petrol.

From the float chamber the petrol flows to the main and compensating jets, 8 and 9 respectively, by means of passage 7, and then through the jets into the channels 10 and 11 above them. From the compensating well 11 some of the petrol must pass into the tube 12 and rise to the same height as the petrol in the float chamber. Situated in the compensating well is a capacity tube 15 which is removable and can be replaced by one of different diameter, thereby varying the quantity of petrol that is in reserve when running slowly, and which is rapidly drawn through the tube 12 on sudden acceleration. Underneath the capacity tube 15 a small washer is fitted to restrict the flow of petrol from the capacity well into tube 12 when the throttle is "snapped" open. This obviates any tendency of a rich "flat" spot.

The top of the compensating well is closed by the plug 16, in which are two ventilation holes. These holes allow the necessary air to pass so that the compensating jet works at atmospheric pressure, and this air passes finally through the tube 12 with petrol which comes through the compensator jet 9. The plug 16 is called the slow-running jet carrier, because attached to it is the slow-running tube 17 and also the slow-running jet 18. The tube dips down into the compensating well, and discharges petrol into the slow-running jet 18.

Petrol, having passed through the slow-running jet 18, enters the passage 19 into which projects a screw 20 for air adjustment. This screw adjusts the amount of suction on the slow-running jet and thereby controls the mixture strength for slow-running. The slow-running passage 19 opens into the main induction tube at 21, just above the edge of the throttle 22 when this is completely closed. As soon as the throttle commences to open, petrol will also pass through the progression jet 23 which ensures acceleration.

For purposes of obtaining a rich mixture for easy starting, a strangler is fitted in the air intake tube. In the strangler flap is a diaphragm which opens under depression and allows more air to pass into the engine immediately after starting. The strangler flap and throttle are interconnected by means of links, so that, on closing the strangler, the throttle flap 22 opens to the correct amount to ensure easy starting.

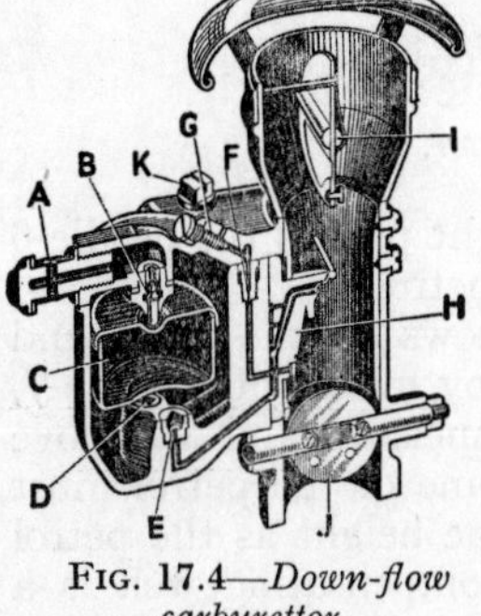

FIG. 17.4—*Down-flow carburettor.*

A number of small drain holes 27 are provided at the base of the air intake to drain off any petrol which may overflow from the jet tubes 10 and 12 when starting the engine from cold. This further reduces the possibility of choking.

4. Down-draught Carburettor.—Fig. 17.4 illustrates a down-draught carburettor in which petrol enters through the union A and passes through the needle valve B into the float-chamber. The float C maintains in the chamber a constant level of petrol, which leaves via the main jet D and compensating jet E. Air is drawn down the choke tube and becomes charged with petrol as it passes the choke-tube jets on its way to the engine. In the down-draught carburettor the force of gravity assists in carrying the petrol towards the engine cylinders. It is claimed that this gives an increase in power at high engine speeds, for, since gravity assists the petrol into the inlet manifold, the carburettor can function satisfactorily with a larger choke area, and thus a greater mass of mixture on full throttle can be passed to the cylinders. Alternatively, if the area of the choke tube is not increased, the main jet can be reduced to give a better fuel consumption.

The adjustable and moving parts on this carburettor will be seen to be: the throttle J, the strangler I, which can be closed when a rich mixture is required for starting the engine, and the screw G, which is an adjustment on the slow-running jet F. The jet F is a subsidiary jet for slow running and an aid to easy starting. With the throttle almost closed the speed at which air is drawn in past F is sufficient to draw petrol from the jet and provide an explosive mixture for the purposes of slow running.

A weak mixture, however, may ignite so slowly that "back firing" through the carburettor may occur owing to the inlet valve opening before the pressure of the gases, which are still burning in the cylinder, is sufficiently reduced.

5. Diffuser-tube Carburettor.—Fig. 17.5 shows a carburettor with the throttle closed and in which a diffuser tube is used as the compensating device. The diffuser tube is open-ended and has rings of holes in the cylindrical side. Petrol floods the tube when the engine is stationary, but, when running, the depression, or lowering of pressure, created at the throat of the choke or Venturi tube, reacts on the diffuser tube from which petrol is drawn. The main jet at the base of the diffuser tube supplies fuel at a rate sufficient to keep the level constant, but as the throttle is opened the depression, acting on the surface of the fuel in the tube, is such that the rate of flow of fuel is increased and the level of fuel in the tube is lowered. Another ring of holes in the diffuser tube then becomes exposed, and, since air flows through them, the rate of flow of fuel from the tube becomes such that the main jet is able to supply fuel at the rate at which it is being drawn off; if not, then the fuel level in the diffuser tube falls still lower and another set of holes is exposed. The reason for incorporating such a device for diminishing the depression, which would otherwise be available for withdrawing fuel from the diffuser tube, is to counteract the tendency of the fuel-air mixture to become over-rich when the air flow through the Venturi tube increases due to further opening of the throttle.

A sudden opening of the throttle momentarily tends to reduce the fuel to air ratio of the mixture, and an accelerator pump is often incorporated in the carburettor and interconnected with the throttle to avoid weakening the mixture by a quick opening of the throttle. Thus, a quantity of fuel is injected into the air stream until the inertia lag of the flowing fuel is overcome. By this

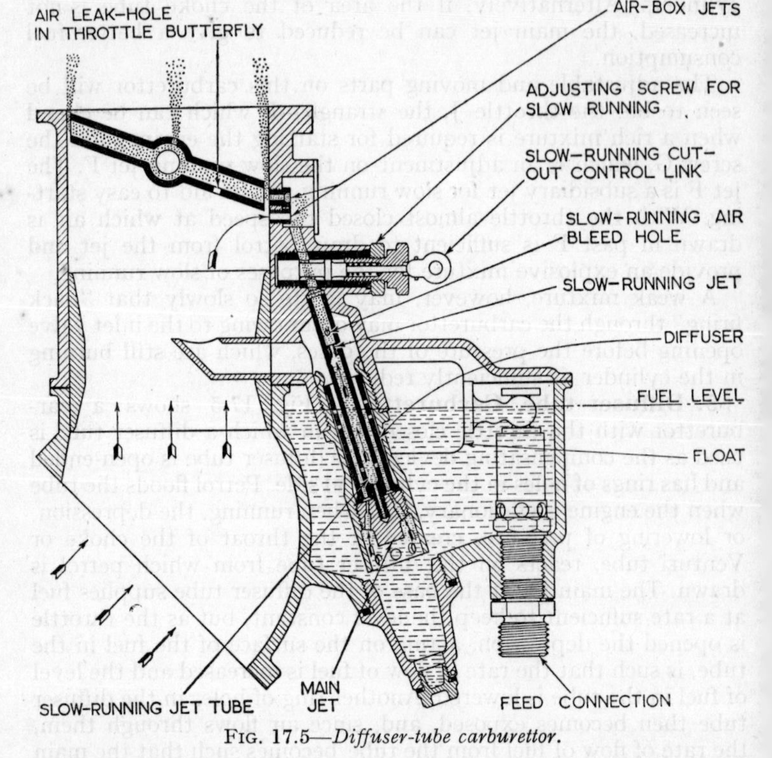

FIG. 17.5—*Diffuser-tube carburettor.*

means rapid acceleration can be achieved and "cutting" of the engine avoided.

An engine can be kept "ticking over" by means of a slow-running jet which continues to operate when the throttle is closed as shown in fig. 17.5.

6. Fuel-injection in Compression-ignition Engines.—The fuel-injection system on compression-ignition engines consists essentially of the fuel pump and the injector. The object of the fuel pump is to deliver, according to the load as indicated in fig. 17.6, the correct quantity of fuel per cycle to the injector which directs the fuel, as finely divided particles suitable for rapid combustion, into the combustion chamber of the cylinder.

In compression-ignition engines the air alone is compressed to about 500 Lb. per sq. in. (the temperature after compression being of the order 600° C.) and, for rapid combustion, the fuel must be injected as finely divided particles into this highly compressed air and directed so as to make its distribution through the air as uniform as possible. Distribution is assisted by turbulence of the air, which is achieved by designing the inlet ports, the combustion chamber, and the top of the piston so that there is rapid motion of the air when the fuel is injected. The idea behind this is that it is easier for the air to find the fuel than for the fuel to find the air—the main objective being to obtain as rapid a relative motion as possible between the air and the burning fuel particles in order not to starve the fuel of the quantity of oxygen necessary for complete combustion.

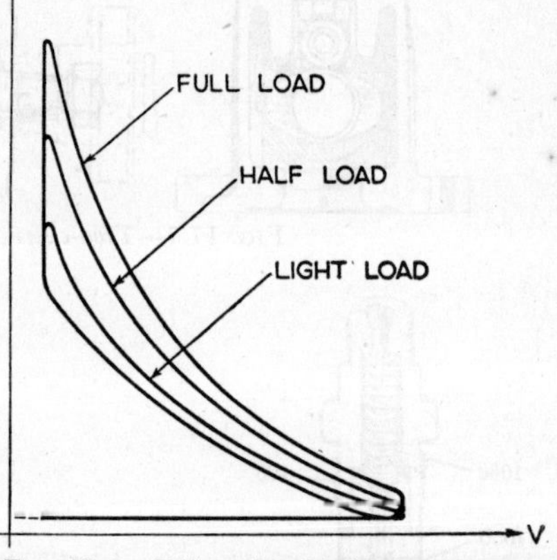

FIG. 17.6—*Effect of fuel-injection in compression-ignition engines.*

Fuel pumps give long service provided clean and highly filtered fuel is served to the plungers and barrels, which are usually ground and lapped to an accuracy of the order $\frac{1}{1000}$ mm.

An important point regarding fuel-injection equipment is that it is less costly to maintain than the carburettors, magnetos, and sparking plugs of petrol engines, and also that breakdowns are less frequent.

Fig. 17.7 is a section through a two-cylinder C.A.V. fuel pump, in which it will be seen that cams impart motion to tappets which in turn impart motion to the plungers. The plunger can be seen in more detail in figs. 17.8, 17.9, and 17.10. The fuel oil is highly filtered by means of a felt-pack filter before entering the barrel of the pump. The amount of fuel delivered to the injector through the spring-loaded valve at the top of the pump barrel depends upon the position of the plunger in the barrel, as will be seen from figs. 17.9 and 17.10. Fig. 17.9 shows the plunger at the beginning of its stroke, and fig. 17.10 shows the point in the stroke at which

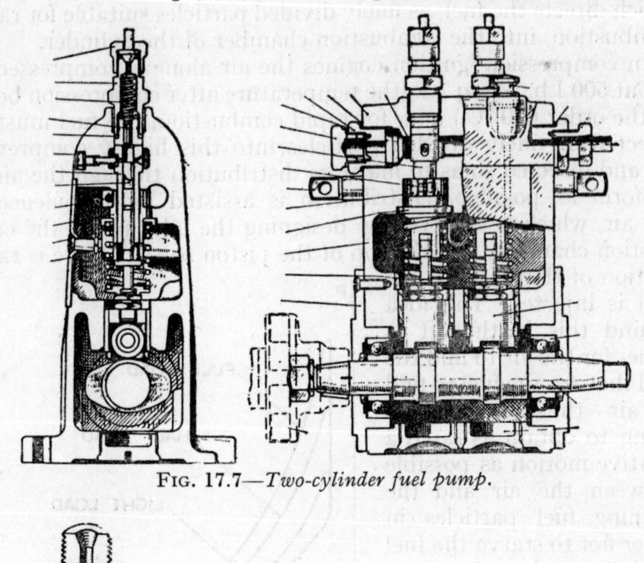

FIG. 17.7—*Two-cylinder fuel pump.*

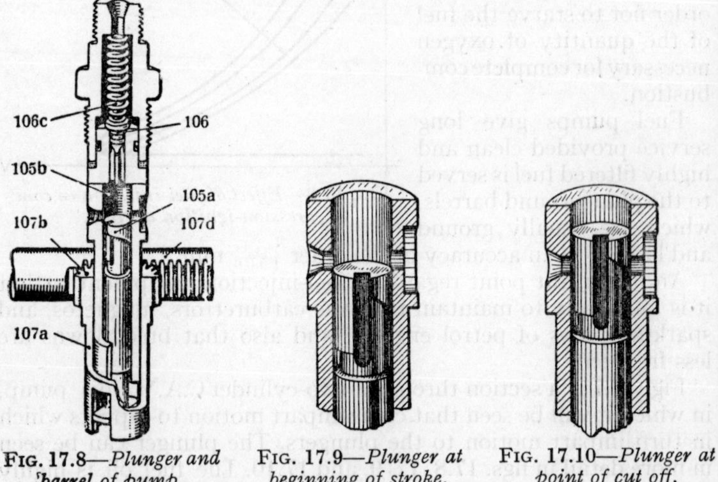

FIG. 17.8—*Plunger and barrel of pump.* FIG. 17.9—*Plunger at beginning of stroke.* FIG. 17.10—*Plunger at point of cut off.*

any oil still undelivered and at the top of the plunger, can flow back down the small slot and through the hole on the right because of a helix-shaped piece cut from the body of the plunger.

The amount of fuel delivered and injected into the engine cylinder depends, therefore, on the rotary position of the plunger in the barrel. This settles the point at which the helix uncovers the hole in the barrel of the pump, and the pressure of the fuel on the top side of the plunger is then suddenly reduced to that on the inlet side. The rotary position of the plunger in the pump barrel is controlled by means of a rack (107d) and wheel (107b). The rack is connected to the governor through link rods, and horizontal

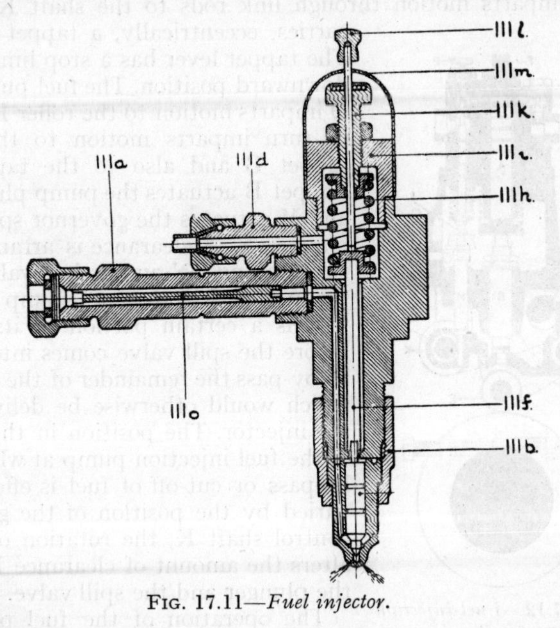

FIG. 17.11—*Fuel injector.*

motion of the rack rotates the plunger one way or the other according as the speed is too high or too low, so that the helix uncovers the hole in the barrel earlier or later. Thus, less or more fuel is delivered to the injector for injection into the cylinder.

Fig. 17.11 shows a section through an injector in which fuel is delivered from the pump along the horizontal pipe (111o). The vertical spindle of the injector is spring-loaded at the top to a pressure which may approach 2,000 Lb. per sq. in., so that the fuel pressure must reach this value before the nozzle will lift to allow fuel to be injected into the engine cylinder. Any fuel which leaks past the vertical spindle is taken off by means of a pipe (111d) fitted above the fuel inlet pipe. The lift of the nozzle is restricted to a definite amount, and a needle (111) can be pushed down the centre at the top in order to tell, by placing one's finger on the head of it, whether or not the nozzle is lifting to allow fuel to be injected into the cylinder.

Fig. 17.12 shows a section of the fuel-injection pump fitted to the constant-speed heavy compression-ignition engine illustrated in fig. 2.14. The amount of fuel delivered to the injector is controlled by means of a governor of the centrifugal type (fig. 2.25). This imparts motion through link rods to the shaft K, which carries, eccentrically, a tappet lever J. The tappet lever has a stop limiting its downward position. The fuel pump cam D imparts motion to the roller E, which in turn imparts motion to the main tappet B and also to the tappet M. Tappet B actuates the pump plunger A, and M actuates the governor spill valve plunger N. A clearance is arranged between plunger N and its ball valve, with the result that the fuel pump plunger travels a certain portion of its stroke before the spill valve comes into action to by-pass the remainder of the fuel oil, which would otherwise be delivered to the injector. The position in the stroke of the fuel-injection pump at which this by-pass or cut-off of fuel is effected, is varied by the position of the governor control shaft K, the rotation of which alters the amount of clearance between the plunger and the spill valve.

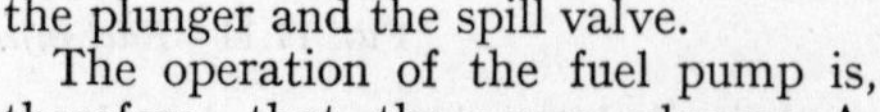

FIG. 17.12—*Fuel-injection pump.*

The operation of the fuel pump is, therefore, that the pump plunger A, which is actuated each revolution from the cam D, through roller E and tappet B, commences to deliver a full charge of fuel oil to the atomiser through the outlet F; but at a certain point in its stroke the spill valve plunger N lifts the spill valve from its seating, and the remainder of the fuel is by-passed.

The suction valve G is of the double-ball type, and the delivery is fitted with a single non-return ball valve at F.

There is a hand priming lever fitted to the pump gear which operates the shaft H, on which cams are machined to operate the lever C. Thus, by hand, the lever C can be moved so as to lift the tappet B and fuel pump plunger A, so enabling the pump to be worked for priming purposes or held out of action to stop the engine. In addition to being able to cut off the fuel supply by means of the priming lever C, each pump is provided with an additional cut-out lever O which carries a small cam on its spindle. By moving this lever the spill valve plunger N can be lifted so that the whole of the fuel is by-passed. This device affords a ready means of cutting out all or each of the cylinders independently.

Fig. 17.13 illustrates the type of injector fitted to the compression-ignition engine of fig. 2.15. The injector is supplied with oil from the pump shown in fig. 17.12 and enters along the pipe R, from which it flows into an annular chamber surrounding the needle holder. The needle B, which has a seating in the steel nozzle E, is loaded by means of a spring F. The load on the spring is adjusted when the engine is on test so that the needle valve opens when the fuel pressure is about 1,500 Lb. per sq. in. The lift of the needle is limited to about $\frac{1}{16}$ in. by means of the adjusting screw O, which is effectively locked in position by the locknuts S. When the requisite pressure is reached by operation of the fuel pump the needle B lifts and the charge of oil is sprayed into the cylinder through the fine holes which are drilled radially in the end of the nozzle E. The injection of fuel continues until the pressure is cut off by the spill valve (fig. 17.12) coming into action, when injection instantly ceases.

The thumb screw L holds the ball valve M on its seating and provides a means of priming the injection system before starting.

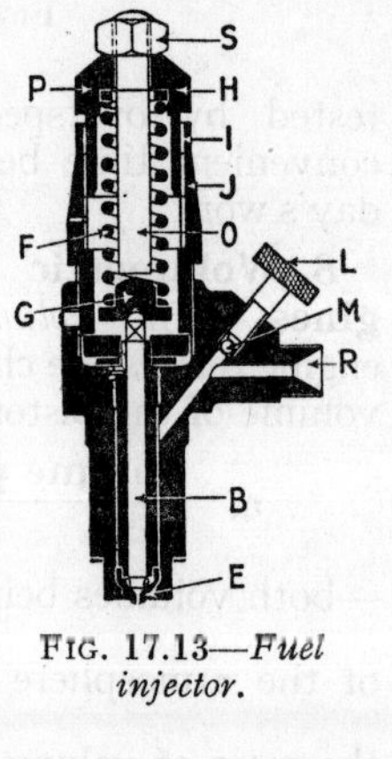

FIG. 17.13—*Fuel injector.*

7. Automatic Safety Device.—Fig. 17.14 shows an automatic fuel cut-out device which comes into action whenever, from any unforeseen cause, the speed of the engine rises beyond that advisable for the safe running of the plant. The engine can thus safely be left unattended for a period.

The mass B attached by the fulcrum pin C and spring E to the web of pulley A moves outwards owing to centrifugal force as the engine speed increases. When the speed has increased to such an extent that the mass B touches the knob of lever F the link G depresses lever H, which releases the tappet K, and the ball valve L is forced on to its seating by the spring M. Thus the fuel supply is cut off from all the pipe lines leading to the pump, and the engine is automatically stopped. The device should be periodically

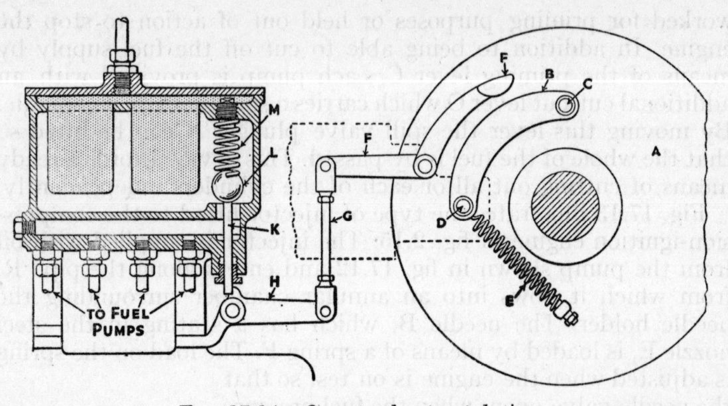

FIG. 17.14—*Overspeed cut-out device.*

tested by overspeeding the engine, say, once a month—a convenient time being just before stopping the engine after a day's work.

8. Volumetric Efficiency of Internal-combustion Engines.—The *volumetric efficiency* of an internal-combustion engine relates the charge actually entering a cylinder to the swept volume of the piston. It may be defined as

$$\eta_v = \frac{\textbf{volume per cycle drawn in during induction}}{\textbf{swept volume of piston}}$$

—both volumes being reckoned at the temperature and pressure of the atmosphere surrounding the engine. Since $V = \left(\frac{RT}{P}\right)m$, the ratio of volumes, when both are reckoned at the same temperature and pressure, may be written :

$$\eta_v = \frac{\textbf{mass of gaseous working agent drawn in per cycle}}{\textbf{mass to fill the stroke volume}}$$

The actual volume (reckoned at the temperature and pressure of the surrounding atmospheric air) drawn into the cylinder of an ordinary un-supercharged engine is, of course, always less than the volume swept out by the piston. It depends on the temperature of the charge entering the cylinder, the back pressure of the gases still in the cylinder at the beginning of the next suction stroke, and the resistance to the flow of fresh charge into the cylinder through the inlet valves and ports. 75 per cent. is an average figure for the volumetric efficiency of an ordinary engine.

Since volumetric efficiency of a compression-ignition engine can be expressed as the ratio of the mass of air used per cycle to the mass of free atmospheric air required to fill the stroke volume, the volumetric efficiency of a supercharged engine can be greater than 100 per cent. if air at about atmospheric temperature is forced into the cylinder at a pressure greater than that of the air surrounding the engine.

For a gas engine in which a gas-air mixture is drawn into the cylinder, the volumetric efficiency may be defined as:

$$\frac{\text{volume of gas-air mixture used per cycle}}{\text{stroke volume of the engine}}$$

both volumes being reckoned at the temperature and pressure of the atmosphere surrounding the engine.

9. Measurement of Air Consumption.—The air drawn into the cylinder of an internal-combustion engine can be measured or estimated in various ways. Three of these are by means of: (i) an orifice through which the air is drawn; (ii) a small gasometer, from which air is drawn into the engine; (iii) exhaust gas analysis, by means of which the air can be estimated from the carbon appearing in the CO_2 and CO of the exhaust gases.

(i) *The Orifice Method of Air Measurement.*—The orifice type of meter is not reliable on pulsating flows. It is not as easy as it appears to smooth the flow of engine suction by means of an air box; with single-cylinder engines this is almost impossible. With multi-cylinder engines running at high speed, however, it is possible to get fairly reliable results by connecting the air inlet to an air box of adequate volume in which is placed an orifice at the opposite end. A manometer tube containing a light liquid can be used to record the pressure-difference over the orifice, and the velocity of the air entering can be estimated by calculation, or from an orifice calibration chart. The mass of air consumed per minute can then be calculated from the equation $\frac{PV}{RT}$, where P and T are the atmospheric pressure and temperature, V is the volume of air flowing through the orifice per minute, and R is the characteristic constant for air, namely, 53·3 ft.-Lb. per lb. °F.

(ii) *The Gasometer Method of Air Measurement.*—For accurate work the air consumed by an engine can be drawn from a small gasometer over a period of time. This method is the most reliable but it is cumbersome. The mass of air consumed can be accurately calculated over that period of time, being the difference between the $\frac{PV}{RT}$ values of the air in the gasometer before and after the period. If the pressure and temperature remain constant, the mass of air consumed between initial and final times will be

$$\frac{P(V_i - V_f)}{RT} = \text{constant} \times (V_i - V_f)$$

(iii) *Estimation of Air Consumption by Analysis of Exhaust Gases.*—If the carbon and hydrogen content of a fuel is known, an estimation of the amount of air drawn into the cylinder per lb. of fuel burnt can be made from an analysis of the exhaust gases. The calculation is based on the assumption that all the carbon present in the fuel finally appears in the CO_2 and CO of the exhaust gas analysis or that the difference term is all nitrogen.

The general case may be worked out on 1 lb. of fuel containing: C lb. of carbon, H_2 lb. of hydrogen, A lb. of ash and other matter. This produces in the *dry* exhaust gas an analysis *by weight* (and *by mass*) per lb. of fuel: CO_2 lb. of carbon dioxide, CO lb. of carbon monoxide, O_2 lb. of oxygen, and N_2 lb. of nitrogen. It will be noted that symbols are used in this analysis to represent numbers not quantities—this being more convenient since a unit mass of 1 lb. of fuel is specified at the beginning.

From the chemical equations for combustion of carbon we know that:

CO_2 lb. of carbon dioxide has come from $\frac{12}{44} \times CO_2$ lb. of carbon, and

CO lb. of carbon monoxide has come from $\frac{24}{56} \times CO$ lb. of carbon.

Hence, since 1 lb. of dry exhaust gas contains CO_2 lb. of carbon dioxide and CO lb. of carbon monoxide, it must have been produced from $\left\{\frac{12}{44}CO_2 + \frac{24}{56}CO\right\}$ lb. of carbon.

And since 1 lb. of fuel contains C lb. of carbon, we deduce that 1 lb. of fuel produces $\frac{C}{\left\{\frac{12}{44}CO_2 + \frac{24}{56}CO\right\}}$ lb. of dry exhaust gas.

Also, since 1 lb. of fuel contains H_2 lb. of hydrogen, we know that this produces $9H_2$ lb. of steam.

Hence, the total mass of exhaust gases produced by the combustion of 1 lb. of fuel is $\left\{9H_2 + \frac{C}{\frac{12}{44}CO_2 + \frac{24}{56}CO}\right\}$ lb.

Of this total mass of exhaust gas $(C + H_2)$ lb. comes from 1 lb. of fuel, and therefore

$$\left\{9H_2+\frac{C}{\left(\frac{12}{44}CO_2+\frac{24}{56}CO\right)}-(C+H_2)\right\} \text{ lb. must be air.}$$

Hence, the mass of air drawn into the engine per lb. of fuel burnt is

$$\left\{8H_2+\frac{C}{\left(\frac{12}{44}CO_2+\frac{24}{56}CO\right)}-C\right\} \text{ lb.}$$

Example 1.—A fuel-oil contains, by weight, 85·4 per cent. carbon and 12·27 per cent. hydrogen. The dry exhaust gas analysis gave the composition by weight: 8·67 per cent. CO_2, 0·11 per cent. CO, 14·20 per cent. O_2, 77·02 per cent. N_2. Calculate (*a*) the air consumption of the engine per lb. of oil burnt; (*b*) the theoretical air required to burn 1 lb. of oil completely; (*c*) the percentage excess air.

(*a*) From the above formula the mass of air actually consumed per lb. of oil

$$=\left\{8\times 0\cdot 1227+\frac{0\cdot 854}{\left(\frac{3}{11}\times 0\cdot 0867+\frac{3}{7}\times 0\cdot 0011\right)}-0\cdot 854\right\} \text{ lb.}$$

$$=(0\cdot 982+35\cdot 55-0\cdot 854) \text{ lb.}$$

$$=35\cdot 68 \text{ lb.}$$

(*b*) Air theoretically required for complete combustion of 1 lb. of oil

$$=\frac{1}{0\cdot 23}\left\{0\cdot 854\times\frac{32}{12}+0\cdot 1227\times 8\right\}=\frac{(2\cdot 272+0\cdot 982)}{0\cdot 23} \text{ lb.}$$

$$=\frac{3\cdot 254}{0\cdot 23}=14\cdot 15 \text{ lb.}$$

(*c*) Hence, the excess air per lb. of fuel is 21·53 lb.,

i.e., excess air = 152 per cent.

Example 2.—The ultimate analysis by weight, of a sample of petrol is carbon 84 per cent., hydrogen 16 per cent. The analysis by volume of the dry exhaust gas of an engine running on this petrol is: CO_2, 12·9 per cent.; O_2, 2 per cent.; N_2, 85 per cent. Calculate how many pounds of air are used per lb. of petrol, and the percentage of excess air.

(*a*) To transform the exhaust gas analysis by volume into an analysis by weight, the volumetric analysis must be multiplied by the respective molecular weights as follows:

			per cent.
CO_2 =	12·9 × 44 =	568 =	18·9
O_2 =	2 × 32 =	64 =	2·1
N_2 =	85·1 × 28 =	2,380 =	79·0
	Total =	3,012	100·0

Thus 100 lb. of dry exhaust gas contain 18·9 lb. of CO_2, which must have come from the combustion of $\frac{18 \cdot 9}{44} \times 12 = 5 \cdot 15$ lb. of carbon.

Thus 1 lb. of carbon is contained in $\frac{100}{5 \cdot 15} = 19 \cdot 4$ lb. of dry exhaust gas.

Hence, since 1 lb. of petrol contains 0·84 lb. of carbon, it will produce $19 \cdot 4 \times 0 \cdot 84 = 16 \cdot 3$ lb. of dry exhaust gas.

Also, since 1 lb. of petrol contains 0·16 lb. of hydrogen, it will produce $9 \times 0 \cdot 16 = 1 \cdot 44$ lb. of steam.

Therefore, the total mass of gases flowing to exhaust per lb. of petrol$=16 \cdot 3 + 1 \cdot 4 = 17 \cdot 7$ lb., of which $(0 \cdot 84 + 0 \cdot 16) = 1$ lb. is petrol and therefore, 16·7 lb. is air.

Hence, the amount of air used per lb. of petrol is 16·7 lb.

The theoretical air required for the complete combustion of 1 lb. of petrol is $\frac{1}{0 \cdot 23}\left\{0 \cdot 84 \times \frac{32}{12} + 0 \cdot 16 \times 8\right\} = 15 \cdot 3$ lb.

$$\therefore \text{ Percentage of excess air} = \left(\frac{16 \cdot 7 - 15 \cdot 3}{15 \cdot 3}\right) \times 100 = 9 \cdot 15 \text{ per cent.}$$

(*b*) *Alternatively*, the air actually consumed can be estimated from the nitrogen present in the exhaust gases, since all the nitrogen present must have been brought in with the air.

In the above problem we see that with every lb. of carbon appearing in the exhaust gases there are $\frac{79}{5 \cdot 15} = 15 \cdot 35$ lb. of nitrogen.

$\therefore$ 1 lb. of petrol containing 0·84 lb. of carbon appears with $15 \cdot 35 \times 0 \cdot 84 = 12 \cdot 9$ lb. of nitrogen, which must have been brought in with $\frac{12 \cdot 9}{0 \cdot 77} = 16 \cdot 7$ lb. of air.

Hence (as before) the mass of air used per lb. of petrol is 16·7 lb.

Example 3.—A single-cylinder four-stroke compression-ignition engine having a stroke volume of 432 cu. in. developed 20 b.h.p. at 500 r.p.m. and consumed 0·4 lb. of oil per b.h.p.-hr. The composition of the oil by weight was: carbon 87 per cent. and hydrogen 13 per cent. An analysis of dry exhaust gas gave a composition by weight of CO_2 10·7 per cent., O_2 11·8 per cent., N_2 77·5 per cent. Calculate the percentage excess air and the volumetric efficiency of the engine if the atmospheric air had a temperature of 59° F. and a pressure of 15 Lb. per sq. in. abs.

Air theoretically required for complete combustion of 1 lb. of oil

$$= \frac{1}{0 \cdot 23}\left\{0 \cdot 87 \times \frac{32}{12} + 8 \times 0 \cdot 13\right\} = 14 \cdot 6 \text{ lb.}$$

From dry exhaust gas analysis we find that 0·107 lb. of CO_2 containing $0 \cdot 017 \times \frac{12}{44}$ lb. of C. appear in 1 lb. of dry exhaust gas.

$\therefore$ 1 lb. of oil containing 0·87 lb. of C produces

$$\frac{0\cdot 87}{0\cdot 107}\times\frac{44}{12}=29\cdot 8 \text{ lb. of dry exhaust gas.}$$

Also 1 lb. of oil containing 0·13 lb. of H_2 produces

$$9\times 0\cdot 13=1\cdot 17 \text{ lb. of steam.}$$

$\therefore$ 1 lb. of oil burns to produce 30·97 lb. of exhaust gas, of which 1 lb. is oil and 29·97 lb. is air.

$$\therefore \text{ Percentage excess air used}=\left(\frac{29\cdot 97}{14\cdot 6}-1\right)\times 100=105 \text{ per cent.}$$

The engine consumes $0\cdot 4\,\frac{\text{lb.}}{\text{h.p.-hour}}\times 20\text{ h.p.}\left[\frac{\text{hour}}{60\text{ min.}}\right]=0\cdot 1333$ lb. of oil per min. and makes 250 cycles per min.

$$\therefore \text{ Mass of air used per cycle}=\frac{0\cdot 1333\text{ lb}_o.}{\text{min.}}\times\frac{1}{250}\frac{\text{min.}}{\text{cycle}}\times 29\cdot 97\,\frac{\text{lb}_a.}{\text{lb}_o.}$$
$$=0\cdot 016\text{ lb}_a./\text{cycle.}$$

Stroke volume $=432$ cu. in. $=0\cdot 25$ cu. ft.

$\therefore$ Mass of atmospheric air required to fill the stroke volume is given by

$$\frac{PV}{RT}=\frac{(15\times 144)\,\frac{\text{Lb.}}{\text{ft.}^2}\times 0\cdot 25\text{ ft.}^3}{53\cdot 3\,\frac{\text{ft.-Lb.}}{\text{lb. °F.}}\times 519°\text{ abs. F.}}=0\cdot 0195\text{ lb.}$$

$$\therefore \text{ Volumetric efficiency}=\frac{16}{19\cdot 5}\times 100=82 \text{ per cent.}$$

10. Scavenge Efficiency.—In high-speed compression-ignition engines combustion of all the fuel is not as a rule completed, in spite of the fact that there is usually an excess of oxygen available. It is found that in order to maintain a clear exhaust, only about three-quarters of the air present in the cylinders of compression-ignition engines can be consumed. At high speeds the volumetric efficiency decreases, as does the ratio of the available oxygen to the quantity of fuel injected, thus increasing the tendency to incomplete combustion.

The scavenge efficiency of an engine is a measure of the degree to which the products of combustion of the previous cycle have been cleared from the cylinder. If all the previous products could be cleared from the cylinder the scavenge efficiency would be 100 per cent. In general, **scavenge efficiency is defined as:**

$$\eta_s=\frac{\textbf{mass of products expelled from the cylinder}}{\textbf{mass of products in cylinder before exhaust valve opens}}$$

$$\text{or } 1-\frac{\text{mass of residual gases left after exhaust valve closes}}{\text{mass of products in cylinder before exhaust valve opens}}$$

11. Supercharging.—During explosion and the process of burning in the cylinder of an internal-combustion engine, the oxygen in the air combines with the elements composing the fuel, resulting in the evolution of heat and high pressure. Oxygen is the "active partner" and the nitrogen in the air is the "sleeping partner"—the latter playing no active part in the chemical reaction of combustion but tends to slow down the rate of combustion and, in fact, reduces the maximum temperature and pressure which would be produced were nitrogen present.

It is usual to speak of the *fuel* being burnt during combustion, but we could equally well regard the *air* as being burnt, for it is the amount of oxygen available for combustion that limits the amount of heat that can be liberated in the cylinder of an internal-combustion engine. With a "rich mixture" the limit to the amount of heat produced is reached when all the oxygen in the air is burnt, and partially burnt fuel passes out with the exhaust. Thus, the power output of any internal-combustion engine depends primarily on the mass of oxygen which can be burnt per unit of time in the cylinders. This can be increased in an engine drawing air from the atmosphere, by increasing the speed of the engine or by supercharging or both. Piston aero-engines give about 10 i.h.p. per lb. of air per minute.

Supercharging is the name given to the process of increasing the pressure of the fuel-air mixture entering an engine to a pressure greater than that of atmospheric air, and is usually achieved by means of a small compressor or blower called a supercharger. Superchargers also whirl the mixture into a more homogeneous state.

Similarly, in compression-ignition engines the mass of air used per minute can be increased either by increasing the speed of the engine or the pressure of the air entering the engine by means of a blower or supercharger—the latter process being known as pressure-charging, supercharging, or boosting.

The mass of the charge, whether it be a fuel-air mixture, as in spark-ignition engines, or simply air, as in compression-ignition engines, depends on the pressure difference between the induction manifold and the inside of the cylinder when the inlet valve is open. In an unsupercharged engine the pressure of the mixture in the induction manifold depends on the atmospheric pressure and on the amount of opening of the throttle of the carburettor. If the throttle is fully open the pressure in the manifold approaches that of the atmosphere surrounding the engine. Thus, in the case of an aero-engine climbing to altitudes where the pressure of the ambient air is lower than that at sea level, less mass of mixture will enter the cylinders, and the power developed will decrease unless the pressure of the mixture is increased by fitting a supercharger or centrifugal blower between the carburettor and the induction manifold.

The power required to drive superchargers or blowers is taken from the engine through a speed-multiplying gear as illustrated in fig. 17.15 or from an exhaust gas turbine as in fig. 17.16 which derives power from the exhaust gases, the energy of which would

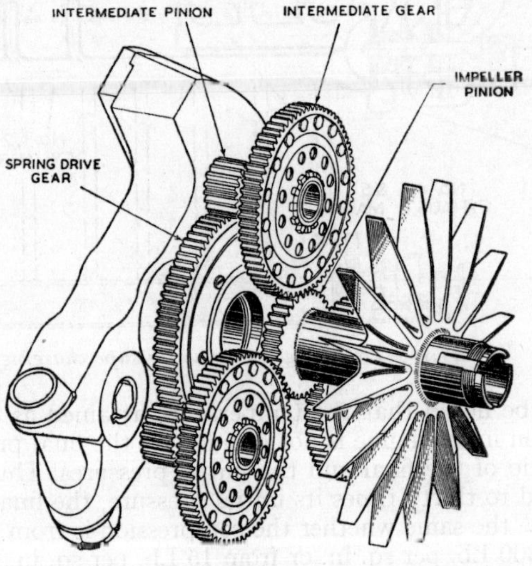

INTERMEDIATE PINION
INTERMEDIATE GEAR
IMPELLER PINION
SPRING DRIVE GEAR

FIG. 17.15—*Speed-multiplying gear for supercharger.*

otherwise go to waste. Exhaust turbo-blowers for pressure-charging, known as the Büchí system after the Swiss engineer, are efficient only on relatively large engines. For industrial and marine engines of, say, over 150 horse-power, such blowers provide the supercharger just when it is most needed and with the minimum reduction in useful power output from the engine. In spark-ignition engines the quantity of fuel-air mixture delivered by superchargers is controlled by partially closing the throttle, thus restricting the amount of mixture or air entering the supercharger; but it will be obvious that a supercharger is being most efficiently used when its speed is such that the throttle is fully open, for there is then the least resistance to the flow of mixture or air entering the supercharger.

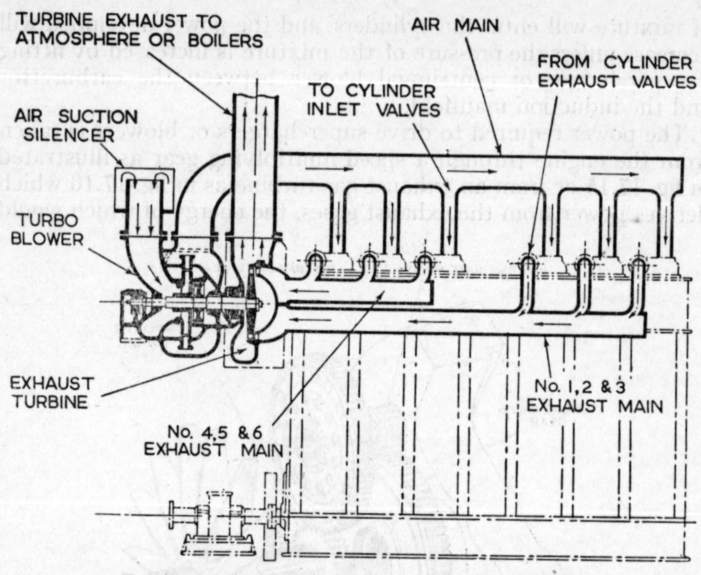

FIG. 17.16—*Exhaust-gas turbine for supercharging.*

It may be noted that the temperature attained as a result of compression in an engine is not decided by the final pressure but by the ratio of the final and the initial pressures. Thus, if air is compressed to thirty times its initial pressure, the final temperature will be the same whether the compression is from 10 Lb. per sq. in. to 300 Lb. per sq. in. or from 15 Lb. per sq. in. to 450 Lb. per sq. in. from the same initial temperature T_i, in accordance with the law:—

$$\frac{T_f}{T_i} = \left(\frac{V_i}{V_f}\right)^{n-1} = \left(\frac{P_f}{P_i}\right)^{\frac{n-1}{n}} = (30)^{\frac{n-1}{n}}$$

The higher the initial temperature of the mixture or air in the cylinder the higher will be the temperature after compression, i.e. before any heat is released by the fuel. Thus, raising the inlet temperature results in the temperatures at all points of the cycle being raised. This is to the detriment of thermal efficiency and mechanical endurance because of the greater losses due to heat transfer, higher specific heats and dissociation. Thus, by reason of higher compression ratio, compression-ignition engines are more sensitive to air-intake temperature than are spark-ignition engines.

The temperature before compression can, however, be lowered in spark-ignition engines by the evaporation of the fuel in a rich mixture (which, because of its richness, has a reduced tendency to detonate) or by the evaporation of a liquid of low boiling point and high latent heat. For example, the evaporation of petrol in air at the mixture strength giving complete combustion will lower the temperature by about 65° F., and such fuels as methyl alcohol and ethyl alcohol by about 250° F. and 190° F., respectively—the alcohol fuels thus having sufficient capacity to counteract nearly all of the temperature rise due to compression in superchargers which, as applied to spark-ignition engines, are usually only fitted to aero and racing engines. While spark-ignition engines can use the evaporation of fuel to cool the fuel-air mixture, the air entering compression-ignition engines has to be cooled by a heat exchanger, although water injection may be used in certain cases. Also, for short periods such as for take-off of aircraft or during combat, water may be injected into the supercharger and by evaporation cool the fuel-air mixture. It is also found that the steam formed serves as an anti-detonant.

Compression-ignition engines respond to supercharging more favourably than spark-ignition engines, for the problems of pre-ignition and detonation do not arise, and the higher the density of the air the shorter is the delay period (see fig. 17.18) resulting in a smoother combustion process. Also, the higher the intake pressure the less sensitive is the engine either to cetane number or to volatility of the fuel, thus enabling a wider range of fuels to be used. Without supercharging, compression-ignition engines will not run on the heavier grades of fuel-oil. In the case of road vehicles the high torque which is needed at low revolutions in order to reduce gear changing and to give good acceleration, is higher in compression-ignition engines than in spark-ignition engines, and in supercharged compression-ignition engines this torque is higher still. In the case of marine propulsion, high torque is only needed at the top end of the speed range and for this an exhaust turbo-blower will provide the necessary supercharge as illustrated in fig. 17.16.

If it is required to double the power output of an engine, the speed may be doubled, in which case the gas loading on the bearings remains unaltered but the dynamic loading is increased to four times as much; or by supercharging to double the initial atmospheric pressure, in which case the gas loading on the bearings is doubled but the dynamic loading remains the same, since the speed has not been altered.

Actually, it is found that by supercharging the petrol engine to twice the atmospheric pressure the power is more than doubled, and the same degree of supercharging or pressure-charging in compression-ignition engines increases their output by about 75 per cent.

Where a group of engines is installed, it may pay to provide a large blower to supercharge the group during periods of overload. Superchargers are always fitted to airplanes and racing cars in which engine-weight per horse-power is required to be small.

12. Turbulence in Internal-combustion Engines.—Turbulence may be said to be violent eddying motion and swirling of fluid. *The object of turbulence in internal-combustion engines is to achieve a rapid relative motion between the air and fuel particles.* If the gases in the cylinder of an engine have eddying and swirling motion at the point of ignition, it is found that this produces quick propagation of flame and its rapid spread throughout a fuel-air charge in the cylinder. The necessity for turbulence can be realised when we consider that in an engine running at 2,400 r.p.m. each stroke is completed in $\frac{1}{80}$ second, and combustion is required to be complete in a fraction of this time. It has been shown in an experiment on an air-petrol mixture in a stagnant condition in a closed vessel that the time from the point of ignition to the point of maximum pressure was 0·03 second. In the cylinder of an engine this time was reduced to less than a tenth of this (0·003 sec.) as a result of turbulence.

The velocity of admission of the explosive mixture through the inlet valves and ports of an engine produces great turbulence which continues during the compression stroke, and, at the point of ignition, assists the flame in spreading rapidly throughout the volume of combustible gases. In compression-ignition engines special designs of cylinder and piston heads (fig. 17.17), shapes and positions of inlet ports, are attended to with a view to producing turbulence. The choice seems to be between the chamber in which swirl is produced by compression, and the chamber in which swirl is induced by induction of air through the inlet ports. In order to maintain the relative velocity between fuel and air, which is so necessary for rapid combustion, the fuel in compression-ignition engines must be injected across and never in the same direction as the air stream. By this means fresh oxygen is brought into contact with the fuel particles to give rapid combustion. The clearance volume in compression-ignition engines is small—say, about 7 per cent. of the stroke volume and, even at full load, contains as much as 30 per cent. of unconsumed oxygen.

Turbulence in an engine is increased with increasing speed of the engine, for the latter has the effect of increasing the velocity of the gas passing through the inlet ports and so increasing the eddying and swirling motion of the inflowing mixture; also, the time during which the turbulence can die down in an engine is reduced when the engine speed is increased. Turbulence is one of the factors which renders possible the high speeds which are attained in modern internal-combustion engines. With a low degree of turbulence it is probable that a good proportion of the fuel-air mixture may burn so slowly after the point of ignition that the heat may only be liberated late in the expansion stroke

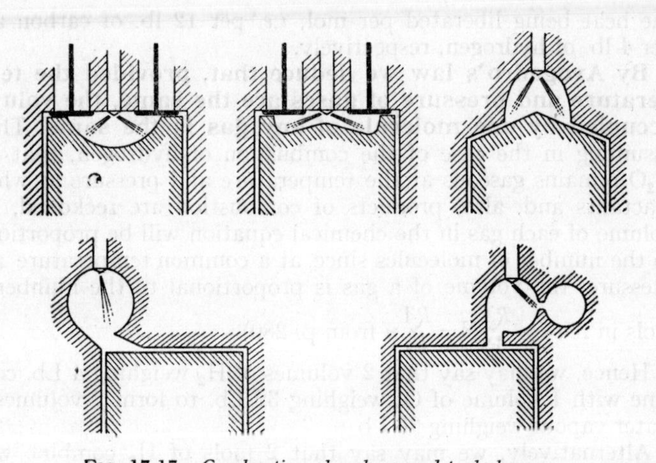

FIG. 17.17—*Combustion chambers and turbulence.*

and so may be wasted in the exhaust gases. Thus, in order to ensure complete combustion and smokeless exhaust we need a high rate of air-swirl to scour away the products of combustion surrounding the fuel oil and to bring fresh supplies of air to the droplets of burning oil. Swirl can, however, be overdone since high air-swirl entails high heat losses by convection.

13. Combustion and Thermo-chemical Equations.—Combustion may be regarded as a process of splitting up fuel and oxygen molecules and resulting in the formation of new molecules (changed with different bonding arrangements) together with the liberation or absorption of heat. A chemical reaction is usually classed as *exothermic* or *endothermic* depending upon whether heat is liberated or absorbed during the reaction. For instance, in the reaction represented by the equation: $C+O_2=CO_2$ the carbon and oxygen contain more intrinsic energy than the carbon dioxide which they produce, the difference being liberated as heat during the reaction. The quantity of heat released—B.Th.U. per lb. of fuel—is usually referred to by engineers as the calorific value of the fuel (defined on p. 13).

The heat of reaction is often shown in a thermo-chemical equation, *e.g.*:

$$C+O_2=CO_2+174{,}600\ \text{B.Th.U.},$$
$$\text{and } 2H_2+O_2=2H_2O\ (\text{gas})+210{,}000\ \text{B.Th.U.}—$$

the heat being liberated per mol, *i.e.* per 12 lb. of carbon and per 4 lb. of hydrogen, respectively.

By Avogadro's law we deduce that, provided the temperature and pressure of gases are the same, the volume occupied by one molecule of any gas is the same. Thus, assuming in the case of the combustion of hydrogen, that the H_2O remains gaseous at the temperature and pressure at which reactants and, also, products of combustion are reckoned, the volume of each gas in the chemical equation will be proportional to the number of molecules since, at a common temperature and pressure, the volume of a gas is proportional to the number of mols in it ($V=\frac{\mathcal{R}T}{P}N=\frac{\mathcal{R}T}{Pf}n$ from p. 280).

Hence, we may say that 2 volumes of H_2 weighing 4 Lb. combine with 1 volume of O_2 weighing 32 Lb. to form 2 volumes of water vapour weighing 36 Lb.

Alternatively, we may say that 2 mols of H_2 combine with 1 mol of O_2 to form 2 mols of H_2O.

A thermochemical equation can, therefore, be said to be an expression from which combining mols or weights or masses can be taken whichever happens to be the more convenient for the particular problem under consideration—the same quantity of heat liberated during the reaction holding good for both cases. Thus the heat liberated is

$$\frac{210{,}000\ \text{B.Th.U.}}{36\ \text{lb.}}=5{,}833\ \text{B.Th.U. per lb. of water vapour; or}$$

$$\frac{210{,}000\ \text{B.Th.U.}}{2\ \text{mol}}=105{,}000\ \text{B.Th.U. per mol of water vapour produced.}$$

14. Chemical Contraction.—If the oxygen of the air is used for the combustion of hydrogen, then the theoretical equation becomes: $2H_2+O_2+3\cdot76N_2=2H_2O+3\cdot76N_2+2\cdot1$ therms, since the ratio, by volume, of nitrogen to oxygen in air is $\frac{79}{21}=3\cdot76$.

Thus, the process of combustion not only changes the kind of molecules but, also, the number of molecules which may be greater than, equal to, or less in number after combustion than the number of molecules of reactants existing before combustion.

In the above case, $6\cdot76$ molecules of reactants become $5\cdot76$ molecules of products of combustion. There is, therefore, molecular contraction of $\frac{6\cdot76-5\cdot76}{6\cdot76}=0\cdot148$ or $14\cdot8$ per cent., but the weights and masses of the reactants and products remain equal. If, in the above reaction, the H_2O is condensed to liquid, the volume of which is negligibly small, then

$$2H_2(g)+O_2(g)+3\cdot76N_2(g)=2H_2O(l)+3\cdot76N_2(g)+2\cdot46 \text{ therms},$$

i.e. the number of *gaseous* mols of products is $3\cdot76$ and of reactants $6\cdot76$. Thus, the percentage *volumetric* contraction is

$$\left(\frac{6\cdot76-3\cdot76}{6\cdot76}\right)\times100=44\cdot4 \text{ per cent.},$$

the volumes being measured at the same temperature and pressure.

The combustion of the general hydrocarbon, C_xH_y, in air can be represented by the equation:

$$C_xH_y+\left(x+\frac{y}{4}\right)O_2+\frac{79}{21}\left(x+\frac{y}{4}\right)N_2=x\,CO_2+\frac{y}{2}H_2O+\frac{79}{21}\left(x+\frac{y}{4}\right)N_2$$

from which it can be deduced that the amount of molecular contraction is $1-\frac{y}{4}$.

Example 1.—Find (i) the percentage molecular contraction or expansion when 1 mol of petrol represented by C_8H_{18} is burnt in air, and (ii) the weight and volume of air theoretically needed to burn 1 gallon of petrol of specific gravity $0\cdot75$.

(i) Applying the above formula we get:

$$C_8H_{18}+(8+4\cdot5)O_2+47N_2=8CO_2+9H_2O+47N_2$$

from which we see that $60\cdot5$ molecules of reactants become 64 molecules of products, i.e. there is a molecular expansion of $5\cdot8$ per cent.

(ii) One mol of C_8H_{18} fuel weighing $96+18=114$ Lb. needs air composed of $12\cdot5$ mols of oxygen weighing $12\cdot5\times32=400$ Lb. and 47 mols of nitrogen weighing $47\times28=1{,}316$ Lb. which together total $59\cdot5$ mols of air weighing 1,716 Lb.

Thus, one gallon of petrol weighing 7·5 Lb. requires

$$1{,}716\times\frac{7\cdot5}{114}=112\cdot8 \text{ Lb. of air,}$$

$$\text{or}\quad 59\cdot5\times\frac{7\cdot5}{114}=3\cdot91 \text{ mols of air,}$$

$$\text{or}\quad 3\cdot91\times358=1{,}400 \text{ cu. ft. of air at s.t.p.}$$

Example 2.—The table gives some particulars of a producer gas:—

Gas	CH_4	CO	H_2	N_2
Per cent by volume.	24	16	52	8
Molecular weight	16	28	2	28

Find, per 100 cu. ft. of producer gas at s.t.p.:—

(*a*) the mass, given that R in PV=RmT for H_2 is 769 ft.Lb./lb.°F.;
(*b*) the volume of air required for complete combustion, given that air contains 20·9 per cent. volume of O_2;
(*c*) the volumetric analysis of the resulting gas if the H_2O condenses
[Part I, B.Sc. Lond.]

(*a*) The mass of hydrogen in 100 cu. ft. of the gas at s.t.p. is:

$$m=\frac{PV}{RT}=\frac{14\cdot7\times144\times52}{769\times492}=0\cdot291 \text{ lb.}$$

Thus, the following table may be drawn up:—

Constituent	Volumetric Analysis or No. of mols N	Molecular Weight i.e mass per mol, M	Product NM	Per cent. Analysis by Weight $\frac{NM}{11\cdot6}=w$	Actual Weight $\frac{0\cdot291}{9\cdot0}\times w$ Lb.
CH_4	24	16	384	33·1	1·072
CO	16	28	448	38·6	1·248
H_2	52	2	104	9·0	0·291
N_2	8	28	224	19·3	0·624
Totals	100	—	1,160	100·0	3·235

Thus, the mass of 100 cu. ft. of gas at s.t.p. is 3·235 lb.

(*b*) The air required and the products of combustion may be deduced from the following table:—

Analysis		Mols of Oxygen required		Products of Combustion				
				Mols of H_2O produced		Mols of CO_2 produced		Mols of other Gases
Constituent	Volumetric, or number of mols of Constituent	Per mol of Constituent	By Constituent	Per mol of Constituent	By Constituent	Per mol of Constituent	By Constituent	Actual mols of Nitrogen
CH_4	24	2	48	2	48	1	24	
CO	16	0·5	8	0	0	1	16	
H_2	52	0·5	26	1	52	0	0	
N_2	8	0	0	0	0	0	0	8
Totals	100	—	82	—	100	—	40	

Mols of N_2 accompanying 82 mols of $O_2 = \frac{79 \cdot 1}{20 \cdot 9} \times 82 = 310$

Therefore, total mols of N_2 in products $= 318$

Thus, 100 mols of producer gas require 82 mols of oxygen which are contained in $82 \times \frac{100}{20 \cdot 9} = 392$ mols of air, and since 1 mol of any gas at s.t.p. occupies 359 cu. ft. we deduce that 100 cu. ft. of producer gas at s.t.p. require 392 cu. ft. of air at s.t.p.

(*c*) From the table it will be seen that the products of combustion are composed as follows:—

Constituent	Total Products		Dry Products	
	Number of mols	Per cent. by Volume	Number of mols	Per cent. by Volume
H_2O	100	21·8	0	0
CO_2	40	8·7	40	11·2
N_2	318	69·5	318	88·8
Totals	458	100·0	358	100·0

Thus, if the H_2O has condensed, the volumetric analysis of the products will be CO_2 11·2 per cent.; N_2 88·8 per cent.

Example 3.—Calculate the volume of a closed vessel containing 1 mol of hydrogen and 4 mols of air at 150 Lb. per sq. in. abs. and 60° F. Estimate the percentage volumetric composition of products after combustion of the mixture, and the pressure of the products in the vessel at 3,540° F.

$PV = \mathcal{R}NT$ is the characteristic equation for a gas or mixture of gases.

$$\text{Hence, } V = \frac{\mathcal{R}NT}{P}$$

$$= 1{,}545 \cdot 5 \frac{\text{ft.-Lb.}}{\text{mol. °F.}} = \frac{5 \text{ mol} \times 520° \text{ abs. F.}}{150 \times 144 \dfrac{\text{Lb.}}{\text{ft.}^2}}$$

$$= 186 \cdot 2 \text{ ft.}^3$$

One mol of air $= 0 \cdot 21$ mol of $O_2 + 0 \cdot 79$ mol of N_2 and

$$H_2 + \tfrac{1}{2}O_2 = H_2O$$

Reactants		Mols of O_2 required for combustion	Mols of Products		
Constituent	Mols		O_2	H_2O	N_2
H_2	1·00	0·5	—	1·00	—
O_2	0·84	—	0·34	—	—
N_2	3·16	—	—	—	3·16
Total	5·00	0·5	0·34	1·00	3·16

Thus, the products of combustion are composed of:

	Volumetric or Mol Analysis	Analysis by Volume per Cent.
O_2	0·34	7·5
H_2O	1·00	22·2
N_2	3·16	70·3
Total	4·50	100·0

$$\text{The pressure } P = \frac{\mathcal{R}NT}{V}$$

$$= 1{,}545 \cdot 5 \frac{\text{ft.-Lb.}}{\text{mol °F.}} = \frac{4 \cdot 5 \text{ mol} \times 4{,}000° \text{ abs. F.}}{186 \cdot 2 \text{ ft.}^3} \left[\frac{\text{ft.}^2}{144 \text{ in}^2.}\right]$$

$$= \frac{1{,}545 \cdot 5 \times 4 \cdot 5 \times 4{,}000}{186 \cdot 2 \times 144} \frac{\text{Lb.}}{\text{in.}^2}$$

$$= 1{,}038 \text{ Lb. per in.}^2 \text{ abs.}$$

Example 4.—Estimate the characteristic gas constants of the reactants and of the products of combustion of Example 3.

Reactants Constituent	Mols N	Molecular Weight or Mass per Mol M	Actual mass of Constituent MN
H_2	1·00	2	2·00
O_2	0·84	32	26·88
N_2	3·16	28	88·48
Total	$5·00=N_r$	—	$117·36=m$

Hence, molecular weight or mass per mol of reactants is

$$M_r=\frac{\Sigma MN}{\Sigma N}=\frac{117·36}{5·00}=23·45\ \frac{\text{lb.}}{\text{mol}}$$

and the characteristic gas constant of the reactants is

$$R_r=\frac{\mathcal{R}}{M_r}=\frac{1{,}545·5\ \frac{\text{ft.-Lb.}}{\text{mol° F.}}}{23·45\ \frac{\text{lb.}}{\text{mol}}}=65·8\ \frac{\text{ft.-Lb.}}{\text{lb. °F.}}$$

Products Constituent	Mols N	Molecular Weight or Mass per Mol M	Actual mass of Constituent MN
O_2	0·34	32	10·88
H_2O	1·00	18	18·00
N_2	3·16	28	88·48
Total	$4·50=N_p$	—	$117·36=m$

Hence, molecular weight or mass per mol of products is

$$M_p=\frac{\Sigma MN}{\Sigma N}=\frac{117·36}{4·5}=26·1\ \frac{\text{lb.}}{\text{mol}}$$

and the characteristic gas constant of the products is

$$R_p=\frac{\mathcal{R}}{M_p}=\frac{1{,}545·5\ \frac{\text{ft.-Lb.}}{\text{mol °F.}}}{26·1\ \frac{\text{lb.}}{\text{mol}}}=59·1\ \frac{\text{ft.-Lb.}}{\text{lb. °F.}}$$

The above example shows that the characteristic law of the reactants or gas mixture before combustion ($PV = R_r mT$ on the "pound system") changes to $PV = R_p mT$ for the products of combustion, whereas on the "mol system" $PV = \mathcal{R} N_r T$ changes to $PV = \mathcal{R} N_p T$. Thus, on the pound system, m remains the same before and after combustion, while the characteristic gas constant R changes, whereas on the mol system the universal gas constant $\mathcal{R}$ remains the same while N, the number of mols, changes.

There is an advantage in using the mol system wherever a characteristic or special gas constant R would otherwise have to be calculated, for it is easier to find N_r and N_p from combustion equations for use on the mol ($PV = \mathcal{R} NT$) system than to calculate the characteristic gas constants R_r and R_p for use on the pound ($PV = RmT$) system from the equation

$$R = \frac{m_1 R_1 + m_2 R_2 + \ldots}{m_1 + m_2 + \ldots} = \frac{\Sigma Rm}{\Sigma m}$$

and this usually after a volumetric (i.e. a mol) analysis has had to be converted into an analysis by weight or by mass.

15. Dissociation.—The quantity of heat required to dissociate or split a compound, say H_2O or CO_2, into its elements again is numerically equal to the heat evolved when the compound is formed by combustion of its elements. At high temperatures H_2, O_2, CO, and other constituents H_2O, CO_2 and N_2 can, owing to dissociation, exist in the same mixture—a proportion of the H_2O and CO_2 molecules being split up due to violent encounters between molecules. The dissociation of CO_2 is more serious than that of the H_2O so far as the performance of internal-combustion engines is concerned since it begins at lower temperatures and is of greater amount. The heat which is absorbed when dissociation takes place is released again when the gases recombine at a lower temperature which may be brought about by expansion of the gases in the cylinder of an engine. A portion of the heat which is released at lower temperatures is required to dissociate molecules at higher temperatures and, hence, the maximum temperature reached is less than that calculated from the calorific value estimated in calorimeters.

16. Detonation and "Knock."—Detonation frequently occurs when certain kinds of fuels are used in internal combustion engines. "Knock" is usually imagined to be caused by a blow delivered against the cylinder or piston by a high-pressure wave travelling at great speed through the gas which forms the working substance of the engine. In spark-ignition engines the explosion wave or high-pressure wave, set up by an extremely rapid rise of pressure, passes through the gas very much faster than the normal speed of flame propagation and strikes the cylinder with a hammer-like blow known as "pinking." It is on the rate of rise of pressure during combustion that smoothness of running to a large extent depends. Detonation is not pre-ignition. It is something which occurs after the spark has started ignition in electric-ignition engines. Detonation *follows* the spark, whereas pre-ignition precedes it.

So long as detonation does not take place, the flame started at the point of ignition spreads through the combustion volume at a speed depending mainly on gas turbulence and on temperature and pressure of the mixture before ignition. But, under certain conditions depending upon the constitution of the fuel, the rate of flame spread becomes accelerated, and a "detonation wave" is set up. All fuel-air mixtures will start pinking if compressed beyond a certain point. Many engines begin pinking after they have been run for a long period because carbon, mainly from burnt lubricating oil collects on top of the piston and gradually increases the compression ratio to the point at which pinking begins. Decarbonising is the remedy in this case. Cylinders and pistons have been broken by the hammer-like blow which detonation can produce, but in most cases just a "knock" is heard. The tendency of hydrocarbon fuels to detonate is at a maximum somewhere between where the mixture strength gives most economical running and that which gives maximum power.

Several substances (or "dopes") have been discovered which, when added to petrol even in a very small proportion ($\frac{1}{900}$ by volume of lead tetra-ethyl is allowed in commercial petrol), have a pronounced "anti-knock" effects. The most important of these is lead tetra-ethyl, $Pb(C_2H_5)_4$. If it is used in too great proportions there is a danger of a deposit of lead in the combustion chamber, which may cause damage to the engine. But if dopes are used correctly in fuels it is possible to reduce the detonation and pinking which frequently occur in ordinary engines.

In a compression-ignition engine the combustion process (according to Ricardo's fig. 17.18) may be considered in three stages: (1) a delay period; (2) a rapid rise of pressure; (3) a period during which fuel burns as it issues from the jets of the injector.

The duration of the delay periods depends primarily upon how much the temperature of the air after compression is in excess of the self-ignition temperature of the fuel. The temperature at which the spontaneous ignition of petroleum fuel oils injected into a cylinder takes place ranges from about 250° C. to 320° C. Thus, allowing a margin of 30°, the temperature of 350° C. should be attained by compression to ensure reliable spontaneous ignition. A compression ratio of 14 : 1 will do this easily, though

18 : 1 is now used in high-speed compression-ignition engines of road vehicles.

Both the rate at which heat will be transferred from the air to the fuel droplet and the rate at which the products of combustion surrounding the droplet will be scoured away from the core, depend on the relative velocity of fuel and air; hence, the lower volatility of the fuel the greater should be the intensity of swirl. The heavier fuel oils have a higher self-ignition temperature, hence, the margin of air temperature over and above the ignition temperature of the fuel is less, and the delay period before ignition begins is lengthened. Pressure as well as temperature, however,

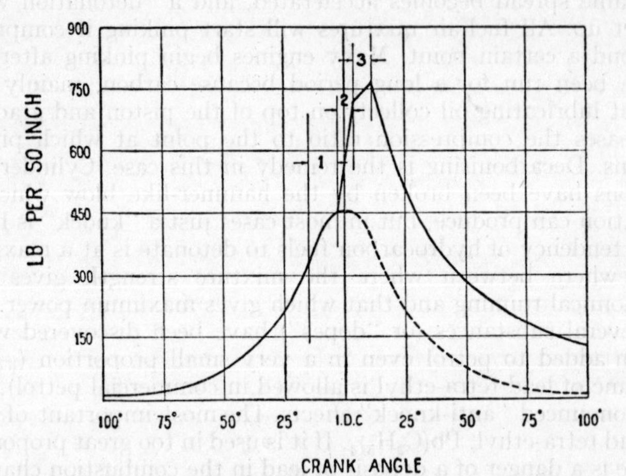

Fig. 17.18—*Combustion in compression-ignition engines.*

plays an important part in initiating the combustion process and in shortening the delay period.

Turbulence may reduce the delay period, provided that the temperature of the air is maintained, though turbulence has the effect of increasing the flow of heat to the cylinder walls and therefore tends to reduce the temperature due to compression. Supercharging also tends to reduce the delay period, and the fuel can usually be doped so as to reduce its self-ignition point. It is necessary to reduce the delay period as much as possible, because a rapid rise of pressure following a long delay period is the cause of "rough-running" and "knock". The third stage depends on the engine speed, and is under the direct mechanical control of the fuel pump. The stresses resulting from "knock" have a detrimental effect on the bearings. Hence, the excessive rate of rise of pressure, which often results in abnormally high maximum pressures, should be reduced as much as possible. Much ingenuity has been displayed in the design of engines in an effort to get maximum energy out of a fuel without encountering troubles caused by "knock."

EXERCISES ON CHAPTER 17

(i)

1. If 15 lb. of air required for the perfect combustion of 1 lb. of fuel, and a mixture strength of 18 is used in an engine, find the percentage weakness of the mixture, basing the calculations on: (*a*) an excess of air; (*b*) a deficiency of fuel.

2. (i) Define " mixture strength " in relation to a fuel-air mixture used in an internal combustion engine.

(ii) Calculate the theoretically correct mixture strength of air to fuel (by weight) for the perfect combustion of a fuel containing 86 per cent. of carbon and 14 per cent. of hydrogen by weight. Air contains 23 per cent. of oxygen by weight.

3. Estimate the percentage analysis by weight, of the exhaust gases from an engine using 17 lb. of air per lb. of fuel, the chemical composition of which is 0·86 per cent. of carbon and 0·14 per cent. of hydrogen by weight. Air contains 77 per cent. of nitrogen by weight.

4. (*a*) Make a diagrammatic sketch of a simple carburettor showing a compensating jet or a diffuser tube. State briefly why the compensating device is necessary, and how it operates.

(*b*) Calculate the mass of air theoretically required for the perfect combustion of 1 gallon of petrol of specific gravity 0·75 and of composition represented by the formula C_8H_{18}. Air contains 23 per cent. of oxygen by weight.

What is the heating value per pound of this fuel-air mixture if the calorific value of the petrol is 19,400 B.Th.U. per lb.?

How many gallons of water result from the combustion of one gallon of petrol? Water weighs 10 Lb. per gallon.

5. A fuel represented by C_7H_{16} is burnt with 100 per cent. excess air, estimate the volumetric analysis of the dry flue gas.

[I.Mech.E., Sec. A.]

6. What are the proportions by weight, of carbon and hydrogen in the oil fuel represented by C_8H_{18}?

Estimate the minimum volume of air at 212° F. and 16 Lb. per sq. in. abs. that will be required for the complete combustion of 1 lb. of this fuel.

7. Define the term "volumetric efficiency" of an internal combustion engine. The diameter of cylinder and the stroke of a four-stroke compression-ignition engine are 24 in. and 30 in. respectively. Oil fuel supplied contains 85 per cent. carbon, 12 per cent. hydrogen, and 3 per cent. of incombustibles by weight. Exhaust contains 13·2 per cent. CO_2, by weight, of total exhaust gases.

(*a*) Estimate what fraction of the weight of air supplied to the engine has been consumed.

(*b*) If the volumetric efficiency is 80 per cent., what weight of fuel is injected per working stroke? [I.Mech.E.]

8. A gas engine works with an air to gas ratio of 7 : 1. The composition of the gas by volume is H_2 0·46, CO 0·24, CH_4 0·20, CO_2 0·04, N_2 0·06. Find the percentage volumetric composition of the total exhaust gas.

9. A closed vessel contains 1 mol of hydrogen and 4 mols of air at 60° F. and 15 Lb. per sq. in. abs. Calculate the volume of the vessel and the percentage molecular contraction after explosion. Also estimate the percentage volumetric contraction after the water vapour has condensed to liquid, the volume of which is assumed negligible. Show that one pound of water vapour would occupy a volume of 103·3 cu. ft. and, with the aid of steam tables, that condensation would commence at about 147° F. Calculate the pressure in the vessel when the temperature has fallen to 60° F. again.

10. An oil engine uses 20·4 lb. of air per lb. of fuel-oil. The fuel-oil has a composition by weight of 85 per cent. carbon and 15 per cent. hydrogen, and the air may be assumed to be free from moisture and to contain 23 per cent. of oxygen and 77 per cent. of nitrogen by weight. Calculate the percentage excess air used and the percentage volumetric analysis of the dry exhaust gas assuming the hydrogen and carbon are completely burnt.

11. The percentage analysis by volume of the producer gas supplied to an engine is:—CO, 12; CH_4, 3; H_2, 26; CO_2, 15; N_2, 44. Calculate the percentage analysis by volume of the dry exhaust gas if the air supplied to the engine is 25 per cent. in excess of that required for complete combustion. Air contains 21 per cent. by volume of oxygen. [Part I, B.Sc. Lond.]

12. A mixture of octane, C_8H_{18}, and ethyl alcohol, C_2H_5OH, in the proportions of 1 molecule of octane to 2 molecules of alcohol is completely burnt in a supply of air 20 per cent. in excess of that required for complete combustion. Determine the volumetric analysis of the *dry* exhaust products. [I.Mech.E., Sec. A.]

13. Define the term *volumetric efficiency* as applied to an internal combustion engine.

Estimate the temperature of the cylinder contents at the end of the suction stroke in an internal combustion engine for which the ratio of compression is 5, the volumetric efficiency referred to prevailing engine room conditions 0·8, the temperature of the residual exhaust gases 1,000° abs. C., and the prevailing temperature in the engine room 15° C.

The pressure throughout induction may be assumed to be atmospheric, the pull in the connecting rod and the inertia forces neglected, and the gases treated as air with constant specific heats.

[I.Mech.E., Sec. A.]

14. An oil engine consumes 20·4 lb. of air per lb. of fuel-oil of analysis 85 per cent. carbon and 15 per cent. hydrogen by weight. Calculate (i) the percentage excess air used; (ii) the partial pressure of the steam in the exhaust gas, whose total pressure is 15 Lb. per sq. in. absolute, and the percentage analysis of the dry exhaust gas by volume; (iii) the heat rejected in the dry exhaust gas and in the steam of the exhaust gas per lb. of fuel-oil if the temperature be 800° F. and the specific heats of dry exhaust gas and of superheated steam be 0·25 and 0·5 B.Th.U./lb. ° F., respectively. Air contains 23 per cent. oxygen by weight. The atmosphere is assumed dry and of temperature 60° F.

15. A four-stroke, four-cylinder engine has a stroke of 4 in. and a bore of 3 in. If heptane (C_7H_{16}) is used as fuel and the ratio of the actual to theoretical mass of air used is 10 : 11, estimate the rate of mass flow of fuel to the engine when running at 3,000 r.p.m. The volumetric efficiency of the engine based on the air drawn from the atmosphere at 14·7 Lb./in.^{2} abs. and 59° F. is 76 per cent.

The characteristic constant for gaseous heptane is

$$R=\frac{\mathcal{R}}{M}=1{,}545\cdot 5\ \frac{\text{ft.-Lb.}}{\text{mol }^\circ\text{F.}}\times\left[\frac{\text{mol.}}{100\text{ lb.}}\right]=15\cdot 46\ \frac{\text{ft.-Lb.}}{\text{lb. }^\circ\text{F.}}$$

16. A four-stroke oil engine has a stroke of 1 ft. and a bore of 8·5 in. and consumes fuel at the rate of 0·61 lb. per b.h.p.-hour when developing 18 b.h.p. at 300 r.p.m.

The fuel oil had a percentage analysis by weight :—carbon 84·4, hydrogen 12·6, oxygen 2·0, and incombustibles 1·0. The percentage volumetric analysis of the dry exhaust gases was CO_2 8·8, CO 0·8, O_2 9·5 and N_2 80·9.

Calculate the percentage of excess air and the volumetric efficiency of the engine working in an atmosphere at 32° F. and 14·7 Lb./in.^{2} abs.

17. Calculate the air supplied per lb. of fuel, the fuel used per minute, the bore and stroke of a four-cylinder four-stroke petrol engine to use the fuel C_9H_{20} of calorific value 19,800 B.Th.U. per lb. and develop 40 b.h.p. when running at 2,400 r.p.m. Assume a brake thermal efficiency of 25 per cent. and a volumetric efficiency of 76 per cent. when drawing from an atmosphere at 14·7 Lb. per sq. in. abs. and 60° F. Also, assume that 10 per cent.

excess air is used and neglect the volume of the fuel in the mixture. The cylinders are "square," i.e. the bore is equal to the stroke.

18. The following data were obtained from a test of a petrol engine running at constant speed.

Brake h.p.	42·2	42·8	43	42·9	41·6	39·9	38·8	36·3
Fuel, lb./min.	0·447	0·398	0·380	0·357	0·328	0·298	0·288	0·272
Air, lb./min.	4·64	4·70	4·80	4·92	4·90	4·80	4·80	4·83

Plot curves of b.h.p. and fuel in lb. per b.h.p.-hour against mixture strength and deduce from them (*a*) the mixture strength for maximum b.h.p. output and also for maximum brake thermal efficiency. Hence, estimate the percentage richness or weakness of the mixture for (*b*) maximum power output and (*c*) maximum efficiency, respectively based, in each case, on

(i) a deficiency or excess of air for 1 lb. of fuel; and
(ii) an excess or deficiency of fuel in the theoretical air, namely, 15 lb. per lb. of fuel, *i.e.* the correct mixture strength (by weight) is 15 to 1.

19. If the brake m.e.p. is 100 Lb./in.^{2} when the engine under test in Question 18 is developing 42·9 b.h.p. calculate the b.m.e.p. for the other powers and plot fuel consumption in lb. per b.h.p.-hour against b.m.e.p. and give reasons for the shape of the curve.

See also Question 12, Chapter 18.

20. (i) The gas supplied to a single-cylinder engine has the following percentage volumetric analysis: H_2 50, CH_4 25, CO_2 10, CO 5, N_2 10. The percentage volumetric analysis of the dry exhaust gases is CO_2 8·5, O_2 5·8, N_2 85·7.

Determine the air-fuel ratio by volume if air contains 21 per cent. oxygen by volume.

(ii) If the gas-consumption rate of this engine is 1,100 cu. ft. per hour when running at 300 r.p.m. on a four-stroke cycle, determine the value of the ratio {volume of air+gas aspirated} per hour÷ {volume swept out by piston per hour during suction strokes only}. Take the swept volume of the engine as 1·0 cu. ft. per stroke, and assume that the pressure and temperature of the air supply to the engine are the same as those of the gas supply.

[Part I, B.Sc. Lond.]

21. A mixture of heptane C_7H_{16}, and air in the proportions 1 : 17·15 by weight is used in an engine. The calorific value of heptane may be taken as 19,400 B.Th.U./lb. Assume air contains 21 per cent. of oxygen and 79 per cent. of nitrogen by volume.

Atomic weights are:—H 1; O 16; C 12; N 14.

Treating the fuel as a gas, calculate the heat available from 1 cu. ft. of the mixture at 32° F. and 14·7 Lb. per sq. in. abs. At these conditions 1 lb. molecule occupies 359 cu. ft. Find also the percentage composition by volume of the dry exhaust gas, assuming complete combustion of the fuel. [Part I, B.Sc. Lond.]

CHAPTER 18

TESTS AND TRIALS OF INTERNAL-COMBUSTION ENGINES

1. Report on Trial of a Four-stroke Compression-ignition Oil Engine

I. OBJECT OF TRIAL

To obtain a power-consumption curve, and thermal and mechanical efficiency curves for the engine when tested over a range of power from no load to full load.

Also to draw up a heat account or heat balance sheet for this range of output of power.

II. THE PLANT

(*a*) *Diagrammatic Sketch, or Line Diagram.*

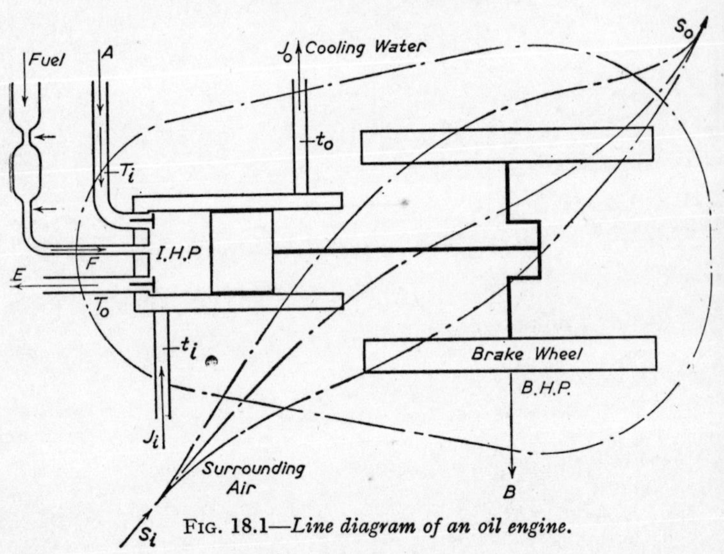

FIG. 18.1—*Line diagram of an oil engine.*

The energy equation for this engine as deduced from fig. 18.1 is:

$$F+A+J_i+S_i=B+E+J_o+S_o.$$

where the symbols represent the rate at which energy flows along the various streams.

When rearranged the equation becomes:

$$F=B+(J_o-J_i)+(E-A)+(S_o-S_i)$$

The latter equation provides the basis for the energy stream diagram of the engine.

(*b*) *Energy Stream Diagram* (*in, say, B.Th.U. per minute*).

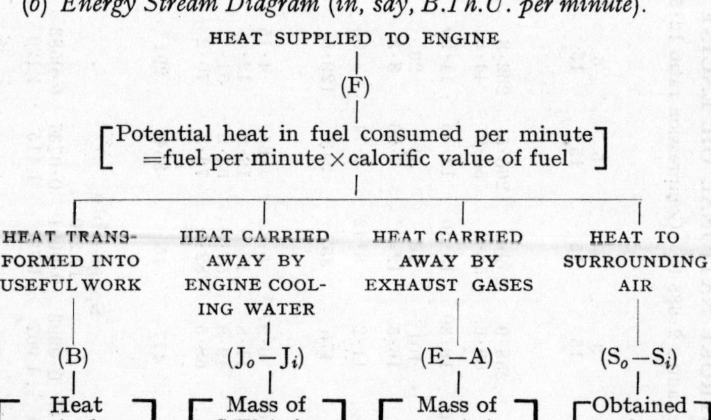

(*c*) *Description of Plant and Method of Testing.*—The engine tested was a four-stroke oil engine of the compression-ignition type (compression ratio 12·5). It was run on light fuel and governed by a spring-loaded governor which, by means of bell-crank levers actuating a shutter valve, by-passed a quantity of fuel oil supplied, thus keeping control of the speed of the engine. The fuel pump began injecting the fuel oil into the cylinder 20° before inner dead-centre and was at full stroke 30° after dead-centre point.

The engine was indicated with an indicator of the spring and piston type, and the b.h.p. obtained from observations made on a rope brake. The fuel consumption was obtained by noting the time for the consumption of a known quantity of fuel.

Rate of flow of cooling water was obtained by noting the head over a standard orifice as the water flowed through it.

Observations were made on fuel, brake, speed, and cooling water every 2 minutes, and indicator diagrams were taken every 3 minutes.

The trial was commenced with the engine running at full load, and afterwards the brake load was reduced in stages to no load. Seven trials were made over the range, full load to no load, each of 15 minutes' duration.

III. REPORT SHEET FOR TRIAL OF A FOUR-STROKE NATIONAL OIL ENGINE

ENGINE DATA: Piston diameter 8 in. Stroke 16 in. Brake radius 2·688 ft. Compression ratio 12·5.

DATE OF TRIAL:

Number of Test.		1	2	3	4	5	6	7
Duration of Test,	min.	15	15	15	15	15	15	15
POWER.								
Revolutions per minute, n		257·2	257·6	258·9	259·5	260·5	262·3	262·9
Mean effective pressure, p	Lb. per sq. in.	87·5	78·6	69·6	58·9	50·9	44·6	28·6
Calculated i.h.p. $=\frac{pla}{33,000}\frac{n}{2}$	h.p.	22·85	20·55	18·30	15·50	13·46	11·90	7·64
Brake weight, w	Lb.	151	126	101	76	51	26	0
Spring balance, s	Lb.	23·3	22·6	16·5	12·5	7·96	3·3	0
Calculated b.h.p. $=\frac{2\pi(w-s)rn}{33,000}$	h.p.	16·8	13·6	11·2	8·42	5·74	3·05	0
Heat equivalent of b.h.p.,	B.Th.U. per min.	713	578	475	357	243	129·5	0
ENGINE COOLING WATER.								
Mass of cooling water per minute,	lb.	9·81	5·16	6·97	5·45	4·65	4·15	3·22
Inlet temperature, t_i	°C.	11·8	11·8	11·8	12·0	12·2	12·4	12·8
Outlet temperature, t_o	°C.	56·2	50·0	49·8	57·8	54·6	51·4	51·3
Rise in temperature $=\frac{9}{5}(t_o-t_i)$	°F.	80	68·7	68·5	82·5	76·3	70·2	69·3
Heat carried away by cooling water,	B.Th.U. min.	785	354	477	450	354	291	223
HEAT SUPPLIED TO ENGINE.								
Fuel: light fuel oil.					Sp. gr. $=0·9$			
Calorific value,	B.Th.U. per lb.				19,200			
Mass of fuel used per min.,	lb.	0·1360	0·1151	0·0993	0·0901	0·0737	0·0583	0·0429
Heat supplied to engine per min.,	B.Th.U.	2,610	2,210	1,907	1,730	1,415	1,120	825

HEAT ACCOUNT (in B.Th.U. per min.).							
Heat supplied to engine.	2,610	2,210	1,907	1,730	1,415	1,120	825
Heat equivalent to b.h.p.	713	578	475	357	243	129·5	0
Heat carried away by cooling water.	785	354	477	450	354	291	223
Heat carried away by exhaust gases, Heat to surrounding air, } by difference	1,112	1,278	955	923	818	699·5	602
	2,610	2,210	1,907	1,730	1,415	1,120	825
EFFICIENCIES.							
Mechanical efficiency, per cent.	73·5	66·1	61·2	54·3	42·6	25·6	0
Thermal efficiency (b.h.p. basis), per cent.	27·2	26·1	24·9	20·6	17·1	11·5	0
Thermal efficiency (i.h.p. basis) per cent.	37·1	39·4	40·7	37·9	40·2	45·0	39·2
Air standard efficiency, $1-\left(\frac{1}{r_c}\right)^{\gamma-1}$	=64·5 per cent.						
Relative efficiency (b.h.p. basis), per cent.	42·2	40·5	38·6	31·9	26·5	17·8	0
DEDUCTIONS.							
Horse-power absorbed in friction.	6·05	6·95	7·1	7·08	7·72	8·85	7·64
Proportion of heat supplied absorbed in friction, per cent.	9·8	13·3	15·8	17·3	23·0	33·4	39·2
Oil consumed per hour, lb.	8·16	6·91	5·95	5·41	4·42	3·50	2·58
Oil per b.h.p.-hour, lb.	0·486	0·508	0·531	0·643	0·771	1·145	—
Brake mean effective press. Lb. per sq. in.	65	52·6	43·0	32·3	21·9	11·6	0
Cost of running per hour on oil costing 1*s.* per gallon, pence	10·9	9·2	7·9	7·2	5·9	4·7	3·4

IV. SPECIMEN SET OF CALCULATIONS FOR TEST I

Power.

R.p.m. $=257\cdot2$; stroke $=16$ in.; m.e.p. $=87\cdot5$ Lb. per sq. in.; piston diameter $=8$ in. Hence, using the numerical formula we get

$$i=\frac{pla}{33{,}000}\left(\frac{n}{2}\right)=\frac{87\cdot5}{33{,}000}\times\frac{16}{12}\times\left(\frac{\pi}{4}\times8^2\right)\left(\frac{257\cdot2}{2}\right)=22\cdot85$$

Brake load $=151$ Lb.; spring balance $=23\cdot3$ Lb.; radius of brake loads $=2\cdot688$ ft. Hence, using the numerical formula we get

$$b=\frac{2\pi tn}{33{,}000}=2\pi\times\frac{(151-23\cdot2)\times2\cdot688}{33{,}000}\times257\cdot2=16\cdot8$$

$\therefore$ Heat equivalent of b.h.p. $=16\cdot8\times\dfrac{33{,}000}{778}=713$ B.Th.U. per min.

Cooling Water.

Rate of flow of cooling water $=9\cdot81$ lb. per min.; inlet temperature $=11\cdot8°$ C.; outlet temperature $=56\cdot2°$ C.

$\therefore$ Heat carried away by engine cooling water

$$=9\cdot81\,\frac{\text{lb.}}{\text{min.}}\times\frac{1\text{ B.Th.U.}}{\text{lb. °F.}}\times44\cdot4°\text{ C.}\left[\frac{9°\text{ F.}}{5°\text{ C.}}\right]=785\text{ B.Th.U. per min.}$$

Heat Supplied to Engine.

Fuel used $=0\cdot1360$ lb. per min.; calorific value of fuel $=19{,}200$ B.Th.U. per lb.

$\therefore$ Heat supplied to engine $=0\cdot1360\times19{,}200=2160$ B.Th.U. per min.

Efficiencies.

$$\text{Mechanical efficiency}=\frac{\text{b.h.p.}}{\text{i.h.p.}}=\frac{16\cdot8}{22\cdot85}=0\cdot735\text{ or }73\cdot5\text{ per cent.}$$

$$\text{Thermal efficiency (b.h.p.) basis}=\frac{\text{heat equivalent of b.h.p.}}{\text{heat supplied}}$$

$$=\frac{713}{2610}=27\cdot2\text{ per cent.}$$

$$\text{Thermal efficiency (i.h.p. basis)}=\frac{22\cdot85\times\dfrac{33{,}000}{778}}{2610}=37\cdot1\text{ per cent.}$$

$$\text{Air standard efficiency}=1-\left(\frac{1}{r_c}\right)^{\gamma-1}=1-\left(\frac{1}{12\cdot5}\right)^{0\cdot41}$$

$$=1-0\cdot355=64\cdot5\text{ per cent.}$$

$$\therefore\ \text{Relative efficiency (b.h.p. basis)}=\frac{27\cdot2}{64\cdot5}=42\cdot2\text{ per cent.}$$

V. GRAPHICAL REPRESENTATION OF RESULTS

(a) ENGINE CURVES

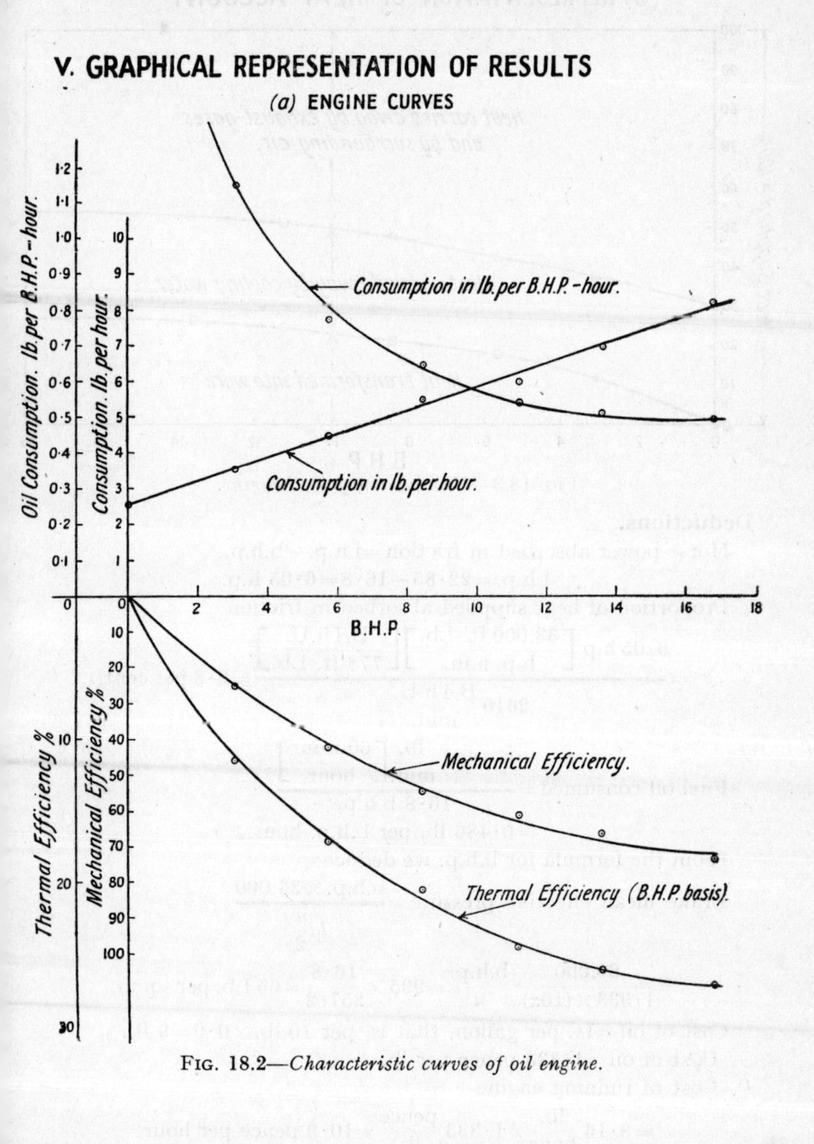

FIG. 18.2—*Characteristic curves of oil engine.*

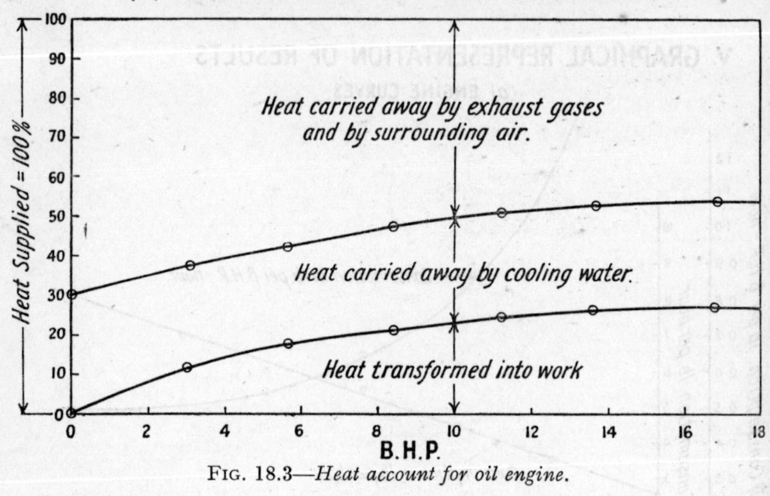

FIG. 18.3—*Heat account for oil engine.*

Deductions.

Horse-power absorbed in friction = i.h.p. − b.h.p.

$$\therefore \text{ f.h.p.} = 22\cdot85 - 16\cdot8 = 6\cdot05 \text{ h.p.}$$

Proportion of heat supplied absorbed in friction

$$= \frac{6\cdot05 \text{ h.p.}\left[\dfrac{33{,}000 \text{ ft.-Lb.}}{\text{h.p. min.}}\right]\left[\dfrac{\text{B.Th.U.}}{778 \text{ ft.-Lb.}}\right]}{2610\,\dfrac{\text{B.Th.U.}}{\text{min.}}} = 9\cdot8 \text{ per cent.}$$

$$\text{Fuel oil consumed} = \frac{0\cdot1360\,\dfrac{\text{lb.}}{\text{min.}}\left[\dfrac{60 \text{ min.}}{\text{hour}}\right]}{16\cdot8 \text{ b.h.p.}}$$

$$= 0\cdot486 \text{ lb. per b.h.p.-hour.}$$

From the formula for b.h.p. we deduce:

$$\text{Brake mean effective pressure} = \frac{\text{b.h.p.} \times 33{,}000}{la\frac{n}{2}}$$

$$= \frac{66{,}000}{1\cdot333 \times (16\pi)} \cdot \frac{\text{b.h.p.}}{n} = 995 \times \frac{16\cdot8}{257\cdot2} = 65 \text{ Lb. per sq. in.}$$

Cost of oil = 1*s*. per gallon, that is, per 10 lb. × 0·9 = 9 lb.

∴ Cost of oil = 1·333 pence per lb.

∴ Cost of running engine

$$= 8\cdot16\,\frac{\text{lb.}}{\text{hour}} \times 1\cdot333\,\frac{\text{pence}}{\text{lb.}} = 10\cdot9 \text{ pence per hour.}$$

VI. CONCLUSIONS AND CRITICISMS

It will be seen from the engine curves, fig. 18.2, that the minimum consumption of fuel per b.h.p.-hour occurs when the engine is developing about 17 b.h.p., and that the thermal efficiency is approaching a maximum at this power. To run the engine at about 17 b.h.p. will, therefore, be the most economical and most efficient power to develop.

This engine has a comparatively low mechanical efficiency, and the high value of the horse-power absorbed in friction should be noted, together with the fact that the engine is of 16-in. stroke and 8-in. piston diameter.

2. Report on Trial of a Petrol Engine

I. OBJECT OF TRIAL

To obtain a power-speed curve, a power-consumption curve, mechanical and thermal efficiency curves for a petrol engine when tested over a range of speed from 600 to 2,200 r.p.m.

II. THE PLANT

(*a*) *Diagrammatic Sketch, or Line Diagram of Plant.*

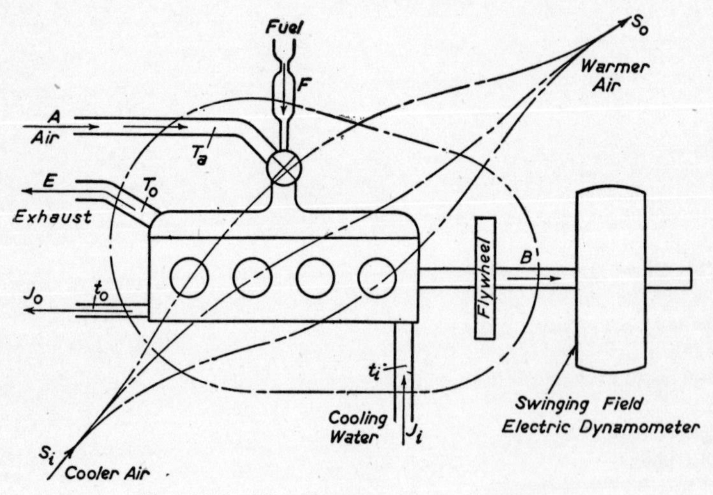

FIG. 18.4—*Line diagram of a petrol engine.*

The energy equation for this engine can be deduced from the line diagram, fig. 18.4 as:

$$F = B + (J_o - J_i) + (E - A) + (S_o - S_i)$$

where the symbols represent the rate at which energy flows along the various streams, and from which the following energy stream diagram is deduced.

(*b*) *Energy Stream Diagram (in, say, B.Th.U. per minute).*

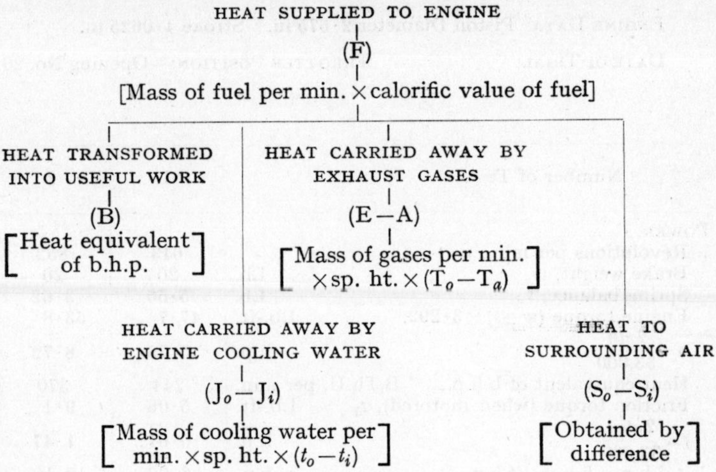

HEAT SUPPLIED TO ENGINE

(F)

[Mass of fuel per min. × calorific value of fuel]

HEAT TRANSFORMED INTO USEFUL WORK

(B)

[Heat equivalent of b.h.p.]

HEAT CARRIED AWAY BY EXHAUST GASES

(E − A)

[Mass of gases per min. × sp. ht. × $(T_o - T_a)$]

HEAT CARRIED AWAY BY ENGINE COOLING WATER

$(J_o - J_i)$

[Mass of cooling water per min. × sp. ht. × $(t_o - t_i)$]

HEAT TO SURROUNDING AIR

$(S_o - S_i)$

[Obtained by difference]

Also:—

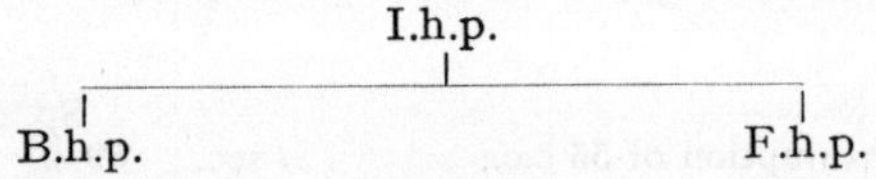

I.h.p.

B.h.p.   F.h.p.

(*c*) *Description of Plant and Method of Testing.*—The engine tested was a four-stroke four-cylinder petrol engine. It was made to develop different powers over a range of speed from 600 to 2,000 r.p.m. in eight tests, each of such duration that the engine consumed 55 c.c. of petrol per test. The throttle opening was set at a particular point and kept there for the whole trial of eight tests, and the carburettor conditions were left constant throughout the trial. The rate of fuel consumption was obtained by noting the time required for the consumption of 55 c.c. each test.

The b.h.p. of the engine was measured by means of an electric dynamometer of the swinging field type. This could also be used as an electric motor for driving the engine when the fuel supply was shut off. An estimation for the friction horse-power of the engine was thus made by direct measurement. The i.h.p. of the engine was taken to be the sum of the measured b.h.p. and f.h.p.

The outlet temperature of the engine cooling water was kept constant, but the rate of flow was not measured during this trial, nor were any exhaustions made on the exhaust gases. A heat balance sheet for the engine was not one of the objects of the trial, hence those two sets of observations were not required.

III. REPORT SHEET FOR TRIAL OF A FOUR-

ENGINE DATA: Piston Diameter 2·675 in. Stroke 4·0625 in.

DATE OF TRIAL: THROTTLE POSITION:—Opening No. 20.

Number of Test.		1	2
POWER.			
Revolutions per min., n		643	852
Brake weight, w	Lb.	20	20
Spring balance, s	Lb.	5·50	3·62
Engine torque $(w-s)\times 3{\cdot}292$,	Lb.-ft.	47·7	53·8
$b=\frac{2\pi tn}{33{,}000}$	h.p.	5·75	8·72
Heat equivalent of b.h.p.,	B.Th.U. per min.	244	370
Friction torque (when motored), t_F	Lb.-ft.	5·06	9·1
$f=\frac{2\pi t_F n}{33{,}000}$	h.p.	0·61	1·47
∴ i.h.p. = b.h.p. + f.h.p.,	h.p.	6·36	10·19
Heat equivalent of i.h.p.,	B.Th.U. per min.	269·5	432
FUEL SUPPLY.			
Fuel.		Sp. gravity 0·734;	
Time for consumption of 55 c.c.,	t sec.	59·9	45·7
Mass of fuel per minute $=\frac{5{\cdot}34}{t}$,	lb.	0·0891	0·1168
Heat supplied to engine per minute,	B.Th.U.	1,720	2,250
EFFICIENCIES.			
Mechanical efficiency,	per cent.	90·3	85·6
Thermal efficiency (b.h.p. basis),	per cent.	14·2	16·4
Thermal efficiency (i.h.p. basis),	per cent.	15·7	19·2
DEDUCTIONS.			
Fuel used per b.h.p.-hour,	lb.	0·931	0·803
Fuel used per i.h.p.-hour,	lb.	0·841	0·687
Proportion of heat supplied absorbed in friction	per cent.	1·5	2·76

CYLINDER FOUR-STROKE PETROL ENGINE

Outlet temp. of engine cooling water kept constant at 136° F.

DYNAMOMETER TORQUE: $(w-s)\times\frac{39\cdot5}{12}$ Lb. ft.

ATMOSPHERIC PRESSURE: 14·7 Lb. per sq. in. abs.
ATMOSPHERIC TEMPERATURE: 60° F.

3	4	5	6	7	8
1,049	1,211	1,402	1,621	1,833	2,008
20	20	20	20	20	20
3·37	3·37	4·0	4·94	6·0	6·81
54·8	54·8	52·6	49·6	46·1	43·4
10·93	12·63	14·03	15·28	16·05	16·57
463	535	594	648	680	702
12·1	13·2	14·7	16·0	16·9	17·3
2·42	3·04	3·92	4·94	5·90	6·60
13·35	15·67	17·95	20·22	21·95	23·17
566	665	762	857	930	983
Calorific value 19,300 B.Th.U. per lb.					
39·0	35·8	32·0	29·5	27·3	26·5
0·1367	0·1489	0·1666	0·1807	0·195	0·201
2,640	2,870	3,220	3,490	3,760	3,880
81·9	80·6	78·1	75·5	73·1	71·6
17·5	18·6	18·5	18·55	18·1	18·1
21·5	23·2	23·7	24·6	24·7	25·3
0·749	0·706	0·711	0·710	0·728	0·729
0·614	0·569	0·556	0·536	0·533	0·521
3·89	4·48	5·16	6·0	6·64	7·22

IV. SPECIMEN SET OF CALCULATIONS FOR TEST I

Power.

R.p.m. = 634; brake load = 20 Lb.; spring balance = 5·5 Lb.
Engine torque $T = (w-s) \times 3\cdot292 = 14\cdot5 \times 3\cdot292 = 47\cdot7$ Lb.-ft.

$$b = \frac{2\pi tn}{33{,}000} = \frac{2\pi \times 47\cdot7 \times 634}{33{,}000} = 5\cdot75 \quad \therefore \text{ b.h.p.} = 5\cdot75 \text{ h.p.}$$

$$\therefore \text{ Heat equivalent of b.h.p.} = 5\cdot75 \times \frac{33{,}000}{778} = 244 \text{ B.Th.U. per min.}$$

Measured friction torque = 5·06 Lb.-ft. = t_F Lb.-ft. = T_F

$$\therefore f = \frac{2\pi t_F n}{33{,}000} = \frac{2\pi \times 5\cdot06 \times 634}{33{,}000} = 0\cdot61 \quad \therefore \text{ f.h.p.} = 0\cdot61 \text{ h.p.}$$

$$\therefore \text{ i.h.p.} = \text{b.h.p.} + \text{f.h.p.} = 5\cdot75 + 0\cdot61 = 6\cdot36 \text{ h.p.}$$

$$\therefore \text{ Heat equivalent of i.h.p.} = 6\cdot36 \times \frac{33{,}000}{778} = 270 \text{ B.Th.U. per min.}$$

Fuel Supply.

Time for consumption of 55 c.c. of specific gravity 0·734 = 59·9 sec.

$$\text{Mass of fuel consumed} = \frac{55 \text{ cm.}^3}{59\cdot9 \text{ sec.}} \times 0\cdot734 \frac{\text{grm.}}{\text{cm.}^3}\left[\frac{\text{lb.}}{453\cdot6 \text{ grm.}}\right]\left[\frac{60 \text{ sec.}}{\text{min.}}\right]$$
$$= 0\cdot0891 \text{ lb./min.}$$

Calorific value of fuel = 19,300 B.Th.U. per lb.

$\therefore$ Heat supplied to engine per min. = 0·0891 × 19,300 = 1,720 B.Th.U.

Efficiencies.

$$\text{Mechanical efficiency} = \frac{\text{b.h.p.}}{\text{i.h.p.}} = \frac{5\cdot75}{6\cdot36} = 90\cdot3 \text{ per cent.}$$

$$\text{Thermal efficiency (b.h.p. basis)} = \frac{\text{heat equivalent of b.h.p.}}{\text{heat supplied}}$$
$$= \frac{244}{1720} = 14\cdot2 \text{ per cent.}$$

$$\text{Thermal efficiency (i.h.p. basis)} = \frac{270}{1720} = 15\cdot7 \text{ per cent.}$$

Deductions.

$$\text{Fuel consumed} = 0\cdot0891 \frac{\text{lb.}}{\text{min.}} \times \frac{1}{5\cdot75 \text{ b.h.p.}}\left[\frac{60 \text{ min.}}{\text{hour}}\right]$$
$$= 0\cdot931 \text{ lb. per b.h.p.-hour.}$$

$$\text{Fuel consumed per i.h.p.-hour} = \frac{0\cdot0891 \times 60}{6\cdot36} = 0\cdot841 \text{ lb}$$

Proportion of heat supplied absorbed in friction

$$= \frac{0\cdot61 \times \frac{33{,}000}{778} \text{ B.Th.U./min.}}{1720 \text{ B.Th.U./min.}} = 1\cdot5 \text{ per cent.}$$

V. GRAPHICAL REPRESENTATION OF RESULTS

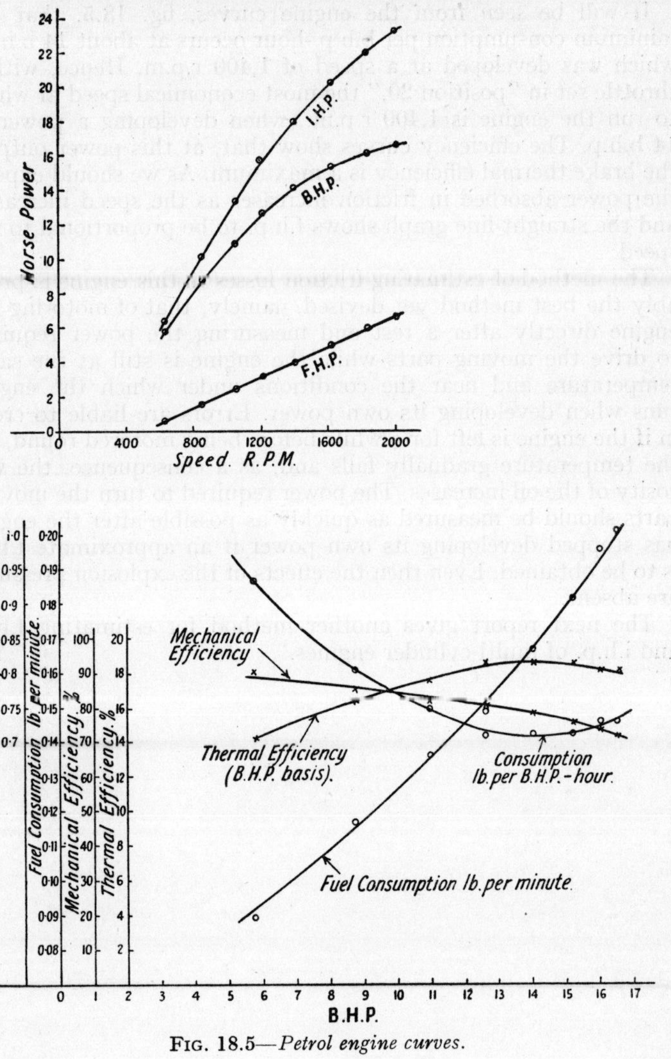

FIG. 18.5—*Petrol engine curves.*

VI. CONCLUSIONS AND CRITICISMS

It will be seen from the engine curves, fig. 18.5, that the minimum consumption per b.h.p.-hour occurs at about 14 b.h.p., which was developed at a speed of 1,400 r.p.m. Hence, with a throttle set in "position 20," the most economical speed at which to run the engine is 1,400 r.p.m., when developing a power of 14 b.h.p. The efficiency curves show that, at this power output, the brake thermal efficiency is a maximum. As we should expect, the power absorbed in friction increases as the speed increases, and the straight-line graph shows f.h.p. to be proportional to the speed.

The method of estimating friction losses in this engine is probably the best method yet devised, namely, that of motoring the engine directly after a test and measuring the power required to drive the moving parts while the engine is still at the same temperature and near the conditions under which the engine runs when developing its own power. Errors are liable to creep in if the engine is left for a while before being motored round, for the temperature gradually falls and, as a consequence, the viscosity of the oil increases. The power required to turn the moving parts should be measured as quickly as possible after the engine has stopped developing its own power if an approximate f.h.p. is to be obtained. Even then the effects of the explosion pressures are absent.

The next report gives another method for estimating f.h.p. and i.h.p. of multi-cylinder engines.

3. Report on Morse Test of a Petrol Engine

I. OBJECT OF TRIAL

To estimate the i.h.p. and f.h.p., the fuel consumption, the thermal and mechanical efficiencies of a multi-cylinder petrol engine when running at constant speed under constant settings of carburettor, magneto, and constant cooling water temperatures, by cutting out the power of one cylinder each in turn (i.e. the Morse test).

Also, to draw up a heat account or heat balance sheet for the engine.

II. THE PLANT

(a) *Diagrammatic Sketch or Line Diagram of Plant.*

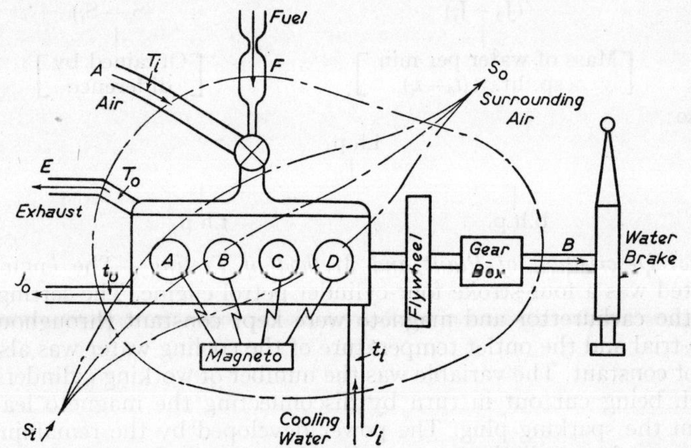

FIG. 18.6—*Line diagram of a petrol engine.*

The energy equation for this plant can be deduced from the diagram, fig. 18.6, as:

$$F = B + (J_o - J_i) + (E - A) + (S_o - S_i),$$

where symbols represent the rate at which energy flows along the various streams, and from which the following energy stream diagram can be deduced.

(*b*) *Energy Stream Diagram (in, say, B.Th.U. per minute).*

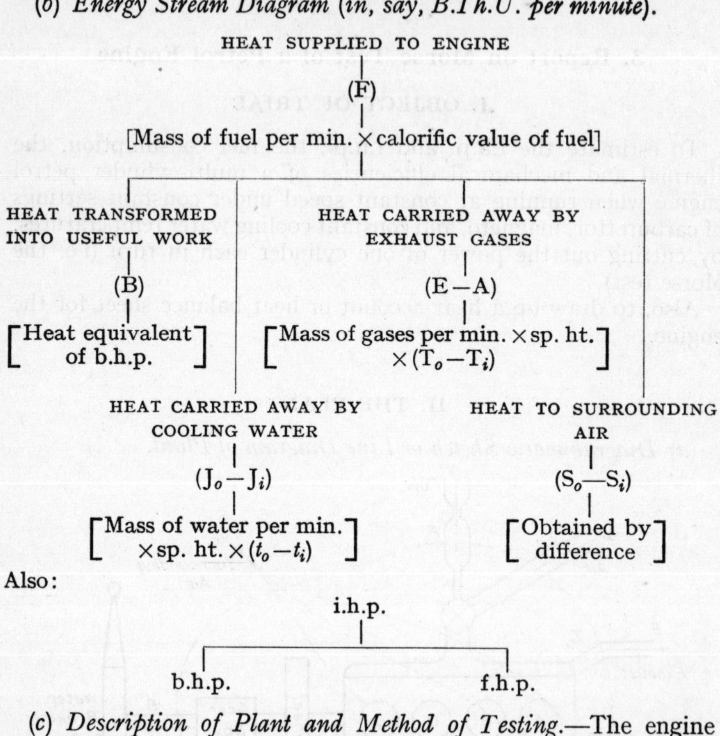

(*c*) *Description of Plant and Method of Testing.*—The engine tested was a four-stroke four-cylinder petrol engine. The settings of the carburettor and magneto were kept constant throughout the trial and the outlet temperature of the cooling water was also kept constant. The variable was the number of working cylinders, each being cut out in turn by disconnecting the magneto lead from the sparking plug. The power developed by the remaining three working cylinders was measured by means of a water-brake. When the cutting out of different cylinders altered the speed slightly, the hand wheel of the brake was turned so as to bring the speed back to the constant speed at which the whole trial was run. The fuel consumption was obtained by noting the time for the consumption of a known quantity. The heat carried away by the cooling water was obtained by noting the rate of flow and the inlet and outlet temperatures.

Five tests are necessary in order to be able to estimate the i.h.p. and f.h.p.—four of the tests being made with each of the cylinders A, B, C, and D cut out in turn, and the fifth test with all four cylinders working. Observations at 2-minute intervals were made over a period of about 10 minutes for each test.

From these five sets of results the i.h.p. and f.h.p. can be obtained in the following way: assume F to be the f.h.p. of each cylinder, then 4 F is the total friction horse-power of the whole engine, and let I_A, I_B, I_C, and I_D, represent the indicated horse-power developed by cylinders A, B, C, and D, respectively, then if cylinder A is cut out, the b.h.p. developed by the remaining three cylinders $=B_1=0+I_B+I_C+I_D-4F$

If cylinder B is cut out, the b.h.p. $=B_2=I_A+0+I_C+I_D-4F$

,, C ,, ,, $=B_3=I_A+I_B+0+I_D-4F$

,, D ,, ,, $=B_4=I_A+I_B+I_C+0-4F$

Hence, by addition, we get

$$(B_1+B_2+B_3+B_4)=3(I_A+I_B+I_C+I_D)-16F \quad . \quad \text{(i)}$$

If the whole four cylinders are working, the brake horse-power developed

$$=B=(I_A+I_B+I_C+I_D)-4F \quad . \quad . \quad . \quad \text{(ii)}$$

Hence, eliminating $(I_A+I_B+I_C+I_D)$ from equations (i) and (ii) we get

$$4F=3B-(B_1+B_2+B_3+B_4) \quad . \quad . \quad . \quad \text{(iii)}$$

And the indicated horse-power of the whole engine

$$(I_A+I_B+I_C+I_D)=4B-(B_1+B_2+B_3+B_4) \quad . \quad . \quad \text{(iv)}$$

III. SPECIMEN SET OF CALCULATIONS

Heat Supplied.

For the " all-in " test the time for consumption of 170 c.c. was 137·5 sec. Specific gravity of fuel=0·733, i.e. density=0·733 grm./c.c.

$$\text{Fuel consumed}=\frac{170\text{ cm.}^3}{137\cdot5\text{ sec.}}\times\frac{0\cdot733\text{ grm.}}{\text{cm.}^3}\left[\frac{\text{lb.}}{453\cdot6\text{ grm.}}\right]\left[\frac{60\text{ sec.}}{\text{min.}}\right]$$

$$=0\cdot120\text{ lb. per min.}$$

$$\therefore\ \text{Heat supplied}=0\cdot120\ \frac{\text{lb.}}{\text{min.}}\times18{,}200\ \frac{\text{B.Th.U.}}{\text{lb.}}$$

$$=2{,}184\text{ B.Th.U. per min.}$$

Cooling Water.

For " all-in " test the rate of flow of cooling water=10·7 lb./min.
Rise in temperature =63·4−15·0=48·4° C.=87·1° F.
∴ Heat carried away by cooling water=931 B.Th.U./min.

Power.

For the " all-in " test the total load $(w+s)$ l.b.=40·8 l.b.

$$\therefore b=\frac{(w+s)n}{4500}=\frac{40\cdot8\times1000}{4500}=9\cdot07\text{, i.e. b.h.p.} = 9\cdot07\text{ h.p.}$$

[*Continued on page 438*

REPORT SHEET ON TRIAL OF A PETROL ENGINE

ENGINE DATA: Bore 69·5 mm.

STROKE: 102 mm.

Horse-power dissipated by water brake is

$b = \dfrac{(w+s)n}{4,500}$ (the spring-balance effect being reversed).

DATE OF TRIAL:

THROTTLE POSITION: Full open. Magneto: Half advanced.

Cylinder cut out.		A	B	C	D	All In.
Duration of Test,	min.	9	9	9	9	9
FUEL SUPPLY.						
Fuel.				specific gravity		0·733
Calorific value of fuel.				18,200 B.Th.U. per lb.		
Time for consumption of 170 c.c.,	sec.	140·3	130·2	133·0	132·7	137·5
Fuel consumed per min.,	lb.	0·117	0·126	0·124	0·124	0·120
Heat supplied to engine per min.,	B.Th.U.	←		(not required)	→	2,185
COOLING WATER						
Cooling water per min.,	lb.	9·13	8·1	8·0	7·93	10·7
Inlet temperature of cooling water,	°C.	17·5	17·0	17·0	16·0	15·0
Outlet temperature of cooling water,	°C.	62·5	63·3	63·7	63·6	63·4
Heat carried away by cooling water per min.,	B.Th.U.	←		(not required)	→	931
POWER.						
Revolutions per min., n		1,000	1,000	1,000	1,000	1,000
Brake load, w	Lb.	20	20	20	20	20
Spring balance, s	Lb.	7·62	8·9	8·4	8·9	20·8
B.h.p. $=\dfrac{(w+s)n}{4,500}$ (for the particular brake used)		6·15	6·43	6·30	6·43	9·07
$B_1+B_2+B_3+B_4$				25·31		
$3\times$ b.h.p. $= 3B$		—	—	—	—	27·21
Friction horse-power of engine $=4F$ (by Equation (iii)).		—	—	—	—	1·9
Indicated horse-power of engine $=I_A+I_B+I_C+I_D$ (by Eqn. (iv)).		—	—	—	—	10·97
Heat equivalent of b.h.p. of engine,	B.Th.U. min.	—	—	—	—	385

			All In. 9
Heat Account (in B.Th.U. per min.)			
Heat supplied to engine.		100%	2,184
Heat equivalent of b.h.p.		17·6%	385
Heat carried away by cooling water.		42·6%	931
Heat carried away by exhaust gases.	Obtained by difference	39·8%	868
Heat to surrounding air.			
		100%	2,184
Efficiencies.			
Mechanical efficiency,	per cent.		82·6
Thermal efficiency (b.h.p. basis),	per cent.		17·6
Thermal efficiency (i.h.p. basis),	per cent.		21·3
Deductions.			
Proportion of heat supplied absorbed in friction,	per cent.		3·7
Consumption of fuel per b.h.p.-hour,	lb.		0·793
Consumption of fuel per i.h.p.-hour	lb.		0·656

$\therefore$ Heat equivalent of b.h.p. $= 9 \cdot 07 \times \dfrac{33{,}000}{778} = 385$ B.Th.U. per min.

From Equation (iii), namely, $4F = 3B - (B_1 + B_2 + B_3 + B_4)$

$$B_1 + B_2 + B_3 + B_4 = 6 \cdot 15 + 6 \cdot 43 + 6 \cdot 30 + 6 \cdot 43 = 25 \cdot 31 \text{ h.p.}$$
$$3B = 3 \times 9 \cdot 07 = 27 \cdot 21 \text{ h.p.}$$

$\therefore$ Friction h.p. of the whole engine $= 4F = 1 \cdot 9$ h.p.

From Equation (iv), namely,

$$(I_A + I_B + I_C + I_D) = 4B - (B_1 + B_2 + B_3 + B_4)$$

the indicated h.p. of the whole engine $= 4 \times 9 \cdot 07 - 25 \cdot 31 = 10 \cdot 97$ h.p.

Efficiencies for the "All-In" Test.

Mechanical efficiency of whole engine

$$= \frac{\text{b.h.p.}}{\text{i.h.p.}} = \frac{9 \cdot 07}{10 \cdot 97} = 82 \cdot 6 \text{ per cent.}$$

$$\text{Thermal efficiency (b.h.p. basis)} = \frac{\text{heat equivalent of b.h.p.}}{\text{heat supplied}}$$
$$= \frac{385}{2184} = 17 \cdot 6 \text{ per cent.}$$

$$\text{Thermal efficiency (i.h.p. basis)} = \frac{10 \cdot 97}{2184} \times \frac{33{,}000}{778} = 21 \cdot 3 \text{ per cent.}$$

Deductions for the "All-In" Test.

Proportion of heat supplied absorbed in friction

$$= \frac{1 \cdot 9}{2184} \times \frac{33{,}000}{778} = 3 \cdot 7 \text{ per cent.}$$

Fuel consumed $= 0 \cdot 120 \times 60 = 7 \cdot 2$ lb. per hour

$$\text{or } 7 \cdot 2 \frac{\text{lb.}}{\text{hour}} \times \frac{1}{9 \cdot 07 \text{ b.h.p.}} = 0 \cdot 793 \text{ lb. per b.h.p.-hour.}$$

GRAPHICAL REPRESENTATION OF RESULTS

The heat account for the engine may be shown graphically thus:

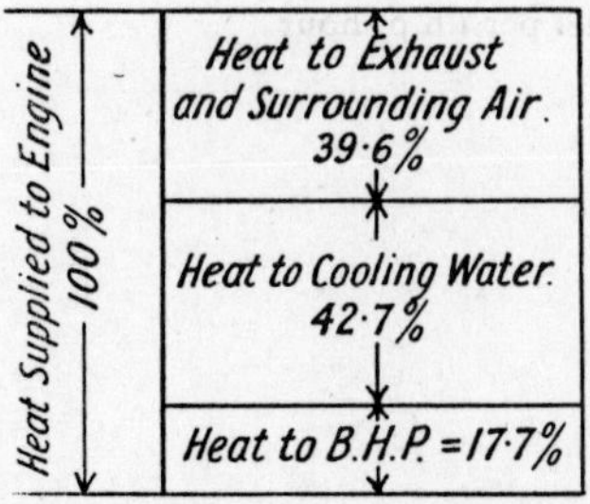

Heat Supplied to Engine 100%
Heat to Exhaust and Surrounding Air. 39·6%
Heat to Cooling Water. 42·7%
Heat to B.H.P. = 17·7%

FIG. 18.7—*Heat account for a petrol engine.*

CRITICISMS AND CONCLUSIONS

In estimating the f.h.p. and i.h.p. of a multi-cylinder engine by this method we have assumed that the friction in each cylinder is the same. This is a reasonable assumption for identical cylinders and pistons, but we have also assumed in equations (i) and (ii) that the friction in the "idle" cylinder is the same as in the working cylinders, which may or may not be true, for it may be that in the firing cylinders the piston rings are exerting greater pressures on the cylinder walls than in the idle cylinder in which there is no pressure due to explosion. If this is so, the friction in the firing cylinders will not be the same as that in the idle one.

To test whether this method of estimating f.h.p. and i.h.p. is reliable or not, another method, such as that previously employed in the trial on the petrol engine (p. 426), should be tried and the results of the two methods compared.

EXERCISES ON CHAPTER 18

(i)

1. A gas engine consumes 200 cu. ft. of coal gas per hour at a temperature of 61° F. and a pressure of 78 cm. of mercury. Calculate the energy supplied per minute to the engine if the calorific value of the gas is 400,000 ft.-Lb. per cu. ft. at 76 cm. of mercury and 32° F.

If the engine develops an i.h.p. of 10 and a b.h.p. of 7·5, calculate the thermal efficiency of the engine on the b.h.p. basis. Find also the mechanical efficiency and the consumption of gas per i.h.p.-hour and per b.h.p.-hour in cu. ft. at s.t.p.

2. You are required to test a gas engine with a view to estimating the power developed in the cylinder and at the brake wheel. It is also required to know the gas consumption and the heat carried away by the engine cooling water per minute. Make a diagrammatic sketch of the plant and apparatus you would employ, and briefly describe how you would use it to measure and estimate the required quantities.

3. The following are the mean values of the observations made during a trial, of 16 minutes' duration, of a four-stroke gas engine; r.p.m. 236 ; explosions per min. 110; mean effective pressure 79 Lb. per sq. in.; piston diameter 7 in.; stroke 15 in. The brake-horse-power was measured electrically as 9. Cooling water flowed at the rate of 13·5 lb. per min. with initial and final temperatures 53° F. and 112° F., respectively. The gas used per minute was calculated to be 3·75 cu. ft. per min. at s.t.p. Calorific value 522 B.Th.U. per cu. ft. at s.t.p.

Calculate the i.h.p. of the engine, the brake thermal and mechanical efficiencies of the engine, the heat carried away by the cooling water per minute, the power absorbed in friction, the consumption in cu. ft. per b.h.p.-hour at s.t.p. Also draw up a heat account for the engine.

4. (*a*) Draw up a heat account for B.Th.U. per minute and per cent. for an oil engine using 3·2 lb. of oil per minute of calorific value 18,900 B.Th.U. per lb. The powers developed were: i.h.p. 400 and b.h.p. 325. Jacket water circulated at the rate of 450 lb. per minute and the temperature rise was 36° F.

(*b*) Sketch the kind of curves you would expect from an oil engine tested at constant speed over a range of power from no load to 10 per cent. overload.

5. The following are the mean values of the observations made during a series of tests of a four-stroke compression-ignition engine:

Number of test.	1	2	3	4	5	6
R.p.m.	206	206	205	204	203	201
Mean effective pressure, Lb. per sq. in.	—	42·8	55·1	70·5	84·1	109
B.h.p.	0	9·5	15·9	23·7	30·2	40
Oil consumed per hour. lb.	5·5	6·9	8·8	11·8	14·1	20·6

The engine has a piston diameter 12 in. and a stroke 18·25 in. Calculate, for each test, the i.h.p. mechanical and brake thermal efficiencies, oil consumption in lb. per b.h.p.-hour. Plot these quantities and also the oil per hour on a b.h.p. base, and estimate from the curves the most economical power at which to run the engine. Calorific value of the oil used 19,100 B.Th.U. per lb.

6. You are required to make a variable speed trial of a multi-cylinder petrol engine with a view to plotting curves, on a speed base, of power output, petrol consumption, thermal efficiency, air consumption and volumetric efficiency.

Make a diagrammatic sketch of the plant and apparatus you would employ. Give a list of the observations you would make, and indicate how you would use them to calculate or estimate the required quantities.

(ii)

7. The following are the mean values of the observations made on a four-stroke compression-ignition engine during a trial of 20 minutes' duration: r.p.m. 250; mean effective pressure 126 Lb. per sq. in.; brake load 94 Lb.; spring balance 20 Lb.; brake wheel+rope radius 2·7 ft.; total oil consumption 1·7 lb.; cooling water flowed at the rate of 6·3 lb. per min. with a rise in temperature of 72° F.; the engine had a piston of 6·5 in. diameter and a stroke of 10·625 in.; the calorific value of the oil was 17,650 B.Th.U. per lb.

Estimate the i.h.p., b.h.p., f.h.p., heat carried away by the cooling water per minute, heat supplied to the engine per minute, brake thermal and mechanical efficiencies. Also, draw up a heat account showing the quantities in B.Th.U. per min. flowing along the various energy streams through the engine, and also as percentages of the heat supplied.

8. The following are the mean values of the observations made during a series of tests of a four-cylinder petrol engine:

Number of cylinder cut out		A	B	C	D	All In
Petrol consumption	lb. per min.	0·202	0·205	0·204	0·200	0·199
Measured b.h.p.		12·4	12·35	10·5	12·01	17·32

The speed of the engine was kept constant throughout the trial at 2,000 r.p.m. Estimate the f.h.p. and i.h.p. of the engine at this speed. Calculate the brake thermal and mechanical efficiencies of the engine if the calorific value of the petrol used was 18,200 B.Th.U. per lb.

9. The fuel used during a test of an internal combustion engine contained 12·5 per cent. of hydrogen by weight, and had a calorific value 19,270 B.Th.U. per lb. The engine consumed 0·5 lb. of fuel per b.h.p. per hour when developing 15·5 b.h.p., the air-fuel ratio of the mixture was 14·3 to 1 by weight. Jacket water was circulated at the rate of 8 lb. per minute with a temperature rise of 91° F. The temperature of the exhaust gases was 1,400° F. and of the engine-room 60° F. When motoring the engine at test speed after the power test the input required was 5·2 horse-power. Estimate the mechanical and brake thermal efficiencies of the engine, and draw up a heat balance sheet in B.Th.U. per minute and per cent. for the test. Assume 0·24 was the mean specific heat of the dry exhaust gases, and the total heat per lb. of steam in the exhaust gases was 1,700 B.Th.U.

10. A fuel consisting of 84 per cent. carbon and 16 per cent. hydrogen is burned completely, the air supplied being 50 per cent. in excess of the chemically correct requirement. Find:—

(*a*) the partial pressure of the water vapour in the products of combustion if the total pressure is 15 Lb. per sq. in. abs. and the temperature is 450° F.;

(*b*) the total heat per lb. of the products, taking 32° F. as datum;

(*c*) the weight of 1 cu. ft. of the products at 450° F.

Air contains 23·1 per cent. O_2 by weight, and the mean specific heats of the dry gases is 0·24 and of superheated steam is 0·5.

11. A six-cylinder four-stroke compression-ignition engine, consumed fuel oil containing 14 per cent. hydrogen and of higher calorific

value 19,250 B.Th.U. per lb. When developing 190 b.h.p. the engine consumed 1·62 lb. of fuel-oil per min. and 85 lb. of air per min. Jacket water circulated at the rate of 133 lb. per min. and its rise of temperature was 56° F. Piston cooling-oil, of specific heat 0·5, circulated at the rate of 78 lb. per min. and had a rise in temperature of 36° F. The temperature of the exhaust gases was 370° F. and of the engine room 68° F. Reckoning from the engine-room temperature as datum, calculate the heat carried away by the dry gas and steam of the exhaust assuming them to have specific heats of 0·24 and 0·48, respectively. Also, draw up a heat balance sheet in B.Th.U. per min. showing how the energy in the fuel oil flowed through the engine. The partial pressure of steam in the exhaust gas may be assumed to be 2 Lb. per sq. in. absolute.

12. A four-stroke automobile engine of total swept volume 173 in³. was tested at constant speed of 2,400 r.p.m. over a range of mixture strength. The numerical formula for the horse-power dissipated by the water brake was $B = \frac{WN}{2{,}800}$, where W is the number of Lb. of load and N the number of revolutions per minute.

Load W. Lb.	38·0	38·6	38·7	38·68	38·5	38	36·2	34	33·1
Fuel. lb. per hour	23·8	23·0	22·4	21·8	21·5	20·4	19·0	18·1	17·8

Plot the fuel consumption in lb. per b.h.p.-hour against brake m.e.p. in Lb. per in.² and discuss the form of curve. Deduce the consumption, the power, and the brake thermal efficiency—

(*a*) for maximum power output;

(*b*) for maximum efficiency taking 18,000 B.Th.U. per lb. as the calorific value of the petrol.

13. A six-cylinder four-stroke petrol engine of bore 90 mm. and stroke 120 mm. gave the following data when tested at 2,500 r.p.m. Torque of six cylinders 215 Lb.-ft. and mean torque of five cylinders 175 Lb.-ft. Petrol containing 15 per cent. of hydrogen by weight and of calorific value 19,300 B.Th.U./lb. was used at the rate of 0·897 lb./min. and air at the rate of 11·3 lb./min. Cooling water flowed at the rate of 81 lb./min. with inlet and outlet temperature of 60° F. and 119° F., respectively. The temperature of the exhaust gases was 890° F. and of the atmosphere in the engine room 60° F.

Estimate the indicated horse-power, the m.e.p. and mechanical efficiency of the engine, stating any assumptions made. Also, assuming the moisture of combustion in the exhaust gases contains 1,500 B.Th.U./lb. above the atmospheric temperature as datum and that the specific heat of the dry exhaust gas is 0·25 B.Th.U./lb. ° F. draw up a heat account for the engine expressed in B.Th.U./min. and as a percentage of the potential heat in the fuel supplied.

14. (i) In a trial of a four-cylinder four-stroke petrol engine of 3·5 in. bore and 3·6 in. stroke the net dynamometer load was 65 Lb. at a radius of 18 in. when the speed was 2,200 r.p.m. At the same speed and throttle opening the engine required 5 : 4 h.p. to motor it with the ignition switched off. Calculate the mechanical efficiency and indicated mean effective pressure.

(ii) During a 3 minute run at this speed and power the engine used 1·05 lb. of petrol of calorific value 18,800 B.Th.U. per lb., and 47 lb. of cooling water with a temperature rise of 105° F.

Draw up a heat balance for the test in B.Th.U. per minute, and briefly justify your inclusion or omission of the friction heat.

[Part I, B.Sc. Lond.]

15. Draw up a heat balance for the test of a spark-ignition engine given the following data:

Calorific value of fuel 19,500 B.Th.U. per lb.; fuel consumed 1·375 lb. per min.; brake power 152 horse-power; exhaust temperature 1,250° F.; cooling water 160 lb. per min. with a rise of temperature 55° F.; room temperature 60° F. Give the heat balance in quantities per minute; assume an air to fuel ratio of 15·1 by weight and the specific heat of the exhaust gas at constant pressure to be 0·28. What are the principal losses unaccounted for?

[I.Mech.E., Sec. A.]

CHAPTER 19

FUELS—SOLID, GASEOUS, AND LIQUID

1. Fuels and Evolution of Heat.—Fuels can be divided into three classes: *solid, gaseous, and liquid.* The two elements forming the bulk of all fuels are carbon and hydrogen, both of which, by union with oxygen, result in the evolution of heat.

The chief of the simpler chemical reactions involved in the combustion of fuels are as follows, the numerals showing B.Th.U. liberated or required per mol of fuel constituent.

$$\begin{aligned}
C+O_2 &= CO_2 & +174{,}600\\
C+CO_2 &= 2CO & -\ 70{,}200\\
2C+O_2 &= 2CO & +104{,}000\\
2CO+O_2 &= 2CO_2 & +244{,}800\\
2H_2+O_2 &= 2H_2O & +246{,}200\\
C+H_2O &= CO+H_2 & -\ 70{,}900\\
C+2H_2O &= CO_2+2H_2 & -\ 71{,}600\\
CO+H_2O &= CO_2+H_2 & -\ 700
\end{aligned}$$

Thus, it will be seen from the first equation that the combustion of 1 lb. of carbon results in the evolution of

$$\frac{174{,}600 \text{ B.Th.U.}}{12 \text{ lb.}} = 14{,}550 \text{ B.Th.U. per lb.}$$

since the mass of 1 mol of carbon is 12 lb. From the fifth equation it will be seen that 1 lb. of hydrogen results in the evolution of

$$\frac{246{,}200 \text{ B.Th.U.}}{4 \text{ lb.}} = 61{,}550 \text{ B.Th.U. per lb.};$$

while, for some of the other reactions, heat has to be supplied, as seen, for instance, in the second equation.

In some fuels the principal constituents, carbon and hydrogen, exist in the form of compounds, called hydrocarbons, having the general chemical formula C_xH_y. The number of hydrocarbon compounds obtainable from coal or crude petroleum is not exactly known, but it is known that there are hundreds of them.

The heating value of fuels is an item of greatest importance. It is common practice to specify two calorific values, the higher or "gross" and the lower or "net" calorific values, especially for fuels containing a fair amount of hydrogen (see p. 14). The reason for this is that hydrogen burns to form water vapour or steam, hence requiring latent heat of evaporation. It is argued that this latent heat of evaporation cannot be utilised in engines or in the furnaces and flues of boilers, and should therefore be deducted from the heat of combustion which is determined by calorimetric measurement. Thus, two calorific values are specified: the higher or "gross" calorific value (H.C.V.) which includes the latent heat of evaporation (or condensation), and the lower or "net" calorific value (L.C.V.) which does not include the latent heat of evaporation of the moisture of combustion or the moisture in the air supplying the oxygen.

As mentioned on p. 14, the finding of the correct value of the latent heat steam of from steam tables for this purpose is not as straightforward as it might at first appear, since the partial pressure which the steam exerts in the final products of combustion can only be calculated accurately if the analysis of the fuel and of the products is known. It is more satisfactory to use the direct experimental figure obtained for calorific value, namely, the gross or higher calorific value (H.C.V.), since this is the heating value of a fuel reckoned from atmospheric temperature as datum.

SOLID FUELS

2. Varieties of Solid Fuels.—The most important of the natural solid fuels are wood, peat, coal, and anthracite. Of the artificial solid fuels, coke and charcoal are the most important.

Coal.—Of all the fuels in existence, coal has claims to being considered the most important, for it exists in great quantities. Most likely it was formed by the decomposition of plants and trees through the agency of pressure and heat. The soft coals, or lignites, resemble wood, while in anthracite there is practically no trace of vegetable origin. An increase in the carbon content and a diminution in the amount of hydrogen and oxygen characterise the change from wood to coal.

Wood.—Wood has ceased to be a commercially important fuel in this country because of its comparatively high price and the large amount of moisture it contains. The latter requires heat from the fuel to evaporate it.

Coke and Charcoal.—The artificial solid fuels, coke and charcoal, are the residues left after the carbonisation or distillation of coal and the distillation of wood, respectively. The distillation of coal is carried out in order to produce illuminating gas or coal gas and also for the production of coke. Coke is used most extensively in the metallurgical industries. It is also used for the making of producer gas, and as a domestic fuel. The amount of volatile matter from coke is very small, but it contains a higher percentage of ash than the coal from which coke is made.

3. Composition of Solid Fuels, and Calorific Values.—Some idea of the composition of average solid fuels (by weight) can be obtained from the following table, but there are many qualities of the same kind of fuel, which therefore differ in composition and calorific value.

Fuel	Percentage Composition (by Wt.)			Approximate Calorific Value
	Carbon	Hydrogen	Oxygen	B.Th.U. per lb.
Wood.	50	6	44	8,500
Peat.	60	6	34	10,500
Coal.	80	5	15	13,500
Anthracite.	95	2·7	2·3	15,000

Analysis of Coal.—The usual ways of determining the composition of coals are by a "proximate analysis" and by an "ultimate analysis."

The *proximate analysis* of coal is that of determining the moisture, volatile matter, fixed carbon, and ash. It is easy and quick compared with an ultimate analysis, and is therefore the one usually performed for commercial purposes, since it furnishes data showing the commercially important properties of coal.

The *ultimate analysis* of coal is one of determining the percentages of the "ultimate" constituents C, H_2, O_2, S, N_2, and ash in the dry coal. The analysis is required for calculative and scientific work.

Calorific Value and Combustion of Solid Fuel.—The calorific value of solid fuel is usually determined by means of the bomb calorimeter, in which a known weight of the sample of coal is burned, and observations made for the estimation of the heat produced. A case has been fully worked out on p. 15.

The combustion of coal and calculations on air supply, together with analysis of products of combustion and flue gases, have been dealt with in Chapter 9 on Boilers, paragraphs 9 and 10.

4. Pulverised Fuel.—It is possible to burn low-grade fuels efficiently if pulverised. For good combustion of any fuel the combustible elements must be surrounded with oxygen necessary for complete combustion. With ordinary hand stoking or mechanical chain-grate stoking it is necessary to admit excess air if there is to be likelihood of complete combustion, and the excess air so admitted reduces the temperature in the combustion chamber, besides increasing the weight of gases which take heat to waste up the chimney stack. By pulverising and forcing the fuel into the combustion chamber in powdered form, the combustible elements in the fuel can be more thoroughly mixed with the air supplied, giving better combustion on a less amount of excess air than is possible in stoker-fired furnaces. The furnace temperature is thus kept up and less heat is wasted via the chimney stack.

It is claimed that pulverised coal firing is as flexible as oil firing and that low-grade and cheap fuels can be burned efficiently.

GASEOUS FUELS

5. Advantages of Gaseous Fuels.—Some advantages claimed for gaseous fuels are:

(1) Combustion of gaseous fuels permits of exact control of (i) quantity; (ii) temperature variations; (iii) length of flame.

(2) Smoke can be eliminated.

(3) Coal, the basis fuel, can be distilled so that gas can be distributed economically to heaters, furnaces, and engines over a very wide area. This is claimed to be much more desirable than conveying coal or other solid fuels over that area.

(4) Cleanliness, in that there is no waste and ash to clear away after combustion.

6. Varieties of Gaseous Fuels.—Of the gaseous fuels used, only in a few localities, such as in Pennsylvania, U.S.A., is natural gas to be found. The other gaseous fuels are artificial and manufactured from solid fuels, the chief of which are: coal gas (otherwise known as illuminating gas or "town gas"), producer gas, water gas, Dowson gas (often called mixed gas), blast-furnace gas, and coke-oven gas.

Natural gas, used extensively in U.S.A., is composed of hydrocarbons of which the chief is methane (CH_4).

Illuminating gas or coal gas is produced at a gasworks with coke as a by-product. It is formed by the destructive distillation or carbonisation of coal, and consists chiefly of hydrogen (H_2), methane (CH_4), and carbon monoxide (CO). It has a calorific value of about 600 B.Th.U. per cu. ft., is comparatively expensive, but is easily accessible from the gas mains and is therefore often used in small plant.

Producer gas is strictly the gas obtained from the incomplete combustion of coke or charcoal in a current of air. It should, therefore, theoretically, consist of a mixture of carbon monoxide and nitrogen according to the chemical equation

$$2C+\left(O_2+\frac{79}{21}N_2\right)=2CO+\frac{79}{21}N_2=2CO+3{\cdot}76N_2$$

Thus, by volume, it should consist of 34·8 per cent. carbon monoxide and 65·2 per cent. nitrogen, but, actually, the gas obtained from a producer differs from the theoretical, for its production depends upon temperature, pressure, size of coal, and velocity of the air passing through the producer.

The calorific value of producer gas is comparatively low because the greater proportion of it is inert nitrogen, but the process of manufacture is cheap and relatively easy.

Water gas is made by blowing steam over highly heated coke. At high temperatures a reaction, which requires heat, takes place according to the equation $C+H_2O=CO+H_2$ resulting in a gas containing, by volume, 50 per cent. carbon monoxide and 50 per cent. hydrogen. At lower temperatures the reaction $C+2H_2O=CO_2+2H_2$ takes place, resulting in a gas containing 33·3 per cent. carbon dioxide and 66·7 per cent. hydrogen, by volume. The gas produced has a comparatively high calorific value of about 300 B.Th.U. per cu. ft.

Dowson gas or mixed gas is a mixture of the above producer gas and water gas. It is manufactured in a producer in one operation and is cheap, giving little trouble in its production. It is made in a large vessel containing coke or other solid fuel (maybe anthracite) through which air and steam are made to pass, either by suction, as in "suction gas" producers, or by pressure. It consists of hydrogen, carbon monoxide, carbon dioxide, and nitrogen. It has a calorific value varying with the details of its production, a likely value being 130 B.Th.U. per cu. ft.

Blast-furnace gas is a by-product from the smelting of iron. The gases leaving the top of an iron blast furnace contain combustible gases, which are collected and used for various purposes such as heating stoves, raising steam in boilers; and when freed from dust and tar by passage through a suitable "scrubber," can be used as fuel in internal-combustion engines. The chief combustible in this gas is carbon monoxide; the blast furnace operates, in fact, as a producer. The exact composition and calorific value of such gas varies with the working of the furnace. The calorific value usually lies between 60 and 90 B.Th.U. per cu. ft.

Coke-oven gas is a by-product from coke-oven plants where the primary concern is to make coke. The composition of this gas is similar to that of coal gas, as would be expected, since both are produced by the heating of coal in retorts. It will be seen from the following Table that coke-oven gas contains a large proportion of hydrogen. This renders it liable to pre-ignition in engines in which the compression ratio is high. The calorific value of this gas varies according to the conditions of working of the oven, but about 450 B.Th.U. per cu. ft. may be taken as a likely value.

7. Composition of Gaseous Fuels, and Calorific Values. —A rough idea of the composition of gaseous fuels (by volume) can be obtained from the following table, but the composition of any one kind of gaseous fuel varies according to the details of its production, and the following figures can therefore only be taken as approximate:

Fuel	Percentage Composition by Volume					Calorific Value per Standard cu. ft.
	H_2	CH_4	CO	CO_2	N_2	B.Th.U.
Coal gas.	48	23	20	4	5	540
Water gas.	50	6	40	4	0	300
Dowson gas.	15	2	28	5	50	150
Blast-furnace gas.	4	1	25	5	65	90
Coke-oven gas.	53	30	10	2	5	450

Determination of Calorific Values of Gaseous Fuels.—The calorific value of gaseous fuels can be determined by means of Boys' calorimeter, illustrated in fig. **19.1**. Gas is fed to the calorimeter under constant pressure and burned at the burner B. The hot products of combustion flow up the funnel E and then past radiator coils. Heat is transferred from the gases to the water circulating through the coils. The water enters at A and leaves at C. Part of the products of combustion is steam, due to the combustion of hydrogen contained in the gas. The steam, on coming into contact with the cold radiator fins, condenses and, therefore, gives its latent heat to the cooling water. The condensed steam falls to the bottom and flows out of the calorimeter through outlet F into a measuring flask. The calorific value of the gas can be obtained from the fact that the heat absorbed by the cooling water is the heat produced by the gas in burning.

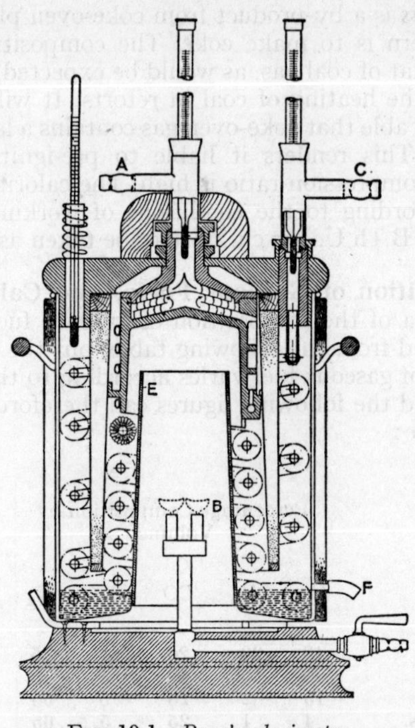

FIG. 19.1—*Boys' calorimeter.*

The observations made during such a test on coal gas were:

Volume of gas used	$=0\cdot583$ cu. ft.
Cooling water circulated	$=21\cdot75$ lb.
Condensed steam collected	$=0\cdot019$ lb.
Rise in temperature of cooling water	$=6\cdot17°$ C.
Pressure of gas above atmosphere (manometer)	$=1\cdot7$ in. of water
Barometric pressure	$=29\cdot78$ in. of mercury.
Temperature of gas	$=14\cdot18°$ C.

From these observations we get: absolute pressure of gas

$$=29\cdot78 \text{ in. Hg}+1\cdot7 \text{ in. } H_2O\left[\frac{1 \text{ in. Hg}}{13\cdot6 \text{ in. } H_2O}\right]=29\cdot91 \text{ in. of mercury.}$$

Volume of gas used, reduced to s.t.p.,

$$=V_o=\frac{PV}{P}\frac{T_o}{T}=\left(\frac{29\cdot91}{29\cdot9}\right)\times0\cdot583 \text{ ft.}^3\times\left(\frac{273}{287\cdot18}\right)=0\cdot555 \text{ cu. ft.}$$

Total quantity of heat received by cooling water

$$=\text{mass}\times\text{sp. ht.}\times\text{rise in temperature}$$

$$=21\cdot75\text{ lb.}\times\frac{1\text{ B.Th.U.}}{\text{lb. °F.}}\times6\cdot17°\text{ C.}\left[\frac{9°\text{ F.}}{5°\text{ C.}}\right]=242\text{ B.Th.U.}$$

which includes the latent heat of condensed steam.

Latent heat of moisture of combustion

$$=0\cdot019\text{ lb.}\times1{,}055\frac{\text{B.Th.U.}}{\text{lb.}}=20\text{ B.Th.U.}$$

Hence, heat received from the products of combustion without reckoning the latent heat of the mosture of combustion

$$=242-20=222\text{ B.Th.U.}$$

Hence, the higher calorific value of the gas $=\frac{242\text{ B.Th.U.}}{0\cdot555\text{ ft.}^3}$

$$=436\text{ B.Th.U. per cu. ft. at s.t.p.}$$

and the lower calorific value $=\frac{222\text{ B.Th.U.}}{0\cdot555\text{ ft.}^3}$

$$=400\text{ B.Th.U. per cu. ft. at s.t.p.}$$

8. Combustion of Gaseous Fuels, and Heating Values of Explosive Mixtures.—The combustible constituents H_2, CH_4 and CO of gaseous fuels burn according to the chemical equations:

$$2H_2+O_2=2H_2O$$
$$CH_4+2O_2=CO_2+2H_2O$$
$$2CO+O_2=2CO_2$$

From the first it will be seen that 2 volumes of hydrogen require, theoretically, 1 volume of oxygen for complete combustion. Since 100 parts of air contain, by volume, 21 parts of oxygen and 79 of nitrogen, it follows that 1 volume of hydrogen requires $\frac{100}{21}\left(\frac{1}{2}\right)$ volumes of air for complete combustion. Similarly, 1 volume of methane requires $\frac{100}{21}(2)$ volumes of air, and 1 volume of carbon monoxide requires $\frac{100}{21}\left(\frac{1}{2}\right)$ volumes of air for complete combustion.

Coal Gas.—The coal gas having the analysis and calorific value given in the above table (paragraph 7) would require, for complete combustion, $\frac{100}{21}\left(\frac{48}{2}+2\times23+\frac{20}{2}\right)=381$ cu. ft. of air per 100 cu. ft. of coal gas. Hence, the heating value of 1 cu. ft. of a mixture of coal gas and its theoretical air—that is, of a charge of 1 cu. ft. of "correctly loaded" air, is $\frac{540\text{ B.Th.U.}}{4\cdot81\text{ ft.}^3}=112$ B.Th.U. per ft.^{3}

Water Gas.—In a similar way, 100 cu. ft. of water gas would require $\frac{100}{21}\left(\frac{50}{2}+2\times 6+\frac{40}{2}\right)=271$ cu. ft. of air for complete combustion. Thus, a charge of 1 cu. ft. of correctly loaded air would have a heating value of $\frac{300 \text{ B.Th.U.}}{3\cdot 71 \text{ ft.}^3}=80\cdot 8$ B.Th.U. per ft.^{3}

Dowson Gas.—Similarly, 100 cu. ft. of Dowson gas would require $\frac{100}{21}\left(\frac{15}{2}+2\times 2+\frac{28}{2}\right)=121\cdot 3$ cu. ft. of air for complete combustion. Thus, a charge of 1 cu. ft. of correctly loaded air would have a heating value of $\frac{150 \text{ B.Th.U.}}{2\cdot 2 \text{ ft.}^3}=68\cdot 2$ B.Th.U. per ft.^{3}

Similarly, 1 cu. ft. of correctly loaded air with *blast-furnace gas* and *coke-oven gas* would have heating values of $\frac{90 \text{ B.Th.U.}}{1\cdot 78 \text{ ft.}^3}=50\cdot 5$ B.Th.U. per ft.^{3} and $\frac{450 \text{ B.Th.U.}}{5\cdot 35 \text{ ft.}^3}=84\cdot 1$ B.Th.U. per ft.^{3}, respectively.

These figures may be tabulated in the following way for those gases whose compositions were given in the table of paragraph 7:

Fuel	Approximate Calorific Value in B.Th.U. per Standard, cu. ft.	Theoretical Air required for Complete Combustion of 1 cu. ft. of Fuel, cu. ft.	Approximate Heating Value of 1 cu. ft. of correctly loaded Air, B.Th.U.
Coal gas.	540	3·81	112
Water gas.	300	2·71	81
Dowson gas.	150	1·21	68
Blast-furnace gas.	90	0·78	50·5
Coke-oven gas.	450	4·35	84

It will be seen from this table that although the calorific values of the fuels vary greatly, there is not so vast a variation in the heating values of the explosive mixtures formed with them. This is because the rich gaseous fuels, such as coal gas and coke-oven gas, are diluted with a large amount of air necessary for complete combustion; while the poor ones, such as blast-furnace gas, are diluted with a comparatively small amount of air.

LIQUID FUELS

9. Uses of Liquid Fuels, and Advantages and Disadvantages of Oil-firing.—Since the development of the oil resources of the world, liquid fuels are now used in many engineering plants which previously used solid or gaseous fuels. In many engines liquid fuel is essential; indeed, some engines are designed for a particular kind of liquid fuel. Other plant, particularly steam-raising plant, is now being fired with liquid fuel both in land and marine installations.

Some of the advantages claimed for liquid fuels in furnaces are:

(1) Greater calorific value, about 19,000 B.Th.U. per lb. as against about 14,000 B.Th.U. per lb. of coal.

(2) Efficient combustion, as indicated by CO_2 recorders, is attainable by thorough mixing of the fuel particles with the air required for combustion.

(3) No dust, no ashes, and no clinker when oil is burnt in boiler furnaces.

(4) The control of steam production is easier and can be more rapid than with solid fuels.

(5) Lighting up is easier, and a furnace can be instantly extinguished by shutting off the fuel supply.

(6) There is no wear and tear of grate bars and no cleaning of fires.

(7) There is a reduction in the manual labour of firemen and a reduction in the cost of handling the fuel. The oil is handled by a pump, and one man can regulate with ease the burners of a number of boilers.

(8) The storage of oil fuel is simpler than the storage of solid fuel, and stored oil does not deteriorate. A ship can be supplied with oil through a pipe with a minimum of manual labour and with the absence of dust. Oil can be stored away in the double bottom, leaving the usual coal bunker space for other purposes. Storage space for oil is about 40 per cent. less than that required for the same heating value in coal.

Some of the disadvantages connected with the use of liquid fuels and oilfiring are:

(1) The cost of oil fuel is relatively high compared with solid fuels.

(2) Special storage requirements are necessary because of the danger of storing oil in large quantities. Insurance costs are therefore higher.

(3) Specially constructed burners and apparatus for spraying the oil are required before efficient combustion can be achieved.

(4) Choking of sprayers is a drawback in oil firing.

10. Constitution of Liquid Fuels.—Liquid fuels consisting of hydrocarbons are mostly obtained by distillation of petroleum or crude oil, these being terms applied to denote oil as it leaves the well. Petroleum is a thick, brown, treacly substance in its crude form and is a mixture of a great number of hydrocarbons. The chief oil-fields of a commercial value from which crude petroleum comes are in U.S.A., Mexico, Russia, and Iran. It is usually necessary to drill and pump the oil from wells at varying depths of the Earth's crust, though frequently it occurs under pressure and squirts out, to result in what is known as a "gusher well." The petroleum is conveyed from the well by means of pipe-lines or oil tankers to a refinery, where it is separated into various commercial products, the most important of which are motor spirit or petrol, paraffin or kerosene, gas oil, fuel oil, lubricating oil, paraffin wax, and bitumen.

Practically all liquid fuels (except the alcohols) are mixtures of hydrocarbons, and hydrocarbons are all similar in so far as their molecules contain nothing but carbon and hydrogen atoms, but they differ among themselves as to the arrangements and number of atoms in a molecule. Difference of arrangement divides the whole field of hydrocarbons into characteristic families. The hydrocarbons in crude oil or petroleum all belong to a number of regular families of compounds obeying the general chemical formulae C_nH_{2n+2}, C_nH_{2n}, C_nH_{2n-2}, C_nH_{2n-4}, C_nH_{2n-6}, C_nH_{2n-8}, C_nH_{2n-10}, C_nH_{2n-12}, C_nH_{2n-14}.

The volatile fuels: petrol, benzol, and kerosene are mixtures of hydrocarbons of which the most important belong to what are known as the aromatic and the paraffin families. Their molecular structures have the general formulae C_nH_{2n-6} and C_nH_{2n+2} respectively. Besides the aromatics and the paraffins there are found in most petrols a certain proportion of the naphthene family, which have the general formula C_nH_{2n}. Another, less important series, of hydrocarbons is the olefine family.

The individual members of the aromatic series (general formula C_nH_{2n-6}) to be found in petrol are:

Hydrocarbon	Formula	Boiling-point, °F.	Specific Gravity
Benzene.	C_6H_6	176	0·884
Toluene.	C_7H_8	230	0·870
Xylene.	C_8H_{10}	248	0·826

The hydrocarbons of the paraffin series (general formula C_nH_{2n+2}) present in petrol are:

Hydrocarbon	Formula	Boiling-point, °F.	Specific Gravity
Pentane.	C_5H_{12}	100	—
Hexane.	C_6H_{14}	156	0·663
Heptane.	C_7H_{16}	209	0·691
Octane	C_8H_{18}	258	0·709
Nonane.	C_9H_{20}	302	0·723
Decane.	$C_{10}H_{22}$	343	0·735
Undecane.	$C_{11}H_{24}$	383	0·746

Those of the naphthalene series (general formula C_nH_{2n}) present in petrol are:

Hydrocarbon	Formula	Boiling-point, °F.	Specific Gravity
Cyclohexane.	C_6H_{12}	178	0·780
Hexahydrotoluene.	C_7H_{14}	212	0·770
Hexahydroxylene	C_8H_{16}	246·2	0·756

11. Varieties of Liquid Fuels.—The natural sources from which nearly all liquid fuels are produced, are: (*a*) petroleum; (*b*) shale; (*c*) coal; (*d*) vegetation.

By chemical processes carried out on the raw materials in the above four categories, several "artificial" fuels can be manufactured and produced:

(1) From petroleum can be produced petrols, kerosene, fuel oils, and lubricating oils.

(2) From shale as it comes from the mines, shale oil can be produced by a process of destructive distillation.

(3) From coal and wood, tars can be produced by a distillation process, and oils can be obtained by refining the resulting tars. Also from coal, synthetic fuels can be produced by a process of hydrogenation.

(4) From the vegetable matters: potatoes, rice, sugar beet—all of which contain cellulose, alcohol fuel can be obtained by fermentation processes.

(5) By mixing together powdered solid fuel and oil, colloidal fuels can be produced.

12. Production and Composition of Liquid Fuels.—(i) Production of Fuels from Petroleum.—*Distillation of Petroleum* into its various fractions will best be understood by considering first the gentle heating in a flask of a mixture of several liquids each having different boiling-points. The liquid with the lowest boiling-point will first evaporate, and if the vapour is caught in a vessel and cooled it will condense, thus the lightest liquid of the mixture will have been separated from the rest. If the temperature of the flask is then gradually raised, the other liquids will evaporate in the order of their boiling-points. This process can be stopped at any particular temperature.

When crude oil or petroleum is heated, first the light spirit is evaporated, then motor spirit (petrol), kerosene (or paraffin), gas oil, and the process is frequently stopped at this point, the residue being used as fuel oil. Each successive fraction distilled usually has a greater specific gravity than the previous one. Gas oils (specific gravity 0·8), the heavier distillates (s.g. 0·9), and residual oils (s.g. 0·95) are called fuel oils. There are many grades of fuel oil, the heaviest being residual oils and the lightest gas oil. Several commercial grades are on the market, ranging between gas oil and residual oils. They are usually made by blending residual oils with gas oil in suitable proportions. The residual oils are usually heavy, dark, and viscous, while the distillates are lighter, clearer, and more fluid.

Thus, at an oil refinery the crude oil or petroleum as it comes from the well containing every variety of hydrocarbon, from those of the thick, tarry fluid to methane (which is blown off as gas), is gradually heated in a large boiler-like vessel or still, and the various "fractions" which distil over are condensed in different receivers according to their boiling-points—the light petrol first, then the kerosene fraction, the fuel oils, and finally the lubricating oils, leaving a heavy viscous residue in the still.

Petrol.—"Petrol" is a colloquial term for a light fuel of which the composition may vary widely. It is a term covering any low-boiling distillate from crude oil or petroleum. Petrol is the lightest of the distillates put to commercial use, and begins to distil at 50° C. At 80° or 90° C. about half of it comes over, and by the time the temperature has been raised to 190° C. all of it has been separated from the petroleum. The range from 50° C. to 190° C. is called the "distillation range" of petrol. This large distillation range indicates that petrol is not a single homogeneous product, but, as stated in paragraph 10, consists of a mixture of hydrocarbons mainly from the aromatic, paraffin, and naphthene families. In commercial petrol the members of the paraffin series predominate up to about 60 per cent. of the whole, and the average composition of petrol may be taken as represented by the formula C_8H_{18}. The calorific value of petrol may be taken as 19,400 B.Th.U. per lb. and of specific gravity 0·72.

It is also possible to produce petrol from heavy oils by a process known as "cracking." After removal of the more volatile fractions from petroleum by direct distillation the remaining heavier fractions can be put through the cracking plant. This treatment involves subjecting these fractions to a high temperature and pressure in the absence of air. The products finally emerging contain a large proportion of the lighter fractions suitable for petrol—for, under the high temperature and pressure of the cracking plant, the large molecules become split up into smaller hydrocarbon molecules of lower boiling-points.

Kerosene (or "paraffin") can have a distillation range from 140° C. to 300° C. It is, therefore, even more of a heterogeneous mixture of hydrocarbons than petrol. The average composition of kerosene may be taken as represented by the formula $C_{10}H_{22}$. Its calorific value may be 19,800 B.Th.U. per lb. and specific gravity 0·81. Kerosene is less volatile than petrol, and carburation is therefore more difficult than with petrol; consequently, it is seldom used in engines of the motor-car type.

Fuel oils are composed of distillates evaporating at temperatures between 200° C. and 350° C. An oil distilled over the above temperature range is likely to have a composition of carbon and hydrogen 84 per cent. and 12 per cent., respectively. The atomic weight of carbon being 12 and that of hydrogen 1, the above composition is equivalent to $\frac{84}{12}=7$ atoms of carbon and $\frac{12}{1}=12$ atoms of hydrogen. The oil may therefore be thought of as one of approximate formula C_7H_{12}. The calorific value may be taken as 19,100 B.Th.U. per lb. and specific gravity 0·89.

Fuel oils have a comparatively high mean temperature of vaporisation, and special engine design is necessary to burn them efficiently. They are successfully burnt in compression-ignition engines by injecting them into air which has been compressed in the cylinder to a high temperature and pressure.

(ii) **Production of Fuels from Shale.**—Shale is a dark grey or black mineral with a laminated structure containing numerous fragments of organic matter such as fossil plants and animals. It has to be mined (chiefly in Scotland), and, on distillation, yields nitrogen compounds and oil. An average yield of crude oil per ton of shale for the Scottish shale industry is about 25 gallons. The crude oil can then be separated at a refinery into several liquid fuels.

(iii) **Production of Fuels from Coal.**—By a process of distillation coal-tar can be produced from coal. The tar is a by-product of coal in gas production, and, if conveyed to a distillery, coal-gas products, of which benzol is one, can be produced.

"Benzol" is a colloquial term for a light fuel produced from coal-tar which may vary in composition. It may be said to be a mixture of the three first members of the aromatic series (see paragraph 10), but chiefly of the first, namely, benzene (C_6H_6). It begins to distil at 80° C. and ends distillation at 120° C. This distillation range of only 40° C. indicates that benzol is a more homogeneous product than either petrol or kerosene, which have distillation ranges of 140° C. and 160° C., respectively. Its volatility is such that it is suitable for use in motor-car engines. It has advantages over petrol, particularly in engines with high compression ratios, in that tendencies to detonation and knocking are reduced. One disadvantage is that benzol freezes at 0° C., and special attention is therefore needed in very cold weather. Benzol is a colourless liquid whose chemical formula may be taken as C_6H_6. The calorific value of average benzol may be taken as 17,100 B.Th.U. per lb. and specific gravity 0·88.

Hydrogenation.—Synthetic fuels can be produced from coal by a process known as hydrogenation. Hydrogen, at about 4,000 Lb. per sq. in. pressure, is brought into contact with powdered coal in retorts at temperatures of 450° C. to 480° C. in the presence of a catalyst. Direct addition of hydrogen takes place, resulting in the formation of a great variety of hydrocarbons from which petrol and fuel oils can be produced.

(iv) **Production of Fuels from Vegetation.**—The chief liquid of vegetable origin which can be used as a fuel is alcohol. It is not very important in Britain as a fuel at the present time, but it is possible that in the future it will be a source of fuel supply, particularly as a substitute for petrol.

If the oil wells in future years should become exhausted of the petroleum from which petrol comes, alcohol can be used as an alternative fuel. Alcohol is a vegetable product the composition of which involves no drain on the world's storage, for it can be produced from potatoes, rice, and sugar beet. By use of a fuel derived from vegetation, mankind is adapting the sun's heat to the development of motive power as it becomes available from day to day; but by using mineral fuels he is consuming a limited legacy of heat which was stored away ages ago and which will quickly be exhausted if the present rate of consumption continues.

The members of the alcohol group available for fuel are methyl alcohol, ethyl alochol, and butyl alcohol, of which the first two, of chemical formula CH_4O and C_2H_6O, respectively, may become important fuels if the supply of hydrocarbon fuels should fail, since both these alcohols can be manufactured fairly easily from vegetable matter. It will be noticed that alcohols contain oxygen in their molecules and are therefore not true hydrocarbons.

Both methyl and ethyl alcohol are highly volatile liquids, having boiling-points of 65° C. and 78° C., respectively. Their specific gravity is about 0·8, and calorific value about 11,700 B.Th.U. per lb.

(v) **Production of Colloidal Fuels.**—Colloidal fuels may be said to be a suspension produced by mixing together powdered solid fuel and oil. It is claimed that such a suspension can be fired by ordinary oil-firing equipment and possesses many of the advantages of oil fuel. A large amount of heat is radiated from the flame of colloidal fuel because of the incandescence of the solid particles contained in it.

13. Important Properties of Fuel Oils.—The most important properties of fuel oils are:

(1) *Specific gravity,* since oil fuel is usually sold by volume and not by weight (*e.g.* gallons, not pounds).

(2) *Heating Value:* an accurate figure for calorific value is required.

(3) *Flash-point and Fire-point:* the flash-point is the temperature at which sufficient vapour is given off to form a momentary flash when a small flame is brought near its surface in a special apparatus. The fire-point is the temperature at which oil gives off enough vapour to burn continuously. This is usually about 20° F. higher than the flash-point.

(4) *The congealing-point,* which is found by means of a cold test. It is the temperature at which the oil becomes pasty—usually due to the crystallisation of paraffin or other matter. The test is important in showing whether or not an oil will flow freely in pipe-lines in cold climates and remain in storage tanks without paraffin wax separating out. If this happens the storage tanks have to be raised above a certain temperature which has to be maintained by heating.

(5) *The viscosity* of an oil is a measure of the internal friction of the oil or of its resistance to flow. The resistance, which is

decreased by raising of temperature, is generally measured by determining the time for a given quantity of the oil to flow at a constant temperature through a small nozzle. Redwood's apparatus is often used, and viscosity is then expressed in "Redwood seconds." Below about 140° F. a small change in temperature makes a very large change in the viscosity of a fuel oil. This has a very important bearing on the spraying and injecting of oil fuels.

(6) *Sulphur Content:* high sulphur content in a fuel oil is undesirable, since corrosion may result from the action of sulphur dioxide (SO_2) and water vapour (H_2O) formed during combustion.

(7) *Moisture and sediment* are found in practically all fuel oils, but should not be present in quantities of more than 2 per cent., or trouble is likely to be experienced in firing.

(8) *Specific heat and coefficient of expansion* of fuel oils vary, the former between 0·4 and 0·5, and an average value for the latter is 0·00004 per °F.

14. Fuels used in Internal-combustion Engines.—The most important properties of a fuel determining its value for use in internal-combustion engines are:

(1) Tendency to detonate should be remote.

(2) Volatility should be high if a carburettor is used.

(3) High calorific value is desired and the heating value of the correct explosive mixture should be high.

(4) The self-ignition temperature of fuels used in spark-ignition engines should be high, while of fuels used in compression-ignition engines it should be low, since, in the latter case, there is no danger of pre-ignition and, with a low self-ignition point, combustion would begin earlier.

(5) The fuels should be free from anything which might lead to a deposit inside the cylinders.

(6) Easy starting of engines is desired. A spark-ignition engine using a fuel with a high latent heat would be difficult to start, since there would be difficulty in supplying the heat of vaporisation from a cold engine. The latent heat of petrol is 144 B.Th.U. per lb., of benzol 180 B.Th.U. per lb.

(7) Low cost of fuels is desired.

The volatile liquid fuels available at the present time consist of petrol, benzol, kerosene, and alcohol. These fuels are mostly used in internal-combustion engines through the agency of a carburettor.

Of the non-volatile fuel oils there are many grades, classed as "heavy oils" and normally used in compression-ignition engines.

An important characteristic regarding the volatile fuels used in internal-combustion engines is that there is less tendency to knock and detonate with the aromatic fuels than with fuels composed mainly of the paraffin series. A fuel consisting entirely of naturally occurring paraffins would be intolerable on account of detonation. Thus, all commercial light fuels contain a large proportion of hydrocarbons of the aromatic series, although aromatics have a heating value about 10 per cent. less than paraffins because of the lower proportion of hydrogen in their molecules. The addition of benzol to petrol simply increases the proportion of aromatic hydrocarbons in the petrol. But the proportion of aromatics cannot be increased much beyond 50 per cent. if the fuel is to be used in conditions where it may be cooled to temperatures below 0° C., on account of the danger of them separating out as solids and blocking up fuel pipes and carburettors. An average aviation petrol would contain some 50 per cent. of mixed paraffin hydrocarbons between pentane and decane (see paragraph 10), 30 per cent. of aromatic hydrocarbons, and 20 per cent. naphthenes. The alcohol fuels, so far as tendency to detonate is concerned, are even better than the aromatics. An automobile fuel can be made of 96 per cent. alcohol with small quantities of naphtha and petroleum to withstand a pressure of 200 Lb. per sq. in. without pre-ignition.

In order to measure the knocking propensity of a fuel it has been decided to test fuels in an engine specially built for the purpose and running under a standard set of conditions.

The fuel is matched against reference fuels consisting of a mixture, in a series of percentages, of a good anti-knock fuel, iso-octane, and a poor anti-knock fuel, heptane. If the knock shown by the fuel is the same as that of a secondary fuel, and tallies with a knock of, say, a 40 per cent.—60 per cent. mixture of heptane and iso-octane, the fuel is said to have an octane number of 60. In a similar manner fuel oils used in compression-ignition engines are matched against a mixture of cetane ($H_{16}C_{32}$) and methyl naphthalene. Fuel oils having cetane numbers of over 50 are used in high-speed compression-ignition engines. Ordinary commercial petrols have octane numbers between 65 and 70 whereas aviation petrols have octane numbers of 100 and over.

The higher the ratio of compression in an engine the greater is the tendency to detonation, and the "highest useful compression ratio" [h.u.c.r.] for a fuel is the highest compression ratio which can be used without detonation occurring when tested in a standard engine. Commercial fuels are composed of many hydrocarbons and, according to the predominance of paraffins or aromatics, of which benzene is one, detonate early or late and have a low or high h.u.c.r., respectively. Since the octane number of a fuel is a measure of its non-detonating or anti-knock qualities, the h.u.c.r. for any fuel is related to the octane number. The anti-knock qualities of fuels can be extended beyond that of pure iso-octane (*i.e.* of octane number 100) by adding dopes. One can extrapolate on the compression ratio, octane number graph and obtain octane numbers over 100 for high-quality or doped fuels. An increase in the octane number of a fuel will allow of an increase in the compression ratio of the engine. The increase in the octane number of petrol from 60 to over 100 has enabled the power output from aero-engines to be increased by about three times and remain within the limit set by the incidence of detonation. For example, 100 octane petrol can be used in an engine of compression ratio 10 to 1 before detonation occurs. In small engines the fuels methyl alcohol and ethyl alcohol detonate at compression ratios 14 and 15 to 1, respectively, whereas acetone detonates at 18 to 1. Ordinary commercial petrol, however, which has an octane number of about 70, has an h.u.c.r. limit of about 7.

15. Determination of Calorific Values of Liquid Fuels.— The calorific value of fuel oil can be determined by means of Junker's calorimeter, illustrated in fig. 19.2. This calorimeter F is based on the same principle as that of Boys, previously described on p. 449. The cooling water flows up the narrow annular space between two thin cylinders. The rate of flow of water can be regulated by the valve T, through which water flows from a reservoir, the head in which is kept at a constant level by means of an overflow arrangement. The fuel oil is contained in the Primus vessel S, from which it is led to the burner E. A small air pressure, recorded on gauge G, is created in S by means of a pump which can be fitted to the valve V, and the fuel is thus forced through the orifice at E. The vessel containing the oil is suspended from one arm of the balance B, by means of which the amount of oil burned can be obtained.

In a test made with this calorimeter, it was decided to burn 10 grm. of oil. When the oil had been burning for some time and conditions were steady, the test was started as the pointer of the balance reached the zero or balancing position. A 10-Grm. weight was then taken off the scale plan and the test continued until the pointer registered balancing position again, which meant that a mass of 10 grm. of oil had burned. The cooling water was collected during the period of the been test and weighed. Temperatures were read at intervals during the test. The condensed steam or moisture of combustion was collected and weighed. Mean values of the observations made were:

Weight of oil burned: 10 Grm. or mass 10 grm.
Weight of cooling water: 22·3 Lb., *i.e.* mass 22·3 lb.
Weight of moisture of combustion: 8·355 Grm. or mass 8·355 grm.
Rise in temperature of cooling water: 10·06° C
Temperature of exhaust gases: 21·8° C.

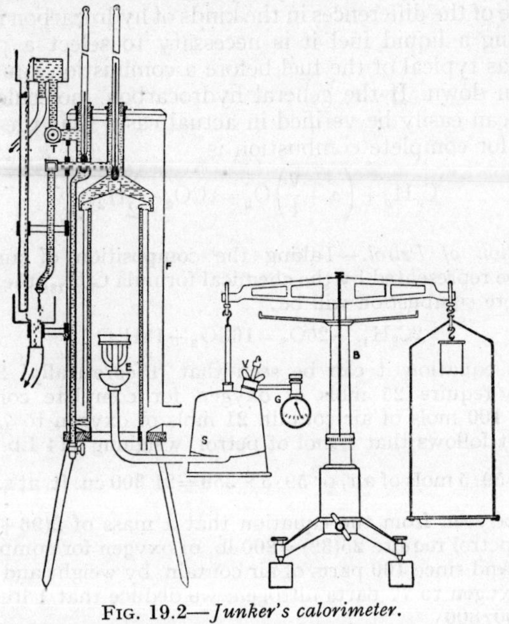

FIG. 19.2—*Junker's calorimeter.*

From these observations we get:

Heat absorbed by cooling water = mass × sp. ht. × rise in temperature

$$=22\cdot 3\text{ lb.}\times\frac{1\text{ B.Th.U.}}{\text{lb. }^\circ\text{F.}}\times 10\cdot 06^\circ\text{ C.}\left[\frac{9^\circ\text{ F.}}{5^\circ\text{ C.}}\right]=405\text{ B.Th.U.}$$

Latent heat of moisture of combustion given to cooling water

$$=8\cdot 355\text{ grm.}\left[\frac{\text{lb.}}{453\cdot 6\text{ grm.}}\right]\times 1{,}055\,\frac{\text{B.Th.U.}}{\text{lb.}}=19\cdot 4\text{ B.Th.U.}$$

∴ Higher calorific value of oil

$$=\frac{405\text{ B.Th.U.}}{10\text{ grm.}}\left[\frac{453\cdot 6\text{ grm.}}{\text{lb.}}\right]=18{,}370\text{ B.Th.U./lb.}$$

and lower calorific value of oil

$$=\frac{(405-19\cdot 4)\text{ B.Th.U.}}{10\text{ grm.}}\left[\frac{453\cdot 6\text{ grm.}}{\text{lb.}}\right]=17{,}500\text{ B.Th.U./lb.}$$

16. Combustion of Liquid Fuels, and Heating Values of Explosive Mixtures.—Combustion will only take place in a fuel-air mixture if the ratio of air to fuel is within certain limits—that is, there is a minimum weakness and a maximum richness beyond which combustion will not take place. Each fuel has its own limits, which are found by experiment.

Because of the differences in the kinds of hydrocarbon molecules constituting a liquid fuel it is necessary to select a particular molecule as typical of the fuel before a combustion equation can be written down. If the general hydrocarbon molecule C_xH_y is taken, it can easily be verified in actual cases that the chemical equation for complete combustion is

$$C_xH_y+\left(x+\frac{y}{4}\right)O_2=xCO_2+\frac{y}{2}H_2O$$

Combustion of Petrol.—Taking the composition of an average petrol to be represented by the chemical formula C_8H_{18}, the equation for complete combustion will be:

$$2C_8H_{18}+25O_2=16CO_2+18H_2O$$

From this equation it can be seen that (theoretically) 2 mols of petrol gas require 25 mols of oxygen for complete combustion. And since 100 mols of air contain 21 mols of oxygen to 79 mols of nitrogen, it follows that 1 mol of petrol, weighing 114 Lb., requires $\frac{100}{21}\left(\frac{25}{2}\right)=59\cdot5$ mols of air, or $59\cdot5\times359=21{,}300$ cu. ft. at s.t.p.

It can be seen from the equation that a mass of $2(96+18)$ lb. $=228$ lb. of petrol require $25(32)=800$ lb. of oxygen for complete combustion. And since 100 parts of air contain, by weight and by mass, 23 parts oxygen to 77 parts nitrogen, we deduce that 1 lb. of petrol requires $\frac{100}{23}\left(\frac{800}{228}\right)=15\cdot3$ lb. of air.

Thus, 1 lb. of petrol requires $15\cdot3$ lb. of air to release a calorific value of 19,400 B.Th.U. Hence, the heating value of 1 lb. of explosive mixture of petrol and its theoretical air, or of 1 lb. of correctly loaded air is $\frac{19{,}400 \text{ B.Th.U.}}{16\cdot3 \text{ lb.}}=1{,}190$ B.Th.U. per lb.

Combustion of Benzol.—Taking the chemical formula representing benzol to be that of pure benzene, namely, C_6H_6, the equation for complete combustion will be:

$$2C_6H_6+15O_2=12CO_2+6H_2O$$

Hence, 1 mol of benzol of mass 78 lb. requires, for complete combustion, $\frac{15}{2}$ mols of oxygen, which are contained in $\frac{100}{21}\left(\frac{15}{2}\right)=35\cdot7$ mols of air or $35\cdot7\times358=128$ cu. ft. at s.t.p.

Or, by mass, $2(72+6)=156$ lb. of benzol require for complete combustion $15\times(32)=480$ lb. of oxygen, which are contained in $\frac{100}{23}\,480=2{,}085$ lb. of air. Hence, 1 lb. of benzol requires, theoretically $\frac{2{,}085}{156}=13\cdot4$ lb. of air for complete combustion.

Thus, 1 lb. of benzol requires 13·4 lb. of air to release a lower calorific value of 17,100 B.Th.U. Hence, the heating value of a charge of 1 lb. of correctly loaded air would be

$$\frac{17{,}100 \text{ B.Th.U.}}{14\cdot4 \text{ lb.}}=1{,}187 \text{ B.T.U. lb.}$$

The combustion of other liquid fuels can be dealt with in the same way, and a few of the results are given in the following table:

Fuel	Chemical Formula	Approximate Calorific Value B.Th.U. per lb.	Theoretical Air to Fuel Ratio for Complete Combustion		Approximate Heating Value of 1 lb. of correctly loaded Air, B.Th.U. per lb.
			By Volume	By Weight	
Petrol.	C_8H_{18}	19,400	59·5	15·3	1,190
Kerosene.	$C_{10}H_{22}$	19,800	73·8	15·2	1,220
Benzol.	C_6H_6	17,100	35·7	13·4	1,187
Alcohol.	C_2H_6O	11,700	14·3	9·1	1,155
Fuel oil.	C_7H_{12}	19,100	47·6	14·5	1,230

We see from the above table (as was seen for gaseous fuels in the table on page 452) that although the calorific value of the fuels vary, there is relatively little difference between the heating values of the explosive mixtures of liquid fuels and their theoretical air.

17. Excess Air, and Satisfactory Combustion in Oil-fired Boilers.—Oil fuels are generally difficult to ignite unless broken up into the form of a very fine spray and mixed with the right proportion of air which supplies the oxygen necessary for combustion.

Oil jets and sprayers are devices for splitting up fuel oil, and many types of injectors are fitted to compression-ignition engines. Some form of sprayer also forms part of the equipment of oil-fired boilers, the burners of which are devices aiming at bringing each particle of oil into contact with its requisite amount of air.

In practice it is not possible to effect satisfactory combustion by giving a fuel the net amount of air theoretically required for complete combustion. The excess air required depends on the fuel. Solid fuels usually require up to 50 per cent. excess air, while oil fuel can be satisfactorily burned with less than 30 per cent. This is one of the advantages connected with oil-fired boilers, for the smaller the amount of excess air used the higher will be the efficiency of combustion. The question thus arises as to what is the minimum quantity of excess air with which it is possible to get satisfactory combustion in furnaces. It should be possible in actual practice to obtain 11 or 12 per cent. CO_2 in the products of combustion from an average fuel oil, in which case there would be no more than 30 per cent. of excess air. Should an attempt be made to cut down the excess air so as to force up the CO_2 beyond a certain point, the production of smoke will almost certainly be the result, and incomplete combustion of a certain proportion of the carbon content of the fuel to CO rather than completely to CO_2. This, as we have previously seen, is undesirable because of the loss of nearly 10,200 B.Th.U. per lb. of carbon burnt.

It is possible, with experience, from the appearance of an oil flame to judge with the eye whether the correct mixture of air and oil is being delivered from the burner. In the absence of a CO_2 recorder, the best method of setting the controls of a burner is first to set the oil valve and oil pressure so as to pass the required quantity of oil into the combustion chamber, and then to get the burner working with a certain amount of excess air by opening the air ducts and shutters. The amount of air should then be slowly reduced until a faint haze is just visible at the top of the chimney-stack, indicating that the "smoking-point" has been reached.

To maintain a reasonably high efficiency the concentration of heat should not exceed about 5,000 B.Th.U. per hour per sq. ft. of heating surface. But this by no means represents the maximum concentration for, by "forcing" an oil-fired boiler, over 10,000 B.Th.U. per sq. ft. per hour can be used.

The volume of the combustion chamber on full load should be about 3 lb. per hour per cu. ft. in ordinary boilers, but, again, this does not represent the maximum, for with boilers using forced draught as much as 17 lb. of oil per hour per cu. ft. of combustion space, representing an input of about 324,000 B.Th.U. per hour per cu. ft. of combustion space, has been consumed.

SUPPLEMENT

ENTROPY, AND SIMPLE APPLICATIONS TO HEAT ENGINES

CHAPTER 20

ENTROPY, AND SIMPLE APPLICATIONS TO HEAT ENGINES

1. Conception of Entropy for Use in Work on Heat Engines.—The conception of entropy presents a difficulty because it does not represent anything tangible or anything which has an immediate physical significance. For use in thermodynamics and analysis of heat engines the idea of entropy can be developed by drawing an analogy between mechanical energy and heat energy when represented as areas with rectangular axes.

Consider mechanical energy first. It is the product of two things, force × displacement (e.g. ft.-Lb. units). It can therefore be represented as an area as shown on fig. 20.1 with force and displacement as rectangular axes.

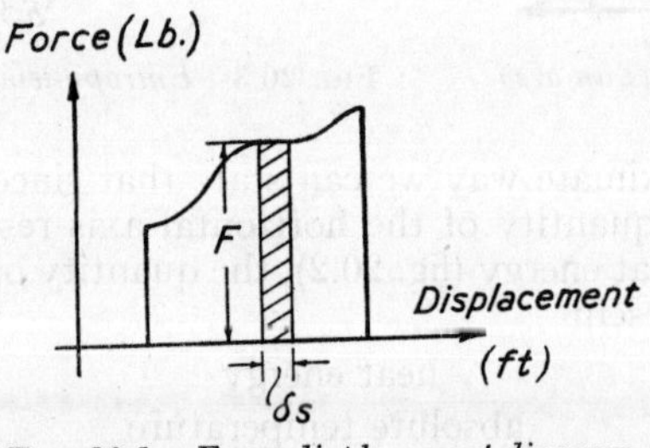

FIG. 20.1—*Force-displacement diagram.*

A man pulling a log of wood over uneven ground may trace out the force-displacement diagram fig. 20.1, in which he pulls with a force F over the small distance δS. The work done (δW) during that small displacement is F × δS, which is equal to the area of the shaded strip,

i.e. $$F \times \delta S = \delta W \quad \text{or} \quad \delta S = \frac{\delta W}{F}$$

Thus, mechanical energy is represented by means of an area, from which we can derive the equation $\int dS = \int \frac{dW}{F}$

We may note also that electrical power is the product of two things, potential difference × current (Volts × Amperes). It can therefore be represented as an area in a way similar to that of mechanical energy.

Since various forms of energy can be represented as areas on rectangular axes, we now decide to represent heat energy as an area in a similar way. Absolute temperature is chosen as one of the axes, since heat and its quality are associated with temperature.

Thus, referring to fig. 20.2, we have so far fixed that the area shall represent heat energy on rectangular axes, one of which is absolute temperature (T), and the quantity of the horizontal axis is yet to be found.

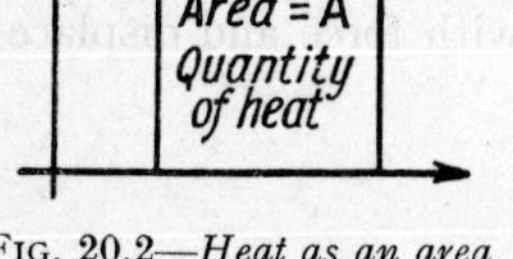

FIG. 20.2—*Heat as an area.*

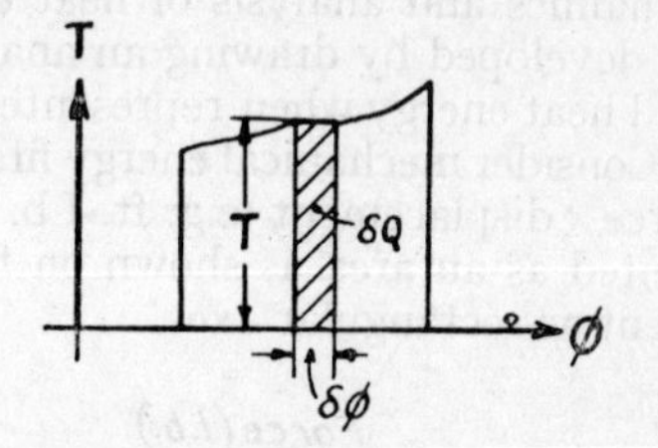

FIG. 20.3—*Entropy-temperature diagram.*

In an approximate way we can state that since absolute temperature × the quantity of the horizontal axis results in an area representing heat energy (fig. 20.2), the quantity of the horizontal axis must represent

$$\frac{\text{heat energy}}{\text{absolute temperature}}.$$

This quantity is given the name "entropy" and the symbol φ.

More strictly, if we consider the strip shown in fig. 20.3, the area of which represents δQ units of heat added to a substance *reversibly* (written ${}_r\delta Q$) at absolute temperature T and which increases the entropy by an amount $\delta\varphi$, then, since ${}_r\delta Q = T\,\delta\varphi$, we arrive at **the equation $\delta\varphi = \frac{{}_r\delta Q}{T}$ which is the definition of change of entropy,** and which is analogous to $\delta S = \frac{\delta W}{F}$ for the force-displacement diagram. The entropy equation, when translated into words, states that the increase in entropy ($\delta\varphi$) of a substance is equal to the heat added (${}_r\delta Q$) to the substance reversibly divided by the absolute temperature (T) of the substance during the reversible addition of heat.

Another definition of entropy can be formulated by translating into words the equation $\delta\varphi \times T = {}_r\delta Q$, namely: **the change in entropy ($\delta\varphi$) of a substance is that quantity which when multiplied by the absolute temperature (T) at which the change took place gives the amount of heat (${}_r\delta Q$) that has been added to or abstracted from the substance reversibly.** The equation is analogous to $\delta W = P \times \delta V$ for a P,V diagram. *It should be noted that* ${}_r\delta Q = T\delta\varphi$ *= area under a trace on the* T,φ *diagram is only correct for a reversible process, as is* $\delta W = P\delta V$ *in the case of work represented as an area on a P, V diagram.*

The equation $\int d\varphi = \int \frac{{}_r dQ}{T}$ **is the strict definition in symbols of change of entropy due to a reversible process.** Real processes are not reversible, however, *but if a substance passes from an initial to a final state via an irreversible—i.e. natural or real—process, the change of entropy is the same as for any reversible process by which the substance could pass from the initial to the final state. This is a consequence of the fact that entropy is a function of the state of a substance and independent of the path by which the state was reached.* Thus, to find the change in entropy of a substance due to a real (i.e. irreversible) process *an equivalent reversible process must first be imagined to replace the real process between the initial and final states before the integration*

$$\int_i^f \frac{{}_r dQ}{T} = \varphi_f - \varphi_i \text{ can be performed.}$$

Example.—If 36 B.Th.U. are added to a substance at the constant temperature 720° abs. F., the increase in entropy of the substance

$$\text{is } \delta\varphi = \frac{{}_r\delta Q}{T} = \frac{36 \text{ B.Th.U.}}{720° \text{ abs. F.}} = 0{\cdot}05 \frac{\text{B.Th.U.}}{°\text{F.}}$$

2. Entropy Change of a Gas.—Since ${}_r\delta Q = T d\varphi$, the first law of thermodynamics $dQ = dE + dW$ for a gas can be written (for a reversible process)

$$_r dQ = T d\varphi = mC_v dT + P dV \quad . \quad . \quad . \quad . \quad \text{(A)}$$

From this equation we can, by eliminating in turn the variables P, V, and T, find expressions for change in entropy as functions of (V,T), (T,P), and (P,V), respectively. We assume the gas obeys the law $PV = RmT$, that C_v remains constant and that the change between initial and final equilibrium states is reversible.

(i) By substituting $P=\frac{RmT}{V}$ in Equation (A) we get

$$\int_1^2 d\varphi = mC_v \int_1^2 \frac{dT}{T} + Rm \int_1^2 \frac{dV}{V}$$

$$\text{or} \quad \varphi_2 - \varphi_1 = mC_v \log_\varepsilon\left(\frac{T_2}{T_1}\right) + Rm \log_\varepsilon\left(\frac{V_2}{V_1}\right)$$

(ii) By differentiating $PV=RmT$ we can substitute

$$PdV = RmdT - VdP = RmdT - \frac{RmT}{P}\,dP \text{ in equation (A),}$$

$$\text{getting} \quad \int_1^2 d\varphi = m(C_v+R) \int_1^2 \frac{dT}{T} - Rm \int_1^2 \frac{dP}{P}$$

$$\text{or} \quad \varphi_2 - \varphi_1 = mC_p \log_\varepsilon\left(\frac{T_2}{T_1}\right) - Rm \log_\varepsilon\left(\frac{P_2}{P_1}\right)$$

(iii) By differentiating $PV=RmT$ we can substitute

$$dT = \frac{PdV + VdP}{Rm} \text{ in Equation (A),}$$

$$\text{getting} \quad \int_1^2 d\varphi = m(C_v+R) \int_1^2 \frac{dV}{V} + mC_v \int_1^2 \frac{dP}{P}$$

$$\text{or} \quad \varphi_2 - \varphi_1 = mC_p \log_\varepsilon\left(\frac{V_2}{V_1}\right) + mC_v \log_\varepsilon\left(\frac{P_2}{P_1}\right)$$

Example 1.—Calculate the change of entropy when the condition of 1 lb. of air changes from a temperature 27° C. and 5 cu. ft. to a volume 20 cu. ft. at 327° C.

From the data given we see that $\frac{T_2}{T_1}=\frac{600}{300}=2$ and $\frac{V_2}{V_1}=\frac{20}{5}=4$.

Hence, the change in entropy can be calculated from the formula

$$\varphi_2 - \varphi_1 = mC_v \log_\varepsilon\left(\frac{T_2}{T_1}\right) + Rm \log_\varepsilon\left(\frac{V_2}{V_1}\right)$$

$$= 1 \text{ lb.} \times 0{\cdot}169 \frac{\text{B.Th.U.}}{\text{lb. °F.}} \times \log_\varepsilon 2$$

$$+ 53{\cdot}3 \frac{\text{ft.-Lb.}}{\text{lb. °F.}} \times 1 \text{ lb.} \left[\frac{\text{B.Th.U.}}{778 \text{ ft.-Lb.}}\right] \log_\varepsilon 4$$

$$= 0{\cdot}1122 \frac{\text{B.Th.U.}}{\text{°F.}}$$

Example 2.—Calculate the decrease in entropy of 1 lb. of air, the temperature of which falls from 127° C. to 27° C. at the constant pressure of 15 Lb. per sq. in. abs.

From the formula

$$\varphi_2-\varphi_1=mC_p \log_\varepsilon\left(\frac{T_2}{T_1}\right)-Rm \log_\varepsilon\left(\frac{P_2}{P_1}\right)$$

$$=1 \text{ lb.} \times 0 \cdot 238 \frac{\text{B.Th.U.}}{\text{lb. }^\circ\text{F.}} \times \log_\varepsilon\left(\frac{300}{400}\right)-0$$

$$=-0 \cdot 06848 \frac{\text{B.Th.U.}}{^\circ\text{F.}}$$

Example 3.—In Example 2 calculate the heat rejected from the air during the process and show that it is approximately equal to the decrease in entropy multiplied by the mean absolute temperature.

$$\text{Heat lost by air}=mC_p(T_1-T_2)=1 \text{ lb.} \times 0 \cdot 238 \frac{\text{C.H.U.}}{\text{lb. }^\circ\text{C.}} \times 100^\circ \text{ C.}$$

$$=23 \cdot 8 \text{ C.H.U.}$$

Decrease in entropy × mean absolute temperature

$$=0 \cdot 06848 \frac{\text{C.H.U.}}{^\circ\text{C.}} \times 350^\circ \text{ C.}=23 \cdot 97 \text{ C.H.U.}$$

Example 4.—Find the change of entropy in the irreversible adiabatic expansion of Joule's experiment. In Joule's experiment in which gas in a cylinder, in a state represented by P_1, V_1, T, rushes into an evacuated cylinder so as to fill both cylinders and achieve a final state P_2, V_2, T, the gas being supposed perfect and thus remaining at constant temperature T, we have an irreversible expansion between terminal equilibrium states. *But although δQ is zero in the real (i.e. irreversible) process, $\delta\varphi$ is not zero in consequence, since the expression $\delta\varphi=\frac{{}_r\delta Q}{T}$ does not apply to irreversible processes.*

In this experiment the same change of state as is actually produced by the real irreversible process could be imagined achieved by an equivalent reversible isothermal process during which heat is allowed to pass through the walls of a cylinder in which the gas is imagined to expand isothermally and reversibly against a moveable piston. The increase of entropy during the real irreversible process is equal to that for the reversible one, namely $\int_i^f \frac{{}_r dQ}{T}$, which is equal to $\frac{Q}{T}$ since the quantity of heat Q passes through the walls reversibly at the constant temperature T. *It should be noted that there is no heat added from an external source during the real irreversible expansion of the gas, but there is, nevertheless, an increase of entropy $\varphi_f-\varphi_i=\frac{Q}{T}$,* where Q is the heat which would be added during the imaginary reversible process and which, by the first law of thermodynamics, $\delta Q=\delta E+\delta W=mC_v\delta T+P\delta V$, is equal to the work done during the reversible isothermal expansion, i.e.

$$Q=\int_i^f PdV=RmT\int_i^f \frac{dV}{V}=RmT\log_\varepsilon\left(\frac{V_f}{V_i}\right).$$

Hence, although in the actual expansion no heat is added to the gas from outside, there is an increase of entropy

$$\varphi_f - \varphi_i = \frac{Q}{T} = Rm \log_\varepsilon\left(\frac{V_f}{V_i}\right).$$

3. Adiabatic, Isentropic and Isothermal Processes represented on the T,φ Chart.—Ideal, reversible, adiabatic and isothermal processes show themselves as vertical and horizontal lines, respectively, on the T,φ chart, as shown in fig. 20.4. An adiabatic process is defined as one which is *thermally insulated*, and an isentropic process as one during which the entropy remains constant. But, although $\delta Q=0$ during an adiabatic process, the equation $\delta\varphi=\delta Q/T$ does not apply unless the process is reversible (i.e. ${}_r\delta Q=T\delta\varphi$). If the process is reversible and adiabatic then ${}_r\delta Q=0$ and therefore $\delta\varphi=0$, i.e. the process is isentropic. Thus, *a reversible adiabatic would be isentropic*, i.e. an adiabatic-isentropic process is represented by expansion *ab* or compression *ba* on fig. 20.4.

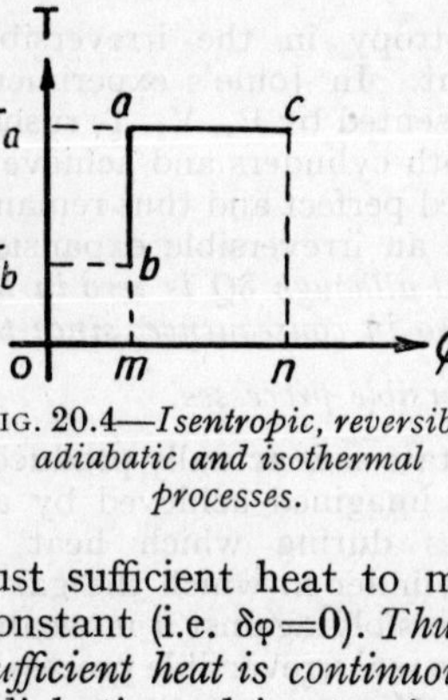

FIG. 20.4—*Isentropic, reversible adiabatic and isothermal processes.*

An isentropic process is not, however, restricted to being an imaginary, ideal process (known as a reversible adiabatic), for, during a real expansion or compression accompanied by the inevitable eddies and friction associated with the irreversibility of all real processes, it is possible to abstract just sufficient heat to maintain the entropy of the substance constant (i.e. $\delta\varphi=0$). *Thus, real processes may be isentropic if just sufficient heat is continuously abstracted.* Hence, we conclude that adiabatic and isentropic processes may be either real (i.e. irreversible) or ideal (i.e. reversible) and that

(i) *In a real adiabatic process* $\delta Q=0$ *but* $\delta\varphi>0$.
(ii) *In a reversible adiabatic process* $\delta Q=0$ *and* $\delta\varphi=0$.
(iii) *In a real isentropic process* $\delta\varphi=0$ *but* $\delta Q<0$.
(iv) *In a reversible isentropic process* $\delta\varphi=0$ *and* $\delta Q=0$, *as in* (ii).

Thus, the labels "reversible adiabatic" and "reversible isentropic" refer to the same ideal and imaginary process (*ab* or *ba* of fig. 20.4) free from eddies, friction and the dissipative effects which accompany all real processes, for both labels imply that $\delta Q=0$ and $\delta\varphi=0$ during the reversible process, i.e. ${}_r\delta Q=\delta E+P\delta V=T\delta\varphi=0$. From this we deduce that in $C_v\delta T+P\delta V=mC_p\delta T-V\delta P=0$ for the reversible compression or expansion of a perfect gas. Hence, $\frac{C_p}{C_v}+\frac{\delta P}{P}\frac{V}{\delta V}=0=\frac{\delta P}{P}+\gamma\frac{\delta V}{V}$, or **$PV^\gamma$=constant for a reversible adiabatic or reversible isentropic process.**

We may note that, as shown in Example 4, although a free expansion or throttling process may take place adiabatically (i.e. $\delta Q=0$), such a process is irreversible ($\delta\varphi>0$) and, therefore, the law PV^γ=constant does not apply to it. The general law joining the terminal equilibrium states of an irreversible expansion or compression is PV^n=constant, where n may vary from unity to a value greater than γ according as δQ varies from a maximum negative value, as in an isothermal process, to zero, as in an adiabatic process, i.e. in a heat-insulated or uncooled process. Referring to fig. 20.7 a reversible adiabatic (signified by suffix a) compression from pressure P_1 to P_2 during which (by definition of reversibility) the gas takes on a succession of equilibrium states, can be represented by the line ① ⓶a, the area under which is zero in accordance with $\int_1^{2a} T d\varphi=\int_1^{2a} {}_r dQ=0$. An irreversible adiabatic, i.e. a real heat-insulated or *uncooled compression* would, because of friction, eddies, and the consequent dissipation of mechanical energy, have terminal equilibrium points ① and ⓶u, and although no heat is added from an external source during this irreversible adiabatic ($\Sigma\delta Q=0$) compression, the entropy of the gas increases by $\varphi_{2u}-\varphi_1$.

An isothermal process is one which takes place at constant temperature. Hence, if the process is a reversible isothermal expansion ac of fig. 20.4, then $d\varphi={}_r\delta Q/T$,

or $$\int_a^c T_a d\varphi=\int_a^c {}_r dQ=T_a(\varphi_c-\varphi_a)=\text{area } macnm$$

which represents the heat added to the substance from an external source during reversible isothermal expansion ac.

A real (i.e. irreversible) isothermal expansion would not, however, require quite as much heat as this to be added from an external source in order to achieve the same change of entropy $(\varphi_c-\varphi_a)$ between the terminal equilibrium states represented by the points a and c on the T,φ diagram of fig. 20.4, since there would be an increase of entropy due to irreversibility caused by eddies and internal friction, irrespective of whether or not heat was added from an external source. During reversible isothermal compression ① ⓶i represented on fig. 20.7 the area under ① ⓶i represents the heat which would need to be abstracted reversibly during reversible isothermal compression, but more heat than this would need to be abstracted to achieve real (i.e. irreversible) isothermal compression since the mechanical energy dissipated into heat by eddies and friction would need to be abstracted as well as that represented by the area under trace ① (2i) of fig. 20.7.

Thus, expressed algebraically, we may state that, **for isothermal expansion or compression (and for all processes) $\delta\varphi \geqslant \delta Q/T$ according as the processes are irreversible or reversible, respectively, and where δQ is the heat added from an external source.** (Also see p. 488).

4. Entropy-temperature Diagrams of Internal-combustion Engine Cycles.—The entropy-temperature diagrams for the hypothetical cycles of internal combustion engines, the P,V diagrams of which are shown in figs. 16.1, 16.4, 16.5, and 16.10, are shown on figs. 20.5 and 20.6.

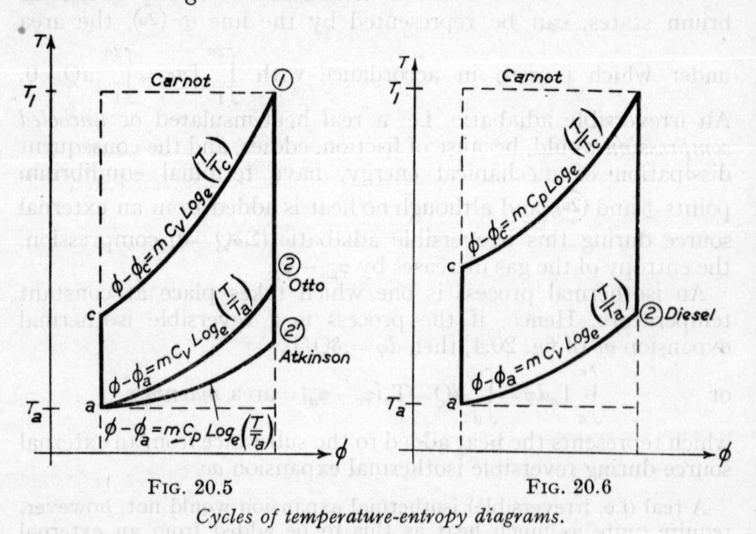

FIG. 20.5 FIG. 20.6

Cycles of temperature-entropy diagrams.

No real engines can follow any of the hypothetical cycles exactly because the latter assume:

(i) Air to be the working agent,

(ii) Compression and expansion to be reversible adiabatic processes.

(iii) No variation of specific heat with temperature.

(iv) Addition and rejection of heat to and from the working agent to take place either at constant volume or at constant pressure.

None of these assumptions is precisely true and, as regards (iv), the heat supplied in practice is due to a process of combustion in all practical and working internal combustion engines.

5. Entropy-temperature Diagram for Compression of Air.—Fig. 20.7 shows the temperature-entropy diagram for:

(i) reversible isothermal compression, represented by the trace ① (2i)

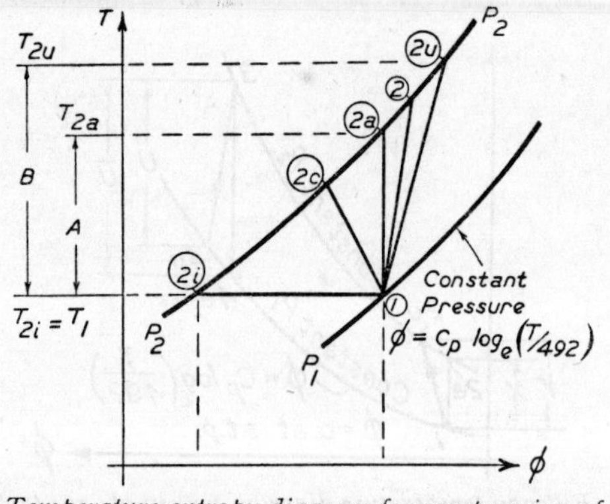

FIG. 20.7—*Temperature-entropy diagram for compression of gas.*

(ii) compression ① (2c), some of the heat of compression being abstracted by means of, say, cooling water,

(iii) reversible adiabatic compression, represented by the trace ① (2a),

(iv) uncooled or heat-insulated compression ① (2u) during which there is no cooling or heat lost by the air undergoing compression, i.e. the compression is irreversible adiabatic between initial and final equilibrium states represented by ① and (2u).

The corresponding P,V diagram is shown in fig. 15.10, and it was shown on page 331, that the " adiabatic efficiency " of an uncooled rotary compressor would be:

$$\frac{\text{energy required for reversible adiabatic compression}}{\text{energy required for actual (i.e. irreversible) adiabatic compression}}$$

i.e. $_{c}\eta_a = \dfrac{H_{2a} - H_1}{H_{2u} - H_1} = \dfrac{C_p(T_{2a} - T_1)}{C_p(T_{2u} - T_1)} = \dfrac{T_{2a} - T_1}{T_{2u} - T_1} = \dfrac{\text{length A}}{\text{length B}}$ on fig. 20.7,

since, for unit mass of gas, $H = E + PV = E + RT$,

hence, $dH = dE + RdT = (C_v + R)dT = C_p dT$

and, therefore, $H_{2a} - H_1 = C_p(T_{2a} - T_1)$.

6. Entropy-temperature Diagrams for Gas-turbine Plant.—In fig. 20.8 the entropy-temperature diagram 1, 2*u*, 3, 4*u* for the working of the open circuit plant of fig. 16.14 is shown relative to the hypothetical diagram 1, 2*a*, 3, 4*a*, 1, in which compression and expansion are assumed to be reversible adiabatic processes.

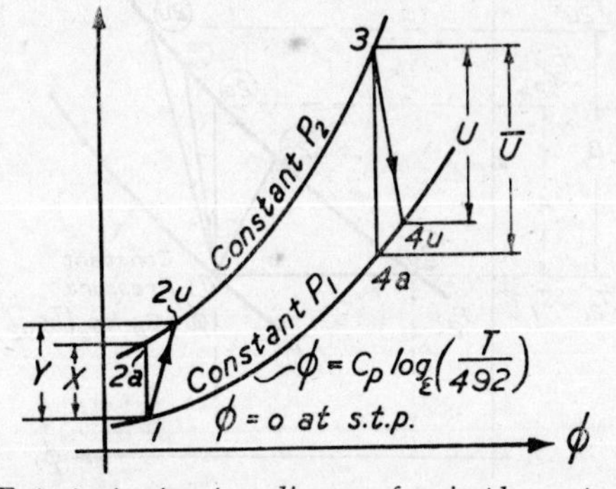

FIG. 20.8—*Entropy-temperature diagram for simple gas-turbine plant.*

The adiabatic efficiency of the compression is

$$_{c}\eta_a = \frac{H_{2a} - H_1}{H_{2u} - H_1} = \frac{T_{2a} - T_1}{T_{2u} - T_1} = \frac{\text{length X}}{\text{length Y}}$$

and the adiabatic efficiency of expansion in the turbine is

$$_{t}\eta_a = \frac{H_3 - H_{4u}}{H_3 - H_{4a}} = \frac{T_3 - T_{4u}}{T_3 - T_{4a}} = \frac{\text{length U}}{\text{length } \bar{U}}.$$

Hence, neglecting the slight mechanical friction at the main bearings, heat lost by radiation, the difference in kinetic energy of working agent in entry and exit ducts, the small drop in pressure in the combustion chamber and the small increase of C_p with temperature, i.e. dealing with the hypothetical case, we deduce that the energy transformed into useful mechanical energy (the specific output of the plant in, say, B.Th.U. per lb. of working agent) is $W = (H_3 - H_{4u}) - (H_{2u} - H_1)$ and the energy supplied is $(H_3 - H_{2u})$ per unit mass of working agent.

Hence, the overall efficiency of the plant is

$$\eta_o = \frac{(T_3 - T_{4u}) - (T_{2u} - T_1)}{(T_3 - T_{2u})} = \frac{{}_t\eta_a \cdot T_3\left(1 - \frac{1}{Z}\right) - \frac{T_1}{{}_c\eta_a}(Z-1)}{(T_3 - T_1) - \frac{T_1}{{}_c\eta_a}(Z-1)}$$

where $Z = \frac{T_3}{T_{4a}} = \frac{T_{2a}}{T_1} = \left(\frac{P_2}{P_1}\right)^{\frac{\gamma-1}{\gamma}} = (r_P)^{\frac{\gamma-1}{\gamma}}$

i.e. $$\eta_o = \frac{\frac{{}_t\eta_a T_3}{Z} - \frac{T_1}{{}_c\eta_a}}{\frac{T_3 - T_1}{Z-1} - \frac{T_1}{{}_c\eta_a}}.$$

Example 1.—Assuming the cycle 1, 2u, 3, 4u, 1 to be followed in the simple plant of fig. 16.14 when $T_1 = 520°$ abs. F., $T_3 = 1{,}900°$ abs. F., $\gamma = 1 \cdot 4$, $C_p = 0 \cdot 24$ B.Th.U. per lb. °F., adiabatic efficiencies of compression and expansion ${}_c\eta_a = 0 \cdot 84$ and ${}_t\eta_a = 0 \cdot 86$. Calculate the specific output and the overall efficiency of the plant when the pressure ratio is 4.

Compare the overall efficiency with the efficiency of the Carnot cycle having the same limits of temperature.

$$Z = \left(\frac{P_2}{P_1}\right)^{\frac{\gamma-1}{\gamma}} = (4)^{\frac{0 \cdot 4}{1 \cdot 4}} = 1 \cdot 486.$$

The specific output is

$$W = (H_3 - H_{4u}) - (H_{2u} - H_1) = C_p\{(T_3 - T_{4u}) - (T_{2u} - T_1)\}$$

$$= C_p(Z-1)\left\{\frac{{}_t\eta_a T_3}{Z} - \frac{T_1}{{}_c\eta_a}\right\}$$

$$= 0 \cdot 24 \frac{\text{B.Th.U.}}{\text{lb. °F.}}(0 \cdot 486)\left\{\frac{0 \cdot 86 \times 1900\ \text{°F.}}{1 \cdot 486} - \frac{520\ \text{°F.}}{0 \cdot 84}\right\}$$

$$= 0 \cdot 24 \times 0 \cdot 486(1100 - 619)\ \text{B.Th.U. per lb.}$$

$$= 56 \cdot 1\ \text{B.Th.U. per lb. of working agent.}$$

The overall efficiency is

$$\eta_o = \frac{\frac{0 \cdot 86 \times 1900}{1 \cdot 486} - \frac{520}{0 \cdot 84}}{\frac{1{,}380}{0 \cdot 486} - \frac{520}{0 \cdot 84}} = \frac{1100 - 619}{2840 - 619} = 0 \cdot 216 \text{ or } 21 \cdot 6 \text{ per cent.}$$

The efficiency of the Carnot cycle having the same limits of temperature is

$$\eta_c = \frac{T_3 - T_1}{T_3} = 1 - \frac{520}{1900} = 0 \cdot 726 \text{ or } 72 \cdot 6 \text{ per cent.}$$

In the case of the closed-circuit plant of fig. 2.22 *with heat exchanger* the hypothetical entropy-temperature diagram for the cycle is shown in fig. 20.9 from which we deduce that, per unit mass of working agent, the heat supplied from an external source is (H_4-H_3) and the specific output of the plant is $(H_4-H_5)-(H_2-H_1)$.

Hence the overall efficiency of a plant following the hypothetical cycle, 1, 2, 3, 4, 5, 6, 1 would be

$$\eta_o=\frac{{}_t C_p(T_4-T_5)-{}_c\bar{C}_p(T_2-T_1)}{{}_b\bar{C}_p(T_4-T_3)}.$$

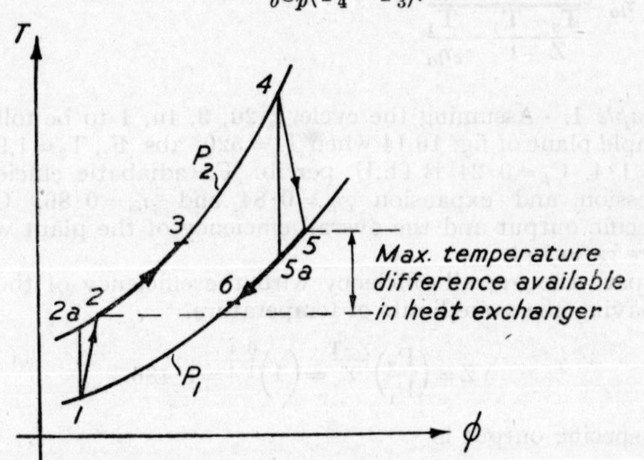

FIG. 20.9—*Entropy-temperature diagram for gas-turbine plant with heat-exchanger.*

7. Entropy of Water and Steam.—Suppose we start with 1 lb. of water at 32° F. or 492° abs. F. under absolute pressure P (of corresponding saturation temperature T_s) and require to change it at that pressure

(i) to water having absolute temperature T_s;
(ii) to saturated steam;
(iii) to superheated steam of absolute temperature T′.

Entropy of Water φ_w—Assuming the specific heat of water remains constant (unity) over the range of temperature (T_s—492° abs. F.), the increase in entropy of 1 lb. of water due to that temperature rise will be given by

$$\int_{\phi_o}^{\phi_w} d\varphi=\int_{T_o}^{T_s}\frac{dQ}{T}=\int_{492\,^\circ\text{abs. F.}}^{T_s} 1\text{ lb.}\times 1\frac{\text{B.Th.U.}}{\text{lb. }^\circ\text{F.}}\times\frac{dT}{T}$$

i.e. $\varphi_w - \varphi_o = \log_\varepsilon\left(\frac{T_s}{492}\right) \frac{\text{B.Th.U.}}{°\text{F.}}$ or, taking the datum, from which entropy is measured, to be the same as was taken for the measurement of heat, namely 32° F., then, at 492° abs. F. the entropy φ_o will be zero. Hence, the entropy of 1 lb. of water at T_s (in °abs. F.) is given by the expression $\varphi_w = \log_\varepsilon \frac{T_s}{492} \frac{\text{B.Th.U.}}{°\text{F.}}$ (specific heat being assumed constant and equal to unity).

Callendar takes into account the variation in the specific heat of water with temperature in the formula

$$\varphi = s \log_\varepsilon\left(\frac{T}{491 \cdot 6}\right) + av\frac{dp}{dt},$$

from which he calculated φ_w in his tables.

Example 1.—Find the entropy of 1 lb. of water at pressure 100 Lb. per sq. in. abs. and temperature 787·5° abs. F. from the formula which assumes that the specific heat of water remains unity. Compare this with Callendar's figure given in the steam tables, and calculate the percentage error.

$$\varphi_w = \log_\varepsilon\left(\frac{787 \cdot 5}{492}\right) = \log_\varepsilon 1 \cdot 6 = 0 \cdot 47 \frac{\text{B.Th.U.}}{°\text{F.}}$$

Callendar's tabulated figure is 0·4742.

$$\therefore \text{ Percentage error} = \frac{0 \cdot 0042}{0 \cdot 4742} \times 100 = 0 \cdot 89 \text{ per cent.}$$

Entropy of Saturated Steam.—After 1 lb. of water has been raised to the saturation temperature, T_s, any further heating will take place at constant temperature T_s. If the fraction q of the latent heat be added, then wet steam, of dryness fraction q, will be produced having entropy $\varphi = \varphi_w + \frac{qL}{T_s}$.

The addition of the whole of the latent heat L will increase the entropy by an amount $\frac{L}{T_s}$, producing dry saturated-steam having entropy $\varphi_s = \varphi_w + \frac{L}{T_s}$.

Entropy of Superheated Steam.—If the 1 lb. of dry saturated-steam at absolute pressure P and absolute temperature T_s is heated at that pressure until the final absolute temperature is T′

the increase in entropy due to the degree of superheat $(T'-T_s)$ will be given by

$$\int_{\phi_s}^{\phi'} d\varphi = \int_{T_s}^{T'} s' \frac{dT}{T},$$

where s' is the specific heat of superheated steam, assumed constant over the range of temperature T_s to T'.

That is, $\varphi' - \varphi_s = s' \log_\varepsilon \left(\frac{T'}{T_s}\right)$, or the entropy of 1 lb. of steam superheated to absolute temperature T' is given by the expression

$$\varphi' = \varphi_s + s' \log_\varepsilon \left(\frac{T'}{T_s}\right)$$

Example 2.—1 lb. of steam at 100 Lb. per sq. in. abs. is assumed to expand reversibly and adiabatically to 5 Lb. per sq. in. abs. If the steam is 0·9 dry at the beginning, calculate the dryness fraction at the end of expansion. Check this by means of the entropy-temperature diagram for steam.

Entropy of steam initially is $\varphi_1 = \varphi_{w1} + \frac{q_1 L_1}{T_1}$

$$= 0{\cdot}4742 + 0{\cdot}9 \times \frac{889{\cdot}7}{787{\cdot}5} = 1{\cdot}4911 \ \frac{\text{B.Th.U.}}{\text{lb. °F.}}$$

Entropy of steam at the end of reversible adiabatic expansion is

$$\varphi_{2a} = \varphi_{w2} + \frac{q_{2a} L_2}{T_2} = 0{\cdot}2348 + q_{2a} \times \frac{1001{\cdot}6}{622{\cdot}0}$$

$$= (0{\cdot}2348 + 1{\cdot}6110 q_{2a}) \ \frac{\text{B.Th.U.}}{\text{lb. °F.}}$$

Since the expansion is reversible and adiabatic, $\varphi_1 = \varphi_{2a}$

$$\therefore \ q_{2a} = \frac{1{\cdot}4911 - {\cdot}02348}{1{\cdot}6110} = \frac{1{\cdot}2563}{1{\cdot}6110} = 0{\cdot}778.$$

On the T,φ chart, a vertical line from $q_1 = 0{\cdot}9$ at 100 Lb. per sq. in. abs. gives $q_{2a} = 0{\cdot}778$ on the line corresponding to 5 Lb. per sq. in. abs.

8. The Temperature-entropy Chart for Water and Steam.—If curves for φ_w and φ_s are plotted on T, φ rectangular axes, we get *ab* and *df* (fig. 20.10), which form the "boundary lines" for water and dry saturated-steam, respectively. The point *b* represents the state of water about to change into steam at pressure p_1 and saturation temperature T_{s1}, having entropy entropy φ_{w1} and total heat h_{w1}. The point *d* represents the state of dry-saturated-steam at pressure p_1 and saturation temperature

T_{s1}, having entropy φ_{s1}, having entropy φ_{s1} and total heat H_{s1}. Any point *c* between *b* and *d* represents wet steam. Dryness lines are drawn to show the dryness fraction of the steam—the line *gi* representing a dryness fraction of 0·5. The dryness fraction of steam represented by *c* is 0·75.

Beyond the dry saturated boundary line, *df*, is the region of super-heat, in which curves of superheat such as *de* are drawn. They are constant pressure lines curving upwards from the various dry saturated points (*d*).

Thus the line *abcde* shows how the entropy and temperature change at pressure p_1 when 1 lb. of water is: (i) raised in temperature from 0° C. or 273° abs. C. to the saturation temperature

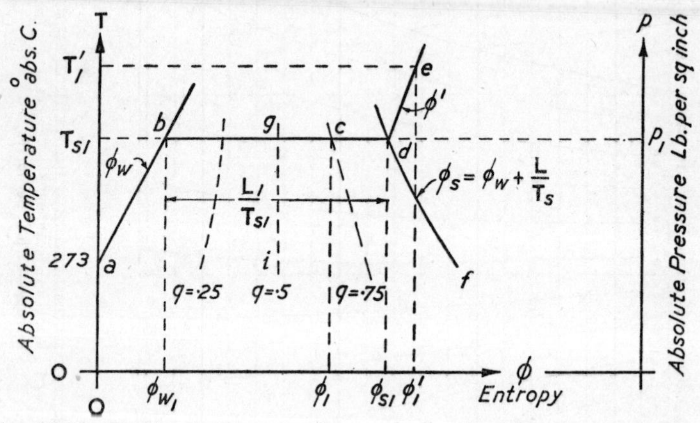

FIG. 20.10—*Temperature-entropy diagram for liquid and dry saturated vapour*

T_{s1}, as represented by point *b*; (ii) taken through all the stages of wetness along *bcd* before becoming dry saturated steam at *d*; (iii) superheated at pressure p_1 until its final temperature is T_1' as represented by the curve *de*.

An entropy temperature chart for water and steam can be plotted from Callendar's steam tables. Such a T, φ chart is shown on fig. 20.11.

9. Representation on T, φ Chart of the Carnot Cycle using Water and Steam as Working Agent.—Having dealt with the Carnot cycle using a perfect gas as working agent on p. 346, we now consider the same ideal cycle when "water-stuff" (which takes, alternately, the forms of water and steam) is used as the working agent.

Fig. 20.12 shows the P,V diagram and fig. 20.13 the corresponding T, φ diagram for a Carnot engine using "water-stuff" (H_2O) as working agent. The commencement of the cycle can be taken as

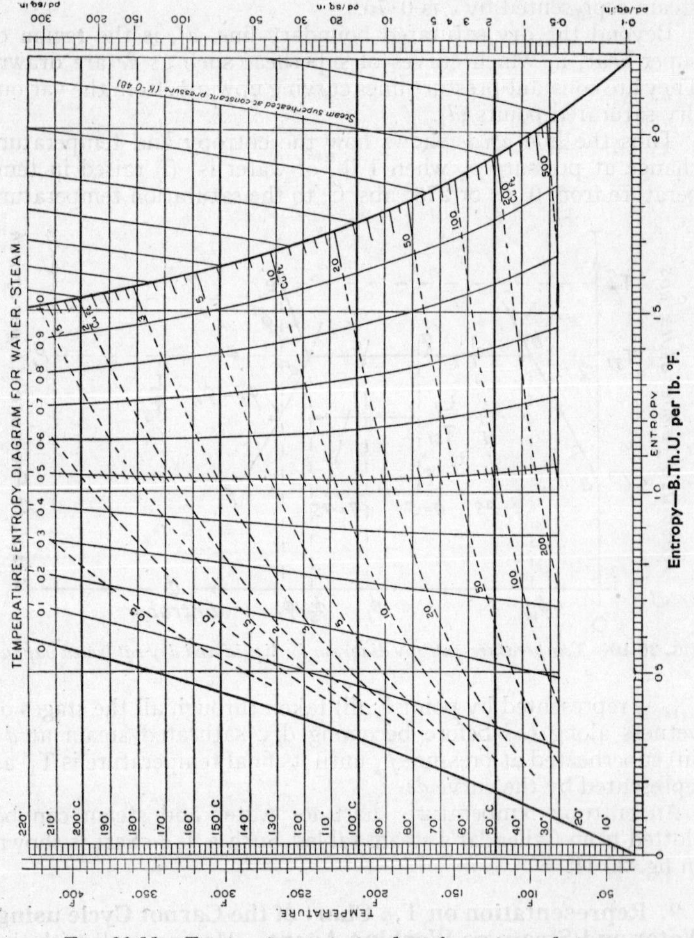

FIG. 20.11—*Temperature-entropy chart for water and steam.*

being at *a,* which represents the state (water) of the working agent at the beginning of the first reversible isothermal process. This process takes place at the temperature T_{s1} and is such that

1 lb. of water is changed into 1 lb. of dry saturated steam by the addition of the latent heat L_1 as shown by *ab* on the T, φ diagram of fig. 20.13. The heat added during the reversible isothermal process *ab* is represented by the area *mabnm*$=L_1=T_{s1}(\varphi_{s1}-\varphi_{w1})$. The second operation of the cycle is the reversible adiabatic expansion represented by *bc* during which the entropy remains constant $(\varphi_b=\varphi_{s1}=\varphi_c)$, and the pressure and temperature drop from P_1, T_{s1} to P_2, T_{s2}. The dryness fraction of the steam represented by *c* is given by the ratio of the lengths $\frac{wc}{ws}$. The third operation, *cd*, is reversible isothermal rejection of heat at pressure P_2 and temperature T_{s2}, during which the entropy decreases by an amount $(\varphi_c-\varphi_d)=(\varphi_{s1}-\varphi_{w1})$. The heat rejected during the reversible isothermal $cd=T_{s2}(\varphi_{s1}-\varphi_{w1})=$area (*ncdmn*).

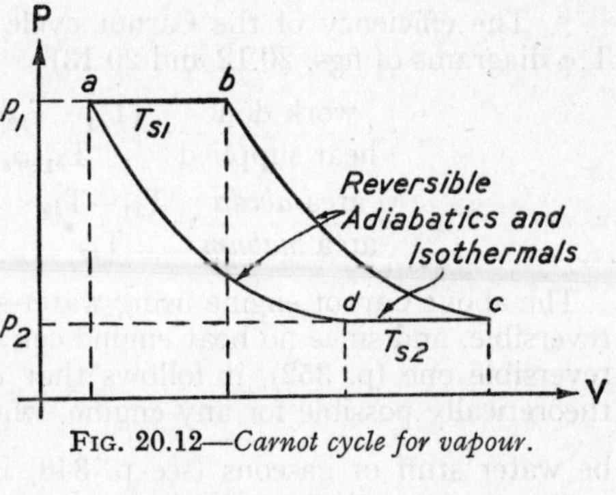

FIG. 20.12—*Carnot cycle for vapour.*

The reversible isothermal rejection of heat is stopped at a point *d* such that reversible adiabatic compression from *d* will bring the working agent back to its original state, *a*, before recommencement of the cycle. The dryness fraction of the steam at P_2, T_{s2}, before reversible adiabatic compression, is given by the ratio of the lengths $\frac{wd}{ws}$, and after compression the working agent is water at P_1, T_{s1}. During the reversible adiabatic compression, *da*, the entropy remains constant, φ_d being$=\varphi_a=\varphi_{w1}$.

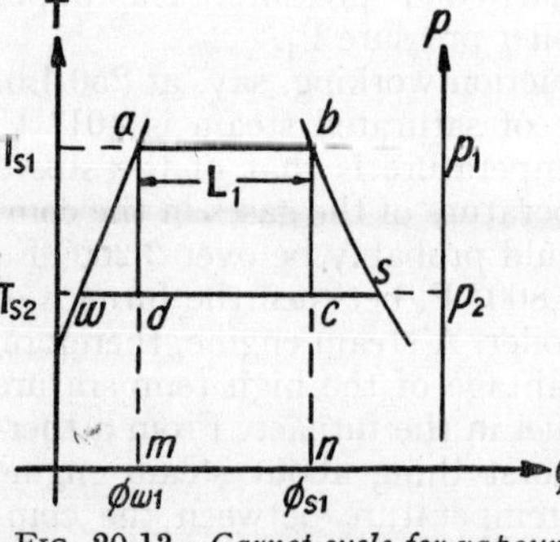

FIG. 20.13—*Carnot cycle for vapour.*

In this cycle of operations it will be noticed that the heat supplied to the working fluid$=T_{s1}(\varphi_{s1}-\varphi_{w1})=$ area under the reversible isothermal *ab*=area *mabnm*.

The heat rejected from the working fluid$=T_{s2}(\varphi_{s1}-\varphi_{w1})=$area under the reversible isothermal *cd*=area *ncdmn*.

Work done=heat supplied—heat rejected.

$$=(T_{s1}-T_{s2})(\varphi_{s1}-\varphi_{w1})=\text{area } abcda.$$

∴ The efficiency of the Carnot cycle (*abcda* on the P,V and T,φ diagrams of figs. 20.12 and 20.13)

$$=\frac{\text{work done}}{\text{heat supplied}}=\frac{(T_{s1}-T_{s2})(\varphi_{s1}-\varphi_{w1})}{T_{s1}(\varphi_{s1}-\varphi_{w1})}$$

$$=\frac{\text{area } abcda}{\text{area } mabnm}=\frac{T_{s1}-T_{s2}}{T_{s1}}$$

The above Carnot engine using water-stuff as working agent is reversible, and since no heat engine can be more efficient than a reversible one (p. 352), it follows that the maximum efficiency theoretically possible for any engine, whether the working agent be water stuff or gaseous (see p. 348) is $\frac{T_1-T_2}{T_1}$, where T_1 and T_2 are the upper and lower temperatures at which heat is added and rejected, respectively. Thus the maximum efficiency of a perfect steam engine, as for all other engines, depends upon the limits of temperature. In a steam engine plant the lower limit T_2 is settled by the pressure P_2 in the condenser—being the saturation temperature T_{s2} at that particular pressure. The upper limit T_1 is T_{s1} as settled by the boiler pressure P_1.

For a boiler of ordinary construction working, say, at 250 Lb. per sq. in. abs., the temperature of saturated steam is 401° F. If there is no superheat, this temperature is that of the steam admitted to the engine. The temperature of the gases in the combustion chamber of the boiler would probably be over 2,200° F., showing that there is a drop of 1,800° F. between the furnace of the boiler and the steam in the boiler. A steam engine, therefore, falls far short of taking full advantage of the high temperature produced by the combustion of fuel in the furnace. From a thermodynamic point of view the worst thing about steam engine plant is the large difference in temperature between the combustion chamber and the steam in the boiler. In practice, this is the most serious breach of reversibility in the transformation of heat into work by a steam engine plant (see p. 132).

Example 1.—Find the Carnot efficiency of an engine working between a boiler pressure of 250 Lb. per sq. in. abs. and a condenser pressure of 1 Lb. per sq. in. abs.

Saturation temperature at 250 Lb. per sq. in. abs. is 860·7° abs F.

Saturation temperature at 1 Lb. per sq. in. abs. is 561·4° abs. F.

$$\therefore \text{Carnot efficiency} = \frac{860 \cdot 7 - 561 \cdot 4}{860 \cdot 7} = \frac{299 \cdot 3}{860 \cdot 7} = 34 \cdot 8 \text{ per cent.}$$

Example 2.—(i) A hot source supplies a quantity of heat, Q_1, at an absolute temperature T_1 to a Carnot (imaginary) engine which rejects heat, Q_2, into a receiver at T_2. Show that the total entropy remains the same when heat is passed through this reversible engine. (ii) Show that there is a net gain of entropy when an actual engine receives a quantity of heat, A_1, at T_1 and rejects heat, A_2, at T_2.

(i) Work done by the (imaginary) Carnot engine

$$= \text{heat supplied} - \text{heat rejected}$$
$$= Q_1 - Q_2$$

$$\therefore \text{Efficiency of Carnot engine} = \frac{Q_1 - Q_2}{Q_1}, \text{ which also} = \frac{T_1 - T_2}{T_1}$$

$$\therefore \frac{Q_2}{Q_1} = \frac{T_2}{T_1} \text{ or } \frac{Q_1}{T_1} = \frac{Q_2}{T_2}$$

That is, the entropy, $\frac{Q_1}{T_1}$, lost by the hot source is equal to the entropy, $\frac{Q_2}{T_2}$, gained by the receiver. Thus, the total entropy of the system remains the same.

(ii) The efficiency of the actual engine receiving heat A_1 and rejecting heat A_2 is $\frac{A_1 - A_2}{A_1}$. This is less than the Carnot efficiency, $\frac{T_1 - T_2}{T_1}$, because an actual engine is not reversible in the ideal sense.

Thus, $$\frac{A_1 - A_2}{A_1} < \frac{T_1 - T_2}{T_1} \text{ or } 1 - \frac{A_2}{A_1} < 1 - \frac{T_2}{T_1}$$

$$\therefore \frac{A_2}{A_1} > \frac{T_2}{T_1} \text{ or } \frac{A_2}{T_2} > \frac{A_1}{T_1}$$

This shows that the entropy, $\frac{A_2}{T_2}$, gained by the receiver is greater than the entropy, $\frac{A_1}{T_1}$, lost by the hot source. The result is a net gain in the entropy of the system $= \left(\frac{A_2}{T_2} - \frac{A_1}{T_1}\right)$ due to the flow of heat from source to receiver through an actual (i.e. irreversible) engine.

This is one particular case of a general principle which states that in a system in which no other but reversible processes occur the net result is that there is neither gain nor loss of entropy, but that during an actual process (which is always irreversible) there is always a net gain of entropy of the system. The principle can be made to form another viewpoint of the second law of thermodynamics mentioned on p. 349.

Changes or processes occurring in a closed system are accompanied either by no change in entropy or by an increase in entropy according as the processes involved are reversible or irreversible, respectively, i.e. $\delta\varphi \geqslant 0$ in a closed system, δQ being zero. In other words, *when an irreversible operation occurs in a closed system it has the same effect on entropy as if the system received heat reversibly from an external source. This is the principle of the increase of entropy, which is a criterion of irreversibility; for, if the entropy of an isolated system increases during a process, the process is irreversible.*

We may now think of the second law of thermodynamics, with reference to entropy, as stating that the total entropy of substances or bodies involved in real processes always increases, or that the entropy of a closed system remains constant only in the idealised imaginary or limiting case in which reversible processes are assumed to occur. The fact that no real action is reversible in the ideal sense led Clausius to make the statement that "entropy of the Universe tends towards a maximum."

The entropy of a system is a maximum when all the energy in the system takes the form of uniformly diffused heat. If this state is reached, no further transformations are possible because there will be no available temperature drop. All natural processes, being irreversible bring the Universe a little nearer to this state. This suggests that the universe is in a condition analogous to that of a wound-up clock, now running down (see also p. 351). It is also said by philosophers that entropy provides the only physical test of the direction of time, in that time, t, must be measured such that $\frac{d\varphi}{dt}$ is a positive quantity.

10. Representation of the Rankine Cycle on the T,φ Chart.—Although the Rankine Cycle has been dealt with on p. 128 it is necessary to consider it again, making use of the T,φ and H,φ diagrams.

Referring to the imaginary Carnot cycle on p. 485, it will be noted that there is only one organ, namely, a cylinder, serving as boiler, engine, and condenser. This is not practicable in an actual working plant, and instead of one organ of the Carnot cycle (fig. 16.1) we have to have the three separate organs: boiler, engine, and condenser, in order to have a practical cycle. The ideal cycle which is aimed at in actual working engines is called the Rankine cycle, described on p. 128. It can also be represented diagrammatically as in fig. 7.1, where we will suppose 1 lb. of dry

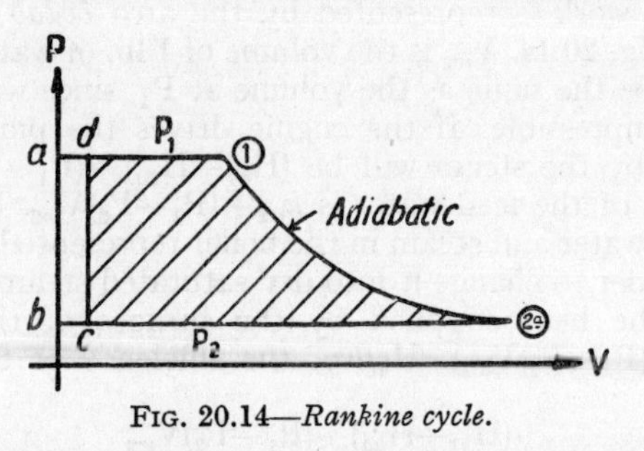

FIG. 20.14—*Rankine cycle.*

saturated steam supplied to the engine at pressure P_1 represented by the admission line *a*① on the P,V diagram, fig. 20.4 and the state shown by the point ① on the dry saturated steam line of the T,φ chart, fig. 20.15.

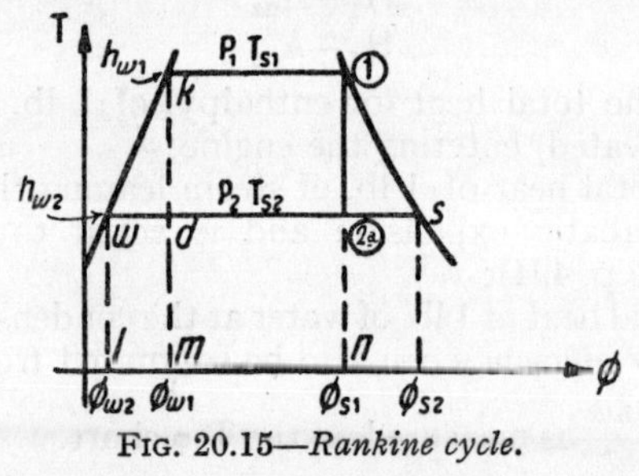

FIG. 20.15—*Rankine cycle.*

Reversible adiabatic expansion is assumed to take place from ① to ②a in the engine, as shown on the P,V diagram and by the line ① ②a (of constant entropy φ_{s1}) on the T, φ chart. Exhaust from the engine is represented by ②a *b* on the P,V diagram. The energy rejected from the engine per lb. after reversible adiabatic expansion is H_{2a}, and the dryness fraction of the steam is given by the ratio of lengths $\frac{w\,(2a)}{ws}$. The work done per lb. of steam passing through the engine is therefore $(H_{s1}-H_{2a})$.

In the condenser, 1 lb. of exhaust steam is condensed to water at pressure P_2 by the abstraction of an amount of heat represented by the area n ⓶a wln. The condensate is then extracted from the condenser with total heat h_{w2} per lb., and pumped into the boiler again after work, $(P_1-P_2)V_{w2}$, has been done on it by the feed pump. This work is represented by the area *bcdab* on the P,V diagram of fig. 20.14. V_{w2} is the volume of 1 lb. of water at P_2 and is taken to be the same as the volume at P_1, since water is practically incompressible. If the engine drives the pump, the net work done by the steam will be $(H_{s1}-H_{2a})-(P_1-P_2)V_{w2}$. The total energy of the feed water is $h_{w2}+(P_1-P_2)V_{w2}$. Heat is supplied to the water and steam in the boiler represented by the area lwk①nl in order to change it into dry saturated steam at pressure P_1. Thus the heat supplied by the furnace of the boiler is $H_{s1}-(h_{w2}+(P_1-P_2)V_{w2})$. Hence, the efficiency of the Rankine cycle is

$$\frac{(H_{s1}-H_{2a})-(P_1-P_2)V_{w2}}{(H_{s1}-h_{w2})-(P_1-P_2)V_{w2}}$$

If the small feed pump term is neglected, the efficiency of the Rankine cycle (as shown previously on p. 128) is

$$\frac{H_1-H_{2a}}{H_1-h_{w2}}$$

where H_1 is the total heat (or enthalpy) of 1 lb. of steam (wet, dry, or superheated) entering the engine;

H_{2a} is the total heat of 1 lb. of steam leaving the engine after reversible adiabatic expansion and is equal to $h_{w2}+q_{2a}L_2$ or $T_{s2}.\varphi_1-G_2$ (see p. 494);

h_{w2} is the total heat of 1 lb. of water at the condenser pressure P_2.

The Rankine efficiency can also be estimated from the ratio of the area $\dfrac{k①⓶a\,wk}{lwk①nl}$ as measured on the T, φ chart.

It has already been mentioned on p. 129 that the Rankine cycle is taken as the standard of comparison for steam engine and steam turbine plant. Although not completely attainable in practice, since it assumes that there is no friction or throttling of steam, reversible adiabatic expansion of steam in the engine cylinder, no loss of heat through cylinder walls and piston, and no losses during pumping of the condensate from condenser to boiler, the cycle, nevertheless, affords a valuable criterion of performance by setting up a standard towards which the operation of real plant can approach, and with which the efficiency of a working steam engine or turbine plant can be compared.

Expansion in a real engine or turbine would not, of course, be reversible adiabatic, and the total heat of the steam after actual expansion would be H_2 which would be greater than H_{2a}, as shown on fig. 20.19. The actual heat drop during expansion would thus be $(H_{s1}-H_2)$ as compared with the "available" heat drop $(H_{s1}-H_{2a})$ which would be achieved if the expansion were reversible and adiabatic.

The relative efficiency, or efficiency ratio, is $\frac{H_{s1}-H_2}{H_{s1}-H_{2a}}$.

The efficiency of the Rankine engine is less than that of the Carnot engine working between the same limits of temperature, because in the former cycle the heat taken in by the working agent is not *all* taken in at the upper limit of temperature T_1. The sensible heat has to be added with the temperature increasing from T_2 to T_1 before the latent heat is added at the constant temperature T_1, whereas in the Carnot engine *all* the heat supplied is taken in at the upper limit of temperature T_1. The effect of this can be seen on the T,φ diagram of fig. 20.15, where the Rankine efficiency is represented by $\frac{k①(2a)wk}{lwk①nl}$ and is less than the Carnot efficiency, which is represented by $\frac{k①(2a)dk}{mk①nm}$.

Example.—Steam at 100 Lb. per sq. in. abs. and dryness fraction 0·9 is admitted to a steam engine and assumed expanded reversibly and adiabatically to a condenser pressure 5 Lb. per sq. in. abs. Calculate the Rankine efficiency when the feed pump term is taken into account, and estimate the percentage error involved when the feed pump term is neglected.

$H_1 = h_{w1} + q_1 L_1 = 298\cdot5 + 0\cdot9 \times 889\cdot7 = 1000\cdot2$ B.Th.U. per lb.

The dryness fraction after reversible adiabatic expansion was calculated in the Example 2 of p. 482 to be $0\cdot778 = q_{2a}$.

Hence, $H_{2a} = h_{w2} + q_{2a} L_2 = 130\cdot2 + 0\cdot778 \times 1001\cdot6 = 909\cdot5$ B.Th.U. per lb.

The feed pump term $(P_1 - P_2)V_{w2}$

$$= (100-5)\,\frac{\text{Lb.}}{\text{in.}^2} \times 0\cdot01639\,\frac{\text{ft.}^3}{\text{lb.}}\left[\frac{144\ \text{in.}^2}{\text{ft.}^2}\right]\left[\frac{\text{B.Th.U.}}{778\ \text{ft.-Lb.}}\right]$$

$$= 0\cdot288 \text{ B.Th.U. per lb.}$$

$V_{w2} = 0\cdot01639$ cu. ft. being the volume of 1 lb. of water at the condenser pressure and temperature.

$$\text{The Rankine efficiency} = \frac{(H_1 - H_{2a}) - (P_1 - P_2)V_{w2}}{(H_1 - h_{w2}) - (P_1 - P_2)V_{w2}}$$

$$= \frac{1099\cdot2 - 909\cdot5 - 0\cdot29}{1099\cdot2 - 130\cdot9 - 0\cdot29} = \frac{189\cdot4}{968\cdot7} = 19\cdot6 \text{ per cent.}$$

The Rankine efficiency, neglecting the feed pump term

$$=\frac{H_1-H_{2a}}{H_1-h_{w2}}=\frac{189\cdot7}{969\cdot0}=19\cdot6 \text{ per cent.}$$

When P_1 is greater, there will be an error, but unless very high pressures are involved the feed pump term is negligible (see page 115).

11. Efficiencies of Rankine and Carnot Cycles Compared. —The Rankine cycle, as has been pointed out on p. 491, does not achieve the maximum efficiency which is theoretically possible by an engine assumed working on the Carnot cycle between the same two limits of temperature T_{s1} and T_{s2}.

On the T,φ diagram of fig. 20.16 the Carnot cycle is represented by *dabcd* and the Rankine cycle by *dabwd*, i.e. the fourth operation, *cd*, of the Carnot cycle is replaced by *cw* and *wd* in the Rankine cycle.

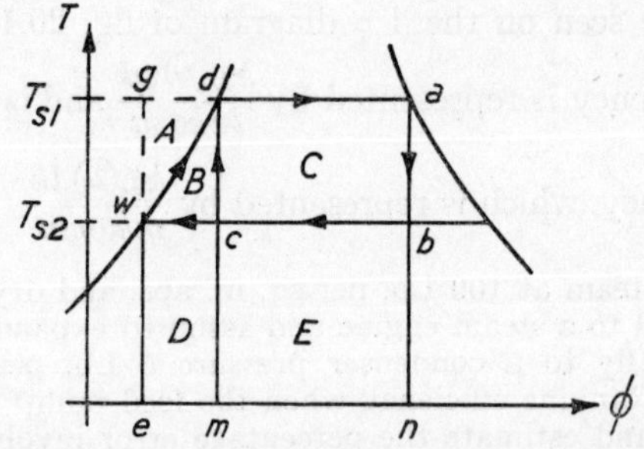

FIG. 20.16—*Rankine and Carnot cycles compared.*

Because this involves the addition of some heat (*wd*) at lower temperatures than the highest (T_{s1}), the efficiency (η_R) of the Rankine cycle is less than that (η_C) of the Carnot cycle assumed working between the same limits of temperature T_{s1} and T_{s2}; for, if the capital letters represent the areas in which they are written it is clear that

$$\eta_R=\frac{B+C}{B+C+D+E} \quad \text{and} \quad \eta_C=\frac{C}{C+E}=\frac{A+B+C}{A+B+C+D+E}$$

$$\text{Therefore, } 1-\eta_R=\frac{D+E}{B+C+D+E} \quad \text{and} \quad 1-\eta_C=\frac{D+E}{A+B+C+D+E}$$

Hence, $1-\eta_C<1-\eta_R$ and $\eta_C>\eta_R$ for the same limits of temperature of working agent.

As mentioned on pp. 132 and 486, a fundamental defect of the orthodox steam boiler is that it permits of a large irreversible temperature drop between the flame in the furnace and the working agent used in the engine or turbine.

12. Calculation of Heat Drop ($H_1 - H_{2a}$) during Reversible Adiabatic Expansion, and Expressions for Rankine Efficiency.—Three cases of reversible adiabatic expansion between pressure limits P_1 and P_2 are shown in fig. 20.17.

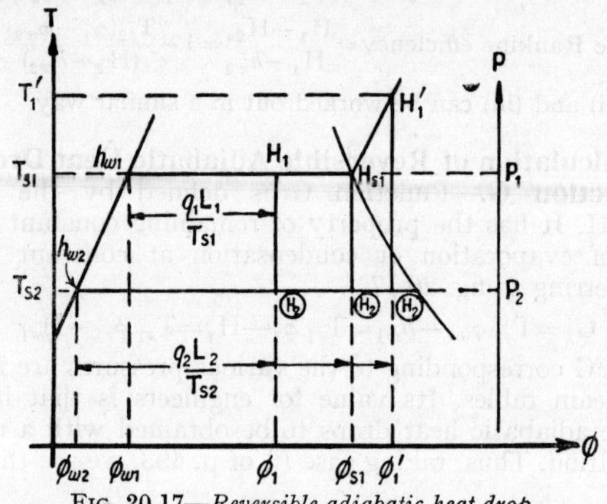

FIG. 20.17—*Reversible adiabatic heat drop.*

(i) Steam initially wet; temperature T_{s1}; total heat

$$H_1 = h_{w1} + q_1 L_1;\ \text{entropy } \varphi_1 = \varphi_{w1} + \frac{q_1 L_1}{T_{s1}};$$

(ii) steam initially dry and saturated; temperature T_{s1}; total heat H_{s1}; entropy $\varphi_{s1} = \varphi_{w1} + \frac{L_1}{T_{s1}}$;

(iii) steam initially superheated at pressure P_1 to a temperature T_1'; total heat $H_1' = H_{s1} + s'(T_1' - T_{s1})$;

$$\text{entropy } \varphi_1' = \varphi_{s1} + s' \log_\varepsilon\left(\frac{T_1'}{T_{s1}}\right)$$

The initial conditions regarding pressure, dryness fraction, or superheat, are usually known, from which the initial total heat and entropy can be found.

After reversible adiabatic expansion from P_1 to P_2, as shown in fig. 20.17, it will be seen that the steam is wet in the three cases. The total heat of the steam after expansion is thus $H_{2a} = h_{w2} + q_{2a} L_2$, and the entropy is $\varphi_{2a} = \varphi_{w2} + \frac{q_{2a} L_2}{T_{s2}}$, which is equal to φ_1, φ_{s1}, or φ_1', according as q_{2a} is the appropriate dryness fraction for the particular one of the three cases considered.

Thus, in case (i), $\phi_{2a}=\varphi_{w2}+\frac{q_{2a}L_2}{T_{s2}}=\varphi_1$

$$\therefore\ q_{2a}L_2=T_{s2}(\varphi_1-\varphi_{w2})$$

$$\therefore\ H_{2a}=h_{w2}+q_{2a}L_2=h_{w2}+T_{s2}(\varphi_1-\varphi_{w2})$$

Thus, the reversible adiabatic heat drop

$$=H_1-H_{2a}=H_1-h_{w2}-T_{s2}(\varphi_1-\varphi_{w2})$$

Hence, the Rankine efficiency $=\frac{H_1-H_{2a}}{H_1-h_{w2}}=1-\frac{T_{s2}(\varphi_1-\varphi_{w2})}{(H_1-h_{w2})}$

Cases (ii) and (iii) can be worked out in a similar way.

13. Calculation of Reversible Adiabatic Heat Drop using the Function G.—Function G is defined by the equation $G=T\varphi-H$. It has the property of remaining constant during a process of evaporation or condensation at constant pressure. Thus, referring to fig. 20.17,

$$G_1=T_{s1}.\varphi_{w1}-h_{w1}=T_{s1}.\varphi_1-H_1=T_{s1}.\phi_{s1}-H_{s1}$$

Values of G corresponding to the various pressures are tabulated in the steam tables. Its value for engineers is that it enables reversible adiabatic heat drops to be obtained with a minimum of calculation. Thus, taking case (i) of p. 493, we see that

$$H_1=h_{w1}+q_1L_1 \quad \text{and} \quad \varphi_1=\varphi_{w1}+\frac{q_1L_1}{T_{s1}}$$

Thus,

$$H_1=h_{w1}+(\varphi_1-\varphi_{w1})T_{s1}=T_{s1}.\varphi_1-(T_{s1}\varphi_{w1}-h_{w1})=T_{s1}.\varphi_1-G_1$$

Similarly, $H_{2a}=T_{s2}.\phi_{2a}-G_2=T_{s2}.\varphi_1-G_2$, since $\varphi_1=\phi_{2a}$ for an reversible adiabatic.

Hence the reversible adiabatic heat drop

$$H_1-H_{2a}=\phi_1.(T_{s1}-T_{s2})-(G_1-G_2)$$

By use of the total heat-entropy chart for 1 lb. of steam (figs. 20.18 and 20.19) the reversible adiabatic heat drop can be obtained as the length of a vertical (i.e., a constant entropy) line measured in B.Th.U. per lb. on the ordinate scale.

Example.—Taking the example on page 491, where steam at 100 Lb. per sq. in. abs. and 0·9 dryness is expanded to 5 Lb. per sq. in. abs., find the reversible adiabatic heat drop and the Rankine efficiency (neglecting the feed pump term).

$$\varphi_1=\varphi_{w1}+\frac{q_1L_1}{T_{s1}}=0\cdot4742+\frac{0\cdot9\times889\cdot7}{787\cdot5}=1\cdot4911\ \frac{\text{B.Th.U.}}{\text{lb. °F.}}$$

[*Continued on page* 496.

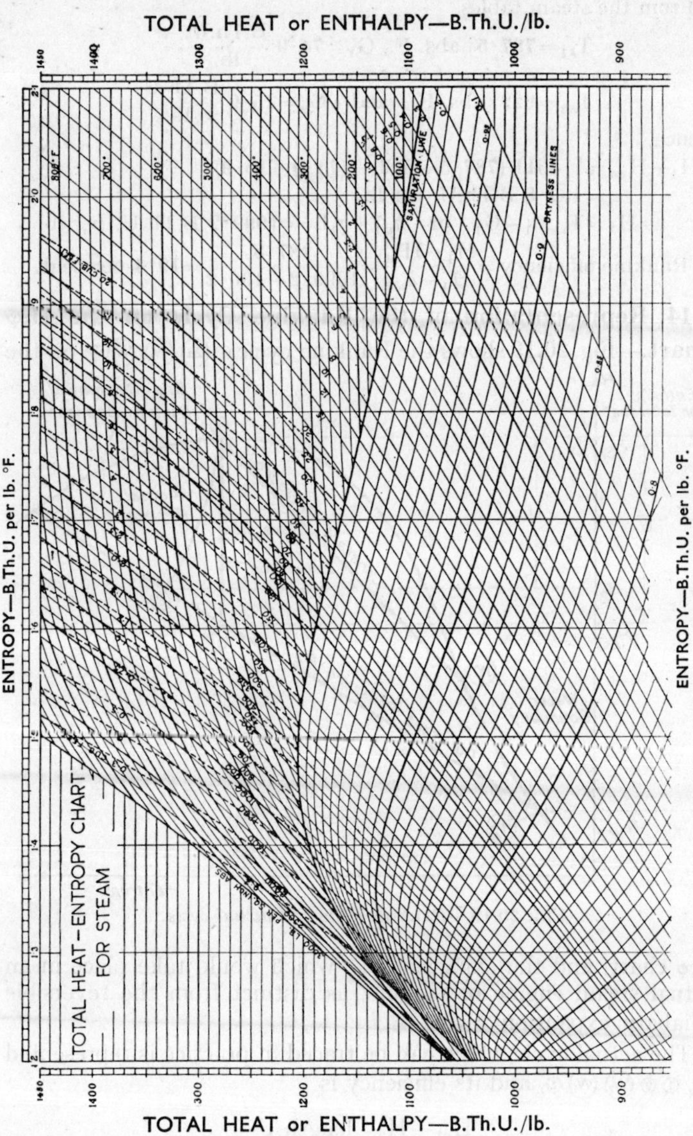

TOTAL HEAT or ENTHALPY—B.Th.U./lb.

TOTAL HEAT–ENTROPY CHART FOR STEAM

ENTROPY—B.Th.U. per lb. °F.

FIG. 20.18—*Enthalpy-entropy chart for steam.*

From the steam tables,

$$T_{s1}=787\cdot5° \text{ abs. F., } G_1=74\cdot9 \frac{\text{B.Th.U.}}{\text{lb.}},$$

$$T_{s2}=622° \text{ abs. F. and } G_2=15\cdot9 \frac{\text{B.Th.U.}}{\text{lb.}}$$

Hence,

$$H_1-H_{2a}=1\cdot4911\ (787\cdot5-622)-(74\cdot9-15\cdot9)$$
$$=187\cdot8 \text{ B.Th.U. per lb.}$$

$$H_1=T_{s1}.\phi_1-G_1 \quad \text{or} \quad h_{w1}+q_1L_1=1099\cdot2 \text{ B.Th.U. per lb.}$$

$$\text{Rankine efficiency}=\frac{H_1-H_{2a}}{H_1-h_{w2}}=\frac{187\cdot8}{1099\cdot2-130\cdot2}=19\cdot4 \text{ per cent.}$$

14. Representation of the Rankine Cycle on the H,φ Chart.—Fig. 20.19 shows the Rankine cycle ① (2a) (W_1) (W_2) ① on the

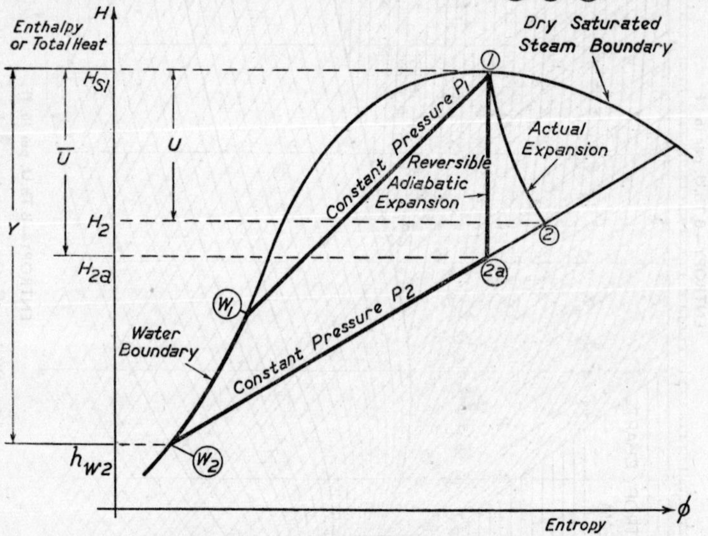

FIG. 20.19—*Rankine cycle and actual cycle.*

H,φ chart, and the expansion ①② which would take place in an actual steam engine or turbine, as distinct from the reversible adiabatic expansion ① (2a).

The actual cycle which can be traced in practice is represented as, ① ② (W_2) (W_1) ①, and its efficiency is

$$\frac{H_{s1}-H_2}{H_{s1}-h_{w2}}=\frac{\text{length U}}{\text{length Y}},$$

whereas the efficiency of the Rankine cycle, ① ②a Ⓦ₂ Ⓦ₁ ①, is

$$\frac{H_{s1}-H_{2a}}{H_{s1}-h_{w2}}=\frac{\text{length } \bar{U}}{\text{length Y}}$$

(neglecting pump terms). Thus, the ratio of the output of the actual cycle to that of the Rankine cycle is

$$\frac{H_{s1}-H_2}{H_{s1}-H_{2a}}=\frac{\text{length U}}{\text{length } \bar{U}}=\text{relative efficiency or efficiency ratio.}$$

Fig. 20.18 shows the H,φ chart from which these lengths can be measured if a graphical method is accurate enough.

Example.—Dry saturated steam at 200 Lb. per sq. in. abs. is admitted to a turbine and exhausted at 0·5 Lb. per sq. in. abs. having a final dryness fraction $q_2=0\cdot82$. Estimate the efficiencies of the actual and Rankine cycles, and the efficiency ratio, neglecting pump terms and radiation.

The H,φ diagrams on fig. 20.19, show the actual and the Rankine cycles, and from a larger H,φ chart (fig. 20.18) can be read $q_{2a}=0\cdot75$. Hence, by use of steam tables we find that, in B.Th.U. per lb., $H_{s1}=1199\cdot5$, $h_{w2}=47\cdot6$, and $H_2=h_{w2}+q_2\times L_2=47\cdot6+0\cdot82\times1048\cdot5=917\cdot6$. Also,

$$H_{2a}=h_{w2}+q_{2a}\times L_2=47\cdot6+0\cdot75\times1048\cdot5=834\cdot6 \text{ B.Th.U. per lb.}$$

Hence, the actual efficiency of the turbine

$$=\frac{H_{s1}-H_2}{H_{s1}-h_{w2}}=\frac{271\cdot9}{1151\cdot9}=0\cdot236 \text{ or } 23\cdot6 \text{ per cent.}$$

and the Rankine efficiency

$$=\frac{H_{s1}-H_{2a}}{H_{s1}-h_{w2}}=\frac{364\cdot9}{1151\cdot9}=0\cdot316 \text{ or } 31\cdot6 \text{ per cent.}$$

$$\text{The efficiency ratio}=\frac{H_{s1}-H_2}{H_{s1}-H_{2a}}=\frac{271\cdot9}{364\cdot9}=0\cdot744 \text{ or } 74\cdot4 \text{ per cent.}$$

15. Clapeyron's Equation.—Now that the Carnot cycle using a vapour has been dealt with (p. 485), it is possible to develop Clapeyron's Equation from such a cycle of operations.

Referring to fig. 20.20, suppose at *a* we start with volume *w* of 1 lb. of liquid at a temperature T, and change it into 1 lb. of dry

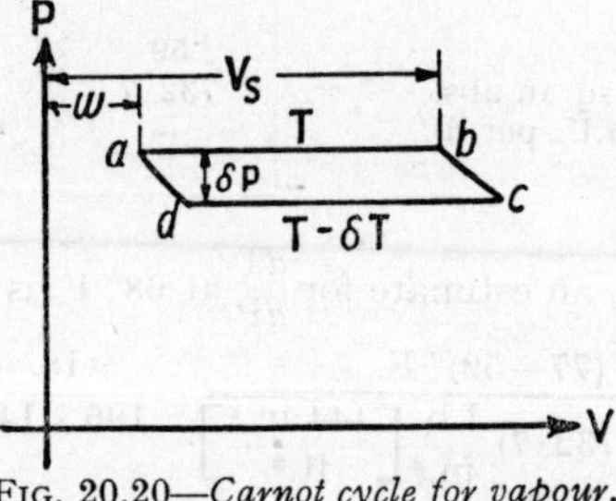

Fig. 20.20—*Carnot cycle for vapour.*

saturated vapour at T by the addition of latent heat L, so that its final volume, V_s, is represented by the point *b*. Complete the Carnot cycle with the two reversible adiabatics *bc* and *da*, and the second reversible isothermal *cd* which is performed at the temperature $(T-\delta T)$. We know that the efficiency of such a Carnot cycle is

$$\frac{\delta T}{T}=\frac{\text{work done}}{\text{heat supplied}}=\frac{\delta P(V_s-w)}{L}. \quad \therefore \quad V_s=w+\frac{L}{T}\frac{dT}{dP}$$

This last equation is known as Clapeyron's equation. Its chief use for engineers is that of deducing the volumes of dry saturated vapours from quantities which can be measured more accurately than a direct measurement of V_s.

Example 1.—Calculate the volume of 1 lb. of dry saturated steam at 100 Lb. per sq. in. abs. from the following data concerning steam at this pressure: saturation temperature 787·5° abs. F.; latent heat 889·7 B.Th.U. per lb.; volume of 1 lb. of water at the saturation temperature 0·0177 cu. ft.; the rate at which the saturation temperature increases with respect to pressure at 100 Lb. per sq. in. abs. is $\frac{0\cdot00505° \text{ F. ft.}^2}{\text{Lb.}}$.

$$V_s=w+\frac{L}{T}\frac{dT}{dP}=0\cdot0177\,\frac{\text{ft.}^3}{\text{lb.}}+889\cdot7\,\frac{\text{B.Th.U.}}{\text{lb.}}\times\frac{1}{787\cdot5° \text{ abs. F.}}$$

$$\times\frac{0\cdot00505° \text{ F. ft.}^2}{\text{Lb.}}\left[\frac{778 \text{ ft.-Lb.}}{\text{B.Th.U.}}\right]$$

$$=0\cdot0177\,\frac{\text{ft.}^3}{\text{lb.}}+4\cdot4263\,\frac{\text{ft.}^3}{\text{lb.}}=4\cdot434\,\frac{\text{ft.}^3}{\text{lb.}}$$

Example 2.—Estimate the volume of 1 lb. of dry and saturated carbon dioxide at 68° F. from the following data: volume of 1 lb. of liquid CO_2 at 68° F. and 825 Lb. per sq. in. abs. is 0·0210 cu. ft.

Temperature in °F.	59	68	77
Pressure in Lb. per sq. in abs.	732·7	825	928·7
Latent heat in B.Th.U. per lb.	—	66·15	—

From the Table, an estimate for $\frac{dT}{dP}$ at 68° F. is

$$\frac{(77-59)° \text{ F.}}{(928\cdot7-732\cdot7)\,\frac{\text{Lb.}}{\text{in.}^2}\left[\frac{144 \text{ in.}^2}{\text{ft.}^2}\right]}=\frac{18}{196\times144}\,\frac{°\text{F. ft.}^2}{\text{Lb.}}$$

Hence, $V_s = w + \frac{L}{T}\left(\frac{dT}{dP}\right)$

$$= 0 \cdot 021 \frac{\text{ft.}^3}{\text{lb.}} + 66 \cdot 15 \frac{\text{B.Th.U.}}{\text{lb.}} \times \frac{1}{(460+68)^\circ \text{ abs. F.}}$$

$$\times \frac{18}{196 \times 144} \frac{{}^\circ\text{F. ft.}^2}{\text{Lb.}} \left[\frac{778 \text{ ft.-Lb.}}{\text{B.Th.U.}}\right]$$

$$= 0 \cdot 021 \frac{\text{ft.}^3}{\text{lb.}} + 0 \cdot 062 \frac{\text{ft.}^3}{\text{lb.}} = 0 \cdot 083 \text{ ft.}^3 \text{ per lb.}$$

EXERCISES ON CHAPTER 20

1. In an internal combustion engine the pressure and temperature of 1 lb. of air after compression are 133 Lb. per sq. in. abs. and 780° F., respectively. Heat is then added at constant volume until the pressure is 500 Lb. per sq. in. abs. Calculate the final temperature and the increase in entropy during this constant volume addition of heat. $C_v = 0 \cdot 169$ B.Th.U. per lb. °F.

2. If 1 lb. of air is raised in temperature from 32° F. to 212° F. at constant pressure, calculate the change in entropy of the air. $C_p = 0 \cdot 238$ B.Th.U. per lb. ° F.

3. Calculate the entropy of 1 lb. of steam at 100 Lb. per sq. in. abs.: (*a*) when the dryness fraction is 0·96; (*b*) when the steam is superheated to 600° F. taking specific heat of superheated steam to be 0·5 B.Th.U. per lb. ° F.

4. One pound of steam initially at 100 Lb. per sq. in. abs. is assumed to expand reversibly and adiabatically to 5 Lb. per sq. in. abs. Calculate the dryness of the steam after expansion; (*a*) if the dryness fraction initially is 0·8; (*b*) if the steam is initially dry and saturated; (*c*) if the steam is superheated initially by 60° F.

Check the calculated results by means of the entropy temperature chart.

5. Calculate the reversible adiabatic heat drop and the efficiency of the Rankine cycle when:

(*a*) Dry saturated steam at 200 Lb. per sq. in. abs. expands to 15 Lb. per sq. in. abs.

(*b*) Steam at 200 Lb. per sq. in. abs. superheated by 320° F. expands to 15 Lb. per sq. in. abs.

(*c*) Dry saturated steam at 200 Lb. per sq. in. abs. expands to 1 Lb. per sq. in. abs.

(*d*) Steam at 200 Lb. per sq. in. abs. superheated by 320° F. expands to 1 Lb. per sq. in.

Check the dryness fraction calculated in parts (*a*) and (*c*) by means of the T,φ chart.

6. Calculate the reversible adiabatic heat drops in parts (*a*) and (*c*) of Question 5, using the function G, and compare the results with the calculations of that question.

7. Deduce the expression known as Clapeyron's Equation. Using the steam tables plot a part of the pressure temperature curve in the region of 200 Lb. per sq. in. abs. and deduce from it the slope at that pressure $\left(\frac{dP}{dT}\right)$. Use this and the steam tables to calculate the volume of 1 lb. of dry saturated steam at 200 Lb. per sq. in. abs. by means of Clapeyron's Equation. Compare with V_s in tables.

8. If the volume of 1 lb. of liquid sulphur dioxide at 68° F. is 0·0112 cu. ft., find the volume of 1 lb. of dry saturated SO_2 at that temperature and 47·57 Lb. per sq. in. abs.

Temperature °F.	59	68	77
Pressure in Lb. per sq. in. abs.	39·8	47·57	56·23
Latent heat of SO_2 B.Th.U. per lb.	—	150·93	—

9. In passing into an engine, steam is " wire drawn " (or throttled) at the stop valve, from 180 Lb. per sq. in. abs. 464° F. to 150 Lb. per sq. in. abs., what is then the condition of the steam? If the steam expands further (*a*) adiabatically and reversibly, (*b*) according to the law PV=constant, to a pressure 2 Lb. per sq. in. abs., what will be the final condition of the steam in the two cases? The specific heat of super-heated steam at 2 Lb. per sq. in. abs. may be assumed to be 0·5 B.Th.U. per lb. ° F.

Specific volume of superheated steam is

$$\frac{1\cdot252(H-835)}{p} \text{ cu. ft. per lb.,}$$

where H is in B.Th.U./lb. and p in Lb./in.^{2} abs.

[I.Mech.E., Sec. A.]

10. Calculate the Rankine efficiency of a steam engine supplied with steam 0·95 dry at 200 Lb. per sq. in. abs. The pressure in the condenser is 2 Lb. per sq. in. abs. Neglect the feed pump term.

11. Steam at a pressure of 200 Lb. per sq. in. abs., 0·982 dryness, passes through a throttle valve and emerges just dry and saturated. Estimate the lower pressure.

12. Make a sketch of either a T,φ or H,φ figure for the compression of air in a centrifugal supercharger, showing the effect of losses.

Air at 9 Lb. per sq. in. abs. and 40° F. is compressed by means of a centrifugal supercharger to 14 Lb. per sq. in. abs. with an adiabatic efficiency of 75 per cent. Find the final temperature and the work done per lb. of air given $C_P=0\cdot238$ and $C_V=0\cdot170$ B.Th.U. per lb. °F. Assume that the supercharger is uncooled and that radiation is negligible.

13. Sketch suitable entropy diagrams to demonstrate the thermodynamic differences between a centrifugal compressor and a reciprocating compressor.

An air-fuel mixture has a volume of 11·32 cu. ft. per lb. at a temperature of 32° F. and a pressure of 14·7 Lb. per sq. in. abs.

The value of γ for the mixture is $1 \cdot 39$. The mixture is compressed in a centrifugal compressor from 10 Lb. per sq. in. abs. to a pressure of 18 Lb. per sq. in. abs., the initial temperature being 25° F. If the adiabatic efficiency, based on the temperature rise, is 83 per cent., calculate the work required to deal with 1 lb. of the mixture.

[Part I, B.Sc. Lond.]

14. Show that the difference in entropy of unit mass of gas between two constant pressures P_1 and P_2 is $\phi_1 - \phi_2 = R \log_\varepsilon \left(\frac{P_2}{P_1}\right)$ at any particular temperature.

$0 \cdot 5$ ft.^{3} of air at 60° F. is compressed from 14 to 120 Lb./in.^{2} abs. according to the law $PV^{1 \cdot 25}$=constant. Calculate the decrease in entropy of the air.

If the compression had been reversible adiabatic according to the law $PV^\gamma = PV^{1 \cdot 4}$=constant, show that there would have been no change in entropy, i.e. the compression would have been isentropic.

If the actual compression had been uncooled, i.e. irreversible adiabatic according to the law $PV^{1 \cdot 5}$=constant, calculate the increase in entropy of the air. $C_p = 0 \cdot 238$ B.Th.U./lb. °F.

15. Deduce from first principles an expression, in terms of T and V, for the gain of entropy of a perfect gas during a change from conditions $P_1T_1V_1$ to conditions $P_2T_2V_2$.

A quantity of carbon dioxide occupies 20 cu. ft. at 750° abs. F. and 400 Lb. per sq. in. abs. Determine the gain of entropy if this carbon dioxide expands isothermally to 100 cu. ft.

[Part I, B.Sc. Lond.]

PROPERTIES OF ONE POUND OF SATURATED STEAM

From the abridged Callendar Steam Tables (fourth edition) published by Messrs. Edward Arnold & Co., by whose permission they are reproduced.

Pressure		Saturation Temperature		Energy in British Thermal Units per lb.				Entropy B.Th.U. per lb. °F.		Volume cu. ft per lb.
		°F.	°abs F.							
Lb./in.² absolute	Vacuum inches of mercury	t_s	T_s	G	h_w	L	H_s	Water ϕ_w	Steam ϕ_s	Dry Sat. V_s
0·5	28·99	79·6	539·3	2·2	**47·7**	1048·5	**1096·1**	0·0924	2·0367	643·0
0·75	28·48	92·3	552·0	3·5	**60·3**	1041·5	**1101·8**	0·1156	2·0025	437·3
1·0	27·97	101·7	561·4	4·7	**69·7**	1036·1	**1105·8**	0·1326	1·9783	334·0
1·25	27·46	109·4	569·1	5·8	**77·3**	1031·7	**1109·0**	0·1460	1·9596	270·4
1·5	26·95	115·7	575·4	6·7	**83·7**	1028·1	**1111·8**	0·1569	1·9442	228·0
2·0	25·92	126·1	585·8	8·5	**94·0**	1022·2	**1116·2**	0·1749	1·9200	173·7
3·0	23·88	141·5	601·2	11·3	**109·4**	1013·2	**1122·6**	0·2008	1·8869	118·7
4·0	21·84	153·0	612·7	13·8	**121·0**	1006·7	**1127·7**	0·2199	1·8632	90·63
5·0	19·80	162·3	622·0	15·9	**130·2**	1001·6	**1131·8**	0·2348	1·8449	73·52
6·0	17·76	170·1	629·8	17·8	**138·1**	996·6	**1134·7**	0·2473	1·8299	61·98
7·0	15·71	176·9	636·6	19·5	**144·9**	992·2	**1137·1**	0·2582	1·8176	53·64
8·0	13·67	182·9	642·6	21·0	**151·0**	988·5	**1139·5**	0·2676	1·8065	47·35
9·0	11·63	188·3	648·0	22·5	**156·5**	985·2	**1141·7**	0·2762	1·7968	42·40
10·0	9·59	193·2	652·9	23·9	**161·3**	982·5	**1143·8**	0·2836	1·7884	38·42
11·0	7·55	197·8	657·5	25·2	**165·9**	979·6	**1145·5**	0·2906	1·7807	35·14
12·0	5·50	202·0	661·7	26·4	**170·1**	976·9	**1147·0**	0·2970	1·7735	32·40
13·0	3·46	205·9	665·6	27·6	**173·9**	974·6	**1148·5**	0·3029	1·7672	30·05

	Gauge Lb./in.²									
14·696	0·0	212·0	671·7	29·4	**180·1**	970·6	**1150·7**	0·3122	1·7574	26·80
15	0·3	213·0	672·7	29·8	**181·2**	970·0	**1151·2**	0·3137	1·7556	26·28
18	3·3	222·4	682·1	32·8	**190·6**	964·0	**1154·6**	0·3276	1·7411	22·17
20	5·3	228·0	687·7	34·6	**196·3**	960·4	**1156·7**	0·3358	1·7327	20·09
25	10·3	240·1	699·7	38·8	**208·6**	952·5	**1161·1**	0·3534	1·7148	16·30
30	15·3	250·3	710·0	42·4	**219·0**	945·6	**1164·6**	0·3682	1·7004	13·73
35	20·3	259·3	719·0	45·8	**228·0**	939·6	**1167·6**	0·3809	1·6883	11·89
40	25·3	267·2	726·9	48·8	**236·1**	934·4	**1170·5**	0·3923	1·6776	10·50
50	35·3	281·0	740·7	54·4	**250·2**	924·6	**1174·8**	0·4112	1·6597	8·516
60	45·3	292·7	752·4	59·2	**262·2**	916·2	**1178·4**	0·4272	1·6450	7·175
70	55·3	302·9	762·6	63·8	**272·7**	908·7	**1181·4**	0·4412	1·6327	6·206
80	65·3	312·0	771·7	67·6	**282·1**	901·9	**1184·0**	0·4533	1·6219	5·472
90	75·3	320·3	780·0	71·5	**290·7**	895·5	**1186·2**	0·4643	1·6124	4·896
100	85·3	327·8	787·5	74·9	**298·5**	889·7	**1188·2**	0·4742	1·6038	4·434
125	110·3	344·4	804·1	82·8	**315·7**	876·4	**1192·1**	0·4958	1·5856	3·587
150	135·3	358·4	818·1	89·8	**330·6**	864·5	**1195·1**	0·5140	1·5705	3·015
175	160·3	370·8	830·5	96·3	**343·7**	853·9	**1197·6**	0·5297	1·5578	2·603
200	185·3	381·8	841·5	102·1	**355·5**	844·0	**1199·5**	0·5437	1·5466	2·290
225	210·3	391·8	851·5	107·5	**366·2**	834·8	**1201·0**	0·5562	1·5366	2·042
250	235·3	401·0	860·7	112·5	**376·1**	826·0	**1202·1**	0·5677	1·5276	1·844
300	285·3	417·3	877·0	121·7	**394·0**	809·8	**1203·8**	0·5881	1·5117	1·543
350	335·3	431·7	891·4	130·0	**409·9**	795·0	**1204·9**	0·6058	1·4979	1·326
400	385·3	444·6	904·3	138·0	**424·2**	781·3	**1205·5**	0·6216	1·4857	1·161
450	435·3	456·3	916·0	145·3	**437·4**	768·2	**1205·6**	0·6358	1·4746	1·032
500	485·3	467·0	926·7	151·8	**449·6**	755·8	**1205·4**	0·6489	1·4646	0·928
600	585·3	486·2	945·9	164·1	**471·8**	732·4	**1204·2**	0·6722	1·4466	0·770
700	685·3	503·1	962·8	175·2	**491·7**	710·5	**1202·2**	0·6927	1·4308	0·655
800	785·3	518·2	977·9	185·5	**509·9**	689·7	**1199·6**	0·7110	1·4165	0·569
1000	985·3	544·6	1004·3	203·8	**542·6**	650·2	**1192·8**	0·7432	1·3909	0·446
2000	1985·3	635·8	1095·5	272·6	**671·8**	464·3	**1136·1**	0·8620	1·2857	0·188
3000	2985·3	695·4	1155·1	321·3	**802·3**	214·1	**1016·4**	0·9728	1·1580	0·086

APPENDIX

SCIENTIFIC METHOD AS A CYCLE OF OPERATIONS

After working through this book it will be well for students to look back on the subject as a whole and to appreciate the inter-connection between, and the cycle formed by, the various phases involved in the treatment, not only this subject of Heat Engines but also of other subjects of engineering and applied science.

On reflection it will be clear that the mechanical and other applied sciences may be thought of and dealt with in three complementary phases, namely:—

(1) **Theory and Analysis**—being the application of fundamental principles or laws, and mathematical operations or logic, to problems after basic assumptions have been made, with a view to establishing useful formulae from which predictions can be made.

(2) **Calculations**—being estimations or predictions from analysis or formulae of the numerical values or magnitudes of quantities involved in the running of plant and machinery of definite size, or estimations from the testing of plant and gear in laboratories.

(3) **Laboratory and Experimental Work**—being a fact-finding task regarding the performance of actual plant on which observations and measurements are made during practical tests and trials.

Analyses and Calculations {i.e. phases (1) and (2)} are usually done on paper in the classroom or design office; and it will be clear that the main stages in the working out of the theoretical side of engineering problems are:—

(i) *Hypothesis and Assumptions*—being a statement of the problem and of the premises and assumptions on which the subsequent analysis is to be based.

(ii) *Scientific Laws*—the relevant basic principles and scientific laws are stated.

(iii) *Mathematics*—the scientific laws are first expressed in symbols and then, by mathematical operations, combined and reduced to useful physical or numerical formulae

$$\left(e.g.\ \text{Power } P = T\omega \text{ or } b = \frac{2\pi t n}{33{,}000}\right)$$

according as symbols are used to represent physical quantities or numbers, respectively.

(iv) *Arithmetic*—involved in the reduction of units arising from the replacement of each symbol by its number and unit in a physical formula (i.e. in which symbols represent quantities as specified by a number and a unit or measure) or by its number in a numerical formula (i.e. in which symbols represent numbers only, the units having been specified at the beginning of the analysis).

Laboratory and Experimental Work {i.e. phase (3)} in engineering and other applied sciences may be analysed and reported under the main headings:—

(i) *Object.*—A concise statement of the aims and objects of the test or trial is made.

(ii) *Plant and Apparatus* is analysed with the aid of, say, a line diagram, energy equation or energy-stream diagram, or otherwise according to the type of plant and experiment.

(iii) *Observations and Results*, taking the form of a report sheet of figures comprising the numerical values of observations and results of calculations, and the graphical representation of results.

(iv) *Conclusions* are drawn as to whether the uses of certain theories and formulae are justified in predicting the results or performance of plant. Alternatively, empirical laws are deduced to fit the graphs resulting from observations made on plant under test.

Tho three main phases constituting scientific method, namely, (1) theory, (2) calculation, and (3) experiment, may also be pictured as a cyclic process or cycle of operations as in the following diagram:

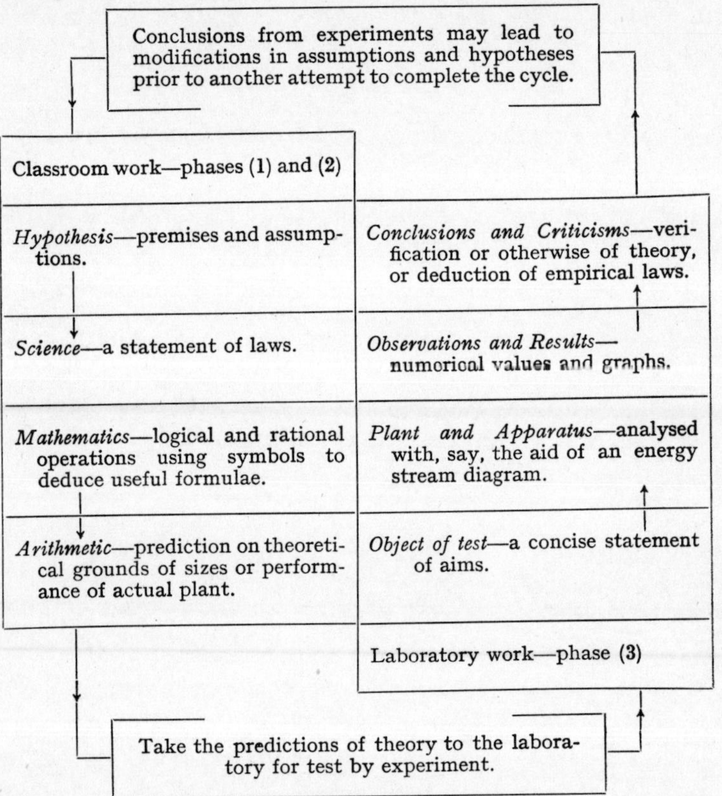

Conclusions from experiments may lead to modifications in assumptions and hypotheses prior to another attempt to complete the cycle.
Classroom work—phases (1) and (2)
Hypothesis—premises and assumptions.
Science—a statement of laws.
Mathematics—logical and rational operations using symbols to deduce useful formulae.
Arithmetic—prediction on theoretical grounds of sizes or performance of actual plant.
Conclusions and Criticisms—verification or otherwise of theory, or deduction of empirical laws.
Observations and Results—numorical values and graphs.
Plant and Apparatus—analysed with, say, the aid of an energy stream diagram.
Object of test—a concise statement of aims.
Laboratory work—phase (3)
Take the predictions of theory to the laboratory for test by experiment.

Assuming, first, this cycle to be begun (top left) by propounding a hypothesis or certain basic assumptions, then, if conclusions from experimental results are wide of those predicted by theory, either the hypothesis, scientific laws, mathematical operations, arithmetic, apparatus, instruments and observations, or several of these are at fault—any or all of which may need to be corrected or modified in order to close the circuit and complete the cycle.

Second, assuming the cycle to be begun (bottom right) in the laboratory (phase 3), then empirical laws may result from observations made during tests and experiments, and provide data for an attempt at formulating a theoretical and scientific explanation.

The above diagram will enable students to appreciate the interconnection between theory and practice and of analytical work in the classroom and testing in the laboratory, and to conceive the two categories as complementary or as the cycle of operations, usually called scientific method.

ANSWERS TO EXERCISES

CHAPTER 1

(3) −15; 5; 70; 130° C.; 33·8; −22; 194; 248° F. (4) 25° C. (6) 258; 278; 343; 403° abs. C.; 493·8; 438; 654; 708° abs. F. (8) 55·5 C.H.U. (9) 157 B.Th.U.; 122,146 ft.-Lb. (10) 1,152 B.Th.U. (11) 1·53 lb. (12) 22·9° C. (15) $17{\cdot}92\times10^{6}$ C.H.U.; $32{\cdot}256\times10^{6}$ B.Th.U.; $25{\cdot}08\times10^{9}$ ft.-Lb.; $12{\cdot}68\times10^{3}$ h.p.-hr.; $9{\cdot}46\times10^{3}$ k.W.hr. (17) (*a*) $11{\cdot}77\times10^{6}$; (b) $16{\cdot}41\times10^{6}$. (18) (*a*) 4·42 lb.; (*b*) 1·54 Ton. (19) 0·4714 lb. per min. (20) 4·06° F. per min. (21) 19,588 and 18,135 B.Th.U./lb.

CHAPTER 3

(1) 20,000 ft.-Lb.; 11·27 in. (2) (*a*) 208,500 ft.-Lb. (*b*) 73·8 Lb. per sq. in.; 208,500 ft.-Lb.; 632 h.p. (3) 1·07 in.; 240 ft.-Lb.; 5·8 h.p.; 1,600 r.p.m. (4) 31·08 Lb. per sq. in.; 32 h.p. (5) 18·5 h.p. (6) 15·1 in. diam.; 22·6 in. stroke. (7) (*a*) 7·55 h.p.; (*b*) 9·2 h.p. (8) 40·4 per cent. (9) 8·8 per cent. (10) 26·1 per cent.; 19·8 per cent.; 76 per cent.; 30·3; 23. (11) 85 b.h.p. (12) 22 b.h.p.; 15 pence. (13) (*a*) 6·25; 4·13; 2·12; (*b*) 264; 175; 90. (14) 50·9 tons; 5·65 tons; 1,020 h.p. (15) 160 b.h.p.; 89·8 Lb. per sq. in. (16) 0·857; 0·368. (17) 2,795 Lb.; 2,030 h.p.; 7·9 per cent.

CHAPTER 4

(2) 633 B.Th.U. (3) 94·2 cu. ft.; 848 B.Th.U. (5) 18·3 per cent.; 2·09. (6) 12; 7·55; 4·45; Mech. efficiency, 63 per cent.; Brake thermal efficiency, 28 per cent.; lb. per b.h.p.-hour, 0·514.

	B.Th.U./min.	Per cent.
Heat supplied.	1,143	100
Heat to b.h.p.	320	28
Heat to cooling water.	378	33
Heat to exhaust. Heat to surrounding air	445	39

(7) 12·7; 9·2; 3·5; 20 per cent.; 27·6 per cent.; 72·4 per cent.; 24·4 cu. ft. per b.h.p.-hr.

	B.Th.U./min.	Per cent.
Heat supplied.	1,950	100
Heat to b.h.p.	391	20
Heat to cooling water.	786	40
Heat to exhaust and surrounding air.	773	40

(8) 7·7; 6·7; 1·0; 326; 284; 42·4; Mech. efficiency, 87·5 per cent.; Brake thermal efficiency, 17·3 per cent.; cu. ft. per b.h.p.-hour, 23·8.

	B.Th.U./min.	Per cent.
Heat supplied	1,655	100
Heat to b.h.p.	284	17·2
Heat to cooling water	676	40·8
Heat to exhaust and surrounding air	695	42·0

(9) Most efficient at 11 b.h.p. (10) 27·9 per cent.; 5·37 and 32·7 ft.³/min.; 69·8 per cent. (11) 19·7 h.p.; 13·85 h.p.; 70·4 per cent.; 40·1 per cent.

Item	B.Th.U./min.	Per cent.
Heat supplied	2,080	100·0
Heat equivalent of b.h.p.	588	28·2
Heat to jacket water	572	27·5
Heat to exhaust gases	431	20·7
Heat to surrounding air	489	23·6
Totals	2,080	100·0

(12) C=3,000; b.h.p.=81·8; f.h.p.=30·3; i.h.p.=112·1; η=73 per cent. (13) 20·8 b.h.p.; 25 i.h.p.; 83·2 per cent.; 31·2 per cent.; 60·4 per cent.

Heat supplied	3,390
Heat equivalent to b.h.p.	882
Heat to cooling water	885
Heat to exhaust and surrounding air	1,623

All the energy used in overcoming friction is changed into heat, part of which flows into the cooling water and the rest flows from the metal to the surrounding air.

CHAPTER 5

(1) 166·7 Lb./in.² abs. (3) 259 B.Th.U. (4) 0·259 B.Th.U.; 646,000 ft.-Lb. (6) 324·43 B.Th.U.; 1110·5 B.Th.U. (7) 0·1 Lb. (8) 34 ft.; 2118·2. (10) 786·1 B.Th.U. (11) 1176·6 B.Th.U.; 3·1569 cu. ft.; 0·0114 per cent. (12) 1095 B.Th.U. (13) 3·624 cu. ft.; 1156 B.Th.U. (14) (*a*) 40 Lb./in.² abs.; 1170·5; 1092·8 B.Th.U./lb.; (*b*) 433·3 B.Th.U.; 0·522. (15) 981·6 B.Th.U.; 0·96; 93·2 B.Th.U. increase. (16) 2·4 Lb.

CHAPTER 6

(2) 1169·6 B.Th.U. (3) (i) 1059·9 B.Th.U.; (ii) 1060·2 B.Th.U.; error 0·028 per cent.; (iii) 1060·1 B.Th.U.; error 0·019 per cent. (4) (i) 1020·7; (ii) 1026·7; error 0·6 per cent.; (iii) 1026·6; error 0·6 per cent. (5) 86·2° F.

(6) 252·2 lb./min. (7) 0·955. (8) 0·444 B.Th.U.; (*b*) 0·055 B.Th.U.; (*c*) 83·215 B.Th.U.

(9)

0·44	0·44	0	0	0·44	0·44
330·16	330·6	330·1	330·1	0·06	0·50
864·5	1195·1	781·28	1111·38	83·22	83·72

(10)

q	H	Exact Volume	Approximate Volume	Exact Work done	Increase in Internal Energy
	B.Th.U. per lb.	cu. ft./lb.	cu. ft./lb.	B.Th.U./lb.	B.Th.U./lb.
1·0	1190·7	3·880	—	82·5	799·0
0·7	926·3	2·7214	2·716	57·6	559·5
0·3	573·7	1·1765	1·164	24·7	239·8

(11) 0·922. (12) 126·8° F. (13) 0·918. (14) (*a*) 1473·1 B.Th.U.; (*b*) 71 B.Th.U.; 85 per cent. (15) 0·745. (16) Superheated by 43° F. (17) 14 Lb. per sq. in. abs. (18) $n=1\cdot134$, 7·9 B.Th.U. lost. (19) (*a*) 43·9 B.Th.U./lb. (*b*) 0·959; (*c*) 0·08 cu. ft./lb. reduction. (20) (*a*) 0·995; (*b*) 72·5° F. superheat; (*c*) 0·816; (*d*) 317·2 B·Th.U./lb. (21) 3·38 in. and 10·55 in.; 10° F. of superheat.

CHAPTER 8

(2) (i) 26,650 ft.-Lb.; (ii) 0·436 lb.; (iii) 7·72 per cent. (3) (i) 0·218 lb.; (ii) 22,220 ft.-Lb.; (iii) 12·9 per cent. (4) (i) 197·3 h.p.; (ii) 50·7 Lb./in.^{2}. (iii) 76 r.p.m. (5) 80 h.p. (6) (i) 5,400 and 7,125 ft.-Lb.; (ii) 0·0573 lb.; (iii) 12·05 per cent. and 14·85 per cent.; (iv) 12·1 per cent. and 20·4 per cent.; (v) 99·9 per cent. and 72·8 per cent. (7) 0·7. (8) 57; 68·2; 83·6 per cent.; 3·76 per cent.

	B.Th.U./min.	Per cent.
Heat supplied	5,580	100
Heat to b.h.p.	210	3·8
Heat to exhaust	4,696	84·1
Heat to surrounding air	674	12·1

(9) 2·2; 117 Lb. per sq. in. (10) 30 h.p. (11) 7·7 in. and 11·5 in.

(12)

	r	2	3	4	5	6	8	10	15
(i)	I.h.p.	107·4	84·7	68·8	57·2	48·5	36·2	27·8	15

(ii) p_A	100	90	80	70	60	50	40	30
I.h.p.	84·7	73·9	63·1	52·3	41·6	30·8	20	9·3

(13) (i) 717,500 B.Th.U.; (ii) 12·6 per cent.; (iii) 29·7 per cent.; (iv) 42·4 per cent. (14) 1·785 ft. stroke; 15·3 in. and 29·4 in. diameter. (15) 105·3 and 248 h.p.; 6·13 and 14·5 Tons. (16) (*a*) 0·66; (*b*) 12·7 per cent.; 26·4 per cent.; 48·2 per cent.

	B.Th.U./min.	Per cent.
(*c*) Heat supplied	86,500	100
Heat to b.h.p.	9,980	11·6
Heat to exhaust	73,275	84·6
Heat to surrounding air	3,245	3·8

(17) (*a*) 5·98 in.; 12·05 in.; (*b*) 1·16 Tons. (18) 108° F. of superheat; 302 B.Th.U. per lb. (19) 40 per cent. (20) 14·3 per cent.; 25·8 per cent.

Item	B.Th.U./min.	Per cent.
Heat supplied	7,650	100
Heat equivalent of b.h.p.	1,018	13·3
Heat to condenser cooling water	6,100	79·7
Heat in condensate	468	6·1
Heat to surrounding air	64	0·9
Totals	7,650	100·0

CHAPTER 9

(1) 8·72 lb. per lb. of coal. (2) 4·82 tons per hour. (3) 11·2 lb. (4) 18·2 lb. of air; 7 lb. excess; 62·5 per cent. (5) 2725 B.Th.U.; 18·6 per cent. (6) 14·39 lb. (7) (i) 11·47 lb.; (ii) 16·35 lb.; (iii) 42·6 per cent.; 1·43. (8) 14·46 lb.

	Percentage by Weight	Percentage by Volume
CO_2	21·8	15·1
SO_2	0·2	—
N_2	78·0	84·9

(11) 0·0776 Lb. per sq. in. (13) (*a*) 61·0 per cent. (*b*) 2,640 B.Th.U.; 1·5 Lb. per sq. in. abs.; 1·361 B.Th.U.

(*c*) Heat balance sheet per lb. of oil.	B.Th.U.	Per cent.
Heat supplied	19,250	100
Heat to water and steam	11,730	61
Heat to chimney	4,001	21
Heat to surrounding air and unaccounted for	3,519	18

(14) 90,800 cu. ft./min. (15) 0·68 Lb./in.^{2} abs. (i) 2370 B.Th.U. (ii) 688 B.Th.U. (16) 236 B.Th.U./hour. (17) 15·65 lb.

Item	B.Th.U. per lb. of fuel
Energy supplied in fuel	19,600
Energy supplied by pump	127
Total	19,727
Heat to water and steam	15,944
Heat to flue gases	3,195
Heat to surrounding air	588
Total	19,727

(18) 90·2 per cent.; 30·5 per cent. (19) 205 B.Th.U./hour. (20) 941° F. (21) (i) 42,100 lb. per hour; (ii) 80·8 per cent. (22) 2,420 B.Th.U./hour.

CHAPTER 10

(3) 108·5° F. (5) 18·57 lb. (8) 0·75 Lb. per sq. in.; 817·5 cu. ft.; 1·87 lb.; 0·535. (9) 115·7° F.; 14·3 lb. (10) 0·115 lb. (11) 0·955; 0·002385 lb. (12) 0·175 lb. (13) 115·5 Lb. per sq. in. abs.; 0·93. (14) 0·739; 1° F. (15) 0·263 Lb.; (*b*) 0·0188 Lb.

CHAPTER 11

(10) 42°; 0·07 in. lead; 0·66 in. steam lap; 0·09 in. exhaust lap. (11) 43°; 0·05 in lead; 0·5 in. steam lap; 0·22 in. exhaust lap; (12) $1\frac{5}{8}$ in.; 33°; $\frac{25}{32}$ in. (13) 1·45 in.; $\alpha=135°$; $\theta_c=95°$.

CHAPTER 12

(5) 910 ft. per sec.; 1,350 ft. per sec.; 97,200 ft.-Lb.; 69·6 per cent. (6) 25°; 33° and 17°. (7) 56,900 and 31,050; 90·5 per cent. (8) 32·5; 1 Lb. (9) 65·4 per cent. (10) 1,049 ft. per sec.; 3·57 h.p.; 92·6 per cent. (11) 401 and 194 ft./sec.; 3,830 ft.-Lb./lb. (12) 156·5 h.p. (13) (i) 24° 2′; (ii) 46,400 ft. Lb./lb. 74·6 per cent.;

	B.Th.U./lb.	Per cent.
Energy supplied	1130·8	100
Energy rejected	1065·2	94·1
Diagram work	59·6	5·3
Heat to surrounding air	6·0	0·6
Totals	1130·8	100·0

CHAPTER 13

(5) 96; 1,382; 99·2; 62·8 ft.-Lb. per lb. per °C. (6) 7·51 cu. ft. (7) 3; 0·21; 2·9; 4·6 lb. (8) 36·4 Lb. per sq. in. (9) 3·74 lb.; 6·75° C. (10) 15·15 Tons. (11) (i) 29·9; (ii) 0·0835; (iii) 51·6. (12) (*a*) 0·0194 lb; (*b*) 10 and 4·7Lb./in.^{2} abs.); (*c*) 71·2 ft. Lb./lb. °F., 0·378, 1·32. (13) 10 Lb. per sq. in abs.; 0·55. (14) (i) 1,860 cu. ft.; (ii) 17·13 Lb./in.^{2} abs.; (iii) 10·5 Lb. per sq. in. abs. (15) 52·5 ft. Lb./lb. °F.; 0·785 lb. (16) O_2, 7·5; H_2O, 22·2; N_2, 70·3; 1038 Lb./in.^{2} abs. (17) (*a*) (i) 1·9 lb.; (ii) 1·193 lb.; (iii) 0·707 lb.; (iv) 169 per cent.; (*b*) (i) 0·464 lb.; (ii) 0·464 lb.; (*c*) (i) 5·72 to 1; (ii) 85·1 C; 14·9 H_2 (18) (*a*) 3·44 ft.^{3}; 400° F.; (*b*) 0·1523 B.Th.U. per °F. loss; (*c*) 101 B.Th.U. rejection. (19) 17·85 lb.; 388 cu. ft.

CHAPTER 14

(1) 10·1 cu. ft.; −45·5° C.; 32,800 ft.-Lb. (2) (*a*) 0·241 cu. ft.; 3,380 ft.-Lb.; (*b*) 0·0768 lb.; 79·5° C. (3) 2 cu. ft.; 331° C.; 76,000 ft.-Lb. (4) (*b*) (i) 0·0612 cu. ft.; 1,128° F.; (ii) 0·02 cu. ft. 59° F.; (*c*) 10,400 ft.-Lb.; 7,900 ft.-Lb. (5) 111 B.Th.U. (9) (*a*) 87·5; 0·442 lb.; (*b*) 1·4; 139·3; 246° C.; 21,350 ft.-Lb. (10) (i) −89° F.; 120 B.Th.U.; (ii) 152,000 ft.-Lb.; (iii) 75 B.Th.U. added. (11) (i) 75 Lb. per sq. in.; (ii) 143 Lb. per sq. in.; 7,100 ft. Lb. (12) 420° F.; 1 cu. ft.; 20·3 B.Th.U. (13) 0·231; 0·275; 34·4 ft.Lb./lb. °F. (14) 3070 ft.-Lb.; 53·7 Lb./in.^{2} abs.; 3·04 B.Th.U. (15) 51·7 Lb. per sq. in. abs. (16) 52·2 C.H.U. (17) 739° F.; 1770 ft./sec.; 56·8 in.^{2} (18) (*a*) infinity, (*b*) zero; 3·41 and 2·416 B.Th.U. per lb. °F. (19) 1,980 ft.-Lb.; −41·7 and 0 B.Th.U.

CHAPTER 15

(1) 24·07 cu. ft.; 11·65 h.p.; 7·67 lb.; 176° F. (2) (i) 46,000 ft.-Lb.; (ii) 43,000 ft.-Lb.; (iii) 14,200 ft.-Lb. (3) 64·2. (4) (*a*) 34·65 Lb. per sq. in.; 61° C.; (*d*) 30·7 h.p. (5) −113° F.; 48·1 lb. (6) 85·3 per cent. (7) 99·6 h.p.; 30 Lb. per sq. in. (9) 1·34 h.p.; 1·16 h.p.; 86·5 per cent.; 1·79 h.p. (10) 58·8 h.p. (11) 20,400 ft.-Lb. (12) 7·3 .hp.; 17·6 lb./min. (13) 83·5 per cent.; 89·6 per cent. (14) 3·11 h.p.; 1260 ft.^{3}/s.h.p. hour. (15) 42·4 Lb./in.^{2} abs.; 21·3 h.p. (16) 76·8 per cent.; 75·3 per cent.; 83·2 per cent. (17) (i) 1·245; 1·53 h.p. (18) 12,750 ft. Lb. (19) 20·6 h.p.

CHAPTER 16

(1) 9·38 in.; 14·06 in. (2) 47·46 per cent.; 24·6 cu. ft. (4) 839° F.; 486 cu. in.; 9·678. (5) 2·446; 50·2 per cent. (6) 13·6 in.; 9·1 in. (7) 227,000 ft.-Lb.; 60·5 per cent. (9) 22·2 per cent.; 45 per cent. (10) 69·2 Lb./in.^{2}; 39·5 h.p.; 780° F. and 2245° F.

(11)

P atmospheres	1	15	64·2	64·2	2·56
V cu. ft.	5	0·33	0·33	0·5	5
t °F.	150	150	2,150	2,460	1,100

(12) 64·7 per cent. (13) 68,200 ft.-Lb. (14) 277 B.Th.U. (15) 41·8 per cent.; 148·5 h.p. per lb./sec.(16) 22·5 per cent.; 77 h.p. per lb./sec. (17) 125 B.Th.U./lb. 50 per cent.; 11·33. (18) 98·5 : 1; 30 per cent.; (19) (i) 220 h.p.; (ii) 320 h.p.; (iii) 100 h.p.; (iv) 15·3 per cent.; (v) 23·5; (vi) 120·8 to 1. (20) 6·78.

CHAPTER 17

(1) (*a*) 20 per cent.; (*b*) 13·3 per cent. (2) 14·84. (3) H_2O 7·0; CO_2 17·5; O_2 2·8; N_2 72·7. (4) 114·3 lb.; 1,193 B.Th.U.; 1·066 gal. (5) CO_2 7; O_2 10·9; N_2 82·1. (6) 84·2 per cent.; 15·8 per cent.; 2·345 cu. ft. (7) (*a*) 0·618; (*b*) 0·0222 Lb. (8) H_2O 11·3, CO_2 6·3, O_2 9·4, N_2 73·0. (9) 1,860 cu. ft.; 10 per cent.; 30 per cent.; 10·5 Lb. per sq. in. abs. (10) 35·6 per cent.; CO_2 10·6, O_2 5·8, N_2 83·6. (11) CO_2 15·2, O_2 3·1, N_2 81·7. (12) CO_2 12·8, O_2 3·7, N_2 83·5. (13) 74° C .(14) (i) 35·4 per cent.; (ii) 1·51 Lb./in.^{2} abs.; (iii) 3710 and 1927 B.Th.U. (15) 0·402 lb./min. (16) 53·6 per cent.; 82·6 per cent. (17) 16·74 lb./lb. of fuel; 0·343 lb./min.; 3·56 in. (18) (*a*) 13; 17; (*b*) Rich by (i) 13·3 per cent.; (ii) 15·4 per cent.; (*c*) Weak by (i) 13·3 per cent.; (ii) 11·8 per cent. (20) (i) 4·31; (ii) 0·65. (21) 396 B.Th.U. per cu. ft.; CO_2 14·5 per cent.; N_2 85·5 per cent.

CHAPTER 18

(1) 1·293 × 10^6 ft.-Lb.; 19·2 per cent.; 75 per cent.; 19·4; 25·9. (3) 12·6; 19·5 per cent.; 71·5 per cent.; 796 B.Th.U.; 3·6 h.p.; 25. Heat to exhaust and surrounding air 779 B.Th.U. or 39·7 per cent.

(4)

Heat supplied	60,500	100
Heat equivalent of b.h.p.	13,800	22·8
Heat to jacket water	16,200	26·8
Heat to exhaust and air	30,500	50·4

(5)

Test	1	2	3	4	5	6
I.h.p.	—	22·8	29·4	37·5	44·5	57·1
Mechanical efficiency, per cent.	0	41·6	54·1	63·5	67·8	70·0
Brake thermal efficiency, per cent.	0	18·4	24·1	26·8	28·6	25·9
Oil, lb. per b.h.p.-hr.	—	0·726	0·553	0·498	0·467	0·515

(7) 14; 9·52; 4·48; 453 B.Th.U.; 1,500 B.Th.U.; 26·9 per cent. 68 per cent.

	B.Th.U./min.	Per cent.
Heat supplied	1,500	100
Heat to b.h.p.	404	26·9
Heat to cooling water	453	30·3
Heat to exhaust and surrounding air	643	42·8

(8) 4·7 h.p.; 22·02 h.p.; 20·3 per cent.; 78·5 per cent.; (9) 74·8 per cent.; 26·4 per cent.;

Heat Balance Sheet	B.Th.U./min.	Per cent.
Heat supplied	2,490	100
Heat equivalent of b.h.p.	657	26·4
Heat to jacket water	728	29·2
Heat to exhaust	835	33·5
Heat to surrounding air	270	10·9

(10) (*a*) 1·45 Lb. per sq. in. abs.; (*b*) 176 B.Th.U.; (*c*) 0·0442 Lb.

(11) 6130 B.Th.U./min.; 2440 B.Th.U./min.

Item	B.Th.U./min.	Per cent.
Heat supplied	31,200	100
Heat equivalent of b.h.p.	8,060	25·8
Heat to jacket water	7,450	23·8
Heat to cooling oil	1,420	4·4
Heat to dry exhaust gas	6,130	19·7
Heat to steam in exhaust	2,440	7·8
Heat to surrounding air	5,700	18·5
Totals	31,200	100·0

(12) (*a*) 0·680 lb./b.h.p. hr.; 33·2 b.h.p.; 20·8 per cent.; (*b*) 0·608 lb./b.h.p. hr.; 31·0 b.h.p.; 23·3 per cent. (13) 114 h.p.; 129 Lb./in.^{2}; 90 per cent.

Item	B.Th.U./min.	Per cent.
Heat supplied	17,350	100
Heat equivalent of b.h.p.	4,340	25·0
Heat to cooling water	4,780	27·6
Heat to dry exhaust gas	2,036	11·7
Heat to moisture of combustion	1,820	10·5
Heat to surrounding air	4,374	25·2

(14) 88·4 per cent.; 120 Lb. per sq. in.

	B.Th.U./min.
Heat supplied	6,580
Heat equivalent b.h.p.	1,732
Heat to cooling water	1,644
Heat to exhaust and surrounding air	3,204
Total	6,580

Friction heat does not appear as a separate item in the heat account because a portion of it is already included (although indeterminate) in the heat to cooling water, and the rest is radiated to the surrounding air.

(15)

Item	B.Th.U./min.
Heat supplied	26,800
Heat equivalent of b.h.p.	6,450
Heat to cooling water	8,800
Heat to exhaust gases	7,330
Heat to surrounding air and in unburnt fuel	4,220
Total	26,800

CHAPTER 20

(1) 4,661° F.; 0·2238 B.Th.U./lb.°F. (2) 0·0741 B.Th.U./lb. °F. (3) 1·5641 B.Th.U./lb. °F.; 1·7524 B.Th..U./lb. °F. (4) 0·710; 0·850; 0·875. (5) (*a*) 189·5 B.Th.U.; 18·6 per cent.; (*b*) 258 B.Th.U.; 21·6 per cent.; (*c*) 337·5 B.Th.U.; 29·8 per cent.; (*d*) 414 B.Th.U.; 31·6 per cent. (7) 2·298 cu. ft. (8) 1·713 cu. ft. (9) $t'=452°$ F., $H'=1250·8$; (*a*) $q=0·835$; (*b*) $t'=392°$ F. (10) 27·3 per cent. (11) 80 Lb. per sq. in. abs. (12) 436° F.; 94·2 B.Th.U. per lb. (13) 18,300 ft.-Lb. (14) $0·00165 \frac{\text{B.Th.U.}}{\text{°F.}}$; $0·000838 \frac{\text{B.Th.U.}}{\text{°F.}}$ (15) $·01367 \frac{\text{B.Th.U.}}{\text{°F.}}$

INDEX